INTRODUCTION to

ATOMIC and NUCLEAR PHYSICS

View of the Cosmotron and Its Shielding

(Courtesy of the Brookhaven National Laboratory)

HENRY SEMAT, Ph.D.

Professor of Physics, The City College
College of the City of New York

INTRODUCTION to ATOMIC and NUCLEAR PHYSICS

THIRD EDITION, *Revised and Enlarged, of Introduction to Atomic Physics*

RINEHART & COMPANY, INC. *New York*

QC
173
.S315
1954

Third Printing, July 1955

Printed in the United States of America

Library of Congress Catalog Card Number: 54-7640

to Ray K. Semat

Preface

The first edition of this book, which appeared in 1939 and which was entitled *Introduction to Atomic Physics*, grew out of a course on Modern Physics I had been giving for several years previous. The friendly reception accorded the first edition prompted author and publisher to bring out a revised edition in 1946. The major changes in the second edition were made in the section on the nucleus; other material was, of course, updated, and various improvements and refinements were made at the suggestion of colleagues and critics.

The new title of the third edition, *Introduction to Atomic and Nuclear Physics*, epitomizes the essential difference between this edition and the earlier ones. Nuclear physics is, of course, a part of atomic physics; however, because of the great advances made in this branch of the subject in the past twenty years, beginning with the discoveries of the neutron, of deuterium, and of induced radioactivity, nuclear physics has come to be considered as a separate branch of physics. The term atomic physics is now considered by physicists to be concerned mostly with those properties of the atom which depend upon their extranuclear structure. However, the latter is determined by some of the nuclear properties, particularly charge, mass, and spin. Hence, in the development of this book, the foundations are laid in Part 1 for the study of both the nuclear and the extranuclear parts of the atom. These include a brief review of the fundamentals of electricity and magnetism, a description of the methods of determining the fundamental constants of atomic and nuclear physics, the experiments which led to the development of the concept of the nuclear atom, and the fundamental experiments showing the wave and particle aspects of both electromagnetic radiation and matter. Using this foundation, the subject of the extranuclear structure of the atom is treated in Part 2, and that of nuclear physics in Part 3. Approximately equal space in this book is devoted to each of the fields normally encompassed by the respective names of atomic and nuclear physics.

The plan and spirit of the original book have not undergone any essential changes. The text is still intended for use at the undergraduate level with students who have had a one-year physics course and a course in the calculus. Part 1, Foundations of Atomic and Nuclear Physics, and Part 2, The Extranuclear Structure of the Atom, have undergone minor revisions since the second edition, mostly to improve them from a pedagogical standpoint and to bring the subject matter up to date. Some of the longer chapters have been subdivided, some new topics as well as diagrams and photographs have been added, and additional problems and references included.

The major change is in Part 3, Nuclear Physics. Chapter 10, on natural radioactivity, has been brought up to date, and several new sections have been added to it. Chapter 11 describes a large variety of experiments on the disintegration of nuclei, and Chapter 12 discusses, in an elementary way, some of the theory of these nuclear processes. Chapter 13, Nuclear Fission, is devoted almost entirely to the physical aspects of fission rather than to the technical aspects. Chapter 14, Elementary Particles, is devoted mostly to the newer particles, the mesons and V-particles, with a brief discussion of the older elementary particles. Chapter 15 discusses the production of new elements and isotopes. Chapter 16 contains a description of the different types of particle accelerators which are used in atomic and nuclear physics. Part 3 contains many new diagrams and photographs as well as a large number of suitable problems.

Throughout the preparation of the various versions of this text I have received invaluable assistance from my colleagues, from teachers who have used the book in one or more editions, and from physicists who have read the manuscripts in whole or in part. I should, therefore, like to extend my sincere thanks to the following: Professor E. F. Barker, University of Michigan; Dr. Dixon Callihan, Oak Ridge National Laboratory; Professor Joseph H. Dexter, College of the City of New York; Mr. H. H. Goldsmith, late of the College of the City of New York; Professor J. M. B. Kellogg, Los Alamos Scientific Laboratory; Professor Paul Kirkpatrick, Stanford University; Dr. Sidney Millman, Bell Telephone Laboratories; Professor Hans Mueller, Massachusetts Institute of Technology; Dr. Edson R. Peck, Northwestern University; Dr. John R. Platt, University of Chicago; Professor Robert L. Weber, The Pennsylvania State University; Professor Lawrence A. Wills, College of the City of New York; Professor Hugh C. Wolfe, Cooper Union; Professor Mark W. Zemansky, College of the City of New York; Dr. Walter H. Zinn, Argonne National Laboratory.

Further, in the preparation of the third edition I have received invaluable help from many physicists in the form of photographs, graphs, and diagrams. These are acknowledged at the appropriate places in the text. In particular, I wish to thank Dr. Maurice M. Shapiro of the Naval Research Laboratory both for supplying me with a large number of photographs and for several helpful discussions on the subject of mesons. I also wish to thank Dr. Charlotte E. Moore of the National Bureau of Standards for supplying me with a corrected list of the first ionization potentials of the elements, and Professor K. B. Newbound of the University of Alberta for his list of problems in nuclear physics, some of which have been incorporated in the text.

I am deeply grateful to Professor Bernard T. Feld of Massachusetts Institute of Technology and to Professor R. L. Sproull of Cornell University, who read the original manuscript of the third edition, for their many valuable criticisms and suggestions, most of which have been incorporated in the book. I also wish to thank my colleague, Professor Harry Soodak, for having read Part 3 and in particular for his many valuable suggestions for Chapter 13 on nuclear fission, and Professor Leo Lederman of Columbia University for having read Chapter 14 on elementary particles and for his many valuable suggestions on the subject of mesons.

Finally, I wish to express my thanks and appreciation to my wife, Ray K. Semat, for typing the manuscripts and for the many other chores involved in the preparation of all three editions.

New York
June, 1954

H. S.

Table of Contents

Preface — *vii*

part **1** **Foundations of Atomic and Nuclear Physics**

1 Elements of Electricity and Magnetism — *3*

2 Charged Atomic Particles — *30*

3 The Nuclear Atom — *75*

4 Electromagnetic Radiation — *97*

5 X-Rays — *121*

6 Waves and Particles — *166*

part **2** **The Extranuclear Structure of the Atom**

7 The Hydrogen Atom — *205*

8 Optical Spectra and Electron Distribution — *233*

9 X-Ray Spectra — *285*

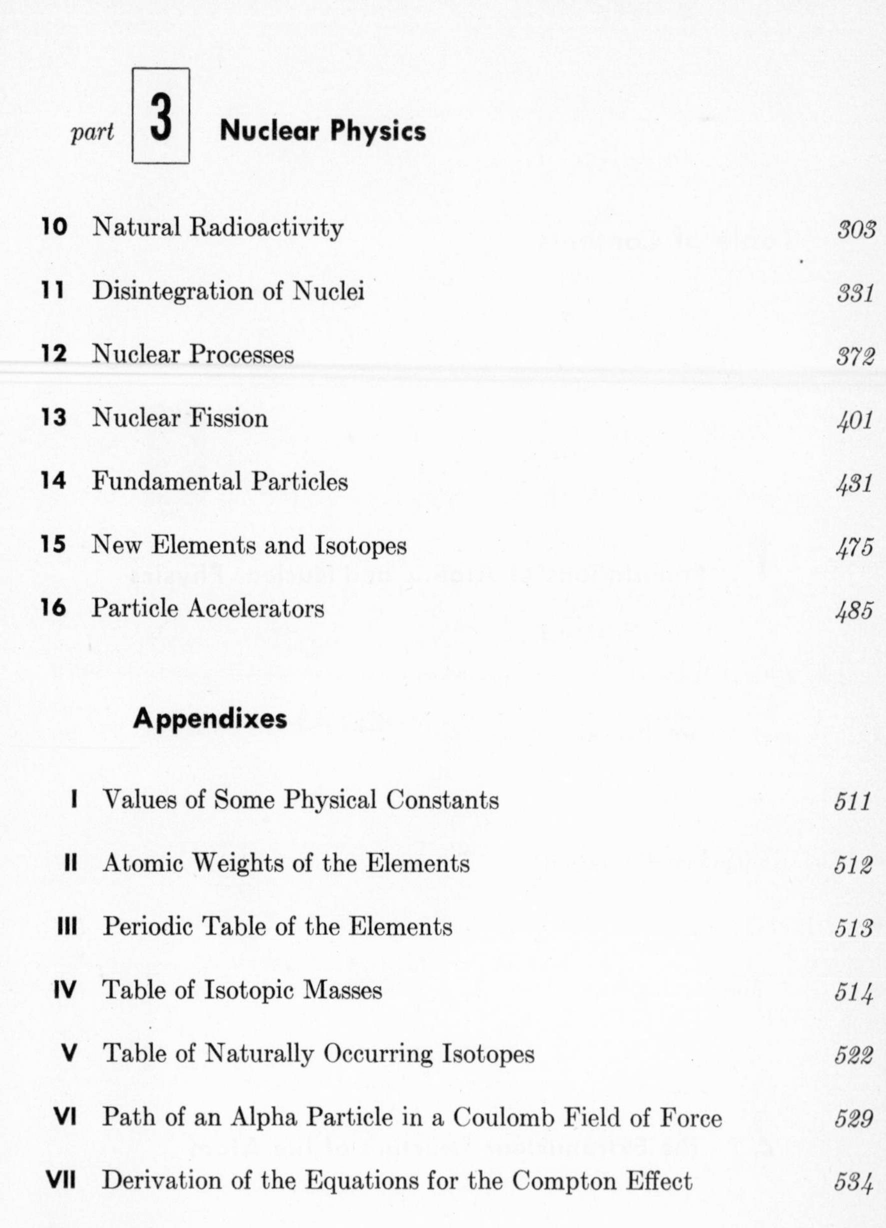

part 3 Nuclear Physics

10 Natural Radioactivity *303*

11 Disintegration of Nuclei *331*

12 Nuclear Processes *372*

13 Nuclear Fission *401*

14 Fundamental Particles *431*

15 New Elements and Isotopes *475*

16 Particle Accelerators *485*

Appendixes

I Values of Some Physical Constants *511*

II Atomic Weights of the Elements *512*

III Periodic Table of the Elements *513*

IV Table of Isotopic Masses *514*

V Table of Naturally Occurring Isotopes *522*

VI Path of an Alpha Particle in a Coulomb Field of Force *529*

VII Derivation of the Equations for the Compton Effect *534*

VIII Evaluation of $\int p_r dr = n_r h$ *538*

Index *543*

FOUNDATIONS of ATOMIC and NUCLEAR PHYSICS

chapter 1

Elements of Electricity and Magnetism

1-1. Introduction

The decade from 1895 to 1905 may be termed the beginning of modern physics. During this period, J. J. Thomson succeeded in demonstrating the existence of the electron, a fundamental unit of negative electricity having very small mass. Becquerel discovered the phenomenon of natural radioactivity and Roentgen discovered x-rays. To these discoveries must be added the bold hypothesis put forth by Planck, that radiant energy, in its interaction with matter, behaves as though it consists of corpuscles or quanta of energy. This led to the development of the quantum theory of radiation and ultimately to quantum mechanics. It was also during this period that Einstein re-examined the fundamental concepts of physics and was led to the development of the special theory of relativity.

It is the aim of this book to present the important experimental data upon which are based our present ideas of the structure of the atom. An atom is to be regarded not as a static structure composed of particles in fixed positions, but rather as a dynamic structure changing in response to outside agencies, affecting them and, in turn, being affected by them. It is by examining the phenomena that occur during these changes that we get our information concerning the structure of the atom as well as an insight into the nature of those quantities which produce or are the result of these changes.

Accumulation of experimental data, particularly from the study of electrochemistry and the discharge of electricity through gases, indicates clearly that the atom is essentially electrical in nature. It will therefore be of value to discuss briefly those fundamental concepts of electricity and magnetism which have been found essential in studying the structure of the atom.

1-2. Coulomb's Law of Force between Electric Charges

If a glass rod is rubbed with a piece of silk, both the glass and the silk become electrified. When two glass rods which have been rubbed with silk are placed near each other, a force of repulsion will be found to exist between them. In a similar manner, if two rubber rods which have been rubbed with wool or cat's fur are placed near each other, there will be a force of repulsion between them. But if one of these rubber rods is brought near one of the electrified glass rods, a force of attraction is found to exist between them. All other electrified bodies can be compared with such glass and rubber rods. *Those electrified bodies which repel the charged glass rod are said to be positively charged or charged with positive electricity, while those electrified bodies which repel the charged rubber rod are said to be negatively charged or charged with negative electricity.* This arbitrary sign convention is adhered to throughout the realm of physics including the atomic domain. The ultimate determination of the sign of any electric charge must rest on a comparison with the charge on a glass rod which has been rubbed with silk or that on a rubber rod which has been rubbed with wool.

Coulomb (1789) made a study of the quantitative law of force between charged bodies. He found that the force between two charged bodies, whose dimensions are small in comparison with the distance between them, is given by

$$\boxed{F = \frac{q_1 q_2}{kr^2},} \tag{1}$$

where q_1 is the magnitude of the electric charge on one body, q_2 the magnitude of the charge on the second body, and r is the distance between them. The force F between the two charges also depends upon the nature of the medium between them; this is expressed by the factor k, called the *dielectric constant*, or the *specific inductive capacity* of the medium. The numerical value of k depends not only upon the nature of the medium but also upon the system of units used in expressing the other quantities in equation (1). In the cgs *electrostatic system of units*, k is set equal to unity when the charges are placed in a vacuum, F is measured in dynes, and r in centimeters. The charge q is then said to be expressed in electrostatic units (esu) of charge. The definition of a unit charge now follows directly from equation (1): *an electrostatic unit charge (1 esu) is one which, when placed in a vacuum one centimeter away from a like equal charge, will repel it with a force of one dyne.* The electrostatic unit of charge is sometimes called the *statcoulomb.* The electrostatic unit of charge is very small; hence, in the practical system of electrical units, a much larger charge is taken as the unit and is called a *coulomb.* A coulomb is equivalent to 3×10^9 esu of charge.

In the cgs electrostatic system of units defined above, the dielectric constant k is a pure numerical constant. For nonconductors or insulators, k is generally greater than unity.

1-3. Intensity of the Electric Field

The fact that a charged body will experience a force when placed at any point in the neighborhood of another body containing a charge Q suggests the idea that an *electric field* exists in the space around the charge Q. This electric field may be explored by placing a very small positive charge q at different points and measuring the force F experienced by it at each point. The *intensity of the electric field* E at any point P is defined as the ratio of this force F to the magnitude of the small positive charge q placed at this point, that is,

$$\boxed{E = \frac{F}{q}.} \tag{2}$$

The test charge q must be sufficiently small so that the electric field is not materially altered by the introduction of this test charge. If F is measured in dynes and q in esu of charge, then E is expressed in dynes per esu of charge.

The intensity of the electric field E at any point is a vector quantity whose direction is that of the force experienced by a *positive* charge placed at that point. A negative charge placed in an electric field will experience a force whose direction is opposite to that of the electric field.

The intensity of the electric field can be evaluated mathematically in many cases. For example, the intensity of the electric field in the space around a point charge Q can be found by imagining a small positive charge q placed at any point P a distance r from the point charge Q. The force F experienced by this positive charge q is, from Coulomb's law,

$$F = \frac{Qq}{kr^2}. \tag{3}$$

Substituting this value of F in equation (2), we get

$$\boxed{E = \frac{Q}{kr^2}} \tag{4}$$

for the intensity of the electric field E at a distance r from the charge Q. In the cgs electrostatic system of units, E is expressed in dynes per esu of charge, or dynes per statcoulomb.

There is a convenient method for mapping the electric field in any region of space to show at a glance its magnitude and direction. If the intensity of the electric field is known at any point, we can imagine a unit area drawn perpendicular to the direction of the electric field at this point and a sufficient number of lines drawn perpendicularly through this unit area so that the number of lines per unit area will represent the magnitude of the intensity of the electric field at this point, and the direction of these lines will represent the direction of this electric field. For example, the electric field around a point charge Q is radial, as shown in Figure 1-1. It can be shown that if one line of force per square centimeter is to represent

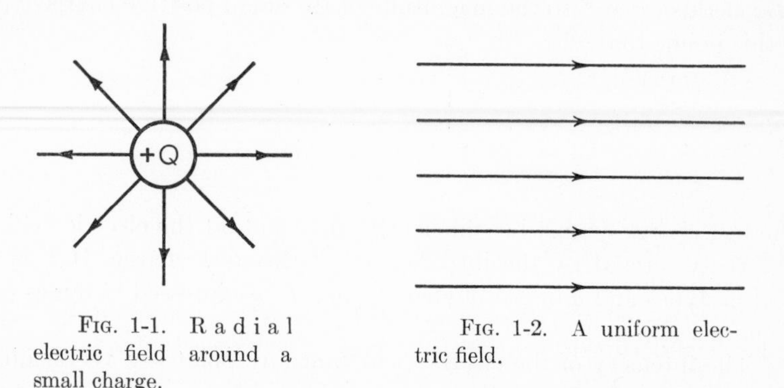

FIG. 1-1. Radial electric field around a small charge.

FIG. 1-2. A uniform electric field.

an intensity of one dyne per esu of charge, then $4\pi Q$ lines will have to be drawn radiating from the point charge Q. If the electric field is uniform throughout a given region of space, that is, if the intensity of the electric field has the same value throughout this region, then it would be represented by a series of parallel, equally spaced lines as shown in Figure 1-2.

1-4. Potential Difference; Potential

A charge q situated at any point in an electric field will experience a force $F = Eq$ where E is the electric field intensity at that point. If this charge is moved from any point A to any other point B, in general work will have to be done in moving it against the forces of the electric field. The *difference of potential* V between A and B is defined as *the ratio of the work done* W *to the positive charge* q *that is moved from* A *to* B, thus

$$V = \frac{W}{q}. \tag{5}$$

It follows directly from the principle of conservation of energy that the difference of potential between two points in an electrostatic field is independent of the path traversed in going from A to B.

In the es system of units, the work W is expressed in ergs, and the charge q in es units of charge or statcoulombs. Hence the difference of potential V will be expressed in ergs per esu of charge. This is sometimes called a *statvolt*. In the practical system of units, W is expressed in joules and q in coulombs; V in this system is expressed in volts. Thus

$$1 \text{ volt} = 1 \text{ joule/coulomb}.$$

Since
$$1 \text{ joule} = 10^7 \text{ ergs}$$

and
$$1 \text{ coul} = 3 \times 10^9 \text{ statcoulombs},$$

$$300 \text{ volts} = 1 \text{ statvolt}.$$

If point A is taken as the zero level of potential, then the difference of potential between A and B is also the *potential of point* B. In practice, the ground is taken as the zero level of potential; the potential of any point is then its difference of potential with respect to ground potential. The potential of a point may be either positive or negative, since V is defined in terms of the work done in moving a positive charge from one point to another.

Of particular interest is the evaluation of the potential at a point A in the neighborhood of a positive charge Q. The electric field intensity E at a distance r from Q is, from equation (4),

$$E = \frac{Q}{kr^2}. \tag{4}$$

If a small positive charge q is moved through a distance dr against the forces of the electric field, the work done per unit charge, which is the difference of potential dV, is, from equation (5),

$$dV = \frac{dW}{q},$$

and since
$$dW = -Fdr,$$

$$dV = \frac{-F}{q}\,dr = -Edr.$$

Substituting the value of E from equation (4),

we get
$$dV = -\frac{Q}{kr^2}\,dr.$$

Let us take a point at infinity as our zero level of potential and imagine the small charge q brought from infinity to point A at a distance a from charge Q. The potential at A is then

$$V_A = -\frac{Q}{k}\int_\infty^a \frac{dr}{r^2},$$

from which

$$V_A = \frac{Q}{ka}. \tag{6}$$

If we were to determine the potential at any other point B at a distance b from charge Q in a similar manner, we would get

$$V_B = \frac{Q}{kb}.$$

The difference of potential V between points A and B is

$$V = V_B - V_A$$

so that

$$V = \frac{1}{k}\left(\frac{Q}{b} - \frac{Q}{a}\right). \tag{7}$$

If the space around the charge Q is a vacuum, then $k = 1$ in the cgs electrostatic system of units and equation (7) becomes

$$V = \frac{Q}{b} - \frac{Q}{a}. \tag{7a}$$

The work done in bringing a charge q to point A where the potential is V_A is, from the definition of potential, simply

$$W = V_A q.$$

Using the value of V_A from equation (6) yields

$$W = \frac{Qq}{ka} \tag{8}$$

for the work done in bringing two charges Q and q to within a distance a of each other. This work produces a *change in the electrostatic potential energy of the system;* hence equation (8) is also the expression for the potential energy $\mathcal{E}_p$ of this system, with the zero level of potential energy taken when the distance $a = \infty$. In general, if r is the distance between two point charges Q and q, the potential energy of the system is

$$\mathcal{E}_p = \frac{Qq}{kr}. \tag{9}$$

If the charges are situated in a vacuum, or, as it is sometimes called, in free space, $k = 1$ in the electrostatic system of units and equation (9) becomes

$$\boxed{\mathcal{E}_p = \frac{Qq}{r}.} \tag{10}$$

1-5. Work Done in Charging a Body

The work done in adding a small charge dq to a body at some potential V is, by definition,

$$dW = Vdq,$$

and the total work done in adding a quantity of charge q to the body is

$$W = \int_0^q Vdq. \tag{11}$$

In order to evaluate equation (11), it is necessary to know the relationship between the potential of the body and the charge on it. Such a relationship is given by the equation

$$C = \frac{q}{V} \tag{12}$$

where C is the *capacitance* of the body; the capacitance of a body is a constant determined by its geometrical configuration and the nature of the dielectric medium surrounding it. The work done in charging a body may now be evaluated with the aid of equation (12), yielding

$$W = \frac{1}{2}\frac{q^2}{C} = \tfrac{1}{2}qV = \tfrac{1}{2}CV^2. \tag{13}$$

If the electric field in any region is uniform, the electric intensity E is constant throughout this region; the difference of potential V, that is, the work done in carrying a unit positive charge through a distance s parallel to this field is

$$V = \int_0^s Edr = Es. \tag{14}$$

A very convenient way of obtaining a comparatively uniform electric field is to use a capacitor consisting of two large parallel plates a small distance s apart. If the plates are kept at a difference of potential V by means of a battery, the electric intensity of the field between the plates will be

$$E = \frac{V}{s}. \tag{15}$$

The electric field will be uniform except at the edges of the plates.

1-6. Coulomb's Law of Force between Magnetic Poles

Permanent magnets have been known and used for centuries. If a thin steel rod which has been magnetized is suspended so that it can swing freely about a vertical axis, the steel rod will come to rest in a very definite position. If there are no other magnetic materials in the immediate neighborhood, the rod will set itself in an approximately north-south position. The end which points north is called the *north-seeking pole*, or, more briefly, the *north pole* of the magnet; the other end is called the *south pole* of the magnet. If the north pole of another magnet is brought near the north pole of the first magnet, a force of repulsion will be found to exist between them; similarly for the south poles of the two magnets. But if opposite poles are brought near one another, there will be a force of attraction between them.

Coulomb investigated the law of force between magnetic poles and found that the force is proportional to the strengths of the magnetic poles, and inversely proportional to the square of the distance between them; or, in the form of an equation, Coulomb's law states that

$$\boxed{F = \frac{p_1 p_2}{\mu r^2},} \tag{16}$$

where F is the force between the two poles, r is the distance between them, p_1 and p_2 represent the strengths of the poles, and μ is a constant of proportionality. The value of μ depends upon the units used and the nature of the medium between the poles; μ is called the *permeability* of the medium. If the magnets are placed in a vacuum, and F is measured in dynes and r in centimeters, then μ can be set equal to unity. The definition of a magnetic pole of unit strength now follows directly from equation (16). A unit magnetic pole, or a pole of unit strength, is one which, when placed in a vacuum one centimeter away from a like equal pole, will repel it with a force of one dyne. The north and south poles of any one magnet are of equal strength.

The system of units defined above is called the *cgs electromagnetic system of units*, or emu. There is no special name given to the unit of pole strength.

1-7. Intensity of the Magnetic Field

The fact that a magnet will exert forces on other magnets suggests the idea that a *magnetic field* exists in the space around the magnet. This magnetic field may be explored by placing the north pole of a long thin magnet at any point in the field and measuring the force experienced by it. The *intensity of the magnetic field H* at any point P is defined as the ratio of the force F to the magnitude of the pole strength p of this exploring magnet which is placed at this point, that is,

$$\boxed{H = \frac{F}{p}.} \tag{17}$$

The strength of the exploring pole must be sufficiently small so that the magnetic field is not materially altered by the introduction of this pole. If F is measured in dynes and p in unit poles, then H is expressed in *oersteds.*

The intensity of the magnetic field H is a vector quantity whose direction at any point in space is that of the force experienced by the north pole of a magnet placed at that point. The south pole of a magnet, when placed in a magnetic field, will experience a force whose direction is opposite to that of the magnetic field at that point. For example, the intensity of the magnetic field at a point A, distant r from the north pole of a bar magnet of strength p_1, can be found by imagining the north pole of another magnet of strength p placed at this point. The force between these two north poles is, from Coulomb's law,

$$F = \frac{p_1 p}{\mu r^2}.$$

The intensity of the magnetic field at A is then

$$H = \frac{F}{p} = \frac{p_1}{\mu r^2}. \tag{18}$$

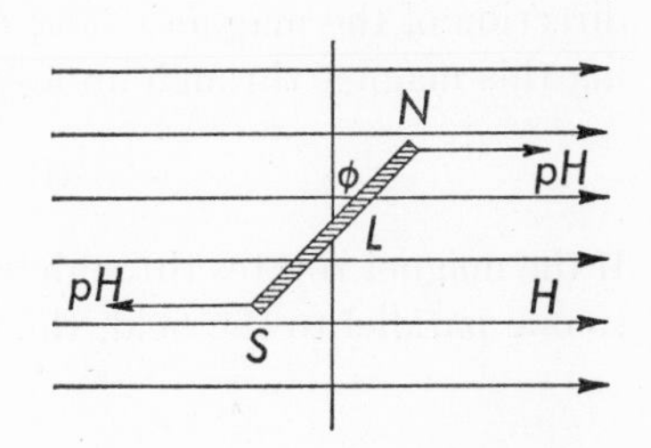

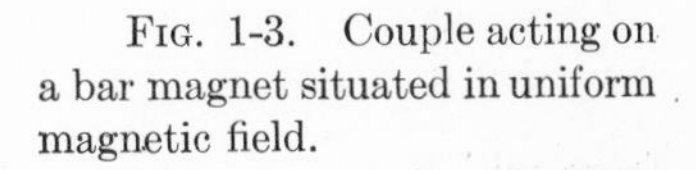
FIG. 1-3. Couple acting on a bar magnet situated in uniform magnetic field.

The direction of H is along a line from the pole p to the point A. The intensity of the magnetic field at A due to the south pole of the magnet can be found in a similar manner. The resultant intensity of the magnetic field at A produced by the bar magnet of pole strength p_1 will be the vector sum of the magnetic field intensities produced by the two poles. The magnetic field may be mapped in a manner analogous to that of the electric field. The number of *magnetic lines of force* drawn perpendicularly through a unit area at any point in space represents the intensity of the magnetic field at this point and the direction of these lines represents the direction of this magnetic field. If the magnetic field is uniform throughout a given region of space, then it would be represented by a series of parallel, equally spaced lines as shown in Figure 1-3. Such a field can be closely approximated experimentally, and has been used extensively in atomic investigations.

1-8. Magnetic Moment of a Magnet

A bar magnet whose diameter is small in comparison with its length can be specified by two quantities, its length L and the strength of either pole p. The product of the pole strength of a magnet and the length of a magnet is known as the *magnetic moment*, M, of the magnet; thus

$$\boxed{M = pL.} \tag{19}$$

If such a small bar magnet is placed in a uniform magnetic field of strength H, as shown in Figure 1-3, each pole will experience a force pH. The two forces on the poles of the magnet constitute a couple. The moment, T, of this couple is

$$T = pH \cdot L \cos \phi = MH \cos \phi, \tag{20}$$

where ϕ is the angle between the magnet and a line perpendicular to the direction of the magnetic field H. The amount of work done, dW, in rotating this magnet through an angle $d\phi$ is

$$dW = MH \cos \phi d\phi.$$

If the magnet rotates through 90° from a position perpendicular to the field to one parallel to the field, the work done by the field will be

$$W = MH \int_0^{\pi/2} \cos \phi d\phi,$$

from which

$$\boxed{W = MH.} \tag{21}$$

Any magnetic substance may be considered as made up of a very large number of very small elementary magnets. When the substance is unmagnetized, these elementary magnets are oriented at random, but when an external magnetic field is applied to this substance, each elementary magnet experiences a couple tending to orient it parallel to the direction of the magnetic field. The degree of orientation of these elementary magnets determines the strength of the poles of a magnetized substance. It is thus clear that work must be done to orient the elementary magnets and hence to magnetize a substance.

1-9. Energy in Electric and Magnetic Fields

It has been shown that work must be done to charge bodies electrically, and also to magnetize substances. A body which has been charged may be considered to possess more energy in virtue of the work done in charging it. One point of view is to consider this energy as residing in the electric field around this charged body. Similarly, the work done in magnetizing a substance may be considered as having been transformed into the energy which resides in the magnetic field surrounding the magnetized substance. Adopting this point of view, we may easily calculate the energy per unit volume in the electric field.

Consider, for example, a parallel plate capacitor consisting of two large metal plates separated by an insulating material whose dielectric constant is k. If q is the charge on either plate, V the difference of potential between the plates, and C the capacitance of the capacitor, the work done in charging this capacitor is

$$W = \tfrac{1}{2}qV = \tfrac{1}{2}CV^2. \tag{13}$$

The capacitance of a parallel plate capacitor is given by

$$C = \frac{kA}{4\pi s}, \tag{22}$$

where A is the area of either plate and s is the thickness of the insulating material between the plates. Since the electric field between the plates is uniform except for end effects, which may be neglected, the electric intensity anywhere in the space between the plates is simply

$$E = \frac{V}{s}. \tag{15}$$

With the aid of the above equations, the work W can be expressed as

$$\boxed{W = \frac{kE^2sA}{8\pi}.} \tag{23}$$

Assuming that the energy resides in the electric field between the plates of the capacitor in the volume sA, the energy per unit volume w in the electric field between the plates is

$$\boxed{w = \frac{kE^2}{8\pi}.} \tag{24}$$

No generality is lost in deriving the above expression for the special case of a uniform electric field, for if the field is not uniform, we can consider a very small region of the field which is practically uniform and deduce the same result.

In a similar manner, the energy per unit volume in a magnetic field can be shown to be

$$w = \frac{\mu H^2}{8\pi}, \tag{25}$$

where μ is the permeability of the medium and H is the intensity of the magnetic field.

1-10. The Electric Current

The motion of a group of electric charges constitutes an electric current. The magnitude of the electric current, i, is the time rate of flow of charges through a given surface S. Thus

$$i = \frac{dq}{dt}. \tag{26}$$

If q is expressed in esu of charge and t in seconds, then i is the esu of current. The practical unit of current is the ampere which is 3×10^9 times as big as the esu of current. The esu of current is sometimes called the *statampere*.

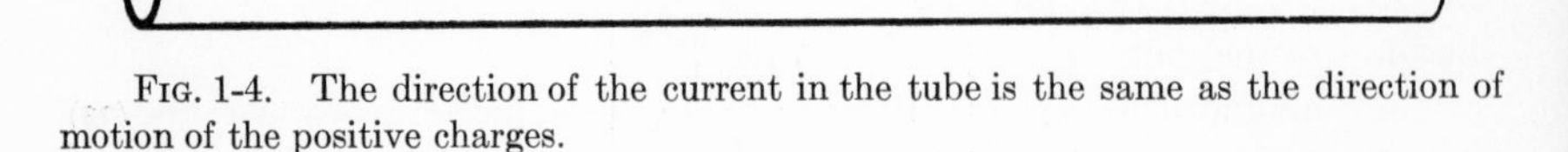

FIG. 1-4. The direction of the current in the tube is the same as the direction of motion of the positive charges.

The direction of the current is taken as the direction of motion of positive charges. If the current consists of the motion of negative charges, the direction of the current is opposite to the direction of motion of the negative charges, as shown in Figure 1-4.

1-11. Magnetic Effect of an Electric Current

Oersted (1820) discovered that a magnetic field exists in the neighborhood of a wire carrying current. Experiments with small magnets or iron filings show that the magnetic field in the neighborhood of a straight wire carrying current is circular in a plane at right angles to the wire with the wire as the center of these circles.

H. A. Rowland (1876) performed a famous experiment to show the equivalence of a moving charge and an electric current in so far as the magnetic effect was concerned. He used an ebonite disk having metallic sectors distributed near its rim. The metallic sectors were charged electrically; then the disk was rotated very rapidly. A magnetic needle near the disk was deflected by the magnetic field set up by the moving charges. When the direction of rotation of the disk was reversed, the deflection of the magnetic needle was also reversed. R. C. Tolman (1929), using a charged cylinder, showed that as far as the magnetic effect is concerned, an oscillating charge is equivalent to an alternating current.

The quantitative relationship between the intensity of the magnetic field at any point in space and the current in the wire was established empirically as a result of the experiments of Biot and Savart (1820), with long straight wires carrying current. If we consider a small section ds of a wire carrying current i, then the intensity of the magnetic field at any point P distant r from this current element is given by the expression

$$\boxed{dH = \frac{kids \sin \theta}{r^2},} \tag{27}$$

where dH is the magnetic field intensity at point P, θ is the angle between r and the current in the element ds, and k is a constant of proportionality. The direction of the magnetic field at point P is perpendicular to the plane containing r and ds as shown in Figure 1-5. A convenient method for determining the direction of the magnetic field intensity H, with reference to the direction of the current i producing it, is to use the *right-hand rule*. For a linear current, assume the thumb of the right hand points in the direction of the current; then the fingers of the right hand will curl in the direction of the lines of magnetic force representing H.

The magnetic field due to a current provides one of the best methods for measuring the magnitude of the current. Instead of utilizing our previous definition of the electric current and then evaluating the constant k, a new unit of current may be defined in terms of its magnetic effect. This is equivalent to replacing ki by a new symbol, i_m, to be defined by means of equation (27), which now takes the form

$$\boxed{dH = \frac{i_m ds \sin \theta}{r^2}.} \tag{28}$$

As an aid in defining this new unit of current, let us calculate the magnetic field intensity, H, produced by a current i_m flowing in a circular

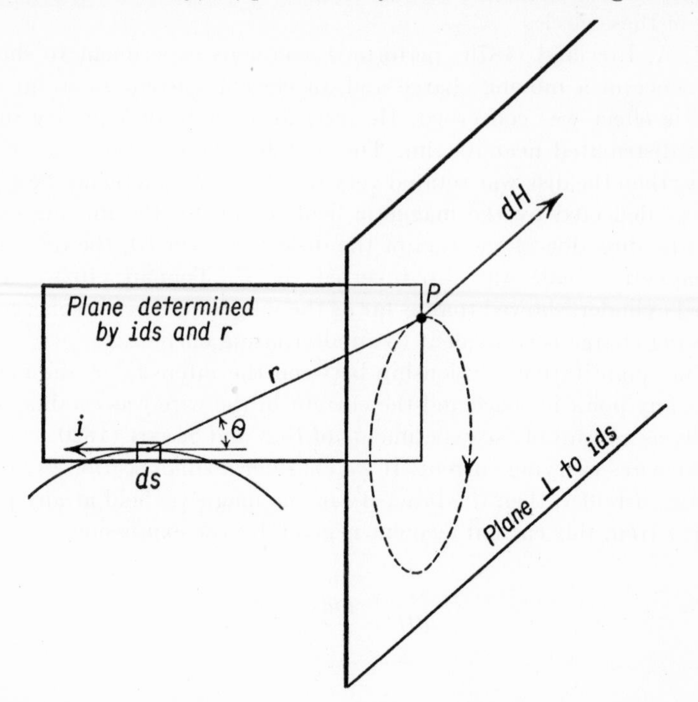

FIG. 1-5. The magnetic field at P is in a plane perpendicular to the plane containing the current element *ids*.

wire of radius r. The magnetic field intensity at the center of the circle, due to the current flowing in a small element of wire ds, is, from equation (28),

$$dH_c = \frac{i_m ds}{r^2},$$

since the angle θ between ds and r is equal to $\pi/2$. Now, from Figure 1-6,

$$ds = r d\phi,$$

so that the magnetic field intensity at the center of the circle due to the entire circuit is

$$H_c = \int_0^{2\pi} \frac{i_m d\phi}{r} = \frac{2\pi i_m}{r}. \tag{29}$$

The magnetic field at the center is perpendicular to the plane of the circle; if the current is in a counterclockwise direction, the magnetic field will be directed out of the plane toward the observer. The new unit of current, known as the *electromagnetic unit of current*, can now be defined with the aid of equation (29). The unit current, in emu, is that current, which, flowing in the arc of a circle one centimeter in length, the radius of the circle being one centimeter, produces a magnetic field of one oersted at the center of the circle. The electromagnetic unit of current is sometimes called the *abampere*. The practical unit of current, the ampere, is 1/10 of the em unit of current. If a current i_m flows in this circle of unit radius, the magnetic field intensity at the center of the circle is

$$H_1 = 2\pi i_m. \tag{30}$$

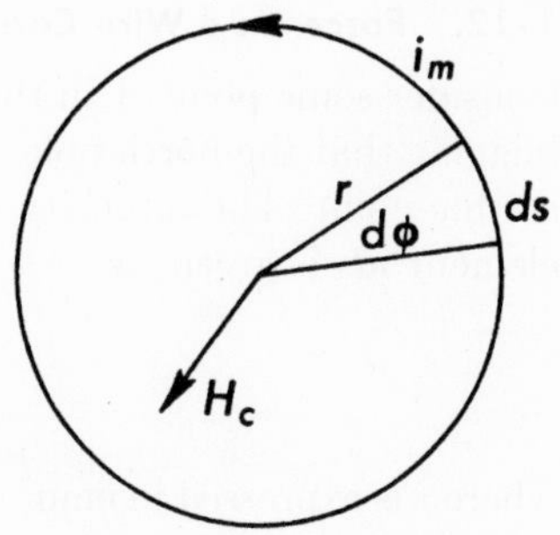

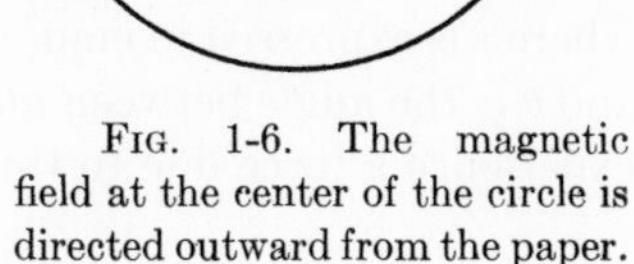

FIG. 1-6. The magnetic field at the center of the circle is directed outward from the paper.

If there are n turns of wire close together in a circle of radius r, each turn carrying current i_m, the intensity of the magnetic field at the center of the circle is

$$\boxed{H_n = \frac{2\pi n i_m}{r}.} \tag{31}$$

The magnitude of a current may be expressed in either electrostatic units or electromagnetic units. Experiments show that the electromagnetic unit of current is about 3×10^{10} times larger than the electrostatic unit of current. The most recent determination of this ratio yields the value as 2.9979×10^{10}. Furthermore, a comparison of the dimensions of these two units of current shows that the ratio is not a dimensionless constant, but that it has the dimensions of a velocity. This ratio will be denoted by the letter c where $c = 2.9979 \times 10^{10}$ cm/sec.

If a current, when expressed in electromagnetic units, has a value i_m, then the numerical value of this current in electrostatic units is

$$i_s = ci_m = 3 \times 10^{10}\, i_m.$$

For example, a current of 5 abamperes is equal to 15×10^{10} statamperes. Also, since 1 abampere is 10 amperes, the above current is equal to 50 amperes. Within the limits of experimental error, c is equal to the velocity of light in a vacuum. This result was of great importance in enabling Maxwell (1865) to establish the electromagnetic theory of light.

Every electric and magnetic quantity can be expressed either in em units or in es units. The ratio of the two units for any quantity always involves the constant c or c^2. For example, to convert a charge q_m expressed in emu to one q_s expressed in esu, we use the equation

$$q_s = cq_m. \tag{32}$$

1-12. Force on a Wire Carrying Current in a Magnetic Field

Consider some point A in the neighborhood of a wire carrying current and imagine that the north pole of a long thin magnet of strength p be situated at this point. The intensity of the magnetic field at A due to any current element ids is given by

$$dH = \frac{ids \sin \theta}{r^2},$$

where i is expressed in emu, r is the distance of the current element from A, and θ is the angle between ids and r. The north pole of the magnet will thus experience a force due to this current element given by

$$dF = pdH = \frac{pids \sin \theta}{r^2}. \tag{33}$$

Assuming Newton's third law, that to every action there is an equal and opposite reaction, the current element will experience an equal force in the opposite direction. In Figure 1-7, two planes are shown at right angles to each other. One plane contains the current element ids and r, the line joining point A to ids. A magnetic north pole of strength p at A will experience a force dF in a direction at right angles to the plane of ids and r. A second plane is drawn through r and dF perpendicular to the first plane. The force dF experienced by the current element ids is also in this second plane and is at right angles to the current element ids.

Now, the magnetic field intensity H_p, at the position of the current element ids at a distance r from the magnetic north pole of strength p, is, from equation (18),

$$H_p = \frac{p}{\mu r^2}. \tag{34}$$

The direction of H_p is along r from A to ids as shown in the figure. Replacing p/r^2 in equation (33) by its value, μH_p, from equation (34), we get, for the force dF on the current element ids,

$$\boxed{dF = \mu H_p \, ids \sin \theta.} \tag{35}$$

This force is at right angles to both the magnetic field intensity H_p and the current element ids; μ is the value of the permeability of the medium at the position of the current element. By introducing a new concept called the

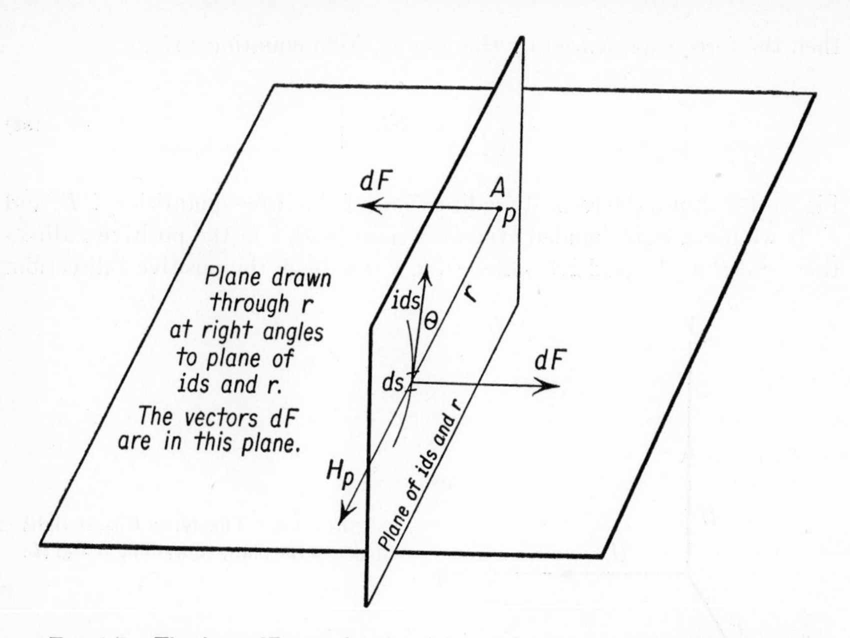

FIG. 1-7. The force dF on pole p at A is equal and opposite to the force dF on the current element ids at a distance r from A.

magnetic induction, or the *magnetic flux density*, designated by the letter B and defined by the equation

$$B = \mu H, \tag{36}$$

equation (35) can be written in the form

$$dF = B\, ids \sin\theta. \tag{37}$$

In the cgs electromagnetic system of units, the magnetic induction is expressed in *gausses*, while H is expressed in oersteds. The value of B in ferromagnetic materials may be several thousand times that of H. In free space, or a vacuum, $\mu = 1$ in the em system of units so that B and H are numerically equal; sometimes they are even used interchangeably.

It follows directly from equation (37) that the force on the current element is a maximum when $\theta = \pi/2$, that is, when the flux density B is at right angles to the current element ids. In the special case in which the current element is part of a straight wire of length L, situated in a uniform magnetic field of flux density B perpendicular to the length of the wire, then the force experienced by the wire is, from equation (37),

$$\boxed{F = BiL.} \tag{38}$$

Figure 1-8 shows the respective directions of the three quantities, i, B, and F. If we use a right-handed system of axes, with i in the positive x direction, and B in the positive y direction, F will be in the positive z direction.

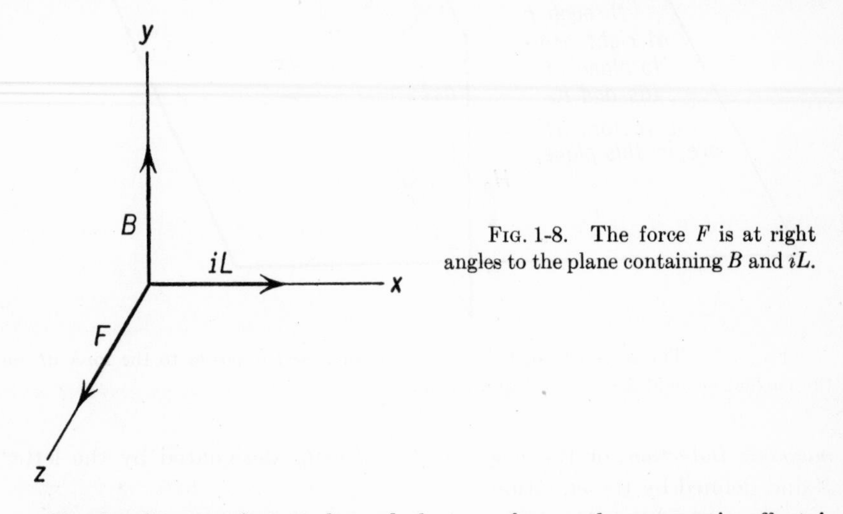

FIG. 1-8. The force F is at right angles to the plane containing B and iL.

Rowland's experiment showed that, as far as the magnetic effect is concerned, a moving charge is equivalent to a current. Suppose we have a motion of charges in any given direction with uniform velocity v. Let n be

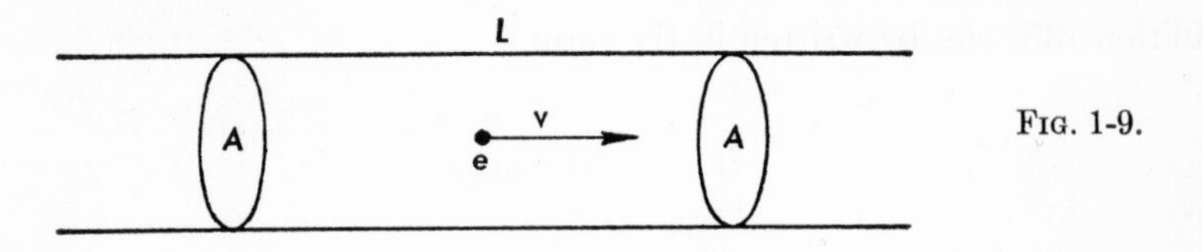

FIG. 1-9.

the number of charges per unit volume moving in a tube of uniform cross-sectional area A, as in Figure 1-9. If the magnitude of each charge in emu is e, then the current in any section of the tube is $i = nAev$. If this tube is in a uniform magnetic field of flux density B perpendicular to the direction of motion, the force on the charges in a length L will be

$$F = BneAvL.$$

The charge q in a length L of the tube is

$$q = neAL;$$

hence the force is

$$\boxed{F = Bqv.} \tag{39}$$

The force is perpendicular to both B and v. A single particle bearing a charge q and moving with a velocity v in a direction perpendicular to a magnetic field of flux density B will also experience a force $F = Bqv$: this force will be perpendicular to both B and v.

1-13. Magnetic Moment of a Plane Circuit Carrying Current

Any plane circuit carrying current i, when placed in a uniform magnetic field of flux density B, will experience a torque T, given by

$$T = iAB \cos \phi, \tag{40}$$

where ϕ is the angle between the plane of the circuit and the direction of the magnetic field. This torque will be a maximum when the plane of the circuit is parallel to the field, and will be zero when the plane circuit is at right angles to the field. If left free to rotate, a plane circuit will always set itself at right angles to the direction of the external magnetic field. This follows directly from the application of equation (35) to each element of the plane circuit. It is left as an exercise for the student to carry out this calculation for some simple geometrical figure such as a rectangle or a circle.

The expression for the torque on a plane circuit carrying current as given by equation (40) can be compared with the expression for the torque on a bar magnet of magnetic moment M when placed in the same magnetic field. The latter is given by equation (20). In making this comparison, let us consider the plane circuit in a vacuum, in which case $\mu = 1$ and $B = H$; it then follows that a plane circuit of area A carrying current i may be assigned a magnetic moment M given by

$$\boxed{M = iA,} \tag{41}$$

where i is expressed in emu.

1-14. Electromagnetic Induction

Michael Faraday in England and Joseph Henry in the United States discovered the phenomenon of electromagnetic induction at about the same time, in 1831. They found that *whenever the magnetic field around a circuit is changed, an electromotive force is induced in this circuit.* The magnetic field may be changed in any number of ways, for example by moving a permanent magnet relative to the circuit, or by bringing another circuit carrying current near the first one, or by varying the current in a neighboring circuit, or by varying the current within the circuit under investigation. It is found experimentally that the magnitude of the electromotive force induced in any circuit is proportional to the time rate of change of the magnetic field around the circuit.

The relationship between the induced electromotive force and the changing magnetic field can best be put in quantitative form by considering the changes in the total *magnetic flux* through the circuit. If we consider any small area dA in a region of permeability μ in which there is a magnetic field of intensity H, the magnetic flux $d\Phi$ through this small area is defined by the equation

$$d\Phi = \mu H_n dA \tag{42}$$

in which H_n is the component of the magnetic field intensity perpendicular to the element of area dA. The total magnetic flux Φ through the area A enclosed by any circuit is then

$$\Phi = \int_0^A \mu H_n dA. \tag{43}$$

In the particular case in which the magnetic field intensity is uniform and perpendicular to the area A, the total magnetic flux is simply

$$\Phi = \mu HA. \tag{44}$$

The *magnetic flux density*, denoted by B, is defined by the equation

$$B = \mu H. \tag{45}$$

In the particular case in which the field is uniform and perpendicular to the area A, the flux is

$$\Phi = BA. \tag{46}$$

In the electromagnetic system of units, H, as we know, is measured in *oersteds:* the magnetic flux density B is measured in *gausses.* The total magnetic flux Φ is measured in *maxwells:* thus a gauss is also a maxwell per square centimeter.

Applied to any plane coil consisting of a single turn enclosing an area A, Faraday's law states that the induced electromotive force V in this circuit is equal to the time rate of change of the magnetic flux through the coil or

$$\boxed{V = -\frac{d\Phi}{dt}.} \tag{47}$$

The minus sign is used to indicate that the direction of the induced electromotive force is such as to give rise to a current which, by its magnetic effect, will oppose the change inducing the current. This is a consequence of the principle of conservation of energy and was first formulated by Lenz (1834).

In equation (47) all quantities are expressed in cgs electromagnetic units. If V is to be expressed in volts when Φ is in maxwells and t in seconds, then the equation takes the form

$$V = -10^{-8} \frac{d\Phi}{dt}. \tag{48}$$

If the coil through which the flux is changing consists of n turns each enclosing the same area A, then the emf induced in the coil is n times that induced in one turn.

Equation (47) is perfectly general and is independent of the material of which the coil is made. Thus an emf will be induced in any closed path surrounding a changing magnetic field whether this closed path consists of a conductor or is merely an imaginary closed path in free space. An induced electromotive force in any closed path implies the existence of an electric field E which is tangent to the path at every point, that is,

$$V = \int_0^s E ds \tag{49}$$

where s is measured along the closed path.

The phenomenon of electromagnetic induction is the basis for many of our most practical devices such as the electromagnetic generator, the transformer, the induction coil, and the electric motor.

1-15. The mks System of Units

In addition to the cgs electrostatic and electromagnetic systems of units defined in this chapter, there is the mks system of units which is being widely used in physics, particularly in electricity and magnetism. There are two versions of the mks system in current use: one is called the rationalized system, the other, unrationalized. Only the latter will be briefly sketched here. The mks system is based upon the meter as the unit of length, the kilogram as the unit of mass, and the second as the unit of time. The unit of force is the *newton*, which is defined as the force necessary to give a mass of one kilogram an acceleration of one meter/sec^2. It therefore follows that

$$1 \text{ newton} = 10^5 \text{ dynes.}$$

When applied to electricity and magnetism, the coulomb is used as the unit of charge. Hence, in using Coulomb's law and the equations based upon it, the constant k cannot be assigned an arbitrary value for a vacuum since the units for charge, force, and distance have already been chosen. Its value may be found by a direct experimental determination; however, for our purposes, it will suffice to assume that

$$1 \text{ coulomb} = 3 \times 10^9 \text{ esu of charge}$$

and to evaluate the force between two positive charges, each of one coulomb, when placed one meter apart, first using equation (1) with electrostatic units and $k = 1$, and then using equation (1) with mks units and setting $k = k_0$ for its value in a vacuum.

Since $$1 \text{ coulomb} = 3 \times 10^9 \text{ statcoulombs}$$

and $$1 \text{ meter} = 100 \text{ cm},$$

application of equation (1), using the cgs electrostatic system of units with $k = 1$, yields

$$F = \frac{3 \times 10^9 \times 3 \times 10^9}{(100)^2} \text{ dynes} = 9 \times 10^{14} \text{ dynes}$$

or $$F = 9 \times 10^9 \text{ newtons.}$$

If we use the mks system of units, then, setting $k = k_0$, $q_1 = q_2 = 1$ coulomb, and $F = 9 \times 10^9$ newtons in equation (1), we can solve for k_0,

thus $$9 \times 10^9 \text{ newtons} = \frac{1 \text{ coul} \times 1 \text{ coul}}{k_0 \times 1\text{m}^2},$$

from which $$1/k_0 = 9 \times 10^9 \frac{\text{ntn} \cdot \text{m}^2}{\text{coul}^2}$$

or $$k_0 = 1.11 \times 10^{-10} \frac{\text{coul}^2}{\text{ntn} \cdot \text{m}^2}.$$

For any material medium k can be set equal to Kk_0. In the mks system k is called the *permittivity* of the dielectric, k_0 is called the permittivity of a vacuum, and K is called the relative permittivity of the dielectric.

In the es system of units, $k_0 = 1$, so that $k = K$, that is, the relative permittivity is equal to the dielectric constant.

The unit of current in the mks system is the ampere, the unit of difference of potential is the volt, and the unit of energy is the joule. The unit of magnetic field intensity, as can be seen from equation (31), is the ampere-turn/meter; this has the same dimensions as the ampere/meter. It follows from equation (31) that

$$1000 \text{ amperes/meter} = 1 \text{ oersted.}$$

The unit of magnetic flux is the *weber*, and the unit of magnetic flux density is the weber/meter^2. The relationship between the weber/meter^2 and the gauss can be found by using equation (38), which shows that

$$1 \text{ weber/meter}^2 = 10{,}000 \text{ gausses.}$$

A weber is a unit of magnetic flux such that a change in magnetic flux of one weber per second through a circuit will induce an emf of one volt in each turn of the circuit.

In the electromagnetic system of units the permeability of a vacuum μ was set equal to one. Its value in the mks system can be determined from the defining equation

$$B = \mu_0 H, \tag{36}$$

where μ_0 is the value of the permeability of a vacuum, by assuming the relationships

$$1 \text{ weber/m}^2 = 10{,}000 \text{ gausses}$$

$$1 \text{ ampere/m} = 10^{-3} \text{ oersted}$$

and substituting these values into equation (36).

Now, in a vacuum, when $B = 1$ gauss, $H = 1$ oersted; converting these to mks values, we get

$$B = 10^{-4} \text{ weber/m}^2.$$

$$H = 1000 \text{ amp/m.}$$

Substituting these values into equation (36) yields

$$10^{-4} \text{ weber/m}^2 = \mu_0 \times 10^3 \text{ amp/m}$$

or

$$\mu_0 = 10^{-7} \text{ weber/amp} \cdot \text{m}$$

as the value of the permeability of a vacuum.

The permeability μ of any medium may then be written as

$$\mu = K_m \mu_0 \tag{50}$$

where K_m is called the relative permeability of the medium and is defined by equation (50).

The relationship between the unit of pole strength in the mks system to that in the em system can be found with the aid of Coulomb's law, equation (16), by using the numerical value of μ_0 shown above. Doing this, we find that

$$1 \text{ mks pole} = 10^8 \text{ em poles.}$$

The conversion factors for some of the quantities for the three systems of units are listed in Table 1-1 for convenience.

The general equations discussed in this chapter can be used with any consistent set of units. In most work in atomic and nuclear physics the cgs systems of units will be found more useful and are more generally used. A few additional units, such as electron volt, ev, and atomic mass unit, amu, which are peculiar to this subject, are widely used in the literature. Further, the theoretical equations applicable to this subject take a much simpler form when used with esu and emu because the constants k_0 and μ_0 need not be incorporated in them, since, as we shall see, the atom consists of a group of particles situated in free space. Hence the mks system of units will rarely be used in the succeeding chapters.

Table 1-1

Conversion Factors

Quantity	mks Unit	cgs es Units	cgs em Units
Force	1 newton	$=10^5$ dynes	$=10^5$ dynes
Energy	1 joule	$=10^7$ ergs	$=10^7$ ergs
Electric charge	1 coulomb	$=3\times10^9$ statcoul	$=10^{-1}$ abcoulomb
Electric current	1 ampere	$=3\times10^9$ statamp	$=10^{-1}$ abampere
Potential difference	1 volt	$=\frac{1}{300}$ statvolt	$=10^8$ abvolts
Electric field intensity	1 newton/coulomb or 1 volt/meter	$=\frac{1}{3\times10^4}$ statvolts/cm	$=10^6$ abvolts/cm
Resistance	1 ohm	$=\frac{1}{9\times10^{11}}$ statohm	$=10^9$ abohms
Magnetic pole	1 mks pole	. . .	$=10^8$ em poles
Magnetic field intensity	1 amp/m	. . .	$=10^{-3}$ oersted
Magnetic flux density	1 weber/m^2	. . .	$=10^4$ gausses
Magnetic flux	1 weber	. . .	$=10^8$ maxwells
Coefficient of self-inductance	1 henry	. . .	$=10^9$ abhenries
Capacitance	1 farad	$=9\times10^{11}$ statfarads	$=10^{-9}$ abfarad

Problems

1-1. (**a**) Show that the potential of an isolated sphere of radius R is equal to q/R, where q is the charge on the sphere. (**b**) Using the result of part (**a**), show that the capacitance of an isolated sphere in a vacuum is equal to its radius.

1-2. (**a**) Determine the potential at a point 0.5×10^{-8} cm from a proton whose positive charge is 4.8×10^{-10} esu. Express the potential in cgs units and in volts. (**b**) Determine the potential energy of an electron when situated at this point.

Ans. (**a**) 0.096 statvolt; 28.8 volts.
(**b**) -4.6×10^{-11} erg.

1-3. (**a**) Determine the potential at a point 5×10^{-12} cm from a nucleus of charge $+80e$, where e is the electronic charge. Express the potential in cgs units and in volts. (**b**) Determine the potential energy of an alpha particle at this position. The charge of an alpha particle is $+2e$.

Ans. (**a**) 7680 statvolts, 2.30×10^{6} volts.
(**b**) 7.37×10^{-6} erg.

1-4. (**a**) An electron of a hydrogen atom moves in a circular orbit of radius 0.53×10^{-8} cm with a frequency of 6.6×10^{15} sec^{-1}. Determine the current in this orbit. (**b**) Calculate the intensity of the magnetic field at the center of this orbit.

Ans. (**a**) 1.05×10^{-3} amp.
(**b**) 1.25×10^{5} oersteds.

1-5. A capacitor, consisting of two parallel plates each of area 80 cm^2 separated a distance of 5mm, has a difference of potential of 300 volts maintained between its plates by means of a battery. Calculate (**a**) the intensity of the field between the plates, and (**b**) the energy per unit volume in this field. (**c**) A very small oil drop carrying a charge of 32×10^{-19} coulomb is introduced between the plates. Calculate the force acting on this oil drop.

Ans. (**a**) 600 volts per cm or 2 dynes per esu of charge.
(**b**) $1/2\pi$ erg per cm^3.
(**c**) 1.92×10^{-8} dyne.

1-6. (**a**) Show that the intensity of the magnetic field at any point distant r from a very long straight wire carrying current i is

$$H = 2i/r.$$

(**b**) Calculate the intensity of the magnetic field at a distance of 10 cm from a very long straight wire carrying a current of 4 amperes.

Ans. 0.08 oersted.

1-7. (**a**) A rectangular loop of wire of length L and width b is placed in a uniform magnetic field of strength H with its plane parallel to the direction of the magnetic field. Show that when a current i is sent through the wire, the loop of wire will experience a torque equal to $iLbH$, where i is in emu. (**b**) A galvanometer coil consists of 600 turns of very fine wire wound on a rectangular frame 4 cm long and 1 cm wide, and is hung by means of a gold wire in a magnetic field of 500 oersteds. What is the torque on the galvanometer coil when a current of 10^{-8} amperes flows through each turn?

Ans. 12×10^{-4} dyne cm.

1-8. With the aid of equation (35), calculate the torque on a circular coil of wire of radius R carrying current i in a uniform magnetic field of strength H parallel to the plane of the coil. Compare this result with equation (40).

1-9. A circular coil of wire of 30 cm radius contains 750 turns wound close together. Determine the intensity of the magnetic field at the center of the coil when the current in the coil is 5 amperes.

Ans. 78.5 oersteds.

1-10. A stream of alpha particles, each carrying a charge of 3.2×10^{-19} coulomb, is sent through a uniform magnetic field of 30,000 gausses. The velocity of each particle is 1.52×10^9 cm/sec and is at right angles to the direction of the magnetic field. Determine the force on each alpha particle.

Ans. 14.6×10^{-7} dyne.

1-11. A thin bar magnet 12 cm long has a pole strength of 500 unit poles. It is placed in a uniform magnetic field of 200 oersteds intensity with the length of the magnet, that is, its axis, at right angles to the direction of the magnetic field. (**a**) Calculate the torque on the magnet in this position. (**b**) Determine the work done by the field in rotating the magnet so that its axis is parallel to the field.

Ans. (**a**) 12×10^5 dyne cm.
(**b**) 12×10^5 ergs.

1-12. A coil of fine wire of 8 cm radius has 500 turns. The magnetic field through the coil is increased at a uniform rate from zero to 12,000 gausses in 0.2 second. Determine the average value of the induced electromotive force in this coil.

Ans. 60.4 volts.

1-13. Calculate the magnetic moment of the plane circuit formed by the motion of an electron in an orbit of hydrogen of radius 0.53×10^{-8} cm with a frequency of 6.6×10^{15} sec^{-1}.

Ans. 9.27×10^{-21} erg/gauss.

1-14. Calculate the average value of the emf induced in a plane circuit of one turn whose radius is 150 cm, if the magnetic field through it is changed from zero to 15,000 gausses in 1/240 sec.

Ans. 2,540 volts.

References

Culver, C. A., *Theory and Application of Electricity and Magnetism*. New York: McGraw-Hill Book Company, Inc., 1947, Chaps. I–VIII, XI.

Frank, N. H., *Introduction to Electricity and Optics*. New York: McGraw-Hill Book Company, Inc., 1950, Chaps. I–VIII, X.
Page, L., and N. I. Adams, *Principles of Electricity*. New York: D. Van Nostrand Company, Inc., 1949, Chaps. I, II, IV, VII, VIII.
Richtmyer, F. K., and E. H. Kennard, *Introduction to Modern Physics*. New York: McGraw-Hill Book Company, Inc., 1947, Chaps. I, II.
Sears, F. W., *Principles of Physics*. Vol. II, *Electricity and Magnetism*. Cambridge, Mass.: Addison-Wesley Press, 1947, Chaps. I–III, XI, XII.
Starling, S. G., *Electricity and Magnetism*. New York: Longmans, Green & Co., 1942, Chaps. I, III, V, VIII, XIII.

chapter **2**

Charged Atomic Particles

2-1. Introduction: Atomic Weights

The concept of atoms was introduced into chemistry as a hypothesis by Dalton (1802), to explain the formation of compounds from simpler substances called elements. The atoms of any one element were assumed to be identical in all their properties including weight. Dalton also formulated the law of multiple proportions which states that if two elements combine in more than one proportion to form different compounds, the weights of one of the elements which unite with identical amounts of the second element are in the ratio of integral numbers. For example, 16 grams of oxygen combine with 12 grams of carbon to form carbon monoxide, CO, while 32 grams of oxygen can also combine with 12 grams of carbon to form another compound, carbon dioxide, CO_2. Shortly afterward, the law of definite proportions was established. This law states that, in any compound, the proportion by weight of the constituent elements is a constant. For example, when mercuric oxide is decomposed, for every 16 grams of oxygen liberated, 200.6 grams of mercury are liberated. When oxygen and mercury are combined to form mercuric oxide, their proportions by weight are always in the ratio of 16 to 200.6.

Many of the elements and compounds were studied in the gaseous state: it was found that the volumes of the elements and compounds involved in a reaction, in which both the initial and final constituents were gases, were connected by very simple relationships. To explain the behavior of gases, Avogadro (1811) put forth the bold hypothesis that equal volumes of different gases, under the same conditions of temperature and pressure, contain equal numbers of molecules. Ampère supported this hypothesis and pointed out that, if correct, it should lead to "a method for determining the relative masses of the atoms and the proportions according to which they enter into combination."

In the combination of hydrogen and oxygen to form water vapor, it is found that when measured at the same temperature and pressure, two liters of hydrogen and one liter of oxygen combine to form two liters of water vapor. The interpretation of this result on the basis of Avogadro's hypothesis is that two molecules of hydrogen and one molecule of oxygen combine to form two molecules of water vapor. The chemical equation expressing this result is

$$2H_2 + O_2 = 2H_2O.$$

This equation also states that, in the free state, hydrogen and oxygen molecules are composed of two atoms each, and water vapor molecules consist of three atoms, two hydrogen atoms and one oxygen atom. From a determination of the combining weights it has been found that 16 grams of oxygen combine with 2.016 grams of hydrogen to form 18.016 grams of water vapor. Since one atom of oxygen combines with two atoms of hydrogen to form water vapor, the relative atomic weights of oxygen and hydrogen are in the ratio of 16 to 1.008. The *chemical system of atomic weights* adopts as a standard 16.00 for the atomic weight of oxygen. The atomic weights of all the other elements are then stated in terms of O = 16.00 as the standard.

Since a molecule of oxygen in the free state contains two atoms, the molecular weight of oxygen is 32.00. The molecular weight of hydrogen, H_2, is 2.016. A quantity of any substance whose mass, in grams, is numerically equal to its molecular weight, is called a *mole*. The volume occupied by a mole of any gas is called a gram molecular volume. At 0°C and 76 cm pressure *the gram molecular volume* of any gas is 22.4 liters. On the basis of Avogadro's hypothesis, every mole of a substance contains the same number of molecules. The number, usually referred to as the *Avogadro number*, will be denoted by the letter N_0.

From the above discussion, it is readily seen that, *in the case of an element, a mass in grams equal numerically to its atomic weight must contain N_0 atoms*. For example, 16 grams of oxygen contain $N_0/2$ molecules and hence contain N_0 atoms. Similarly for any other diatomic molecule. For a monatomic molecule such as helium or neon, it is obvious, of course, that there are N_0 atoms in a gram-atomic weight of the element. Hence, if the Avogadro number N_0 can be determined, the mass in grams of any atom will be known. Since we are evidently dealing with large numbers of atoms, the atomic mass determined in this manner may be only an average value. It has been found that in many cases the masses of the atoms of an element are not all identical. (See §2-8.)

The Avogadro number N_0 can be determined by several methods. Two of these methods will be discussed in this chapter. One method is based upon a study of electrolysis; the other is based upon a study of the Brownian motion of particles suspended in a fluid.

2-2. Electrolysis

Solutions of acids, bases, and salts are known to be conductors of electricity. The conductivity of these solutions is due to the presence of *ions* in the solution. An ion is an atom or a group of atoms charged electrically.

On the modern theory of the structure of the atom (§3-6), an atom consists of a positively charged *nucleus* surrounded by a number of negatively charged particles called *electrons.* In the neutral atom, the sum of all the electronic charges is equal, numerically, to the positive charge of the nucleus. An atom is said to be ionized if the total electronic charge is not equal numerically to the positive charge of the nucleus; similarly, a group of atoms is said to be ionized if the total electronic charge differs numerically from the total positive charge of their nuclei. If there is a deficiency of electrons, the ion is positively charged, and if there is an excess of electrons, it is negatively charged. It has been found empirically that the charge on any ion can be expressed in terms of integral multiples of a fundamental quantity of electricity which has been shown to be equivalent to the charge of an electron (§2-4). If the charge on an ion is equivalent to one electron, it is said to have a valence of unity; if the charge on an ion is equivalent to two electrons, it has a valence of two, and so on.

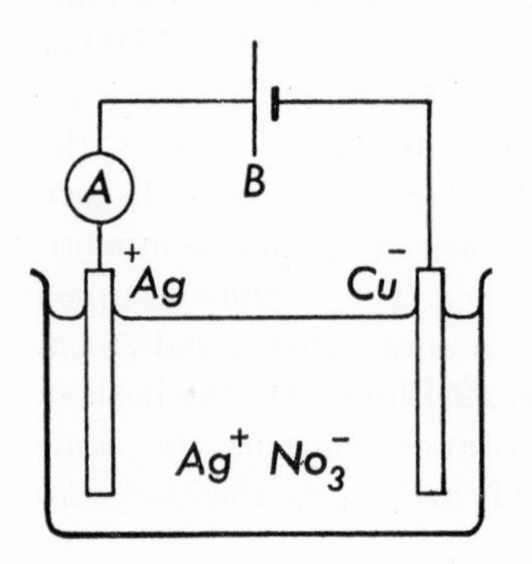

Fig. 2-1.

As a typical example of electrolysis, let us consider a chemical cell containing a solution of silver nitrate, $AgNO_3$, a silver anode connected to the positive terminal of a battery, and a copper cathode connected to the negative terminal of the battery, as shown in Figure 2-1. The silver nitrate in the solution is dissociated into silver ions, Ag^+, and nitrate ions, NO_3^-. Under the action of the electric field between the electrodes, the Ag^+ ions migrate toward the cathode, and the NO_3^- ions migrate toward the anode. If the chemical cell is examined after the current has been flowing in the circuit for some definite time, it will be found that a mass M of metallic silver Ag has been deposited on the cathode and an equal mass M of metallic silver has been removed from the anode, leaving the concentration of the solution unchanged. A simplified analysis of the action of this cell is as follows: when a silver ion, Ag^+, reaches the cathode, it acquires an electron from it, thus forming a neutral atom which adheres to the cathode. At the anode a silver atom breaks up into a silver ion and an electron; the ion, Ag^+, goes into solution to replace the one which was removed, while the electron is forced through the external part of the circuit. Thus an atom is removed from the anode for each atom deposited on the cathode. The silver ions are transferred through the solution and the electrons are transferred through the external metallic portions of the circuit.

The behavior of electrolytic cells can be summarized in terms of two laws first formulated by Faraday. The first law states that the quantity of any substance liberated from the solution depends only upon the total charge passing through the circuit, or

$$\boxed{M = kQ,} \tag{1}$$

where M is the mass of the material liberated at one electrode, Q is the quantity of charge transferred, and k is a factor of proportionality called the *electrochemical equivalent* of the substance. From this equation, it is evident that k is the mass liberated per unit charge transferred, usually expressed in grams per coulomb.

Faraday's second law states that for any substance the mass liberated by the transfer of a quantity of electricity Q is proportional to the *chemical equivalent* of the substance, or

$$\boxed{M = Q\frac{A}{v}\frac{1}{F},} \tag{2}$$

where A/v, the ratio of the atomic weight to the valence of the element, is the chemical equivalent of the element, and F is a constant of proportionality known as the *Faraday constant.*

From equations (1) and (2), it will be noted that

$$F = \frac{A}{kv}\cdot$$

The value of F can be determined from the results of the experiments on electrolysis. For the case of silver, where $k = 0.0011180$ grams per coulomb, $A = 107.88$ grams per gram-atomic weight, and v is unity, we get

$$F = \frac{107.88}{0.0011180} = 96{,}500 \text{ coulombs/gm-at wt.}$$

Thus the transfer of 96,500 coulombs of charge will deposit a gram-atomic weight of a monovalent element.

Since the valence of silver is unity, for every atom of silver deposited on the cathode, a charge equivalent to one electron has been transferred through the solution. If e is the charge of one electron, then N_0e is the total charge transferred when one gram-atomic weight of silver is deposited on the cathode. Or

$$\boxed{F = N_0e = 96{,}500 \text{ coulombs/gm-at wt.}} \tag{3}$$

The value of the Avogadro number can be determined from a knowledge of the value of the electronic charge. The present accepted value of e is 4.80×10^{-10} statcoulomb or 1.60×10^{-19} coulomb, so that $N_0 = 6.025 \times 10^{23}$ atoms per gram-atomic weight.

If the Avogadro number N_0 could be determined independently with the same degree of precision as the electronic charge e, it would be a check on the determination of e as well as additional confirmation of Avogadro's hypothesis. The first direct determination of the Avogadro number was made by Perrin in 1908 in an investigation of the motion and distribution of very small particles suspended in a fluid.

2-3. Brownian Motion

If fine particles suspended in a fluid are examined in the field of a microscope, it will be observed that they are in constant haphazard motion. This random motion continues indefinitely and is found to depend upon several factors, such as the size of the particles, the viscosity of the fluid in which they are immersed, and the temperature of the system. The motion of these particles was first observed by Brown in 1827. Many observers recognized that these particles behave in the same way that molecules of an ideal gas are supposed to behave. The random motion of these particles may be likened to the thermal motion of gas molecules.

The explanation of the Brownian motion, first given by Einstein and Smoluchowski (1905), is based on the assumption that the particles in suspension are continually bombarded by the molecules of the fluid and that this bombardment produces an unbalanced force which accelerates the particle. The motion of the particle through the fluid is opposed by another force due to the viscosity of the fluid. From this theory the distribution of particles in a field of force and their displacement in the course of time can be calculated. Perrin performed these two different types of experiments on Brownian motion, one on the vertical distribution of the particles in the fluid, the other on the displacement of the particles in a given time interval. As a result of many determinations of N_0 under different experimental conditions, Perrin adopted

$$N_0 = 6.85 \times 10^{23}$$

as the best value for the Avogadro number, yielding the value

$$e = 4.2 \times 10^{-10} \text{ esu}$$

for the electronic charge.

Later work by Millikan and Fletcher on Brownian motion in a gaseous medium such as air yielded the value $N_0 = 6.03 \times 10^{23}$, while Westgren (1915), working with colloidal gold, silver, and selenium particles, obtained the value $N_0 = 6.05 \times 10^{23}$. Avogadro's hypothesis was thus confirmed experimentally about a century after it was formulated.

R. T. Birge, who has been making a very exhaustive and critical study of the experimental determinations of the different fundamental physical constants, considers recent determinations of the Avogadro number to be among the most reliable of any of the physical constants. One method which has attained great precision and has yielded generally consistent results is the determination of the Avogadro number from measurements of the densities of crystals and their structure as determined by x-ray analysis (see §5-12).

The present value of the Avogadro number is

$$N_0 = 6.025 \times 10^{23} \text{ atoms/gm-at wt.}$$

When the above value is combined with the present value of the Faraday

$$F = 9652.0 \text{ emu per gram-atomic weight,}$$

the value of the electronic charge becomes

$$e = 4.803 \times 10^{-10} \text{ esu of charge.}$$

(See Appendix I.)

2-4. Determination of the Charge of an Electron

The earliest experiments on the determination of the electronic charge were performed by Townsend (1897) and J. J. Thomson (1898). Their method consisted in allowing water vapor to condense on ions, thus forming a cloud, and then determining the charge carried by the cloud. The number of individual droplets in the cloud was then computed by weighing the water condensed from the cloud and dividing it by the average weight of a single droplet. The latter was determined by measuring the rate of fall of these droplets through air, assuming Stokes' law to hold. On the assumption that each droplet was condensed on a single ion carrying charge e, they obtained values for e of the order of 3×10^{-10} esu.

A very important by-product of this type of investigation was the discovery by C. T. R. Wilson (1897) of a method for producing these clouds. If air that is saturated with water vapor and ionized by some agency is expanded suddenly, the air is cooled and the water vapor condenses on the ions in the air.

H. A. Wilson (1903) made a decided improvement in the method for determining the electronic charge by forming clouds between two capacitor plates which could be connected to the terminals of a battery. The experimental procedure was first to determine the rate of fall of the top surface of the cloud under the influence of gravity alone, and then to produce a second cloud and charge the capacitor plates so that the droplets would be urged downward by both gravity and the force due to the electric field. The numerical results for the electronic charge were about the same as those obtained by Townsend and Thomson. All of these experiments suffered from the fact that the weight of a drop of water did not remain constant during the time of observation. Further, the exact number of ions on which each drop was condensed was not known.

Millikan, while repeating the experiments of H. A. Wilson, found that single drops of water could be held stationary between the two plates of

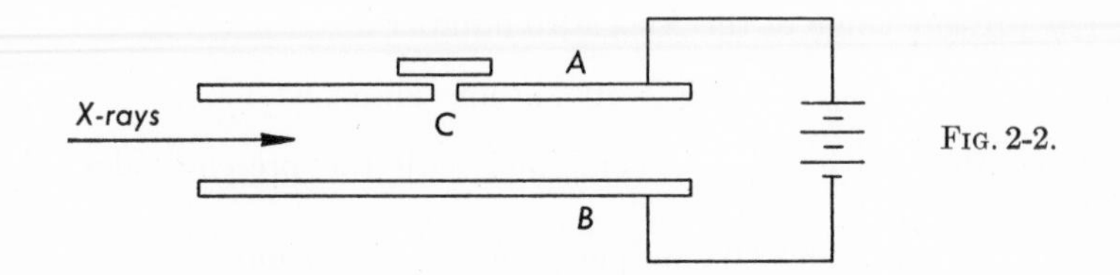

FIG. 2-2.

the capacitor by adjusting the voltage between the plates so that the weight of the drop could be balanced by the force due to the electric field between the plates. While working with these "balanced drops" he noticed that occasionally the drop would start moving up or down in the electric field. This drop had evidently captured an ion, positive in one case, negative in the other case. This made it possible to determine the charge carried by an ion irrespective of the original charge carried by the drop of water. To avoid the errors due to evaporation Millikan decided to use drops of oil instead of water.

The apparatus consisted essentially of two brass plates A and B about 22 cm in diameter and about 1.5 cm apart, as sketched in Figure 2-2. These plates were placed in a large metal box to avoid air currents. In this experiment small drops of oil are sprayed into the box by means of an atomizer. After a while one of these drops drifts through the pinhole C in the top of plate A and can then be observed with the aid of a telescope. Indirect illumination of the drop is provided by a lamp on the side. When there is no electric field between the plates, the forces acting on the oil drop are its weight m_1g, the buoyant force, m_0g, of the air, and a resisting force due to the viscosity of the medium. Let us set

$$m_1g - m_0g = mg,$$

where mg is the effective weight of the oil drop in the air. From experiment it is known that the resisting force is proportional to the velocity of the oil drop. Equilibrium will be reached when the velocity of the drop reaches such a value that the resisting force becomes equal to the effective weight of the oil drop. The oil drop will then continue to move downward with uniform velocity. Calling this value of the velocity v_1, we can write

$$mg = Kv_1, \tag{4}$$

where K is a factor of proportionality. For very small drops, this value of the velocity is reached very quickly. If the capacitor plates are now connected to the battery so that plate A is positive, the velocity of the oil drop will be changed suddenly. This change is due to the fact that the oil drop is charged when it comes from the atomizer. If q represents the charge on the oil drop, then the force on it due to the electric field is

$$F = \frac{V}{d}q, \tag{5}$$

where V is the difference of potential between the plates and d is the distance between the plates. If the charge on the oil drop is negative, then the force due to the electric field will be upward and the new velocity v_2 will be given by

$$F - mg = Kv_2, \tag{6}$$

where v_2 is considered positive in the upward direction. Combining equations (5) and (6), we get

$$\frac{V}{d}q - mg = Kv_2. \tag{7}$$

In Millikan's experiment the air between the capacitor plates was ionized by various methods such as allowing x-rays or the radiations from radioactive substances to pass through it. The oil drop occasionally acquired an additional ion, either positive or negative, and its velocity in the electric field was observed to change. Or it may have lost an ion in its passage through the ionized air. If v_3 represents its new velocity after the acquisition of an ion of charge q_n, then from equation (7)

$$\frac{V}{d}(q + q_n) - mg = Kv_3. \tag{8}$$

Solving equations (7) and (8) for q_n, we get

$$\boxed{q_n = \frac{d}{V}K(v_3 - v_2).} \tag{9}$$

The experiment consists in determining q_n, the charges on the ions captured or lost by the oil drop during the time of observation, which, in some cases, lasted for several hours. The velocity of the oil drop was measured by timing the passage of its image between two cross hairs in the telescope a known distance apart. The difference of potential V was of the order of several thousand volts. The only quantity left to be evaluated in the determination of q_n is the factor K. If Stokes's law for the velocity of spheres falling through a viscous medium holds, then $K = 6\pi\eta a$ where η is the coefficient of viscosity of the air and a is the radius of the oil drop. A series of experiments was performed to verify the accuracy of Stokes's law. It was found that for very small drops, Stokes's law had to be modified, the correction being given with sufficient accuracy if K is written

$$K = \frac{6\pi\eta a}{1 + \dfrac{b}{pa}}, \tag{10}$$

where p is the pressure of the air in centimeters of mercury and b is an empirically determined constant. The value of the coefficient of viscosity was determined in another series of experiments, and the value used by Millikan is $\eta = 0.0001825$ cgs units.

From many determinations of q_n, it was found that q_n could always be represented by

$$q_n = ne, \tag{11}$$

where n is an integer and e represents the elementary charge equivalent to that of an electron. The value of the charge of an electron from Millikan's work (1917) is

$$e = 4.770 \times 10^{-10} \text{ esu of charge.}$$

It must be emphasized that the value of e is the same for both positive and negative charges since q_n, the ionic charge captured or lost by the oil drop, could be either positive or negative, depending on chance.

Later experimental evidence, particularly from the study of x-ray wavelengths (§5-12), indicated that this value of e was too small. Shiba, in 1932, pointed out that the error in Millikan's determination of e was probably due to an error in the determination of η. Many experiments have since been performed for the redetermination of this constant. The weighted average of seven different determinations of the coefficient of viscosity of air at 23°C is

$$\eta = 1832.5 \times 10^{-7} \text{ cgs unit.}$$

When this value of η is used with Millikan's measurements, the value of the electronic charge becomes

$$e = 4.8071 \times 10^{-10} \text{ esu of charge.}$$

An interesting modification of Millikan's oil drop experiment was devised by Hopper and Laby (1941). In this experiment the oil drop was allowed to fall through a horizontal electric field between two vertical plates. Under the action of its weight mg and the force due to the horizontal electric field, the oil drop moves at an angle to the vertical. Because of the resistance provided by the viscosity of the air, the oil drop quickly reaches the limiting velocity v at an angle θ to the vertical. It then con-

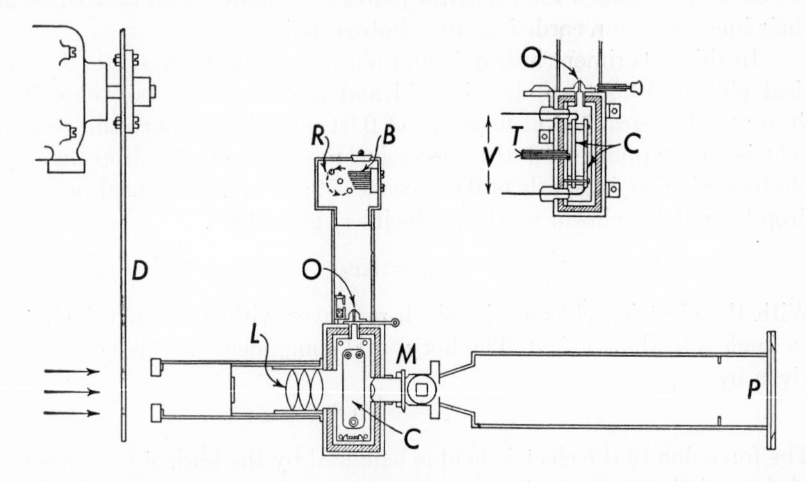

Fig. 2-3. Apparatus used by Hopper and Laby for determining the electronic charge. B is a steel wire brush; R, a rotating bar; O, the opening for oil drops; C, capacitor plates; D, rotating metal disk; L, condenser lens system; M, microscope objective; P, photographic plate; T, thermocouple; and V, leads for applying voltage to capacitor plates.

tinues to travel in a straight line with this uniform velocity v. For an oil drop of radius 5×10^{-4} cm, calculations show that it takes less than 0.003 seconds to reach within 1 part in 10,000 of its terminal velocity.

Hopper and Laby found that the most effective method for producing oil drops of the proper size was to place a drop of oil on the wires of a fine steel brush; a rotating bar (see Figure 2-3) first pushes the wires of the brush back and then suddenly releases them, producing a copious supply of oil drops of about the desired range of sizes. Drops of castor oil and apiezon oil were used in this experiment. These drops were produced in a box which was mounted vertically on a well-insulated copper box containing the vertical plates of the capacitor. The tube connecting these two boxes was fitted with a tap which served to separate drops of different sizes, to protect the air in the copper box from external disturbances, and to allow the drops to enter so that they are in focus as they fall past the microscope objective. The temperature of the air in the copper box was controlled by means of a thermostat; the temperature was kept constant and slightly above room temperature. The drops were illuminated intermittently at intervals of 0.04 second, each flash lasting for 1/1500 second. This was accomplished by allowing light from an arc to pass through a slot cut near the edge of a disk; this disk was rotated by means of a synchronous motor at a speed of 25 revolutions per second. A shutter in front of the condenser lens was kept open for two seconds, during which time the oil drops between the capacitor plates were illuminated fifty times and their images were recorded on the photographic plate.

In this experiment a drop is first allowed to fall between the two vertical plates without an electric field and the successive positions of the drop are photographed at intervals of 0.04 second. The horizontal electric field is then applied and the successive positions of the drop are again photographed at intervals of 0.04 second. With no electric field on, the oil drop falls with uniform vertical velocity v_y given by

$$mg = Kv_y.$$

With the electric field on, the oil drop moves with uniform velocity v at an angle θ to the vertical. The horizontal component of this velocity v_x is given by

$$v_x = v \sin \theta. \tag{12}$$

The force due to the electric field is balanced by the horizontal component of the resisting force so that

$$\frac{V}{d} ne = Kv_x, \tag{13}$$

where V is the difference of potential between the plates, d the distance between them, and ne the charge on the oil drop. From equations (12) and (13), we get

$$ne = \frac{d}{V} Kv \sin \theta. \tag{14}$$

Figure 2-4 is a typical plate showing the paths of both deflected and undeflected oil drops. The velocities v_y and v can be calculated by measuring the distances between the images of the oil drop, and the angle θ can be measured from the plate. Hence the total charge ne carried by the oil drop can be computed. This is another way in which this experiment differs from Millikan's experiment. The values of n in this experiment were rather large, from about 40 to 300. The larger the oil drop used, the larger was the value of n.

Hopper and Laby did not measure the viscosity of the air in this experiment. Instead, they calculated the weighted mean of nine previously determined values and adopted $\eta = 1830 \times 10^{-7}$ cgs units for the viscosity of air at 23°C. With this value of η they obtained the value $e = 4.802 \times 10^{-10}$ esu for the value of the electronic charge.

Using the method of least squares averaging instead of arithmetical averaging of the differences in the positions of the oil drops, and the value $\eta = 1832.5 \times 10^{-7}$, R. T. Birge recalculated the value of e from

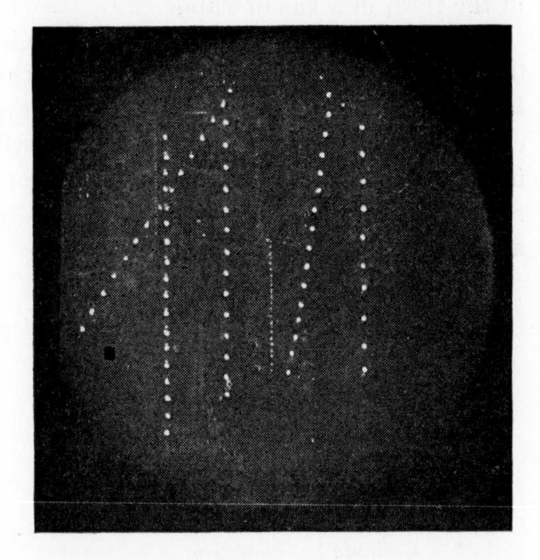

FIG. 2-4. Photograph of deflected and undeflected paths of oil drops (photograph retouched). (Courtesy of V. D. Hopper and T. H. Laby.)

Hopper and Laby's measurements, and obtained $e = 4.8137 \times 10^{-10}$ es units for the electronic charge.

In this book we shall adopt the currently accepted value

$$\boxed{e = 4.803 \times 10^{-10} \text{ esu of charge}} \tag{15}$$

for the electronic charge. (See Appendix I.)

2-5. Electric Discharge through Gases

The phenomenon of the discharge of electricity through gases has been known for many years and has been utilized for the study of many problems connected with atomic structure. In its simplest form a discharge tube consists of a long glass tube with a circular electrode sealed into each end, as shown in Figure 2-5. A smaller side tube is sealed into it so that the pressure of the gas in the tube may be controlled by connecting it to a pumping system.

Let us consider the phenomena when there is air in the tube. Electrode A is connected to the positive side of a source of high potential such as an induction coil, and electrode C is connected to the negative side. When the pressure of the air inside the tube is reduced to a few millimeters of mercury, the electric discharge fills the entire space between the electrodes with a pink or reddish glow. If the light from this tube is examined with a spectroscope, it will be found to consist of a series of lines characteristic of the gases within the tube. This type of discharge is frequently used in studying the spectra of various substances which can be obtained in the form of a gas or vapor.

When the pressure of the air within the tube is reduced to about 0.1 mm of mercury the appearance of the discharge is approximately as follows: there is a bluish velvety glow around the cathode C, called the cathode glow; then a dark space, called the Crookes dark space, then the negative glow, followed by the Faraday dark space, and then, filling the rest of the tube up to the anode, is the striated positive column, and just around the anode is the anode glow.

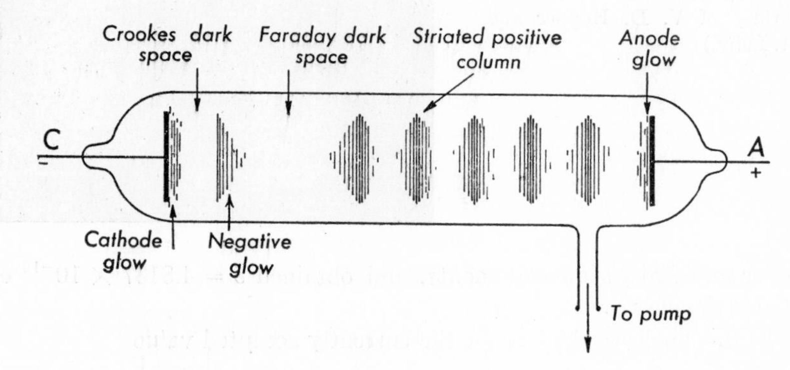

FIG. 2-5. Appearance of the electric discharge when the pressure of the air in the tube is about 0.1 mm of mercury.

The electric field is not uniform along the length of the tube but varies widely as we pass from one electrode to the other. The field is most intense in the Crookes dark space. The width of this dark space depends upon the pressure. As the pressure is reduced, this dark space widens out until at a pressure of about 0.001 mm, it fills the entire tube. At this pressure the positive column and negative glow have disappeared.

The phenomena observed in the discharge tube may be explained qualitatively by assuming that neutral molecules or atoms are ionized by collisions with ions or free electrons, and also that positive ions recombine with free electrons or with negative ions to form neutral atoms or molecules. Under the action of the electric field, the positive ions are accelerated toward the cathode, while the negative ions and electrons are accelerated toward the anode, and thus acquire considerable kinetic energy. A charged particle will lose some of its energy in a collision with a neutral atom or molecule if this collision results in the ionization of the neutral particle, since, in the process of ionization, work must be done to separate the positive from the negative charges. On the other hand, energy will be released when an electron and an ion recombine to form a neutral atom or molecule. Some of this energy may be emitted in the form of light characteristic of the gas in the tube.

When the pressure of the gas is comparatively low, about 0.001 mm of mercury, the mean free path of the ions and atoms is very large, so that an ion or electron makes very few collisions in traversing the length of the tube. The positive ions, for example, will thus have a great deal of kinetic energy when they strike the cathode. The result of this bombardment of the cathode by the positive ions is that the cathode emits particles called *cathode rays*. These cathode rays travel away from the cathode in practically straight lines perpendicular to the surface of the cathode since the direction of motion is determined almost exclusively by the very intense field in the immediate neighborhood of the cathode.

These cathode rays can be deflected by electric and magnetic fields, and the direction of the deflection shows that they are negatively charged. Certain substances such as glass and zinc sulfide emit fluorescent radiations when bombarded by cathode rays. Cathode rays will also affect a photographic plate. These effects may be used to detect and measure the cathode rays.

2-6. Determination of e/m for Cathode Rays

J. J. Thomson (1897) first successfully determined the nature of the cathode rays and showed that they are *electrons;* he was also the first to measure the ratio of the charge of the cathode ray to its mass, denoted by the symbol e/m.

A typical cathode-ray tube, as shown in Figure 2-6, consists of a circular disk C as the cathode, and a cylindrical anode A with a small circular hole bored through it along the axis of the cylinder. Two parallel plates of length L separated a distance d are placed behind the anode and a zinc sulfide screen is placed at the end of the tube. A gas discharge is maintained between the anode and the cathode by means of some source of high potential. Most of the cathode rays coming from C strike the anode. Some cathode rays, however, pass through the hole in the anode and proceed with uniform velocity v until they strike the fluorescent screen S at O, producing a bright spot.

If a difference of potential V is applied between the plates PP', then the cathode rays will be deflected upward toward the positive plate by a force F, given by

$$F = \frac{V}{d} e = ma, \tag{16}$$

in which e is the charge on a cathode ray, and m is its mass. Since the electric field between the plates is uniform, the path of the cathode rays will be parabolic in the region between the plates. After they leave this space, they will continue with uniform rectilinear motion until they strike the screen at O'. To determine e/m, the acceleration of the particle must be measured. This can be done indirectly by noting that the amount of the deflection y parallel to the electric field between the plates is given by

$$y = \tfrac{1}{2}at^2, \tag{17}$$

and that the time t during which the particle is accelerated is given by

$$t = \frac{L}{v}, \tag{18}$$

where L is the length of the plates and v is the velocity of the rays parallel to the plates. The velocity of the cathode rays can be found very simply with the aid of a magnetic field applied at right angles to the electric field

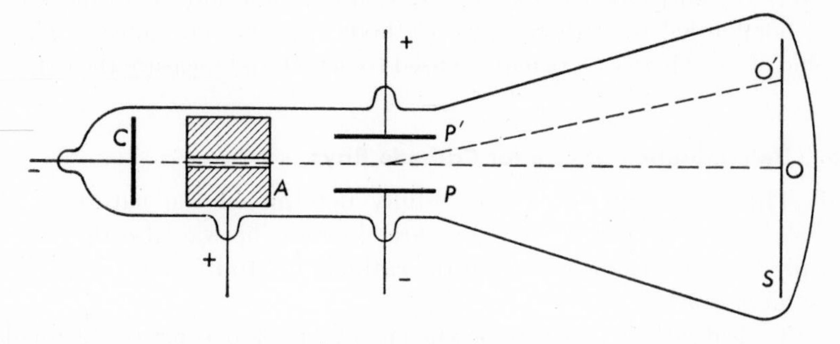

FIG. 2-6. A cathode-ray tube.

and acting over the same length of path L. This magnetic field may be supplied by an electromagnet having its N pole on the side toward the reader and its S pole on the side of the tube away from the reader. If the strength of the magnetic field is B, the cathode ray will experience an additional force F_1 given by

$$F_1 = Bev. \tag{19}$$

The direction of the deflection due to the magnetic field will be downward; this field can be adjusted so that the cathode rays are not deviated from their original path, as is evidenced by the return of the fluorescent spot to point O. This will occur when the forces due to the electric and magnetic fields are equal, in which case

$$\frac{V}{d}e = Bev, \tag{20}$$

from which
$$v = \frac{V}{dB}. \tag{21}$$

The expression for e/m thus becomes

$$\frac{e}{m} = 2\frac{V}{dB^2L^2}y. \tag{22}$$

All the quantities on the right-hand side of the equation are measurable quantities. The deflection y at the end of the path in the electric field is proportional to the distance OO' which is measured on the fluorescent screen.

A consistent set of units must be used for all the quantities in equations (16) to (22). If e, V, and B are expressed in the em system of units, and the other quantities in cgs units, the value of e/m will be expressed in emu of charge per gram. The present accepted value of e/m is

$$\boxed{\frac{e}{m} = 1.7589 \times 10^7 \text{ emu/gm.}} \tag{23}$$

Measurements of e/m with electrons from other sources (for example, electrons emitted by hot filaments and electrons ejected from metallic plates by the action of light) all yield the same value within the limits of experimental error. The value given above is the weighted average of many such determinations.

The mass of an electron may now be computed using the above value of e/m and the known value of e. Using $e = 1.602 \times 10^{-20}$ emu, we find the mass of an electron to be

$$\boxed{m_e = 9.107 \times 10^{-28} \text{ gm.}} \tag{24}$$

It is instructive to compare the mass of an electron with that of the hydrogen atom. Since a gram-atomic weight of hydrogen contains N_0 atoms, the mass of a hydrogen atom is

$$M_H = \frac{1.008}{6.025 \times 10^{23}} \text{ gm,}$$

from which
$$M_H = 1.673 \times 10^{-24} \text{ gm.} \tag{25}$$

The ratio of the mass of a hydrogen atom to that of an electron is thus

$$\boxed{M_H/m_e = 1837.} \tag{26}$$

2-7. Variation of Mass with Velocity

One of the predictions of Einstein's special theory of relativity is that the mass of a particle should vary with its velocity according to the equation

$$m = \frac{m_0}{\sqrt{1 - \dfrac{v^2}{c^2}}}, \tag{27}$$

where m_0 is the mass of the particle when at rest, m its mass when it is moving with velocity v, and c the velocity of light. This prediction can be tested by determining the masses of electrons which are moving with speeds comparable with the speed of light. Convenient sources of high-speed electrons are available in the form of certain radioactive elements which emit such electrons continually. These electrons are sometimes called *beta rays* or *beta particles*. The electrons which are most suitable for these experiments are those which are emitted with definite velocities characteristic of the emitting elements; they form the so-called "sharp lines" in the beta-ray spectra of the radioactive elements (see §10-8). Kaufmann, Bucherer, and others performed a series of experiments on the determination of e/m of beta rays of different speeds. Assuming, as a consequence of the laws of electrodynamics, that the total charge on a particle is conserved, then any variation in the value of e/m with the speed of the particle should be due to the variation in mass according to the equation

$$\frac{e}{m} = \frac{e}{m_0}\sqrt{1 - \frac{v^2}{c^2}}. \tag{28}$$

In Bucherer's experiment, a small grain of radium fluoride R was placed between two parallel circular disks AB at their centers, as shown in Figure 2-7. The spacing between the disks was about 0.25 mm. A photographic film P was bent in a cylindrical form concentric with the disks AB. This apparatus was placed in a vacuum chamber. An electric field Y was maintained between the plates by means of a battery. The whole apparatus was placed in a uniform magnetic field of strength B parallel to the planes of the disks. The beta particles coming out radially from the source R experienced a force Ye due to the electric field, and a force $Bev \sin \theta$, due to the magnetic field, where θ is the angle between v and B. If the resultant force on a beta particle was not zero, it was deflected either up or down and could not escape from the narrow space between the disks. If, however, the force on any of the beta rays due to the magnetic field was equal and opposite to that due to the electric field, then these particles traveled radially from R and struck the photographic film P. For these beta particles

$$Bev \sin \theta = Ye, \tag{29}$$

from which

$$\sin \theta = \frac{Y}{Bv}. \tag{30}$$

Since both Y and B are in em units, the ratio Y/B has the dimensions of a velocity. In one of Bucherer's experiments, the ratio Y/B was made equal to $\frac{1}{2}c$. Since on the basis of the relativity theory the velocity of a beta particle cannot exceed the velocity of light, hence by setting $v = c$,

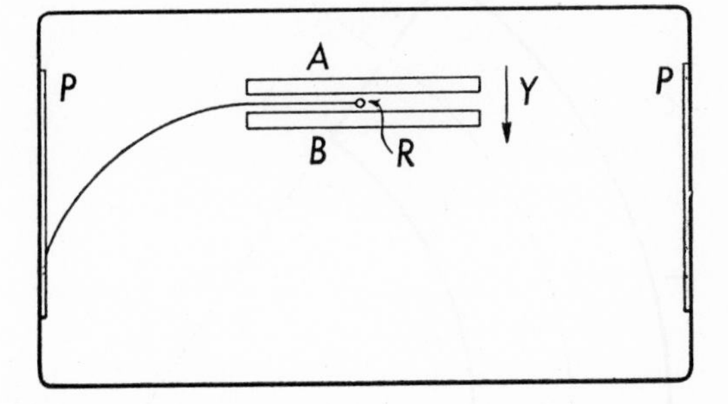

FIG. 2-7. Simplified diagram of the apparatus used in Bucherer's experiment. The magnetic field is perpendicular to the plane of the paper and directed toward the reader.

we obtain the limiting value of $\sin \theta$, which is $\frac{1}{2}$, so that $\theta = 30°$ or $150°$. In this case only those beta particles which were projected initially at angles with the magnetic field lying between 30° and 150° could get to the photographic film.

After leaving the region between the disks, the beta particles continued traveling in the magnetic field until they reached the film. In general these particles moved in helical paths, but those coming out perpendicular to the magnetic field moved in circles of radius r given by

$$Bev = mv^2/r \tag{31}$$

from which e/m could be calculated. Putting this value of e/m in equation (28) should give the constant value e/m_0 for all values of v. A typical set of Bucherer's experimental results is given in the following table:

Table 2-1

v/c	$e/m_0 \frac{\text{emu}}{\text{gm}}$
0.3173	1.752×10^7
0.3787	1.761
0.4281	1.760
0 5154	1.763
0.6870	1.767

These values of e/m_0 are constant within the limits of experimental error. The results are thus in good agreement with equation (27) derived on the basis of the special theory of relativity.

One criticism of Bucherer's experiment is that it lacked the precision claimed owing to the fact that, in the arrangement used, the electrons were not focused by the magnetic field and hence the resolving power was

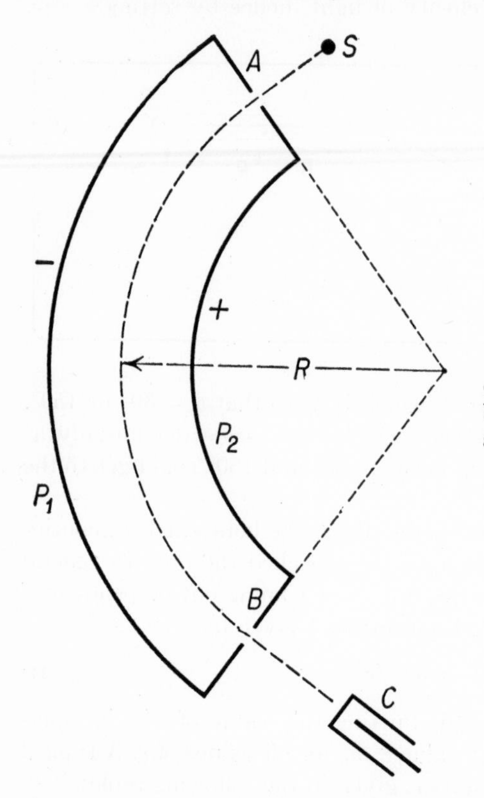

FIG. 2-8. Electrons travel in a circular path in the radial electric field between the two concentric plates P_1 and P_2.

very poor. A more precise determination of the variation of mass with velocity was made by M. M. Rogers, A. W. McReynolds, and F. T. Rogers, Jr., in 1939 using the electrons which form the sharp lines of the beta-ray spectra of radium (B + C). The momenta of these electrons were first determined by subjecting them to a magnetic field B at right angles to their velocities. The force on each electron is

$$Bev = \frac{mv^2}{r} \tag{32}$$

so that

$$\boxed{mv = Ber.} \tag{33}$$

There are three sharp lines in the beta-ray spectra of Ra (B + C) corresponding to the three values of $Br = mv/e$ listed in Table 2-2.

These magnetic deflection experiments were then followed by electric deflection experiments. Referring to Figure 2-8, we find that S is the source of the electrons and consists of a platinum wire coated with Ra (B + C). The electrons from S travel through a radial electric field in the space between two concentric plates P_1P_2 of a cylindrical capacitor. The electrons enter this field through a narrow slit A, are deflected in a circular path of radius R by the radial electric field of intensity Y and leave through the slit B. They are detected by a Geiger counter C. (See §3-4.)

The force on each electron in the radial electric field is

$$Ye = \frac{mv^2}{R},$$

from which

$$YR = \frac{mv^2}{e}. \tag{34}$$

The potential difference between the plates at which the largest number of electrons was recorded was taken as that required to produce the electric field Y which caused these particles to move in the circular path of radius R. The three values of YR obtained in these experiments are listed in Table 2-2.

The velocity v of each of these three groups of electrons forming the beta-ray lines could be calculated by using equations (33) and (34), which yield

$$v = \frac{YR}{Br}. \tag{35}$$

These equations also yield

$$\frac{m}{e} = \frac{(Br)^2}{YR}. \tag{36}$$

Assuming that

$$m = \frac{m_0}{\sqrt{1 - v^2/c^2}} \tag{27}$$

and

$$\frac{m}{e} = \frac{m_0}{e} \cdot \frac{1}{\sqrt{1 - v^2/c^2}}, \tag{37}$$

it is possible to compare the measured value of m/e with the accepted value of m_0/e, obtaining the values of m/m_0 for the three different groups of electrons listed in the table. The values of m/m_0 calculated from equation (27) for the measured values of v are given in the last column of Table 2-2.

Table 2-2

Line	Br in gausses-cm	V in volts	YR emu-cm	v in cm/sec	v/c	$\frac{m}{m_0}$ (Obs.)	$\frac{m}{m_0}$ (Calc.)
1	1406.0	9,970	2.671×10^{13}	1.8998×10^{10}	0.6337	1.298	1.293
2	1671.1	13,017	3.487×10^{13}	2.0868×10^{10}	0.6961	1.404	1.393
3	1931.5	16,200	4.341×10^{13}	2.2470×10^{10}	0.7496	1.507	1.511

The correctness of the prediction that the mass of a particle varies with its velocity according to equation (27) is thus amply verified. It has also been verified in many other experiments involving not only electrons but other particles as well, and is always taken into account in the design of instruments, such as high energy particle accelerators, for both positively and negatively charged particles. We shall consider the significance of the variation of mass with velocity and the relationship of mass and energy in §§2-14 and 2-16.

2-8. Isotopes

One of the hypotheses introduced by Dalton into atomic theory was that all of the atoms of any one element were identical in all respects, including that of mass. On this basis, the numbers representing the weights of the elements would give the relative masses of the atoms of these elements. Others, however, suggested that the atoms of any one element need not be identical in mass, that the numbers representing the chemical atomic weights are only average values of the different weights of the atoms of the particular element. The basis of this suggestion was the hope that the weights of all atoms could be expressed by integral numbers. Prout (1815) first formulated this idea in his hypothesis that the atoms of all the elements are made up of hydrogen atoms. If this hypothesis were correct, the weights of all the atoms would be expressed as integers with that of hydrogen as unity. Careful determinations of atomic weights, however, showed that the atomic weights of many elements were not integral numbers relative to that of hydrogen. By the latter half of the nineteenth century Prout's hypothesis had been discarded in favor of Dalton's hypothesis. But with the discovery of radioactivity at the end of the nineteenth century and the study of the radioactive elements produced in the process of natural radioactive disintegration (§10-2), sufficient experimental evidence was presented to support the suggestion that the atoms of an element need not be identical in mass, and renewed efforts were made to determine whether atomic masses could be represented by whole numbers.

Several groups of elements having identical properties but different atomic weights are formed in the process of radioactive disintegration. This means that the elements within any one group must occupy the same place in the periodic table of the elements (Appendix III). Soddy suggested the name *isotopes* for the elements occupying the same place in the periodic table.

The search for isotopes among the nonradioactive elements was begun by J. J. Thomson about 1910. The first element successfully investigated was neon. It is the lightest element whose atomic weight, 20.2, differs appreciably from an integral number. The method used was the determination of the ratio of the charge to the mass of the positive ions formed in an electrical discharge tube containing neon gas.

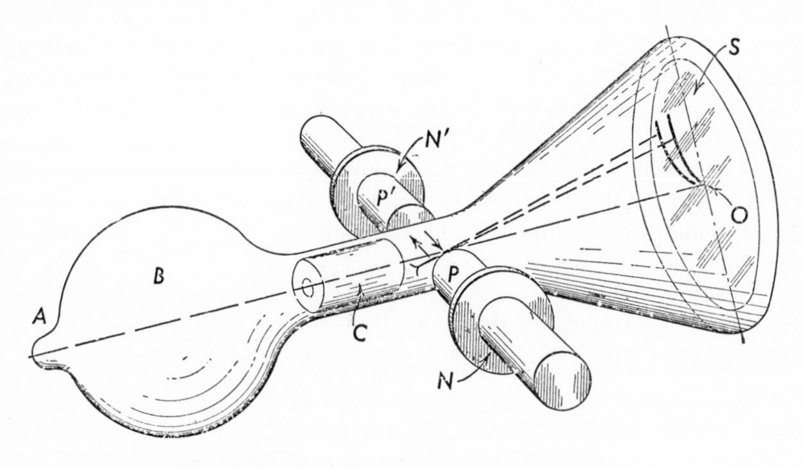

FIG. 2-9. J. J. Thomson's positive-ray tube.

2-9. Positive-Ray Analysis

In Thomson's method of positive-ray analysis, positive ions are formed in the gas in the space between the anode A and the cathode C of the tube B, sketched in Figure 2-9. The tube is operated at a voltage of about 50,000 volts. The cathode consists of a long cylinder about 7 cm long with a hole less than a millimeter in diameter along the axis of the cylinder. Those positive ions which travel along the axis of the tube pass through the hole in the cathode and emerge as a very narrow beam. When there is no electric or magnetic field acting on these ions, they strike the fluorescent screen or photographic plate S at point O.

In analyzing the beam, both electric and magnetic fields are used. The pole pieces PP' of an electromagnet are placed outside the tube just behind the cathode. These pole pieces are insulated from the rest of the electromagnet by means of thin mica sheets NN', so that the pole pieces can be used as the plates of a capacitor by being connected to a battery. The electric and magnetic fields are parallel and act simultaneously on the beam of positive ions passing through them.

Assume that the beam moves in the x direction and that the electric and magnetic fields are in the positive y direction. Because of the action of the electric field alone, the positive ions will be accelerated in the y direction by a force

$$F_y = YE = Ma_y, \tag{38}$$

where Y is the electric field intensity due to the difference of potential across the capacitor plates, E the charge carried by the positive ion, M its mass, and a_y its acceleration in the y direction. The deflection of the ion in the y direction will be

$$y = \tfrac{1}{2}a_y t^2 = \frac{1}{2}\frac{YE}{M}\frac{L^2}{v^2}, \tag{39}$$

where L is the length of the capacitor plates and v is the original velocity of the ion in the x direction.

The force on an ion due to the magnetic field is perpendicular to both B and v, and for small deflections this force may be considered as accelerating the ion in the z direction. This force is

$$F_z = BEv = Ma_z, \tag{40}$$

where B is the strength of the magnetic field and a_z is the acceleration of the ion in the z direction. The deflection in the z direction is given by

$$z = \tfrac{1}{2}a_z t^2 = \frac{1}{2}\frac{BE}{M}\frac{L^2}{v}. \tag{41}$$

It will be noticed that the deflection produced by the magnetic field varies inversely as the first power of the velocity, while the deflection produced by the electric field varies inversely as the second power of the velocity. Eliminating v from the equations (39) and (41), we get

$$z^2 = \frac{L^2}{2}\frac{B^2}{Y}\frac{E}{M}y = C\frac{E}{M}y, \tag{42}$$

which is the equation of a parabola, since $C = \dfrac{L^2B^2}{2Y}$ is a constant in any one experiment. All positive ions with the same value of E/M will form a single parabola; those moving with the greatest velocity will be deflected least and will be closest to the origin, which is the original undeflected position O. If the direction of the magnetic field be reversed during one half of the exposure, the negative half of the parabola will be obtained and thus give a convenient method for determining the position of the y axis on the photographic plate.

The first element to be analyzed by the parabola method was neon of atomic weight 20.2. Two parabolas were identified as due to two isotopes of neon of atomic weights 20 and 22, respectively. These parabolas are represented in the graphs in Figure 2-10. Several other elements were analyzed by this method and found to consist of several isotopes each. While the parabola method was capable of showing the existence of isotopes, it was not sufficiently accurate for the precise determination of the

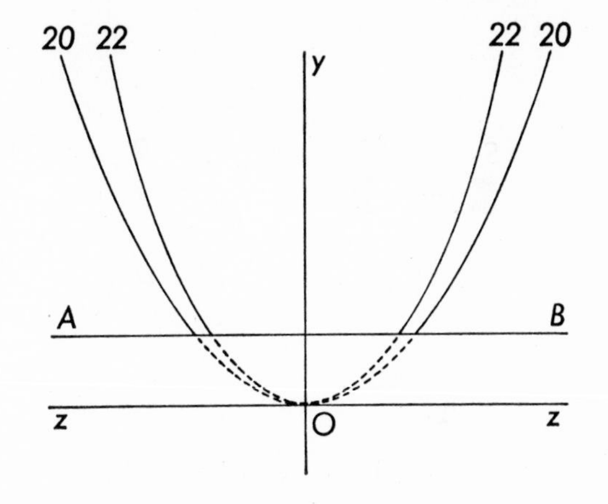

FIG. 2-10. Graph showing the two parabolas of the neon isotopes. The points of intersection of the line AB with the parabolas represent the positions of the ions of maximum energy; all other ions reach points above AB.

masses of these isotopes. Aston redesigned the instrument so that it became an instrument of precision for the determination of the masses of isotopes and their relative abundance in a given sample of material. This instrument has received the name of *mass spectrograph.* Mass spectrographs of somewhat different designs were developed by Dempster, Bainbridge, Mattauch, Nier, and other experimenters.

2-10. Aston's Mass Spectrograph

Aston's method is an improvement on J. J. Thomson's method in that all positive ions of the same mass fall on a single line on the photographic plate instead of being spread out into a parabola. The stream of positive ions coming through the hole in the cathode of the discharge tube passes through two defining slits S_1 and S_2, as shown in Figure 2-11, and then into the electric field between the capacitor plates P_1P_2. The deflections of the ions depend upon their *energies.* Those of kinetic energy $\frac{1}{2}Mv^2$ and charge E are deflected parallel to the electric field Y between the plates by an amount

$$d_1 = \frac{1}{2}\frac{YE}{M}\frac{L^2}{v^2}, \tag{43}$$

where L is the length of the path between the plates. The diaphragm D is placed behind the plates so as to permit only those ions which have been deflected through the same distance d_1 to pass through its opening. This narrow bundle of rays which has been deflected through a small angle θ is allowed to pass through the diaphragm D into the magnetic field B at right angles to the plane of the paper. This magnetic field is produced by a large electromagnet, the position of the pole pieces being indicated by

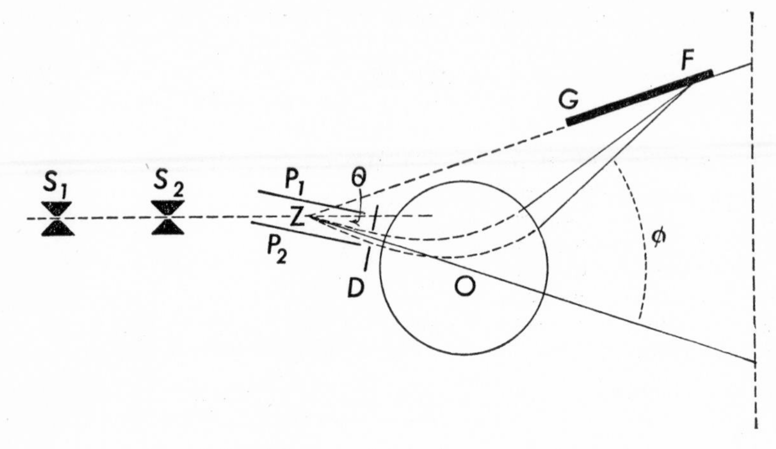

FIG. 2-11. Diagram of Aston's mass spectrograph.

the large circle in the diagram. This magnetic field deflects the ions in a direction opposite to that due to the electric field by an amount

$$d_2 = \frac{b^2}{2v}\frac{BE}{M}, \tag{44}$$

where b is the length of the path in the magnetic field.

Those positive ions which pass through the diaphragm D have a small range of energies depending upon the size of the slit in the diaphragm and the position of this slit. As shown by equation (43), the ions with smaller energies are deflected downward more than the ions of larger energies; that is, the deflection in the electric field is inversely proportional to the square of the velocity of the ion. The magnetic field is directed so as to deflect the particles upward, and the amount of this deflection varies inversely as the first power of the velocity of the ions as shown by equation (44). The paths of the slow-moving ions will therefore intersect those of the faster-moving ions at some point F which is determined by the geometry of the apparatus. Thus ions having the same value of E/M but slightly different energies are brought to a single focus on the photographic plate GF. Other ions having the same range of energies but a different value of E/M are brought to a focus at a different point on the photographic plate. It can be shown that these foci for different values of E/M

lie along a line ZF passing through the center Z of the plates of the capacitor and that the angle between ZF and the original path of the ions is equal to θ. The photographic plate is placed along this line to detect the positive ions.

Each line on the photographic plate represents a definite value of E/M. Several different methods are used for the determination of the masses. In general, substances whose masses are accurately known are mixed with elements whose isotopes are to be determined. The positions of the lines representing the known masses are then used as reference points in measuring the masses of the isotopes.

Aston later (1925) improved the design of his spectrograph so that it became an instrument of very great precision. It was used for the discovery of isotopes, for the accurate determination of their atomic masses, and for the determination of the relative abundance of the different isotopes of a given element.

2-11. Dempster's Mass Spectrometer and Spectrograph

A. J. Dempster was among the early pioneers in mass spectroscopy. His first instrument was a spectrometer rather than a spectrograph. In this spectrometer the positive ions all acquire practically the same energy before entering the magnetic field. The magnetic field is large enough and the path through it long enough to deflect these ions through 180°. The source of positive ions is usually a salt containing the element to be investigated. This salt is deposited on the anode. When the anode is heated by an electric current, or by the bombardment of electrons from a filament, positive ions are liberated from the anode. In later work with metallic elements, the metal itself was vaporized and the vapor then ionized by bombardment with electrons. The positive ions pass through a hole in an iron plate P, shown in Figure 2-12, and are accelerated to the slit S_1 by a difference of potential V between P and S_1. The energy acquired by the ions in going from P to S_1 is

$$VE = \tfrac{1}{2}Mv^2. \tag{45}$$

The ions entering through S_1 are bent in the form of a semicircle by a magnetic field B perpendicular to the plane of the paper, and focused upon the second slit S_2. The radius R of the semicircular path traversed by these ions is given by

$$BEv = \frac{Mv^2}{R}\cdot \tag{46}$$

The value of E/M for the ions which reach S_2 is then given by

$$\frac{E}{M} = \frac{2V}{B^2R^2}\cdot \tag{47}$$

The ions which pass through S_2 are detected and measured by the charge deposited on the plate connected to the electrometer.

One of the advantages of this instrument is that even though the beam of ions which enters the slit S_1 is slightly divergent, the effect of the magnetic field is to reconverge the beam after deflecting it through 180°. It can be shown that if a divergent beam of ions is sent perpendicularly

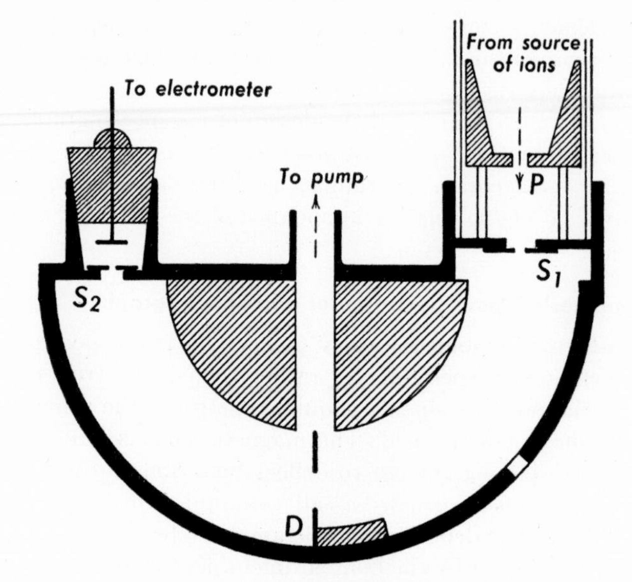

Fig. 2-12. Diagram of Dempster's mass spectrometer.

through a magnetic field in such a way that the central part of the beam enters and leaves the magnetic field normal to the edges of the pole pieces producing the magnetic field, then the beam of ions will be brought to a focus on a line which extends from the source through the center of curvature of the central beam. The magnetic field thus acts as a *lens* and forms an image of the slit through which the ions pass.

In practice, the magnetic field is kept at a constant value and the difference of potential V between P and S_1 is varied. The number of ions passing through S_2 is then measured by the electrometer for different values of the potential V. A typical curve giving the results of the experiment on potassium is shown in Figure 2-13. The two peaks correspond to two isotopes of potassium of mass numbers 39 and 41.

Dempster also designed a mass spectrograph in which the positive ions coming through the slit S pass through a radial electric field between two cylindrical capacitor plates C_1 and C_2, as shown in Figure 2-14, and then enter the magnetic field perpendicular to the plane of the diagram.

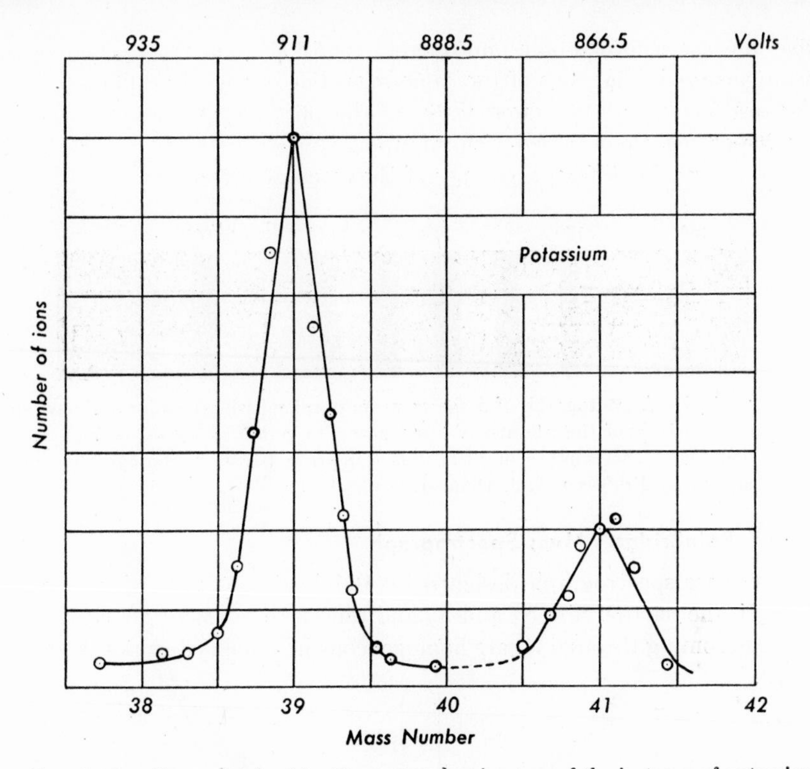

FIG. 2-13. Curve obtained by Dempster showing two of the isotopes of potassium of mass numbers 39 and 41.

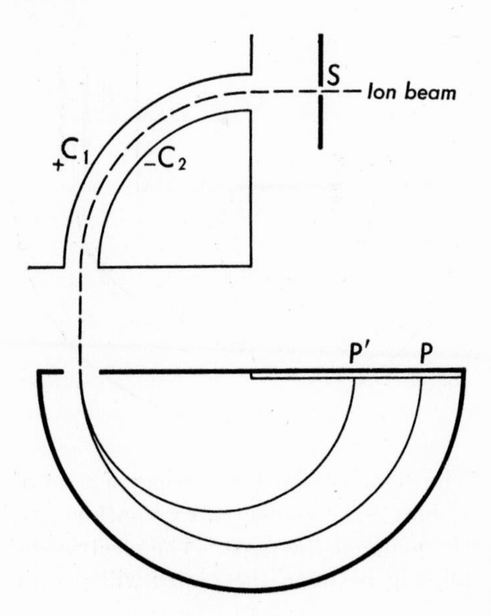

FIG. 2-14. Dempster's mass spectrograph utilizing cylindrical capacitor plates.

The ions are recorded on a photographic plate PP'. The advantage of this arrangement is that ions of the same mass but of slightly different velocities are focused at the same place on the photographic plate. A typical mass spectrogram obtained with this apparatus is illustrated in Figure 2-15, which shows the different isotopes of the element ytterbium.

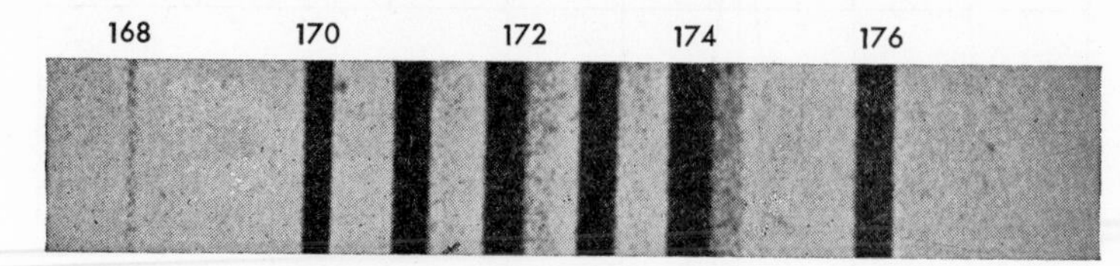

FIG. 2-15. A photograph of a spectrogram obtained with Dempster's mass spectrograph in a study of the isotopes of ytterbium. The numbers above the lines are the mass numbers of the isotopes of ytterbium. (Reprinted from a photograph supplied to the author by Professor A. J. Dempster.)

2-12. Bainbridge's Mass Spectrograph

In the mass spectrograph designed by Bainbridge, the positive ions pass through the narrow slits S_1 and S_2 and then into a *velocity selector* so that the ions coming through S_3 are homogeneous in velocity but not in energy.

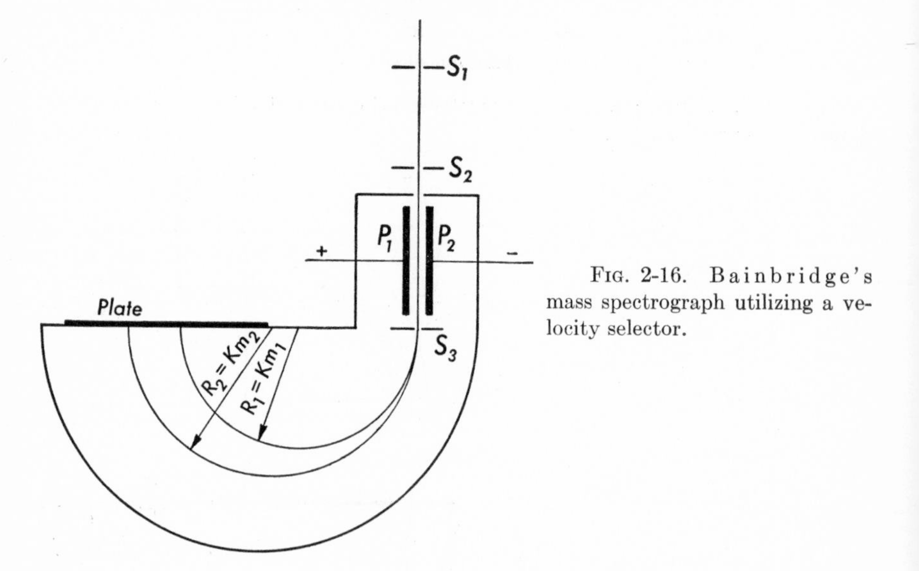

FIG. 2-16. Bainbridge's mass spectrograph utilizing a velocity selector.

The velocity selector consists of a set of capacitor plates P_1P_2, as shown in Figure 2-16, connected to a battery, and a magnetic field perpendicular to the plane of the paper. The electric and magnetic fields acting on the ions moving between the plates will permit those ions to pass through which satisfy the condition that

$$v = \frac{V}{dB}, \tag{21}$$

where v is the velocity of the ions, V/d the intensity of the electric field between the plates, and B the flux density of the magnetic field in this region. The ions which pass through slit S_3 are now acted upon by a second magnetic field B_1 perpendicular to the plane of the paper. The force acting on each ion is given by

$$B_1Ev = \frac{Mv^2}{R},$$

from which

$$M = \frac{B_1E}{v}R = KR. \tag{48}$$

The ions travel in a circular path for 180° and then strike a photographic plate. Since the ions all have the same velocity, the masses of the ions are directly proportional to the radius R of the circular path. Thus the mass scale of this instrument is linear.

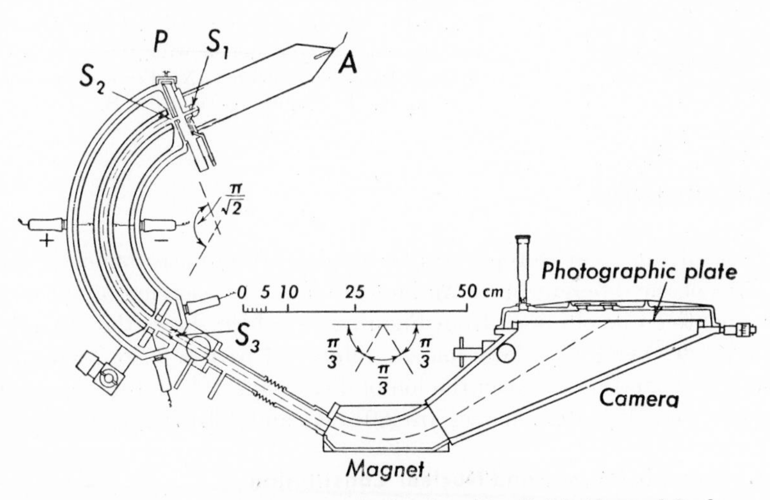

FIG. 2-17. The mass spectrograph developed by Bainbridge and Jordan.

A mass spectrograph of high precision and resolving power has been developed by Bainbridge and Jordan, as sketched in Figure 2-17. In this apparatus a beam of ions from the gas discharge tube A passes through a narrow slit S_1 at the end of the tube, and enters a radial electric field through a second slit, S_2. The ions are bent through an angle of $\pi/\sqrt{2}$ radians by the radial electric field and emerge through the slit S_3. They then continue in straight lines until they reach the magnetic field where they are bent through an angle of $\pi/3$ radians, after which they travel in straight lines to the photographic plate. In this arrangement of electric and magnetic fields, ions with the same value of E/M and a distribution

FIG. 2-18. A photograph of a spectrogram obtained by Bainbridge and Jordan, showing the ten isotopes of tin and one of iodine. The mass numbers of the isotopes are given in the figure. (From a photograph supplied by K. T. Bainbridge and E. B. Jordan.)

of velocities within a certain range are focused at a single place on the photographic plate. The mass scale is linear over a large portion of the plate.

The mass spectrogram of tin, Figure 2-18, showing its ten isotopes, is typical of the results obtained with this instrument. The relative abun-

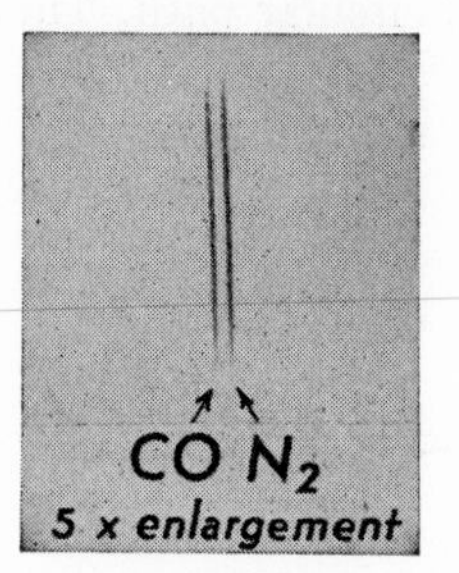

FIG. 2-19. Photograph obtained with the Bainbridge and Jordan mass spectrograph showing the separation of the ions of CO and N_2. Enlarged 5X. (From a photograph supplied by K. T. Bainbridge and E. B. Jordan.)

dance of the different isotopes can be obtained from measurements of the densities of the different lines. An indication of the resolving power of the instrument can be obtained from Figure 2-19, which shows the separation of the ions CO and N_2, whose masses differ by 1 part in 2500. Figure 2-20 shows the separation between the ion of deuterium, H^2, and the molecular hydrogen ion, H_2^1, whose masses are 2.014741 and 2.016290, respectively.

2-13. Isotopic Masses and Nuclear Constitution

As the result of the investigations with the mass spectrograph, it has been established that about 280 different isotopes occur in nature. The atomic weights of these isotopes differ very little from whole numbers. The number of naturally occurring isotopes per element varies from one for elements fluorine and gold, to ten for the element tin. Since there are about 100 different elements, there are, on the average, about 3 isotopes per element. A table of naturally occurring isotopes and their relative abundance is given in Appendix V.

It is now well established from experiments on the scattering of alpha particles (§3-7), and from the study of x-ray spectra (§9-1), that an atom consists of a very small nucleus with a net positive charge, surrounded by a sufficient number of electrons so that the normal atom is electrically neutral. The results of these experiments lead to the conclusion that the charge of the nucleus of an atom can be represented by Ze, where e is numerically equal to the charge of an electron but positive in sign, and Z is an integer. There are also Z electrons outside the nucleus of a neutral atom. The number Z is called the *atomic number* of the element. The atomic number Z ranges in value from 1 to 100 for presently known elements.

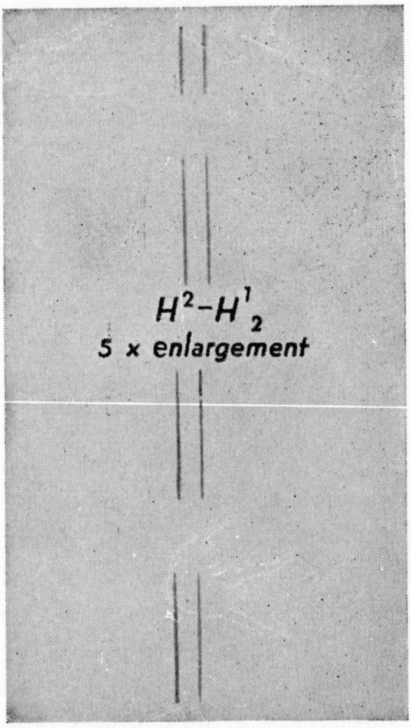

H^2-H^1_2
5 × enlargement

FIG. 2-20. Photograph obtained with the Bainbridge and Jordan mass spectrograph showing the separation of the ions of deuterium, H^2, and molecular hydrogen, H^1_2. (From a photograph supplied by K. T. Bainbridge and E. B. Jordan.)

The isotopes of any one element, though they have different atomic weights, all have the same atomic number Z. One conclusion from this fact is that the atoms of the various isotopes of any element have exactly the same number of extranuclear electrons. The chemical properties of an element must therefore be ascribed mainly to the arrangement and action of the electrons outside the nucleus. Differences in atomic weights among isotopes of the same element must therefore be due to differences in nuclear structure.

The results of the measurements of isotopic masses with mass spectrographs show that the atomic masses of all the isotopes are very nearly integers on a scale in which the atomic mass of the most abundant isotope of oxygen is assigned the value of 16 exactly. This is called the *physical scale of atomic masses;* a table of values of isotopic masses is given in Appendix IV. It will be convenient to introduce the term *mass number* for the integer A nearest the atomic mass of an isotope. The unit of atomic mass, that is, one amu, is thus one sixteenth the mass of the oxygen atom of mass number 16. We know that N_0 atoms of this isotope have a mass of 16 grams. Hence 1 atom of mass number 16 has a mass of 16 gm/N_0.

Therefore
$$1 \text{ amu} = \frac{1}{16}\frac{16 \text{ gm}}{N_0}$$

or
$$\boxed{1 \text{ amu} = \frac{1 \text{ gm}}{N_0},} \tag{49}$$

so that
$$1 \text{ amu} = \frac{1}{6.025 \times 10^{23}} \text{ gm},$$

or
$$1 \text{ amu} = 1.66 \times 10^{-24} \text{ gm}. \tag{49a}$$

The fact that the atomic masses of all isotopes are very nearly integers suggests the idea that nuclei are made up of particles, called *nucleons*, each of mass number $A = 1$. At present two particles of nuclear size and of mass nearly unity are known. These are the *proton* and the *neutron*. The proton is the positively charged nucleus of the hydrogen atom of mass number 1. This hydrogen atom consists of a positively charged nucleus, called the proton, and an electron outside the nucleus. Since the mass of the hydrogen atom is about 1840 times the mass of the electron, practically the entire mass of the hydrogen atom is due to the proton. The mass of the proton in atomic mass units is 1.007595. The other nuclear particle of unit mass number was discovered experimentally in 1932 by Chadwick as a result of experiments on artificial disintegration (§11-1). The neutron has no electric charge and its mass is 1.008987 amu.

Prior to the discovery of the neutron, the nucleus was supposed to be made up of protons and electrons. With the tremendous amount of new experimental data on nuclear phenomena which became available after the discovery of the neutron, it became necessary to discard the older hypothesis in favor of one in which the nucleus consists of protons and neutrons. There are several arguments against the existence of electrons in the nucleus. Some of these arguments will be presented in the appropriate places in the text.

On the hypothesis that a nucleus of an atom consists of protons and neutrons, *the mass number A represents the total number of particles in the nucleus. The atomic number Z is the number of protons in the nucleus,* and

$N = A - Z$ is the number of neutrons in the nucleus. N is sometimes called the *neutron number* of the isotope. The isotopes of any one element differ only in the number of neutrons in the various nuclei. The convention adopted for representing this information can be illustrated with a typical case such as oxygen. The atomic number of oxygen is 8; there are three known stable isotopes of oxygen of mass numbers 16, 17, and 18. These are represented by the symbols ${}_8O^{16}$, ${}_8O^{17}$, and ${}_8O^{18}$, respectively, the atomic number being written as a subscript on the lower left-hand side of the chemical symbol of the element, and the mass number as a superscript on the upper right-hand side of the chemical symbol. The atomic number is sometimes omitted, since the chemical symbol uniquely determines it. Thus the isotopes of oxygen will sometimes be designated as O^{16}, O^{17}, O^{18}.

2-14. Mass and Energy

It might at first be supposed that the mass of a nucleus should be the sum of the masses of its constituent particles. A survey of the data, however, shows that the mass of a nucleus is, in general, less than the sum of the masses of its constituent particles in the free state. To account for this difference in mass, use is made of the *principle of equivalence of mass and energy,* a principle first developed by Einstein in his theory of relativity. Einstein's principle states that a mass m is equivalent to an amount of energy $\mathcal{E}$, and the equation relating these quantities is

$$\boxed{\mathcal{E} = mc^2,} \tag{50}$$

where c is the speed of light.

Thus c^2 may be considered as the conversion factor in changing a quantity of energy from mass units to the more conventional energy units. For example, if m is expressed in grams and $\mathcal{E}$ in ergs, then c must be expressed in cm/sec. Taking $c = 3 \times 10^{10}$ cm/sec, a mass of 1 gram is equivalent to

$$\begin{aligned}\mathcal{E} &= 1 \text{ gm} \times (3 \times 10^{10} \text{ cm/sec})^2\\ &= 9 \times 10^{20} \text{ ergs.}\end{aligned}$$

Similarly a mass of 1 kilogram is equivalent to

$$\begin{aligned}\mathcal{E} &= 1 \text{ kg} \times (3 \times 10^{8} \text{ m/sec})^2\\ &= 9 \times 10^{16} \text{ joules.}\end{aligned}$$

Energy units other than the erg or the joule have been found to be more convenient and more useful in atomic and nuclear physics. Among these are the *atomic mass unit,* amu, and the *electron volt,* ev. The atomic mass unit has already been defined, (§2-13); its value in grams is

$$\boxed{1 \text{ amu} = 1.66 \times 10^{-24} \text{ gm.}} \tag{51}$$

Using the precise value of $c = 2.99793 \times 10^{10}$ cm/sec in equation (50), we get

$$\boxed{1 \text{ amu} = 1.492 \times 10^{-3} \text{ erg.}} \tag{52}$$

The other convenient energy unit, the *electron volt*, is the kinetic energy an electron acquires when it is accelerated in an electric field produced by a difference of potential of one volt. Since the work done upon an electron by a difference of potential V is Ve,

$$\boxed{1 \text{ electron volt} = 1 \text{ ev} = 1.60 \times 10^{-12} \text{ erg.}} \tag{53}$$

Multiples of this unit frequently used are

$$1 \text{ kev} = 1000 \text{ ev}$$

$$1 \text{ Mev} = 10^{6} \text{ ev.}$$

The conversion factor for amu to Mev is

$$\boxed{1 \text{ amu} = 931.2 \text{ Mev.}} \tag{54}$$

The mass of an electron, for example, is frequently expressed in terms of its energy equivalent in electron volts. Since its mass is

$$m_e = 9.109 \times 10^{-28} \text{ gm,}$$

its energy in ergs is from equation (50)

$$\mathcal{E} = 8.185 \times 10^{-7} \text{ erg}$$

which is equivalent to

$$\mathcal{E} = 0.511 \text{ Mev.} \tag{55}$$

The energy of an electron at rest, in amu is

$$\mathcal{E} = 0.000548 \text{ amu.} \tag{56}$$

If Δm is the decrease in mass when a number of particles combine to form the nucleus of an atom, then the principle of equivalence of mass and energy states that an amount of energy

$$\Delta\mathcal{E} = \Delta mc^2 \tag{57}$$

is released in this process. This amount of energy represents the *binding energy* of the particles in the nucleus.

To illustrate the relationship between mass and energy and the meaning of *binding energy of a nucleus*, let us consider the isotope of lithium of mass number 7. Since its atomic number is 3, the lithium nucleus is composed of 3 protons and 4 neutrons. The masses of these particles, including one electron with each proton and three electrons with the lithium nucleus, are

$$\begin{aligned} 4\,{}_0n^1 &= 4 \times 1.008987 = 4.03595 \\ 3\,{}_1\mathrm{H}^1 &= 3 \times 1.008145 = \underline{3.02444} \\ 4\,{}_0n^1 + 3\,{}_1\mathrm{H}^1 &= 7.06039 \\ {}_3\mathrm{Li}^7 &= \underline{7.01822} \\ \Delta m &= 0.04217 \text{ amu} \end{aligned}$$

or

$$\Delta m = 39.27 \text{ Mev.}$$

In subtracting, the masses of the electrons cancel out. The difference in mass between these particles in the free state and in the nucleus of lithium is 0.04217 amu, or the binding energy of the ${}_3\mathrm{Li}^7$ nucleus is 39.26 Mev. The nucleus of ${}_3\mathrm{Li}^7$ thus has a very stable structure. In any attempt to disrupt this nucleus, energy will have to be supplied from some external source.

It may be noted that the use of atomic masses rather than nuclear masses in calculations of nuclear energy changes is correct in all cases except the one in which a nuclear transformation takes place with the emission of a positron (§11-5).

2-15. Binding Energies of Nuclei

The results of the measurements of the atomic masses of the isotopes can be presented in a variety of ways, each instructive and useful in its own manner. One method is in terms of the binding energies of the different nucleons. The binding energy $\mathcal{E}_B$ of a nucleus is *defined as the difference between the sum of the masses of the Z protons and N neutrons in the free state and the mass of the nucleus containing the* $A = Z + N$ *nucleons.* In performing the calculation, the mass of the neutral atom of ${}_1\mathrm{H}^1$ can be used instead of the mass of the proton, and the mass of the appropriate neutral atom of mass number A can be used instead of the mass of the nucleus since the masses of the electrons will cancel out. Thus the binding energy of a nucleus is given by the equation:

$$\boxed{\mathcal{E}_B = Z \cdot M_H + NM_n - M,} \tag{58}$$

where M_H is the atomic mass of hydrogen of mass number 1, M_n is the mass of the neutron, and M is the atomic mass of the isotope of atomic number Z

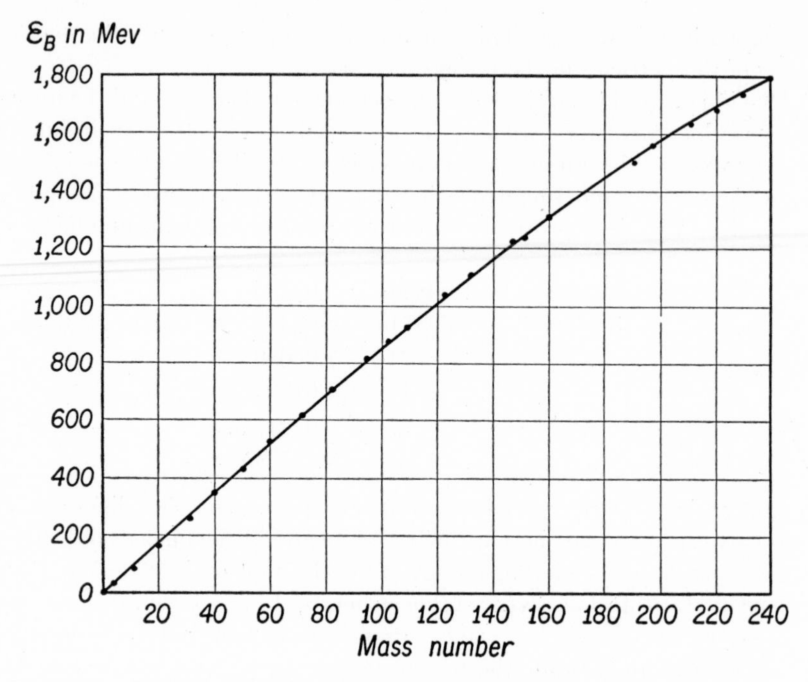

FIG. 2-21. Binding energy of nuclei, in Mev, as a function of the mass number A.

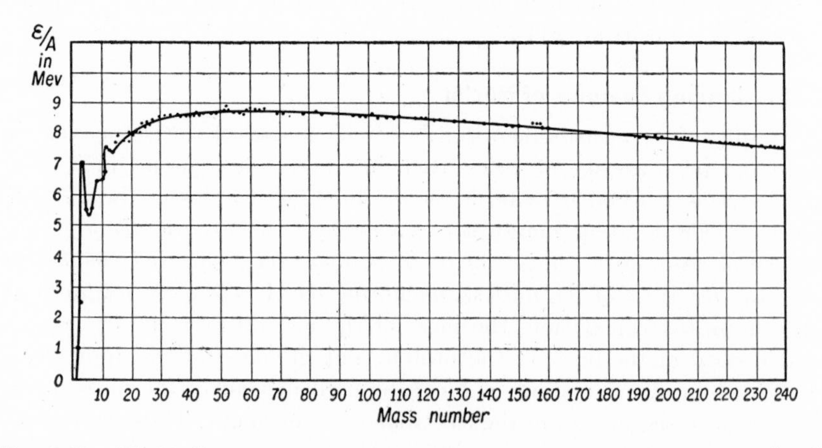

FIG. 2-22. The binding energy per nucleon in Mev, as a function of the mass number A.

and mass number A. The binding energy may either be expressed in amu or converted to Mev. Figure 2-21 is a graph of the binding energies of the nuclei, expressed in Mev, as ordinates, against the mass numbers A as abscissae. To a first approximation, the binding energy increases practically linearly with the mass number. Figure 2-22 shows the binding energy per nucleon, $\mathcal{E}_B/A$, plotted against the mass number A. The graph shows that for values of A greater than about 20, the binding energy per nucleon increases slowly from about 8 Mev to 8.5 Mev in the neighborhood of

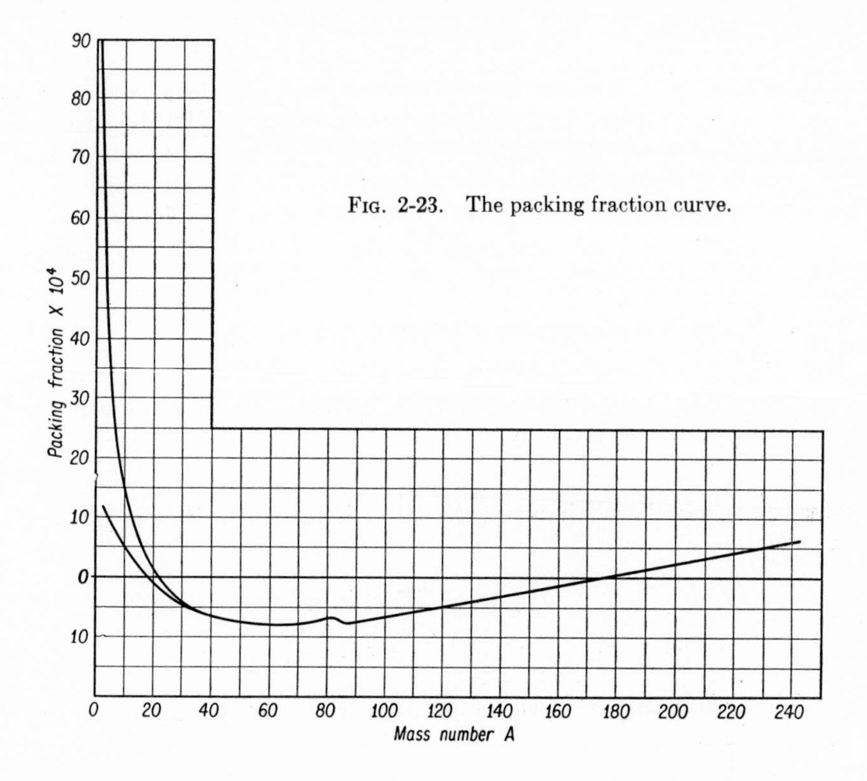

FIG. 2-23. The packing fraction curve.

$A \simeq 60$, then decreases slowly to about 7.5 Mev for the heaviest elements. For values of A between 1 and 20, the variations in $\mathcal{E}_B/A$ are considerable. In any study of nuclear forces, stability of nuclei, and other nuclear properties, the variations of $\mathcal{E}_B$ and $\mathcal{E}_B/A$ for different values of A may be very significant. We shall postpone such a discussion until Chapter 10, after we have investigated in greater detail some of the nuclear properties and nuclear processes.

Other convenient ways of presenting the data obtained from atomic mass determinations are in terms of the *mass defect* and the *packing fraction* of the individual nuclei. The mass defect Δ is defined *as the difference between the atomic mass M of an isotope and its mass number A*, thus

$$\Delta = M - A. \tag{59}$$

The *packing fraction* F, a term first introduced by Aston, is defined *as the mass defect of the whole atom per nucleon*, that is

$$F = \frac{\Delta}{A} = \frac{M - A}{A}. \tag{60}$$

The curve of packing fractions against mass numbers is shown in Figure 2-23. For mass numbers between about 20 and 180, the packing fractions have small negative values with minimum values in the region of $A \simeq 60$. For values of A above 180, the packing fractions are positive and increase in value with increasing mass number. For the very light elements, the packing fractions are comparatively large with large variations among them. The packing fraction of 0^{16} is zero by definition.

2-16. Energy and Momentum of a Relativistic Particle

A particle of rest mass m_0 moving with a velocity v comparable with the velocity of light c is termed a *relativistic particle*. The momentum p of a relativistic particle is given by

$$p = mv \tag{61}$$

where m is its relativistic mass; the latter is related to its rest mass by the equation

$$m = \frac{m_0}{\left(1 - \frac{v^2}{c^2}\right)^{1/2}}. \tag{27}$$

The relationship between the total energy $\mathcal{E}$ and the total mass m of the particle is

$$\mathcal{E} = mc^2. \tag{50}$$

In describing a relativistic particle, it is a common practice to state its momentum and kinetic energy, or its momentum and total energy. A very useful equation is one between the momentum and the total energy $\mathcal{E}$. By eliminating v and m from equations (27), (50), and (61), we get

$$p^2 = \frac{\mathcal{E}^2}{c^2} - m_0^2c^2, \tag{62}$$

and

$$p = \frac{[\mathcal{E}^2 - (m_0c^2)^2]^{1/2}}{c}. \tag{63}$$

If the total energy of a particle consists simply of its kinetic energy $\mathcal{E}_k$ and its rest mass energy, m_0c^2, then

$$\mathcal{E} = \mathcal{E}_k + m_0c^2,$$

or

$$\mathcal{E}_k = \mathcal{E} - m_0c^2,$$

so that

$$\mathcal{E}_k = mc^2 - m_0c^2,$$

from which

$$\boxed{\mathcal{E}_k = m_0c^2\left[\frac{1}{\left(1 - \frac{v^2}{c^2}\right)^{1/2}} - 1\right].} \tag{64}$$

The relativistic expression for the kinetic energy of a particle will reduce to the more familiar nonrelativistic expression when $v \ll c$. This can be seen by expanding the first term in the bracket of equation (64) by the binominal theorem, thus:

$$\left(1 - \frac{v^2}{c^2}\right)^{-1/2} = 1 + \frac{1}{2}\frac{v^2}{c^2} + \cdots$$

neglecting terms in v/c above the second power. Then equation (64) becomes

$$\mathcal{E}_k = m_0c^2\left[1 + \frac{1}{2}\frac{v^2}{c^2} - 1\right]$$

or

$$\mathcal{E}_k = \tfrac{1}{2}m_0v^2.$$

In dealing with high energy particles it is a common practice to express the energy of a particle in Mev. Since the product pc has the dimensions of energy, the momenta of such high energy particles are customarily expressed in terms of the energy unit divided by c, that is as Mev/c. For example, if the total energy of an electron is 1.5 Mev, then its momentum p is, from equation (63),

$$p = \frac{[(1.5)^2 - (0.5)^2]^{1/2}\text{ Mev}}{c}$$

since its rest mass is approximately 0.5 Mev.
Solving for p yields

$$p = 1.4\text{ Mev}/c.$$

2-17. Radius of the Electron

There is no definite information concerning the structure or shape of the electron, though experimental evidence indicates that it cannot be infinitesimal in size but must have some finite size. The simplest assumption is that the electron is a sphere of radius a. Various methods have been suggested for evaluating the radius of the electron, all leading to results of the same order of magnitude.

One method for assigning a radius to an electron is to equate its electrostatic energy to its rest mass energy, that is

$$\frac{e^2}{a} = m_0c^2 \tag{65}$$

from which

$$\boxed{a = \frac{e^2}{m_0c^2}\cdot} \tag{66}$$

Substitution of the values of e, m_0, and c yields

$$a = 2.82 \times 10^{-13} \text{ cm}$$

for the radius of the electron.

Problems

2-1. The following data were recorded during a performance of an oil drop experiment:

plate distance	1.60 cm
distance of fall	1.021 cm
potential difference	5085 volts
viscosity of air	1.824×10^{-4} gm/cm sec
density of oil	0.92 gm/cm^3
average time of fall	11.88 sec
successive times of rise	22.37 sec
	34.80 sec
	29.25 sec
	19.70 sec
	42.30 sec

Calculate the successive changes in charge on the oil drop and obtain an average value of e from these data. Assume $b/pa = 0.03$.

2-2. (**a**) Prove that Y, the distance between O and O' on the fluorescent screen of Figure 2-6 is given by

$$Y = y \cdot \frac{2D}{L},$$

where D is the distance from the center of the plates to the screen.

The following are the important dimensions of a cathode-ray tube:

distance from anode to screen	33.0 cm
length of plates	7.8 cm
distance between plates	2.4 cm

The plates are placed close to the anode.

(**b**) In the balance method of determining e/m, the voltage across the plates was 2800 volts and the magnetic field was 8.20 gausses. When only the magnetic field was on, the deflection on the fluorescent screen was 2.40 cm. Calculate e/m.

(**c**) With the same tube but using the magnetic deflection only, when the accelerating potential between the anode and the cathode was 32,500 volts, a magnetic field of 5.6 gausses produced a displacement of 2.10 cm on the fluorescent screen. Calculate the value of e/m.

2-3. Using the data on the masses of isotopes from Appendix IV, calculate the binding energy of a neutron in a ${}_3Li^7$ nucleus. Express the result in both amu and Mev.

Ans. 0.00774 amu or 7.20 Mev.

2-4. An electron emitted from a heated filament is accelerated to the anode by a difference of potential of 300 volts between the filament and the anode. Calculate (**a**) its kinetic energy in ergs, (**b**) the velocity of the electron when it reaches the anode.

Ans. (**a**) 4.8×10^{-10} erg.
(**b**) 1.03×10^{9} cm/sec.

2-5. An electron moving with a kinetic energy of 5000 ev enters a uniform magnetic field of 200 gausses perpendicular to its direction of motion. Determine the radius of the path of this electron.

Ans. 1.20 cm.

2-6. Singly charged lithium ions of mass numbers 6 and 7, liberated from a heated anode, are accelerated by means of a difference of potential of 400 volts between the anode and the cathode and then pass through a hole in the cathode into a uniform magnetic field perpendicular to their direction of motion. If the magnetic flux density is 800 gausses, determine the radii of the paths of these ions.

Ans. 8.83 cm and 9.54 cm.

2-7. One method of actually determining masses of isotopes with a mass spectrograph is to take a series of *doublets*, that is, ions differing slightly in mass (see Figure 2-19), and then determine the difference between their masses. Three such doublet measurements are given below:

$$H_2^1 - H^2 = 1.53 \times 10^{-3} \text{ amu}$$
$$H_3^2 - \tfrac{1}{2}C^{12} = 42.19 \times 10^{-3} \text{ amu}$$
$$C^{12}H_4^1 - O^{16} = 36.49 \times 10^{-3} \text{ amu}$$

The term "$\frac{1}{2}$C" means that the carbon was doubly ionized while the others were all singly ionized. From the above data determine the masses of the isotopes H^1, H^2, and C^{12}.

Ans. $H^1 = 1.00813.$
$H^2 = 2.01473.$
$C^{12} = 12.00398.$

2-8. Plot a graph of the momentum of a relativistic particle as a function of the total energy. Use a scale for energy in which the rest mass energy of a particle is unity. Determine, from this graph, (**a**) the momentum of an electron, in Mev/c, whose total energy is 200 Mev; (**b**) the momentum of a proton whose total energy is 4600 Mev.

2-9. A K-conversion electron emitted by Cs^{137} as a sharp line of its beta-ray spectrum has a momentum, as measured by the curvature of its path in a magnetic field, of 3380 gausses cm. Express its momentum (**a**) in cgs units and (**b**) in units of Mev/c. Determine (**c**) its total energy, and (**d**) its kinetic energy, in Mev.

Ans. (**a**) 5.41×10^{-17} gm cm/sec.
(**b**) 1.01 Mev/c.
(**c**) 1.135 Mev.
(**d**) 0.624 Mev.

2-10. (**a**) Show that the velocity of a relativistic particle is given by

$$v = c\frac{p}{\sqrt{p^2 + m_0^2c^2}}$$

where p is its momentum.

(**b**) Determine the velocity of an electron whose momentum, when determined by the curvature of its path in a magnetic field, is quoted at 2500 gausses cm.

(**c**) Determine the momentum of this electron in units of Mev/c.

2-11. (**a**) Show that the velocity of a relativistic particle of rest mass m_0 and total energy $\mathcal{E}$ is given by

$$v = c\left[1 - \left(\frac{m_0c^2}{\mathcal{E}}\right)^2\right]^{1/2}.$$

(**b**) Determine the velocity of a particle whose total energy is twice its rest mass energy. (**c**) Determine its kinetic energy.

Ans. (**b**) $0.866c$
(**c**) m_0c^2.

2-12. A stream of electrons is projected with a velocity v from a point source at an angle θ to the direction of a uniform field of strength B. (**a**) Describe the paths of these electrons. (**b**) If θ is the semivertex angle of a cone, show that the electrons will meet, or be focused, at the end of each cycle of its motion.

2-13. Uranium isotopes of mass numbers 235 and 238 are to be separated from a piece of uranium by using a mass spectrometer which will deflect them through

180° into two collectors 4.0 cm apart. If the singly charged ions have energies of 2000 ev when entering the magnetic field, calculate (**a**) the magnetic flux density necessary to achieve this separation and (**b**) the radii of the paths of the ions.

2-14. The following mass doublet separations were obtained by A. O. Nier in a recent investigation with the double-focusing mass spectrometer:

Doublet	$\Delta M \times 10^4$ amu
a. $(C^{12})_4 - S^{32}O^{16}$	331.82
b. $C^{12}(O^{16})_2 - C^{12}S^{32}$	177.82
c. $(C^{12})_3(H^1)_8 - C^{12}(O^{16})_2$	729.67
d. $(C^{12})_6(H^1)_4 - C^{12}(S^{32})_2$	873.26

Using O^{16} as the standard, determine the atomic masses of H^1, C^{12}, and S^{32}. Compare these results with the values given in the table of Appendix IV.

2-15. Calculate the rest mass energy of a proton in Mev.

2-16. Assume that the curve for binding energy against mass number is a straight line for values of A greater than 30. Determine the slope of this line. Interpret the significance of the value of this slope.

2-17. (**a**) Using equations (58) and (60), show that the binding energy per nucleon is given by

$$\frac{\mathcal{E}_B}{A} = \frac{Z}{A}(M_H - M_n) + (M_n - 1) - F$$

where F is the packing fraction.

(**b**) The packing fraction of lead, $Z = 82$, $A = 206$, is 2.22×10^{-4} amu. Determine the binding energy per nucleon for this isotope. Compare the result with the value obtained from Figure 2-22.

References

Brownian motion

Millikan, R. A., *Electrons + and −*. Chicago: The University of Chicago Press, 1947, Chap. VII.

Perrin, J., *Atoms*. New York: D. Van Nostrand Company, Inc., 1917, Chaps. III, IV.

Electronic charge

Millikan, R. A., *Electrons + and −*. Chicago: The University of Chicago Press, 1947, Chaps. IV, V.

Isotopes

Aston, F. W., *Mass Spectra and Isotopes.* New York: Longmans, Green & Co., 1942.

Richtmyer, F. K., and E. H. Kennard, *Introduction to Modern Physics.* New York: McGraw-Hill Book Company, Inc., 1947, Chap. XI.

Stranathan, J. D., *The Particles of Modern Physics.* Philadelphia: The Blakiston Company, 1942, Chap. V.

Relativity

Abro, A. d', *The Evolution of Scientific Thought—from Newton to Einstein.* New York: Dover Publications, 1950, Part II.

Bergmann, P. G., *Introduction to the Theory of Relativity.* New York: Prentice-Hall, Inc., 1942, Part I.

Born, M., *Einstein's Theory of Relativity.* London: Methuen & Company, Ltd., 1924, Chaps. V, VI.

Einstein, A., *The Meaning of Relativity.* Princeton, N. J.: Princeton University Press, 1953.

———, *Relativity.* New York: Hartsdale House, 1947.

Richtmyer, F. K., and E. H. Kennard, *Introduction to Modern Physics.* New York: McGraw-Hill Book Company, Inc., 1947, Chap. IV.

Tolman, R. C., *The Theory of the Relativity of Motion.* Berkeley: University of California Press, 1917, Chaps. I-IV.

chapter **3**

The Nuclear Atom

3-1. Discovery of Natural Radioactivity

The discovery of radioactivity by Henri Becquerel in 1896, shortly after the discovery of x-rays by Roentgen in 1895, marked the beginning of the modern approach to the study of the structure of the atom. Becquerel was interested in determining whether there was any relationship between the phosphorescence of certain salts after irradiation by ordinary light and the fluorescence of the glass of an x-ray tube which was emitting x-rays. One of the salts used was the double sulfate of uranium and potassium. He wrapped a photographic plate in very thick black paper, placed a crystal of the uranium salt on it and exposed the whole thing to sunlight. When the plate was developed, a silhouette of the phosphorescent substance appeared in black on the negative, showing that radiations came from the uranium salt. He then varied this experiment by placing a coin, or a metallic screen pierced with an open-work design, between the uranium salt and the photographic plate, and, on developing the plate, found the image of each of these objects on the negative.

In attempting to repeat the above experiments, Becquerel ran into some cloudy weather; he put all the materials away in a drawer and waited for a sunny day. A few days later, he developed this photographic plate and found that the dark silhouettes again appeared with great intensity, even though the salt had not been exposed to much sunlight. To make certain that this activity goes on without the aid of an external source of light, he built a light-tight box and performed a series of experiments with the photographic plate at the bottom of the box. In one experiment uranium salt crystals were put directly on the photographic plate; he obtained very dark silhouettes of the crystals. In another experiment he put a piece of aluminum between the salt crystals and the photographic plate; he again obtained silhouettes, but these were slightly less intense than those obtained without the aluminum plate. He then concluded that the active radiations came from the uranium salt and that the external light had no influence whatever on this activity.

Becquerel then proceeded to experiment with different compounds of uranium, both in crystalline form and in solutions, and found that radiations were emitted by all of them, whether they did or did not phosphoresce. He was thus led to the conclusion that it was the element uranium which was responsible for these radiations. He confirmed this conclusion by repeating the above experiments with some commercial powdered uranium. Further experiments showed that the radiations from uranium would also cause the discharge of electrically charged bodies. Shortly thereafter, Rutherford investigated the penetrating power of the radiations from uranium and showed that they were of two types, a very soft radiation easily absorbed in matter which Rutherford called *alpha rays*, and a more penetrating type of radiation which he called *beta rays*. It is apparent now that the radiation which affected the photographic plate in Becquerel's experiment consisted of beta rays.

The method used by Rutherford in studying these radiations was an electrical method based upon the ionization produced by the radiation in its passage through a gas. The ionization currents so produced can be used for quantitative measurements. Using such a method, Mme Curie showed that the activity of any uranium salt was directly proportional to the quantity of uranium in the salt, thus demonstrating that radioactivity is an atomic phenomenon.

M. and Mme Curie subjected uranium pitchblende to a systematic chemical analysis, and, using an electrical method, measured the activity of the different elements obtained from the pitchblende. In 1898 they succeeded in discovering two new radioactive elements, polonium and radium. Radium was precipitated in the form of radium chloride. The activity of radium was found to be more than a million times that of a similar quantity of uranium. In 1910, Mme Curie and Debierne obtained pure radium metal by means of electrolysis of the fused salt. The atomic weight of radium as determined by Hoenigschmidt is 225.97. Radium fits in at the end of the second group in the periodic table; it is chemically similar to calcium, strontium, and barium. Many more radioactive substances have been discovered since then, thus filling many of the gaps which existed in the periodic table prior to the discovery of radioactivity.

3-2. Radiation Emitted by Radioactive Substances

In addition to the alpha and beta rays, naturally radioactive substances emit a third type of radiation called *gamma rays*. The existence of these three distinct types of radiation can be demonstrated very simply. A small quantity of some radioactive salt is placed at the bottom of a long narrow groove in a lead block, Figure 3-1. A fairly parallel beam will come from the radioactive material R through the slit S. Rays going in all other directions will be absorbed by the lead. This lead block is placed in an airtight chamber and a photographic plate P is placed a short distance above it. To avoid absorption of the rays, the air is pumped out of the chamber. A strong magnetic field is applied at right angles to the plane of the paper. After a reasonable exposure, three distinct lines will be found on the photographic plate. If the magnetic field is directed away from the reader, the positively charged particles or alpha rays will be deflected to the left in the figure, the negatively charged particles or beta rays will be deflected to the right, and the neutral rays or gamma rays will not be deviated at all.

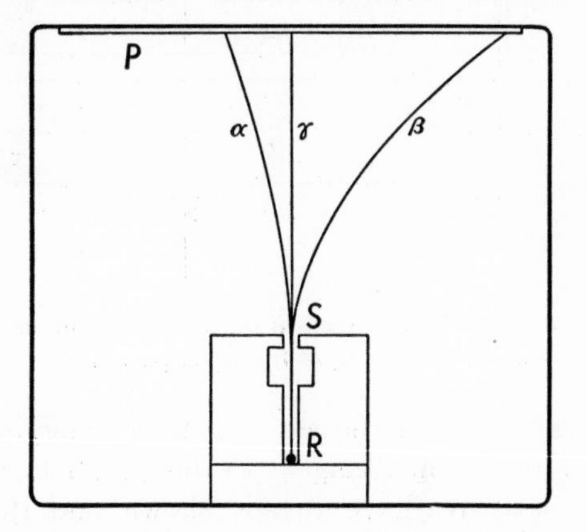

FIG. 3-1. Paths of the rays from a radioactive substance R in a magnetic field perpendicular to the plane of the paper. The magnetic field is directed into the paper.

In very early experiments Henri Becquerel was able to show that the beta particles were similar to cathode rays moving with very great velocities. He succeeded in deflecting them first in magnetic fields and then in electric fields, using photographic methods of detection. From the results of these experiments he determined the value of e/m for some of the slower speed beta rays and found this ratio to be about the value then known for electrons. Since then more accurate determinations have been made (see §2-7) which show that beta particles emitted by naturally radioactive substances are negatively charged electrons.

3-3. Determination of *E/M* for Alpha Particles

One of the best determinations of the ratio of the charge E to the mass M of the alpha rays was made by Rutherford and Robinson using the alpha particles emitted by the gas radon ($Z = 86$), and two of its products of disintegration, radium A and radium C′. In the apparatus sketched in Figure 3-2, the alpha particles coming from the radioactive materials contained in the thin-walled glass tube S pass between two silvered glass plates A and B, then through a narrow slit S_1, and strike the photographic plate P placed about 50 cm from the slit. The photographic plate was wrapped in aluminum leaf to protect it from light and from the glow of the source S. With no difference of potential between the plates a thin stream of undeflected alpha particles passes through the narrow slit S_1 and strikes the photographic plate. When a difference of potential V is maintained between the plates, the alpha particles travel in parabolic paths in the electric field. Only those alpha particles that enter the electric field at some suitable small angle θ with the plane of the plates will be able to

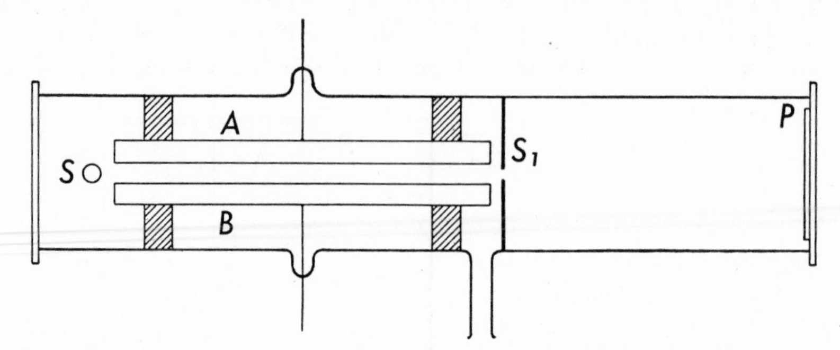

FIG. 3-2. Diagram of the apparatus used by Rutherford and Robinson for the determination of E/M for alpha particles.

get through the slit S_1. After emerging from this slit they travel in a straight line, tangent to this parabola, until they strike the photographic plate. We have already shown that the deflection of a charged particle from its original line of motion produced by the action of an electric field

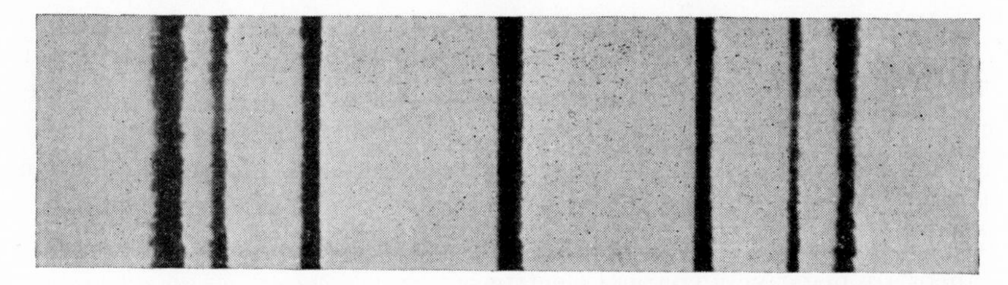

FIG. 3-3. Lines on the photographic plate obtained by the electrostatic deflection of the alpha particles. (From Rutherford, Chadwick, and Ellis, *Radiations from Radioactive Substances*. By permission of The Macmillan Company, publishers.)

is proportional to E/Mv^2, where E is the charge of the particle, M its mass, and v its velocity. Hence, by measuring the displacement of the line on the photographic plate from the line produced by the undeviated particle, the value of E/Mv^2 can be calculated.

An enlargement of the photograph obtained by the electrostatic deflection method is shown in Figure 3-3. Three distinct lines are visible on each side of the central line. The central line is due to the action of the alpha particles before the field is applied. Lines on both sides of the central line are produced by reversing the electric field. The outermost lines are due to the alpha particles of radon, the next pair of lines to the alpha particles of radium A and the innermost pair to those from radium C′.

To determine the value of E/M of the alpha particles, it is necessary to perform another experiment to determine the velocity v of the alpha particles from the same source. This was done by subjecting the alpha particles from this source to a magnetic field B perpendicular to the direction of their motion, that is, perpendicular to the plane of the figure, and having them strike another photographic plate placed at P. We have already shown that the deflection produced by the magnetic field is propor-

FIG. 3-4. Lines on the photographic plate obtained by the magnetic deflection of the alpha particles. (From Rutherford, Chadwick, and Ellis, *Radiations from Radioactive Substances*. By permission of The Macmillan Company, publishers.)

tional to E/Mv; the latter value can be determined by measuring the displacement of the line from the line produced by the undeviated particles. Figure 3-4 is an enlargement of the photograph obtained in the magnetic deflection experiment. By reversing the magnetic field, lines were obtained on the other side of the undeviated line. By combining the results of these two experiments, the value of E/M for the alpha particles was computed. The best value was determined from the measurements of the alpha particles of radium C′ and yielded

$$\frac{E}{M} = 4820 \frac{\text{emu}}{\text{gm}} \cdot$$

3-4. Nature of the Alpha Particles

The value of E/M for alpha particles having been accurately determined, a measurement of either E or M independently would give sufficient evidence as to the nature of these particles. One method of determining E is to count the number of alpha particles, N, emitted by some radioactive substance in a given time interval, and then determine the charge NE carried by these particles. Two methods frequently used for counting alpha particles are (a) the scintillation method, and (b) the Geiger counter method.

In the scintillation method, alpha particles strike a screen containing a thin layer of powdered zinc sulfide. The energy of the alpha particle is transformed into energy of fluorescent radiation by the small crystals of zinc sulfide. This radiation is in the visible region of the spectrum. Each alpha particle which strikes the screen produces a single scintillation. These scintillations may be viewed with a microscope and the number of alpha particles appearing in the field of view may be counted.

One type of counter known as a Geiger counter consists essentially of a cylinder C and a fine wire W mounted parallel to the axis of the cylinder and insulated from it, as shown in Figure 3-5. The cylinder contains a gas, such as air or argon, at a pressure of about 5 to 12 cm of mercury. A difference of potential slightly less than that necessary to produce a discharge through the gas is maintained between the wire and the cylinder wall.

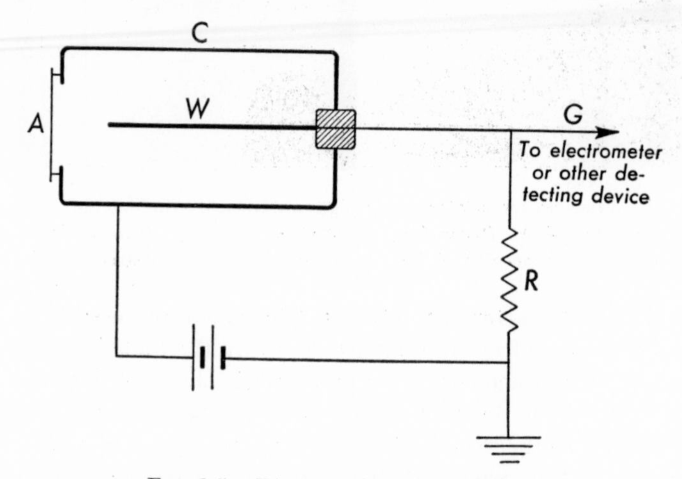

FIG. 3-5. Diagram of a Geiger counter.

Alpha particles can enter the Geiger counter through the aperture A, which is usually covered with a thin sheet of mica, glass, or aluminum. An alpha particle ionizes the gas along its path; these ions are accelerated by the electric field and produce more ions by collision with neutral atoms and molecules so that the ionization current builds up very rapidly. A very high resistance is connected between the wire and ground so that the energy due to the ionization current is rapidly dissipated. The effect is thus the production of a very large current lasting for a very short interval of time. This momentary current registers as a "kick" in an electrometer connected at G. This momentary current may be amplified so that it is capable of operating a loud-speaker, or a mechanical counter. By the proper choice of the value of the resistance R, the time constant of the circuit may be made sufficiently small so that each alpha particle which enters the chamber produces a momentary electrical surge which is recorded.

By counting the number of alpha particles entering the aperture A from any source placed a convenient distance away, the total number of alpha particles emitted by the source in a given time may be computed.

Using this method Rutherford and Geiger found that 3.57×10^{10} alpha particles per second are emitted by one gram of radium. The present accepted value is 3.70×10^{10} alpha particles per second.

Knowing the rate at which alpha particles are emitted by a given mass of radioactive material, one may measure the charge on the alpha particles by allowing these particles to charge up a plate connected to an electrometer. Using the alpha particles from radium C, Rutherford and Geiger found the charge E to be 9.3×10^{-10} esu, while Regener, using the alpha particles of polonium, obtained the value $E = 9.58 \times 10^{-10}$ esu. Within the limits of experimental error, the charge on the alpha particle is equivalent to twice the electronic charge. Using the latter value of E and the previously determined value of E/M for computing the mass of the alpha particle, we get

$$M = 6.62 \times 10^{-24} \text{ gm.}$$

Comparing this with the mass of the hydrogen atom, we get

$$\frac{M}{M_{\text{H}}} = \frac{6.62}{1.67} = 4.$$

The mass of the alpha particle is almost four times that of hydrogen, that is, it has the same atomic weight as helium ($Z = 2$). Since the alpha particle carries a charge of $+2e$ and has a mass equal to that of the helium atom, it is probably the nucleus of a helium atom. To make this identification certain, Rutherford and Royds (1909) carried out a spectroscopic analysis with the aid of alpha particles emitted by radon.

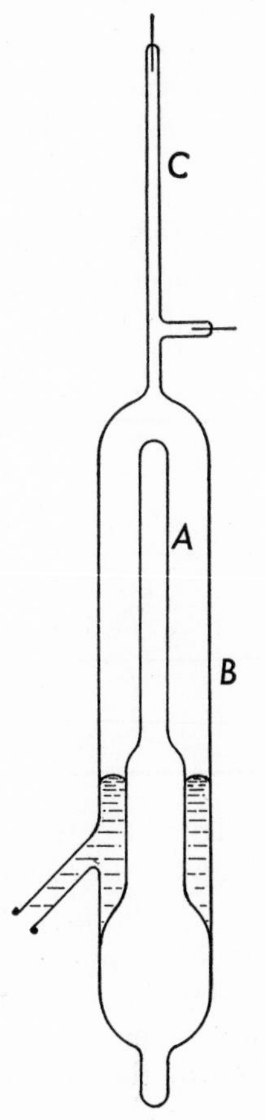

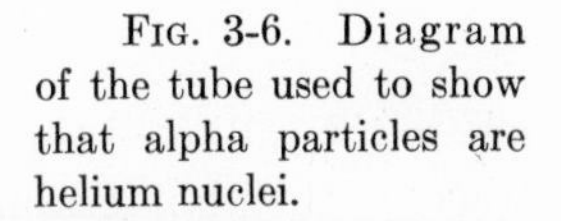
Fig. 3-6. Diagram of the tube used to show that alpha particles are helium nuclei.

In this experiment (see Figure 3-6), some radon was put into the thin-walled glass tube A. This tube was placed in a thick-walled glass tube B that had sealed on to it a capillary tube C into which two electrodes were sealed. Tubes B and C were pumped out and the system was allowed to stand for a few days. The alpha particles emitted by the radon passed through the thin walls of tube A and collected in tube B. The gases collecting in tube B could be compressed and forced into the capillary tube C by letting mercury in through a side tube. After six days enough gas was accumulated and forced into C so that a high voltage across its electrodes produced an electric discharge through the gas. The light coming from this tube was examined with a spectroscope which clearly showed the spectral lines of helium. Control experiments showed that ordinary helium gas could not penetrate through the thin walls of tube A. This spectroscopic evidence proves conclusively that alpha particles are helium nuclei.

3-5. Velocities of the Alpha Particles

The velocities of emission of alpha particles can be measured by allowing them to pass through a magnetic field perpendicular to the direction of motion. In the magnetic spectrograph used by Rosenblum, and sketched

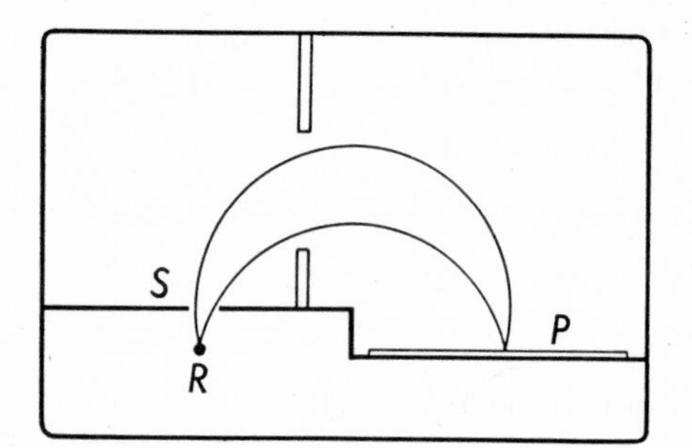

FIG. 3-7. Magnetic spectrograph used for measuring the velocities of alpha particles. The magnetic field is perpendicular to the plane of the paper and directed toward the reader.

in Figure 3-7, the radioactive material R is deposited on a fine wire, and the alpha rays coming through the narrow slit S are bent in a circular path by the magnetic field B perpendicular to the plane of the figure. After traversing a semicircle, the alpha rays of any one velocity are focused on the photographic plate P. The air in the chamber is pumped out to avoid loss of velocity by the alpha particles. The radius of the circle is given by the expression

$$BEv = \frac{Mv^2}{r},$$

where the radius of the circle, r, is half the distance from the source to the trace on the photographic plate, and v is the velocity of the alpha particle. The magnetic field in this experiment was about 36,000 gausses. Rutherford and his co-workers used a similar apparatus but substituted an ionization chamber for the photographic plate. W. Y. Chang has recently (1948) remeasured the velocities of the alpha particles from polonium and other radioactive sources, using a large, semicircular focusing magnetic spectrograph. The radii of the alpha particle paths were of the order of 30 cm in a magnetic field of the order of 11,000 gausses, giving greater resolution than in the earlier experiments.

The results of the experiments on the velocities of emission of alpha particles show that these velocities are of the order of 10^9 cm/sec. In many cases the velocity spectrum consists of only a single line, that is, all the alpha particles emitted from this type of element have exactly the same velocity. In another large group of elements, the velocity spectrum consists of two or more lines very close together. In a few cases there are several groups of lines covering a comparatively large velocity range. A few of the results of these measurements are given in Table 3-1.

Table 3-1

Velocities of Alpha Particles from Some Isotopes

Isotope		Velocity in cm/sec
Actinium A		1.882×10^9
Polonium		1.597
Radium	α_1	1.517
	α_2	1.488
Radium A		1.699
Radium C	α_1	1.628
	α_2	1.623
	α_3	1.603
Radium C′		1.922
Radon		1.625
Thorium C	α_1	1.711
	α_2	1.705
	α_3	1.665
	α_4	1.645
	α_5	1.642

3-6. Rutherford's Nuclear Theory of the Atom

Rutherford, in 1911, proposed a nuclear theory for the structure of the atom. He was led to this theory by the results of an experiment by Geiger and Marsden on the scattering of alpha particles by matter. They observed that some of the alpha particles were scattered through angles greater than 90°, that is, they emerged on the side of incidence. To explain such large-angle scattering of fast-moving alpha particles, Rutherford assumed that there was an intense electric field within the atom and that the alpha particle was deflected by a single atom. To provide such an intense electric field, Rutherford assumed that the entire positive charge of the atom was concentrated in a very small nucleus and that the electrons occupied the space outside the nucleus.

In developing the theory of the scattering of alpha particles by atomic nuclei, Rutherford assumed that both the nucleus and the alpha particle behaved as point charges, that Coulomb's law was valid for such small distances, and that Newtonian mechanics was applicable. To test this theory, he instituted a series of experiments on the scattering of alpha particles by thin films of matter. These experiments were performed by Geiger and Marsden in 1913 and repeated with greater accuracy by Chadwick in 1920. They verified Rutherford's nuclear theory of the structure of the atom and showed that the charge on the nucleus of an atom is Ze, where Z is the atomic number of the element and e is the electronic charge.

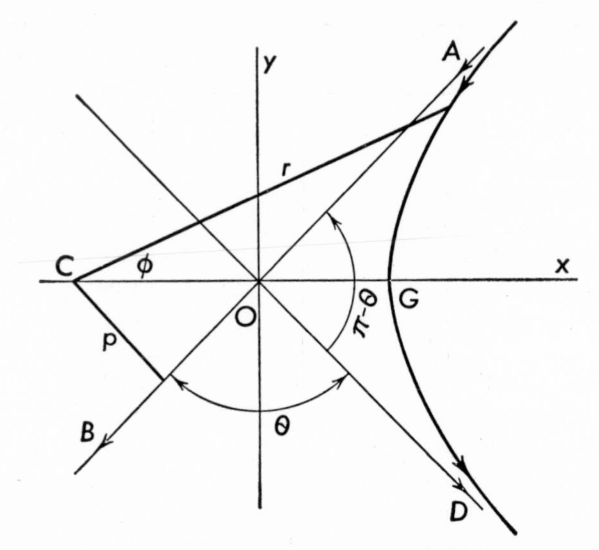

FIG. 3-8. The hyperbolic path of an alpha particle in the field of force of a nucleus.

3-7. Single Scattering of Alpha Particles by Thin Foils

Consider a nucleus of charge Ze stationary at point C, and an alpha particle of mass M and charge E approaching it along the line AB, as shown in Figure 3-8. The original velocity of the alpha particle in the direction of AB is V. There will be a force of repulsion between the two charges given by Coulomb's law

$$F = \frac{ZeE}{r^2}, \tag{1}$$

where r is the distance between the alpha particle and the nucleus. Because of this force of repulsion, the alpha particle will be deflected from its original direction, and will move in a hyperbolic path with the nucleus at the focus on the convex side of this branch of the hyperbola. When it leaves the region close to the nucleus, the alpha particle will be moving in the direction of OD, making an angle θ with its original direction of motion, AB. It can be shown (see Appendix VI) that the angle of deflection, θ, is given by

$$\cot\frac{\theta}{2} = \frac{MV^2}{ZeE}\,p, \tag{2}$$

where p is the distance from the nucleus at C to the original line of motion AB. In the actual experiments on the scattering of alpha particles, a large number of particles were directed against a thin metallic foil. It is therefore necessary to calculate the number of alpha particles scattered through a given angle θ, or, what amounts to the same thing, the probability that an alpha particle will be deflected through this angle θ. We shall assume that the foil is so thin that the alpha particles suffer no loss in velocity in passing through it.

Suppose that a stream of alpha particles is directed normally on a thin foil of matter of thickness t containing n atoms per unit volume. The number of atoms per unit area of this foil, and also the number of nuclei per unit area of foil, is nt. Any alpha particle whose initial velocity would bring it within a distance p of a nucleus will be deflected through an angle equal to or greater than θ, where θ is given by equation (2). To determine the probability that an alpha particle would come within this distance, imagine a circle of radius p drawn around each nucleus; then the area occupied by all such circles in a unit area of foil is $\pi p^2 nt$. The probability that an alpha particle would come within this distance p of a nucleus is the ratio of the area $\pi p^2 nt$ to unit area. Since every alpha particle which would come within a distance p of a nucleus will be deflected through an angle equal to or greater than θ, the probability that an alpha particle will be deflected through such an angle, or the fraction of the total number of alpha particles which will be deflected through an angle equal to or greater than θ, is given by

$$f = \pi p^2 nt = \pi nt\left(\frac{ZeE}{MV^2}\right)^2 \cot^2\frac{\theta}{2}, \tag{3}$$

using the value of p from equation (2).

The probability that the original direction of motion of an alpha particle would fall between the radii p and $p + dp$, or the probability that an alpha particle would be deflected through an angle lying between θ and $\theta + d\theta$ is

$$df = 2\pi pntdp$$

or

$$df = -\pi nt\left(\frac{ZeE}{MV^2}\right)^2 \cot\frac{\theta}{2}\csc^2\frac{\theta}{2}\,d\theta. \tag{4}$$

In the experiments on the scattering of alpha particles, the scattered particles were detected by the scintillations produced on a fluorescent screen. To compare results for different angles of scattering, it is necessary to know the number of alpha particles falling on unit area of the fluorescent screen. To determine this number, consider a stream of alpha particles which are incident normally on the thin foil T as shown in Figure 3-9. The

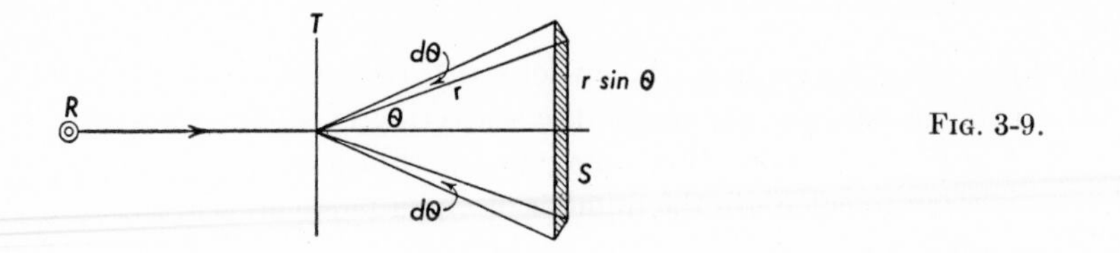

FIG. 3-9.

alpha particles which are scattered through an angle θ will travel along the elements of a cone of semivertex angle θ. Similarly, the alpha particles which are scattered through an angle $\theta + d\theta$ will travel along the elements of a cone of semivertex angle $\theta + d\theta$. If the fluorescent screen is to be placed at right angles to the direction of motion of the scattered particles, its shape must be that of a zone of a sphere of radius r and width $rd\theta$. Since the radius of this zone is $r \sin \theta$, an element of area dA of the fluorescent screen formed in this way is

$$dA = 2\pi r \sin\theta \cdot rd\theta = 2\pi r^2 \sin\theta d\theta$$

$$= 4\pi r^2 \sin\frac{\theta}{2}\cos\frac{\theta}{2}\, d\theta. \tag{5}$$

If Q is the total number of alpha particles incident on the foil, then the number striking unit area of the screen is, from equations (4) and (5),

$$N = Q\,\frac{\pi nt\left(\dfrac{ZeE}{MV^2}\right)^2 \cot\dfrac{\theta}{2}\csc^2\dfrac{\theta}{2}\, d\theta}{4\pi r^2 \sin\dfrac{\theta}{2}\cos\dfrac{\theta}{2}\, d\theta}$$

so that

$$\boxed{N = \frac{Qnt(Ze)^2E^2}{4r^2(MV^2)^2\sin^4\dfrac{\theta}{2}}}. \tag{6}$$

A study of equation (6) shows that if Rutherford's nuclear theory of the atom is correct, then the number of alpha particles falling on unit area of a screen at a distance r from the point of scattering must be proportional to

a. the reciprocal of $\sin^4 \theta/2$,

b. the thickness t of the scattering material,

c. the reciprocal of the square of initial energy of the particle or $1/(\frac{1}{2}MV^2)^2$,

d. the square of the nuclear charge, or $(Ze)^2$.

3-8. Experimental Verification of Rutherford's Nuclear Theory of the Atom

Each of the above deductions was tested and verified experimentally in a series of experiments carried out in Rutherford's laboratory. The angular distribution of the alpha particles scattered by a thin foil F, as shown in Figure 3-10, was measured by Geiger and Marsden. The alpha particles from a radon source R passed through a diaphragm D and were scattered

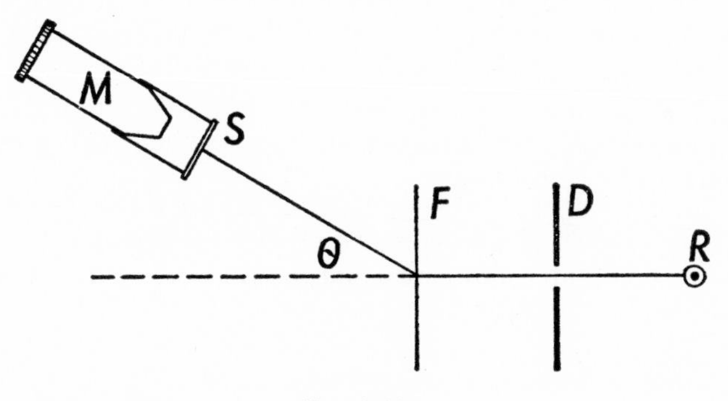

FIG. 3-10.

by the thin foil F. The alpha particles which were scattered through an angle θ struck a zinc sulfide screen S and the scintillations were viewed through the microscope M. The microscope and screen were rotated about an axis passing through the center of the foil F, and the number of particles striking the screen in a given time was measured at different angles over a range of angles from 5° to 150°. Gold and silver foils were used in the experiment. Some of the results are given in Table 3-2 for gold as the scattering element. If the number of particles, N, scattered per unit time through an angle θ is proportional to the reciprocal of $\sin^4 \theta/2$, then the product $N \times \sin^4 \theta/2$ should be a constant. The last column in Table 3-2 lists the values of these products; these values are approximately constant and lie within the limits of error of the experiment.

To test the dependence of scattering on the thickness of the foil, the angle of scattering was kept at about 25° and foils of different thicknesses and also of different materials were used. The alpha-particle source was

Table 3-2

Scattering of Alpha Particles from Gold Foil			
Angle of Deflection θ	$\dfrac{1}{\sin^4 \dfrac{\theta}{2}}$	Number of Scintillations in Unit Time N	$N \times \sin^4 \dfrac{\theta}{2}$
150°	1.15	33.1	28.8
135°	1.38	43.0	31.2
120°	1.79	51.9	29.0
105°	2.53	69.5	27.5
75°	7.25	211	29.1
60°	16.0	477	29.8
45°	46.6	1435	30.8
30°	223	7800	35.0
15°	3445	132,000	38.4

radium (B + C). The results of the experiments are shown in Figure 3-11, in which the number of particles per minute, N, scattered through an angle of 25°, is plotted as ordinates, and the thickness, t, of the scattering

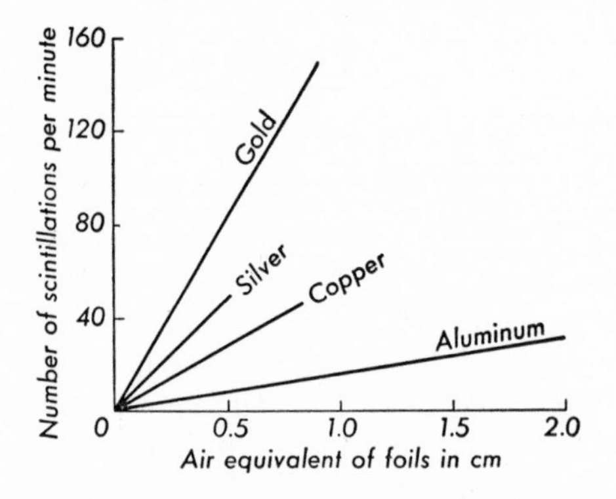

FIG. 3-11. Curves showing that the number of alpha particles scattered through a given angle is directly proportional to the thickness of the scattering foil. Each curve is the result of an independent set of measurements.

foil of a given material is plotted as abscissae. It is seen that for any one element, the number of particles scattered per minute is directly proportional to the thickness of the scattering foil. In the graph, the thickness of each foil is expressed in terms of an equivalent length of air path, that is, a thickness of air path which produces the same loss in energy of the alpha particle traversing it as that produced by the material under investigation.

In another series of observations, the velocity of the incident alpha particle was changed by placing absorbing screens of mica between the source and the scattering foil. The velocities of the alpha particles were determined empirically by first finding the range R of the alpha particles in air (§10-7), and then applying Geiger's rule that

$$R = aV^3 \tag{7}$$

where a is a constant. The results of the experiment are shown in Table 3-3.

Table 3-3

Variation of Scattering with Velocity

Range of Alpha Particles	Relative Values of $\frac{1}{V^4}$	Number of Scintillations in Unit Time N	NV^4
5.5	1.0	24.7	25
4.76	1.20	29.0	24
4.05	1.50	33.4	22
3.32	1.91	44	23
2.51	2.84	81	28
1.84	4.32	101	23
1.04	9.22	255	28

If the number of particles scattered through an angle θ is inversely proportional to the square of the energy of the particles, then the product NV^4 should be constant. The values of this product over a wide range of velocities are given in the last column of Table 3-3. These values are considered constant within the limits of error of the experiment.

The experiments of Geiger and Marsden have been interpreted as establishing the essential correctness of Rutherford's nuclear theory of the atom. However, these experiments were not sufficiently accurate to provide a reliable determination of the atomic number Z. It was not until 1920 that Chadwick succeeded in measuring the nuclear charge directly. In the meantime, Bohr had adopted Rutherford's nuclear hypothesis in his brilliant work on atomic spectra, and Moseley, from his work on x-ray spectra, was able to determine the nuclear charge and showed that it was equal to Ze.

3-9. Direct Determination of the Nuclear Charge

In Chadwick's experiment, alpha particles from the source R, as shown in Figure 3-12, were scattered by a thin foil AA' which was made in the form of an annular ring. The alpha particles which were scattered through an angle θ were counted by the scintillations they produced on the zinc sulfide screen placed at S on the axis of the cone RAA' such that $RA = AS$. The total number of alpha particles falling on the foil AA' could be determined by counting the number reaching S directly from R, since the areas of the screen S and the foil AA' were known. When the scattered rays were investigated, the direct rays from R were cut off by means of the lead plate L. Account was taken of the fact that the annular ring was of

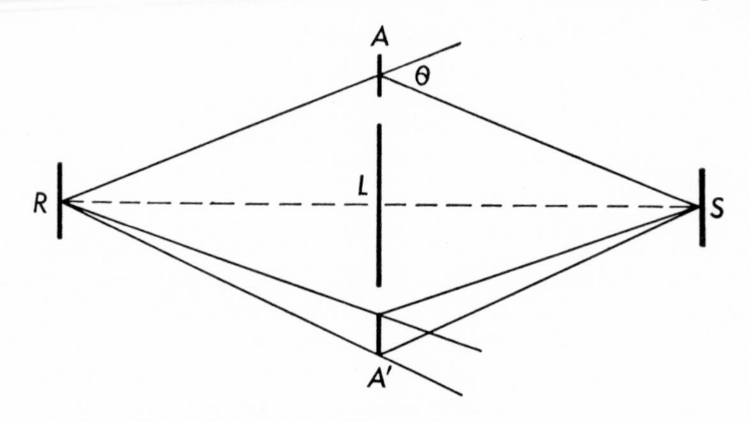

Fig. 3-12. Diagram of the arrangement used by Chadwick in his experiments on the scattering of alpha particles.

finite width. The results of Chadwick's experiments using platinum, silver, and copper foils are tabulated below:

Table 3-4

Element	Nuclear Charge Ze	Atomic Number Z
Cu	$29.3e$	29
Ag	$46.3e$	47
Pt	$77.4e$	78

Within the limits of experimental error, these results are in agreement with Rutherford's nuclear theory of the atom and provide the only direct measurement of the nuclear charge.

3-10. Nuclear Sizes: Radii

The results of experiments on the scattering of alpha particles may be used to calculate the distance of approach of the alpha particle to the nucleus (GC in Figure 3-8). The distance of approach will be smallest when the scattering angle θ is greatest, that is, 180°. For this case, the direction of the initial velocity V is along the line joining the centers of the nucleus and the alpha particle. At the point of closest approach the alpha particle comes to rest momentarily, so that its energy at this point is simply the Coulomb potential energy ZeE/b where b is the distance of closest approach. Equating the potential energy to the initial kinetic energy of the alpha particle, we get

$$\frac{ZeE}{b} = \tfrac{1}{2}MV^2,$$

from which

$$\boxed{b = \frac{2ZeE}{MV^2}.} \tag{8}$$

In the actual experiments the angle of scattering did not exceed 150°; for this angle the distance of approach was 3.2×10^{-12} cm for gold and about 2×10^{-12} cm for silver. The distance of closest approach b would thus be somewhat smaller than these values. Considering the process of scattering as a type of collision between two particles, the alpha particle and the nucleus, the distance of closest approach gives an upper limit to the size of the nucleus. Thus the radius of the gold nucleus is less than 3.2×10^{-12} cm. Rutherford also performed experiments on the scattering of alpha particles by lighter nuclei such as aluminum and helium. For the case of helium, the closest distance of approach calculated from the results of the experiment yielded a value of about 3×10^{-13} cm.

There are other experimental data from which estimates can be made of the sizes of nuclei. We shall discuss some of these experiments in Part III. These results can be expressed in the following empirical equation for the radius R of a nucleus of an isotope of mass number A:

$$\boxed{R = r_0 A^{1/3},} \tag{9}$$

where r_0 is the radius parameter. Numerical values of r_0 vary from about 1.2×10^{-13} cm to 1.5×10^{-13} cm. The latest data favor the value $r_0 = 1.2 \times 10^{-13}$ cm and will be adopted for all numerical calculations in this book.

3-11. Nuclear Cross Section

The concept of a *nuclear cross section* is a very useful one in nuclear physics. One must not assume that a nucleus is necessarily spherical in shape, or that it behaves as a solid elastic sphere of radius R toward projectiles such as alpha particles. We sometimes talk of the "geometrical" cross section given by πR^2 where R is the radius as given by equation (9). However, a more useful concept is the *cross section of a nucleus for a given process*, such as the cross section for the scattering of charged particles, or the cross section for the absorption of certain particles or for the absorption of radiation such as gamma rays. The term *cross section* used in this sense *is a measure of the probability of the occurrence of the given process.* As an example of this let us refer once again to the single scattering of alpha particles by nuclei, sometimes called *Coulomb scattering.* It was shown that the probability f that an alpha particle would be scattered by a nucleus through an angle equal to or greater than θ is given by

$$f = \pi p^2 nt, \tag{3}$$

where n is the number of nuclei per unit volume, t is the thickness of the scattering material, and p is the impact parameter. We can now define a nuclear scattering cross section, σ_s, as

$$\boxed{\sigma_s = \pi p^2;} \tag{10}$$

hence

$$f = \sigma_s nt. \tag{11}$$

The scattering cross section σ_s is thus proportional to the probability of scattering.

If a beam containing N alpha particles is sent through the substance of thickness t, then the number N_s of particles that will be scattered through an angle equal to or greater than θ is

$$N_s = fN = \sigma_s ntN,$$

from which

$$\boxed{\sigma_s = \frac{N_s}{Nnt}.} \tag{12}$$

Equation (12) can be used for determining scattering cross sections from empirical data.

The concept of a nuclear cross section can be extended to other types of nuclear processes. For example, if we are interested in the absorption of certain particles by nuclei, then we can define the *absorption cross section* as

$$\sigma_a = \frac{N_a}{Nnt}, \tag{13}$$

where N_a is the number of particles absorbed by the nuclei when the incident beam contains N particles.

A large number of nuclear cross sections are of the order of 10^{-24} cm^2. It has been found convenient to use a separate name for this area. The name adopted is a *barn*, that is,

$$1 \text{ barn} = 10^{-24} \text{ cm}^2. \tag{14}$$

3-12. Differential Scattering Cross Section

Just as the scattering cross section σ_s is a measure of the probability that a particle will be scattered through an angle equal to or greater than θ, the *differential scattering cross section* $d\sigma_s$ is a measure of the probability that a particle will be scattered through an angle whose value lies between θ and $\theta + d\theta$. Referring to equation (10),

$$\sigma_s = \pi p^2; \tag{10}$$

therefore,

$$d\sigma_s = 2\pi p dp. \tag{15}$$

In the case of the single scattering of alpha particles, it was shown that

$$\cot\frac{\theta}{2} = \frac{MV^2}{ZeE}p. \tag{2}$$

Introducing the value of b from equation (8),

$$b = \frac{2ZeE}{MV^2}, \tag{8}$$

we can write that

$$p = \frac{b}{2}\cot\frac{\theta}{2}, \tag{16}$$

and hence

$$d\sigma_s = \frac{\pi b^2}{4}\cot\frac{\theta}{2}\csc^2\frac{\theta}{2}\,d\theta. \tag{17}$$

Referring to Figure 3-13, the particles which are scattered through an angle whose value lies between θ and $\theta + d\theta$ are contained within a solid angle $d\omega$ whose value is

$$d\omega = 2\pi \sin\theta d\theta. \tag{18}$$

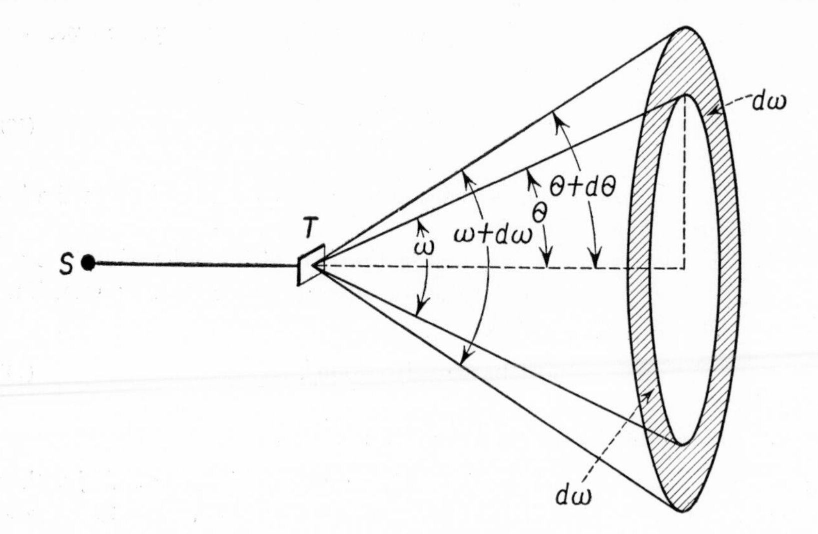

FIG. 3-13. The solid angle $d\omega$ is that included between the two concentric cones of semivertex (plane) angles θ and $\theta + d\theta$ corresponding to the solid angles ω and $\omega + d\omega$, respectively. S is the source of alpha particles and T is the scattering substance.

Substituting this value of $d\theta$ in equation (17) yields

$$d\sigma_s = \frac{\pi b^2}{4} \cot\frac{\theta}{2} \csc^2\frac{\theta}{2} \frac{d\omega}{2\pi \sin\theta},$$

from which

$$\boxed{d\sigma_s = \frac{b^2}{16 \sin^4 \frac{\theta}{2}} d\omega.} \tag{19}$$

Equation (19) is simply the Rutherford scattering law and is to be compared with equation (4). The differential scattering cross section can be interpreted as a measure of the probability that a particle will be scattered within a solid angle whose value lies between ω and $\omega + d\omega$. Differential cross sections for other types of nuclear processes can be defined in a manner analogous to that used in defining the differential scattering cross section.

Problems

3-1. (a) Show that the path of an alpha particle in the electrostatic deflection experiment performed by Rutherford for the determination of E/M (§3-3) is a parabola given by

$$y = x \tan\theta - \tfrac{1}{2}\left(\frac{V}{d}\frac{E}{M}\right)\frac{x^2}{v_0^2 \cos^2\theta}$$

where θ is the angle which the initial velocity v_0 makes with the line joining the source S and the slit S_1, and V is the difference of potential between the plates.

(b) Show that only those alpha particles which are directed initially at an angle θ given by

$$\sin 2\theta = \frac{V}{d} \frac{E}{M} \frac{L}{v_0^2}$$

will get through the slit S_1. L is the distance from S to S_1.

(c) Calculate the value of the angle θ in this experiment for the alpha particles from radon when $V = 2000$ volts; the distance between the plates is 4 mm and the length of each plate is 35 cm.

Ans. $\theta = 55$ minutes.

3-2. Alpha particles from polonium are directed normally against a thin sheet of gold of thickness 10^{-5} cm. The density of gold is 19.32 gm/cm^3. Determine the fraction of the incident alpha particles scattered through angles greater than 90°.

Ans. 8.5×10^{-6}.

3-3. **(a)** Protons of 1 Mev energy are scattered by nuclei of gold. Assuming the Rutherford type of scattering, calculate the distance of closest approach. **(b)** Compare this distance with the radius of the proton. **(c)** Determine the distance of closest approach of deuterons of the same energy.

Ans. **(a)** and **(c)** 11.4×10^{-12} cm.

3-4. Using the value of the radius of a nucleus given by equation (9), determine the average density of nuclear matter.

Ans. 2.3×10^{14} gm/cm^3.

3-5. Alpha particles from ThC′ are deflected in a strong magnetic field. Their momentum, expressed in terms of the field strength B and radius of curvature r of the path, is found to be $Br = 427.07$ kilogausses cm. Determine **(a)** the kinetic energy of these alpha particles; and **(b)** their velocity.

Ans. **(a)** 2.058×10^9 cm/sec.
(b) 8.80 Mev.

3-6. Alpha particles from a polonium source are deflected in a magnetic field $B = 25{,}000$ gausses and travel in a circular path of radius r, such that $Br = 331.76$ kilogausses cm. Determine **(a)** the radius of the path and **(b)** the kinetic energy of the alpha particles.

Ans. **(a)** 13.27 cm.
(b) 5.30 Mev.

3-7. Thorium C emits alpha particles of two different velocities. When traversing a magnetic field of strength $B = 20{,}000$ gausses they travel in circular paths of radii r_1 and r_2 such that $Br_1 = 354.34$ kilogausses cm and $Br_2 = 355.51$ kilogausses cm. Assuming that these alpha particles start from a point source and travel in semicircular paths, **(a)** determine the separation of the two alpha-particle lines in this spectrum; and **(b)** calculate their kinetic energies.

Ans. **(a)** 1.17 mm.
(b) 6.059 Mev; 6.098 Mev.

References

Cork, J. M., *Radioactivity and Nuclear Physics.* New York: D. Van Nostrand Company, Inc., 1950, Chaps. I–VI.

Rasetti, F., *Elements of Nuclear Physics.* New York: Prentice-Hall, Inc., 1936, Chaps. I–IV.

Rutherford, E., J. Chadwick, and C. D. Ellis, *Radiations from Radioactive Substances.* London: Cambridge University Press, 1930, Chaps. II, VIII.

chapter **4**

Electromagnetic Radiation

4-1. Early Theories of the Nature of Light

Ever since the days of Newton and Huygens—that is, since the latter part of the seventeenth century—there have been two fundamentally different theories concerning the nature of light. Newton proposed a corpuscular theory of light without specifying definitely the nature of these corpuscles; Huygens proposed a wave theory to explain exactly the same phenomena that were explained by Newton on his corpuscular theory. In one important case, that of the velocity of light in material media, deductions from these two theories led to divergent results. On the basis of Newton's corpuscular theory, light should travel faster in the denser medium, while on the basis of the wave theory, light should travel slower in the denser medium. It was not until the middle of the nineteenth century that the velocity of light in a dense medium, water, was determined by Foucault and Fizeau, and found to be less than that in a vacuum. By this time, the wave theory had become fairly well established, mainly because of the work of Young, Fresnel, and Arago on the phenomena of interference and diffraction of light. Further, the polarization of light by reflection, and by double refraction through crystals, could be explained on the assumption that light waves were transverse waves. The wave theory of light was the only one which could explain satisfactorily all the optical phenomena then known.

4-2. Maxwell's Electromagnetic Theory of Light

Although the wave theory of light was definitely established, the nature of the waves remained a puzzle. It was at first thought that these waves were similar to the transverse waves which are propagated through an elastic solid. A luminiferous ether, filling all of space and having some of the properties of an elastic solid, was postulated as the medium through which light waves were propagated. Maxwell, in his work on electricity and magnetism (1864), showed that a disturbance consisting of transverse electric and magnetic fields should be propagated through the ether with the speed of light. Hertz (1887) succeeded in producing electromagnetic waves by means of an oscillatory current and showed the correctness of Maxwell's theory. Modern wireless telegraphy and radio are practical developments based upon the work of Maxwell and Hertz.

Serious difficulties arose in connection with the properties of the luminiferous ether through which these waves were assumed to be propagated. Einstein's theory of relativity (1905) resolved these difficulties by showing that such an ether was not necessary for the propagation of electromagnetic waves. As a consequence of this theory, light waves are now regarded as electromagnetic oscillations, consisting of variations in the intensities of transverse electric and magnetic fields, each of which may exist in free space, that is, space completely devoid of matter.

On the basis of classical electrodynamics, it is shown that an accelerated charge radiates energy in the form of electromagnetic waves. The electromagnetic wave consists of an electric field of intensity Y and a magnetic field of intensity H always at right angles to each other. The magnitudes of these electric and magnetic intensities at a distance r from a charge e are given by

$$\boxed{Y = H = \frac{ae}{rc^2} \sin \phi,} \tag{1}$$

where a is the acceleration of the charge and ϕ is the angle between r and the direction of the acceleration, as shown in Figure 4-1. Y and H are

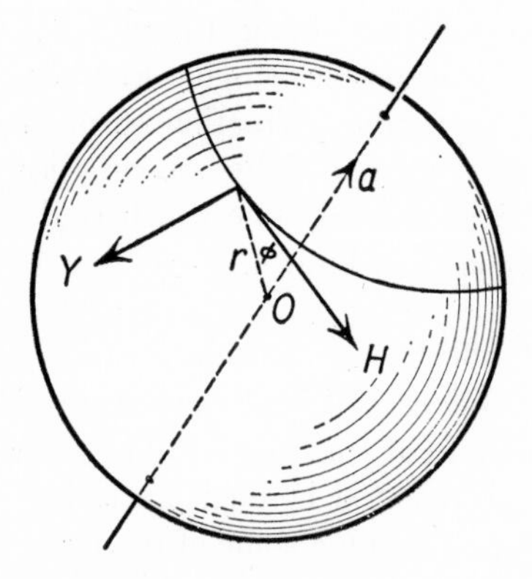

FIG. 4-1. The electric intensity Y and the magnetic intensity H are tangent to the surface of the sphere.

numerically equal when Y is expressed in esu, H is expressed in emu, and the charge e is expressed in esu. Equation (1) holds only when the velocity of the charge is much smaller than the velocity of light. The electric and magnetic fields are always at right angles to the direction of propagation and move through space with the velocity of light.

It has been shown that the energy per unit volume in an electric field in free space is equal to $Y^2/8\pi$, and that the energy per unit volume in a magnetic field in free space is equal to $H^2/8\pi$. The energy per unit volume, w, in the electromagnetic wave is, therefore,

$$w = \frac{Y^2}{8\pi} + \frac{H^2}{8\pi} = \frac{Y^2}{4\pi}. \tag{2}$$

Since this energy is propagated with velocity c, the amount of energy, I, which flows in unit time through unit area perpendicular to the direction of propagation is

$$I = \frac{cY^2}{4\pi}. \tag{3}$$

Hence I represents the instantaneous value of the intensity of the electromagnetic wave at any point in space. It will be noted, by referring to equation (1), that the intensity of the electromagnetic wave produced by a charge which is accelerated along the axis is a maximum in a direction at right angles to the acceleration, and is zero in a direction parallel to the acceleration.

The rate at which energy is radiated from an accelerated charge can be calculated by integrating the intensity I over the surface of a sphere of radius r containing the accelerated charge at its center. Referring to Figure 4-2, consider a small element of surface area included between two small circles of radii $r \sin \phi$ and $r \sin (\phi + d\phi)$, and of area

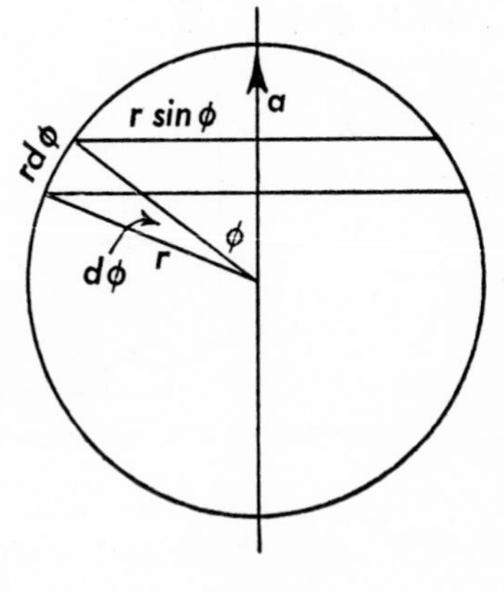

FIG. 4-2.

$$dA = 2\pi r \sin \phi \cdot r d\phi.$$

The amount of energy, dS, which passes through this element of surface in unit time is

$$dS = IdA = \frac{cY^2}{4\pi} \cdot 2\pi r^2 \sin \phi d\phi.$$

Substituting the value of Y from equation (1), and integrating over the whole surface, we get

$$S = \int_0^A IdA = \frac{1}{2}\frac{a^2e^2}{c^3}\int_0^\pi \sin^3 \phi d\phi,$$

yielding

$$\boxed{S = \frac{2}{3}\frac{a^2e^2}{c^3}.} \tag{4}$$

In this equation S represents the rate at which energy is radiated from the accelerated charge; it depends upon the square of the acceleration and also upon the square of the charge. It is thus independent of the direction of the acceleration and of the sign of the charge.

The simplest type of electromagnetic wave is a plane wave in which the electric field intensity is in one direction only, say the y direction, which vibrates with a single frequency, and which has a single wavelength λ. Such a wave is called a *linearly polarized monochromatic* electromagnetic wave; the direction of polarization is taken as the direction of vibration of the vector representing the electric field intensity. In the example above the direction of polarization is the y direction. Since an electromagnetic wave is a transverse wave, its direction of propagation is at right angles to the direction of vibration of the electric vector which represents the intensity of the electric field. A linearly polarized monochromatic electromagnetic wave

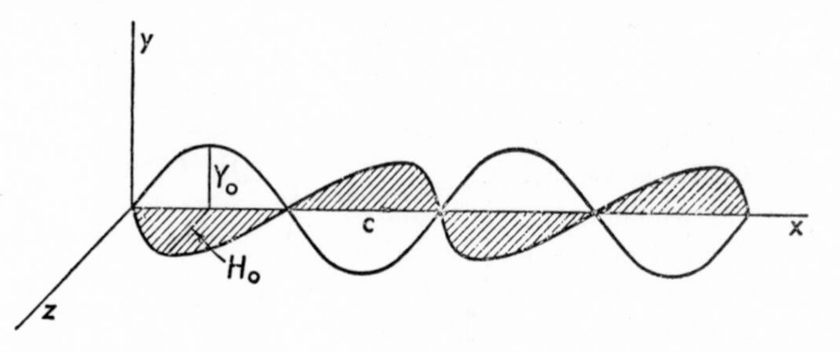

FIG. 4-3. Graph showing the values of the intensities of the electric and magnetic fields in a plane electromagnetic wave at a given instant of time.

consists not only of an electric field but a magnetic field as well. The magnetic field is always at right angles to the electric field, varying periodically and always in time phase with the electric field. Such a linearly polarized electromagnetic wave traveling, say, in the x direction, can be represented by the following two equations:

$$Y = Y_0 \sin \frac{2\pi}{\lambda} (x - ct) \tag{5a}$$

$$H = H_0 \sin \frac{2\pi}{\lambda} (x - ct), \tag{5b}$$

where Y is the electric intensity at any point in the path of the wave at any instant of time, H is the intensity of the magnetic field at the same point at the same time, but always at right angles to the electric vector Y. Both Y and H are in a plane at right angles to the direction of propagation. In Figure 4-3, Y is chosen parallel to the y axis and H parallel to the z axis. Y_0 and H_0 are the amplitudes of the electric and magnetic intensities, respectively. This plane wave is propagated in the x direction with the velocity c.

The average intensity of the wave is the average value of the energy flowing through unit area in unit time. Since the rate at which electromagnetic energy flows through unit area is given by $I = c\frac{Y^2}{4\pi}$, the average intensity can be obtained by averaging I over a convenient interval of time, say half a period, yielding

$$I_{\text{av}} = \frac{1}{\frac{T}{2}}\int_0^{T/2} I dt = \frac{2}{T}\int_0^{T/2} \frac{c}{4\pi} Y_0^2 \sin^2 \frac{2\pi}{\lambda}(x - ct)dt,$$

or

$$\boxed{I_{\text{av}} = \frac{cY_0^2}{8\pi}.} \tag{6}$$

The average intensity of the electromagnetic wave is thus proportional to the square of the amplitude of the electric intensity, which, of course, is equal to the square of the amplitude of the magnetic intensity.

In the case of light, a plane electromagnetic wave can be produced very simply by placing a small source of light at the focus of a converging lens or mirror and producing a parallel beam, that is, one in which the wave front is a plane. A linearly polarized plane wave can be obtained by passing a plane parallel beam of light through a Nicol prism, by reflecting the parallel beam from a glass plate set at the polarizing angle, or by passing the parallel beam of light through a sheet of polaroid. Again the direction of polarization is the direction of vibration of the electric vector representing the intensity of the electric field of the light wave.

A Nicol prism may also be used as an analyzer to determine whether the beam is polarized. The Nicol prism is rotated about the beam of light as an axis, and, if a position of the prism can be found in which no light can pass through it, the beam is said to be linearly polarized. The direction of vibration of the electric vector is then easily determined since the Nicol prism does not transmit light in which the direction of vibration is parallel to the long diagonal of the face of the prism.

An interesting and important type of polarization is produced when a linearly polarized beam of light is allowed to pass through a thin sheet of some doubly refracting crystal such as mica. If the linearly polarized monochromatic beam of light is incident on the thin sheet of mica with its direction of vibration at 45° to the axis of the crystal, then the electric vector will be resolved into two components at right angles to one another which travel through the crystal with different velocities. For a certain value of the thickness of the crystal one beam will emerge a quarter of a period behind the other, that is, they will be out of phase by a quarter of a wavelength. A crystal of such thickness is called a quarter-wave plate. The vibrations of the electric vectors in the two beams are at right angles to one another and they differ in phase by a quarter of a period. Thus when one component is a maximum the other component is zero, yielding a resultant vector which describes a circle. Such a beam is said to be *circularly* polarized. The direction of rotation of the circularly polarized beam may be either clockwise or counterclockwise, depending upon the nature of the crystal and upon the angle between the electric vector of the incident beam and the crystal axis, i.e., whether the angle is $+45°$ or $-45°$. When the circularly polarized beam is passed through a second quarter-wave plate with its axis parallel to the first one, the beam becomes linearly polarized again.

4-3. The Zeeman Effect

It is known that the light emitted by any element consists of sharp lines of definite wavelengths, and hence of definite frequencies characteristic of the element. The light evidently comes from the atoms of the element and, on the classical theory, is due to the periodic motions of the charges within the atom. Since moving charges are affected by electric and magnetic fields, it should be possible to produce changes in the emitted light by subjecting the source of radiation to electric and magnetic fields. Faraday attempted to find such an effect by placing a sodium flame in a strong magnetic field but failed to detect any change in the character of the light. Zeeman (1896), with apparatus of greater resolving power, succeeded in producing this effect and in determining the nature of the charge emitting the light.

To produce the Zeeman effect, the source of light, such as a sodium flame or a mercury arc, is placed between the poles of a powerful electromagnet. The light coming from the source is examined by means of a spectroscope of high resolving power. The light may be viewed in a direction perpendicular to the magnetic field, or parallel to the magnetic field; to make the latter possible, a hole is drilled in one of the pole pieces along the axis of the magnet. If one of the intense lines in the spectrum of the element is focused in the spectroscope, then, when the magnetic field is applied, it is found that this line splits into several component lines. Furthermore, although the original line was unpolarized, each of the component lines is polarized. In the simpler *normal* Zeeman effect, there are three components when the light is viewed perpendicular to the direction of the magnetic field and only two components when the light is viewed parallel to the magnetic field. In the more complex or *anomalous* Zeeman effect, the line is split into many more components. Consideration of the anomalous Zeeman effect will be left to a later chapter (Chapter 8), since the classical theory is unable to account for this anomalous effect.

In the normal Zeeman effect, when the light is viewed in a direction perpendicular to the direction of the magnetic field, three component lines are observed, one in the same position as the original line, and two components separated by equal distances on either side of this central line, as shown in Figure 4-4. By means of an analyzer such as a Nicol prism it can

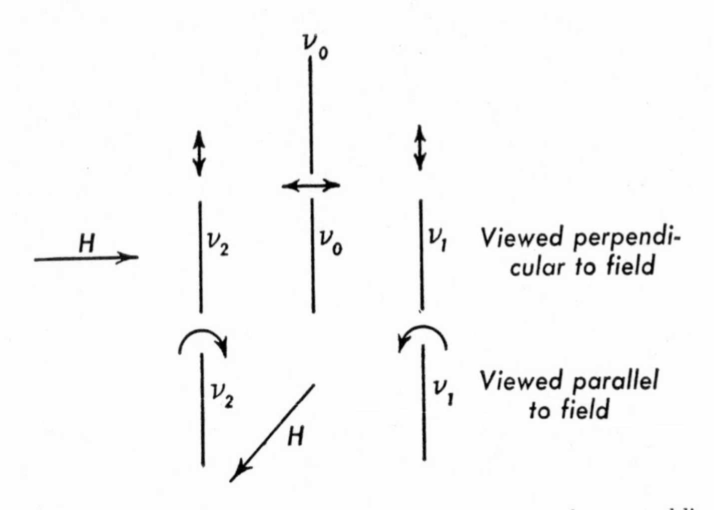

FIG. 4-4. The normal Zeeman effect showing the splitting of a spectral line when the source of light is in a magnetic field.

be shown that the outer components are polarized at right angles to the undisplaced component. The direction of vibration of the electric vector in the outer components is perpendicular to the magnetic field; in the inner component the electric vector is parallel to the magnetic field. When the light is viewed parallel to the magnetic field, there is no undisplaced line; only the two outer components are present in the same positions as in the perpendicular case. These two components are circularly polarized in opposite directions.

The classical explanation of the normal Zeeman effect is based on Lorentz's electron theory. Assume that an electron in the atom is moving in a circular orbit of radius r under the action of some central force F_0, as shown in Figure 4-5. Then from Newton's second law of motion

$$F_0 = \frac{mv_0^2}{r} = m\omega_0^2 r \tag{7}$$

where v_0 is its linear velocity in the orbit and ω_0 is its angular velocity. If an external magnetic field is applied perpendicular to the plane of the orbit of the electron, two effects will be produced. During the time that the magnetic field is being established, there will be an electric field tangent to the orbit because of the emf produced by the changing magnetic flux through it. At the same time there will be an additional force on the electron which will be perpendicular to the direction of the magnetic field and to the velocity of the electron, that is, the force will be radial. A simple analysis shows that if the tangential electric field is such as to cause an increase in the velocity of the electron, the radial force will be directed toward the center, thus providing the additional force needed to keep it moving in the same orbit with this higher velocity. Conversely, if the tangential electric field is such as to decrease the velocity of the electron, then the radial force due to the magnetic field will be directed away from the center, thus decreasing the centripetal force to the amount needed to keep the electron moving in the same circular orbit at the smaller velocity. The simplified analysis given above is a special case of a very famous theorem due to Larmor which will be discussed in greater detail in Chapter 8.

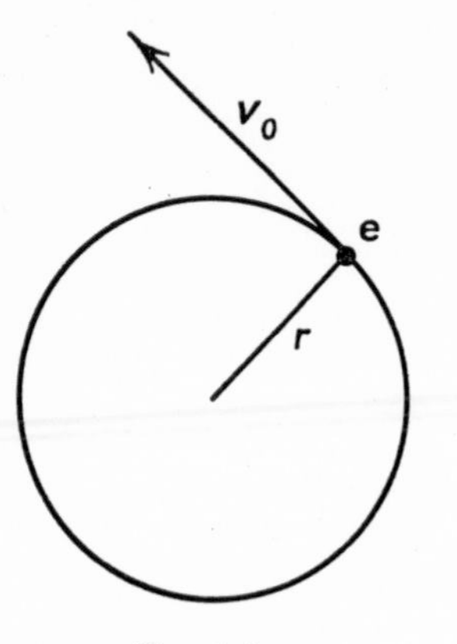

FIG. 4-5.

Suppose that the velocity of the electron has been increased to v_1 by the application of the magnetic field of intensity H; then the force F_H due to the magnetic field is

$$F_H = Hev_1 = He\omega_1 r$$

where

$$v_1 = \omega_1 r.$$

The symbol H is frequently used rather than B, since the space between the constituent particles of an atom is a vacuum, and in the em system of units, the permeability $\mu = 1$, so that $B = H$. Since this force is directed toward the center, the total force acting radially is

$$F_0 + F_H = m\omega_1^2 r.$$

Substituting the values for F_0 and F_H, we get

$$m\omega_0^2 r + He\omega_1 r = m\omega_1^2 r. \tag{8}$$

Solving equation (8) for ω_1, we get

$$\omega_1 = \frac{\dfrac{eH}{m} \pm \sqrt{\left(\dfrac{eH}{m}\right)^2 + 4\omega_0^2}}{2}.$$

It can be shown that $\left(\dfrac{eH}{m}\right)^2 \ll 4\omega_0^2$;

therefore we can write $$\omega_1 = \omega_0 + \frac{eH}{2m}. \tag{9}$$

Only the positive sign is retained since the effect of the magnetic field is small and can produce only a slight change in the magnitude of the angular velocity. If the charge should be rotating in the opposite direction, its angular velocity will be decreased by the amount $eH/2m$, so that, in general, its angular velocity will be

$$\omega = \omega_0 \pm \frac{eH}{2m}. \tag{10}$$

This equation may be put in terms of the frequency of rotation with the aid of the equations

$$\omega = 2\pi\nu$$

$$\omega_0 = 2\pi\nu_0,$$

where ν is the frequency corresponding to the angular velocity ω. Equation (10) then becomes

$$\boxed{\nu = \nu_0 \pm \frac{eH}{4\pi m}.} \tag{11}$$

The quantity $eH/4\pi m$, where e is in electromagnetic units, is called the normal Zeeman separation in a magnetic field of intensity H. The quantity e/m can thus be determined from a measurement of the normal Zeeman separation of a single spectrum line. Most recent determinations of e/m from measurements of the Zeeman effect yield

$$\frac{e}{m} = 1.759 \times 10^7 \frac{\text{emu}}{\text{gm}},$$

which is practically identical with the value of e/m obtained for electrons by means of electric and magnetic deflection experiments.

To compare prediction with experimental observation, consider the direction of the magnetic field H as that of the positive x axis; the current in the electromagnet producing this field can be represented as circular in the Y-Z plane, as shown in Figure 4-6. In the actual source of light, the atoms will have all possible orientations. Since light is a transverse wave motion, only those components of the acceleration of the electron which are perpendicular to the line of sight will be effective in sending radiation in this direction. Those electrons moving in orbits parallel to the Y-Z plane will have their frequencies increased or decreased by an amount $eH/4\pi m$. Any uniform circular motion can be resolved into two simple harmonic vibrations at right angles to one another and differing in time phase by a quarter of a period. If the light coming from these electrons is viewed along the z axis, only the y component of the vibration will be observed and the frequencies will be

$$\nu_1 = \nu_0 + \frac{eH}{4\pi m} \tag{12}$$

and

$$\nu_2 = \nu_0 - \frac{eH}{4\pi m}. \tag{13}$$

Since only the y component of the acceleration is effective in sending light in this direction, these components will be linearly polarized with the

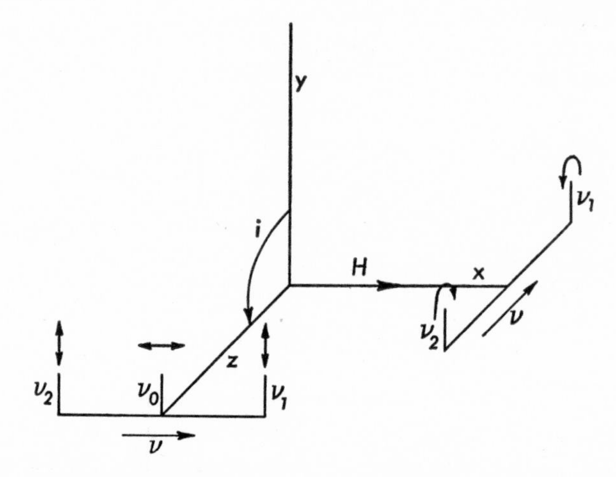

FIG. 4-6. The direction of vibration of the components of a spectral line exhibiting the normal Zeeman effect in relation to the direction of the current producing the magnetic field.

direction of vibration perpendicular to the magnetic field. If the light is viewed along the x axis, both the y and z vibrations will be effective in sending out radiations and the two component lines will be circularly polarized. Experiment shows that the higher frequency component is circularly polarized in the same direction as that of the current in the electromagnet. An analysis of the direction of the force due to the magnetic field shows that only a negative charge rotating in the same direction as that of the polarization can have its frequency increased by the magnetic field (see Figure 4-6). The component of lower frequency is circularly polarized in the opposite direction and again must be due to a negative charge rotating in this direction. Thus it appears that the light emitted by an atom originates in negatively charged particles for which the value of e/m is identical with that observed for electrons.

To explain the presence of the undeviated component of frequency ν_0, consider those vibrations which are parallel to the x axis. Since the motion of the electron is parallel to the direction of the magnetic field, there will be no additional force acting on it and its frequency will be unchanged. This component will therefore be observed when the light is viewed perpendicular to the magnetic field; the light of frequency ν_0 will be linearly polarized with the direction of vibration parallel to the direction of the magnetic field. This component will not be observed when the source is viewed parallel to the magnetic field, since no light can be emitted parallel to the direction of vibration of the charge.

4-4. Photoelectric Effect

The photoelectric effect was first observed by Hertz in his work on the production of electromagnetic waves. Hertz noted that the air in the spark gap became a better conductor when it was illuminated by ultraviolet light

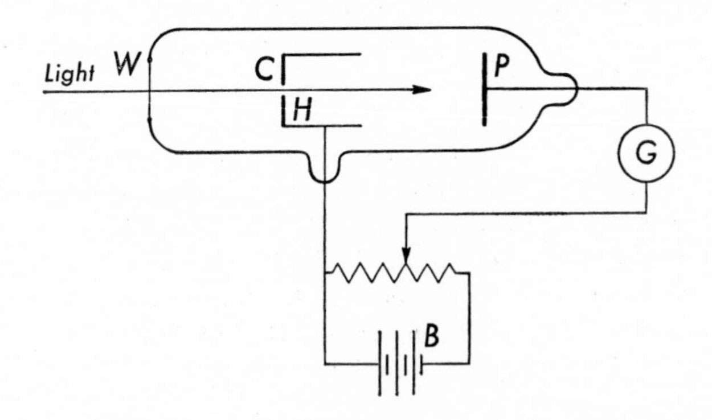

Fig. 4-7. Experimental arrangement for measuring the photoelectric current.

from an arc lamp. Hallwachs (1888) found that when ultraviolet light was incident on a negatively charged zinc surface, the surface lost its charge rapidly. If the surface was positively charged, there was no loss of charge under the action of the light. A neutral surface became positively charged when illuminated by ultraviolet light. It is evident that only negative charges are emitted by the surface because of the action of the ultraviolet light. Measurements of e/m for these negative charges by the usual electric and magnetic deflection methods show that these charges are electrons.

A typical arrangement for the study of the photoelectric effect is shown in Figure 4-7. A glass tube has a quartz window W sealed onto it to permit ultraviolet light to enter the tube. P is the photoelectric surface to be investigated and C is a hollow cylinder to collect the electrons emitted by P. A small hole in the base of the cylinder permits light to reach the plate P. In this type of work it is very important that the surface of the plate P be as clean as possible. Not only must the air be pumped out of the tube; the entire tube must be baked during the pumping operation to get rid of as much gas as possible if the results of the experiment are to have any quantitative significance. Further, to ensure that no electrons come from the cylinder C because of the action of scattered light, C is usually coated with copper oxide or some other substance which is comparatively insensitive photoelectrically. However, when C and P are made of different materials, it is found that a *contact* difference of potential exists between them. This contact difference of potential may be of the order of one or two volts. If the contact difference of potential between C and P is such as to make C negative with respect to P, it will oppose the motion of the electrons. In all photoelectric experiments correction must be made for this contact difference of potential. In the discussion which follows, the values of the potential difference between C and P have been corrected for this effect.

When light from some source such as a quartz mercury arc lamp is incident on the plate P, the electrons emitted by the plate are collected by the cylinder C. A difference of potential is maintained between P and C by means of a potentiometer arrangement, and the photoelectric current is measured by a sensitive galvanometer G. The photoelectric current is found to depend upon two factors: (a) the intensity of the incident light, and (b) the wavelengths of the incident beam. To determine the effect of each of these factors, monochromatic light of known wavelength must be used. There are two points of interest in the photoelectric effect: one is the velocity with which the electrons are emitted by the surface; the other is the number of electrons emitted under known conditions.

4-5. Velocity of the Photoelectrons

If monochromatic light of wavelength λ and intensity I is incident upon the surface P, the electrons emitted from the surface will be acted upon by the electric field between the plate P and the collecting cylinder C. With a potentiometer arrangement, the electric field can be varied by varying the difference of potential between P and C. If C is made positive with respect to the plate, the electrons will be accelerated toward C; if C is made negative, the electrons will be retarded. The current, as registered by the galvanometer, is proportional to the number of electrons per second reaching the cylinder. If the photoelectric current i is plotted against the difference of potential V between C and P, as shown in Figure 4-8, it is found that for all positive values of V the current is constant, but as C is made negative with respect to P, the current decreases rapidly and becomes zero at some value V_0. If the intensity of the monochromatic beam of light is increased from I_1 to I_2, and the experiment is repeated, the photoelectric current is increased in the same ratio for all values of V. As V is made negative, the photoelectric current decreases sharply and reaches zero at the same value of the voltage V_0, which is called the *stopping potential* for this particular wavelength λ.

There are two results of great importance that have been obtained in this experiment. The direct proportionality between the maximum current and the intensity of the light indicates that the number of electrons per

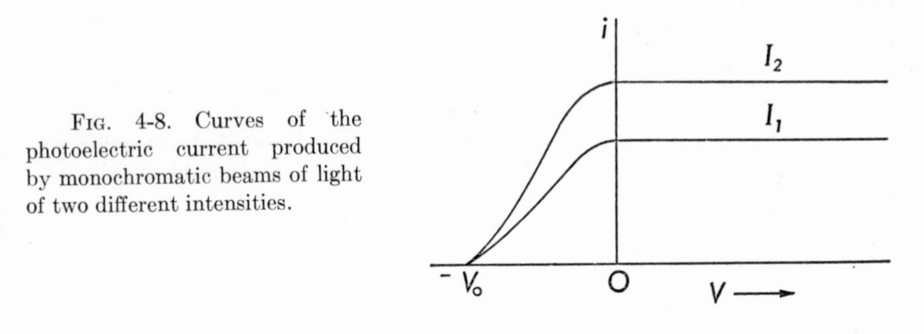

FIG. 4-8. Curves of the photoelectric current produced by monochromatic beams of light of two different intensities.

second emitted by the surface P is directly proportional to the intensity of the incident beam of light. The fact that the stopping potential V_0 is independent of the intensity of the beam can be interpreted only by assuming that the kinetic energy of the electrons emitted by the surface does not exceed a certain maximum value give by

$$\boxed{V_0 e = \tfrac{1}{2} m v^2_{\text{max}}.} \tag{14}$$

Those electrons which leave the surface with kinetic energies less than the maximum are stopped by smaller values of the potential difference. This explains the decrease in the current when the potential difference between C and P is made negative.

The dependence of the stopping potential on the wavelength of the light was investigated by Millikan (1916) in a series of very careful experiments using sodium and potassium as the photoelectric surfaces. The surfaces were illuminated by light of different wavelengths. The stopping potential, V_0, was determined for each particular wavelength. The results of Millikan's experiments can best be represented in a graph, Figure 4-9, in which $V_0 e$ is plotted against the frequency, ν, of the light incident upon the given surface. The curve is a straight line given by the equation

$$V_0 e = \tfrac{1}{2} m v^2_{\text{max}} = h(\nu - \nu_0) = h\nu - h\nu_0, \tag{15}$$

where h is the slope of the line and ν_0 is the smallest frequency which can cause the emission of an electron from the surface. The frequency ν_0 is known as the *threshold frequency* and depends upon the nature of the surface. The slope h, however, is a constant which is independent of the nature of the surface. This constant h is known as the *Planck constant* and plays an exceedingly important role in atomic phenomena. The value of the Planck constant h determined photoelectrically depends upon the value of the electronic charge. Using the early value $e = 4.77 \times 10^{-10}$ esu, Millikan

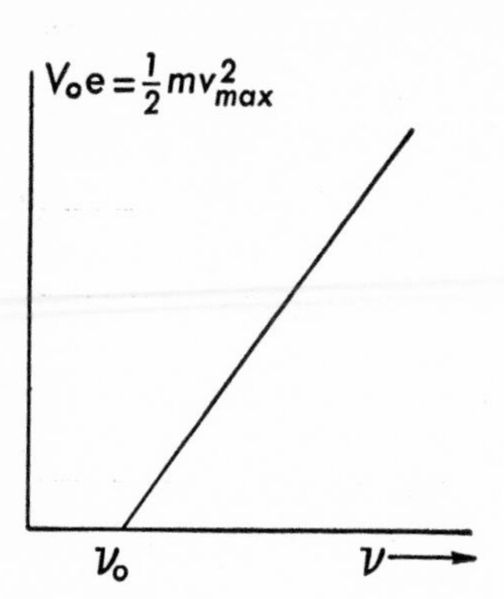

FIG. 4-9. Dependence of the stopping potential on the frequency of the incident radiation.

found that $h = 6.55 \times 10^{-27}$ erg seconds. More recent determinations of this constant, particularly from measurements of the short wavelength limit of the continuous x-ray spectrum, have yielded more precise values for the Planck constant. The present accepted value is

$$h = 6.625 \times 10^{-27} \text{ erg sec.}$$

4-6. Einstein's Photoelectric Equation

The direct dependence of the energy of the photoelectron upon the frequency of the incident light cannot be explained by the electromagnetic wave theory of light. On this classical theory there should be a relationship between the intensity of the incident light and the energy of the photoelectron. The intensity of an electromagnetic wave depends upon the square of the amplitude of the electric vector and is independent of the frequency of the light. To explain the photoelectric effect, Einstein (1905) made use of the concept of a *quantum of energy*, a concept which was first introduced into physics by Planck (1900), in order to explain the distribution of energy among the various wavelengths in the radiation from a "black body" at temperature T. According to Planck's theory, whenever radiation is emitted or absorbed by such a body, the energy is emitted or absorbed in whole *quanta*, where a *quantum of energy* is given by

$$\boxed{\mathcal{E} = h\nu} \qquad (16)$$

in which ν is the frequency of the radiation and h is the Planck constant.

Such a quantum of energy has since received the name *photon*. The energy of a quantum or a photon is directly proportional to the frequency of the radiation. In Einstein's explanation of the photoelectric effect, the entire energy of a photon is transferred to a single electron in the metal, and when the electron comes out of the surface of the metal it will have an amount of kinetic energy given by

$$\boxed{\tfrac{1}{2}mv^2 = h\nu - p.} \tag{17}$$

Equation (17) is known as Einstein's photoelectric equation and is identical with equation (15) if $p = h\nu_0$.

The photoelectric effect is not confined to the action of light upon metallic surfaces. It can occur in gases and liquids as well as in solids. The

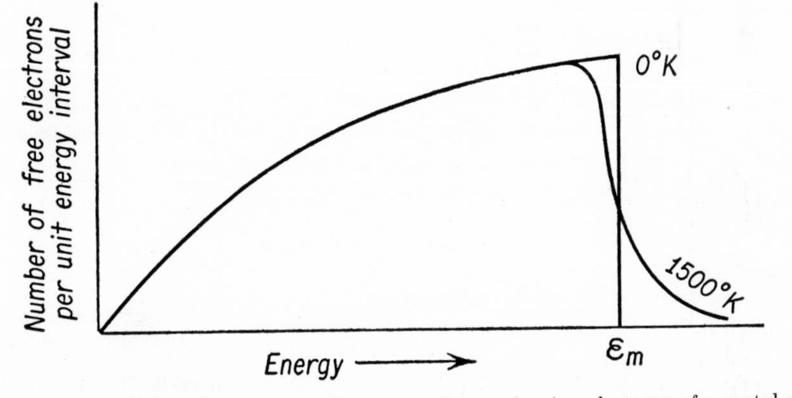

Fig. 4-10. Distribution of energies among the conduction electrons of a metal at 0°K and at 1500°K.

nature of the light effective in producing the photoelectric effect includes the whole range of electromagnetic waves from the very short gamma rays and x-rays down into the infrared region of wavelengths. The quantity p should yield valuable information concerning the origin of the photoelectrons. For example, in the case of the surface photoelectric effect in conductors, it was assumed that p is equal to the work done by the electron in getting through the surface of the metal. According to the modern theory of electron conduction in metals, originally developed by Sommerfeld, the conduction electrons have a wide range of energy values inside the metal. The energy distribution of the conduction electrons, based upon a statistical theory developed by Fermi and Dirac, is shown in the graph of Figure 4-10, in which the number of conduction electrons within a given energy range is plotted against the energy. The energy range depends only slightly upon the temperature of the conductor. At 0°K, the theory predicts a sharp upper limit $\mathcal{E}_m$, for the energy of the conduction electrons given by

$$\mathcal{E}_m = \frac{h^2}{2m}\left(\frac{3n}{8\pi}\right)^{2/3}, \tag{18}$$

where h is the Planck constant, m the mass of the electron, and n the number of free or conduction electrons per unit volume. At higher tem-

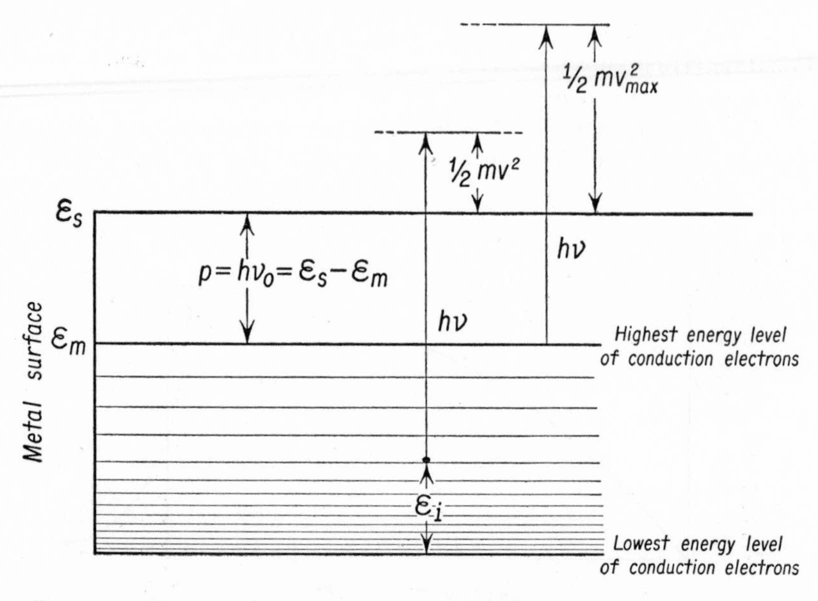

FIG. 4-11. Energies of conduction electrons inside a metal lie between 0 and $\mathcal{E}_m$. A photon of energy $h\nu$ ejects an electron with kinetic energy $\frac{1}{2}mv^2$; another photon of equal energy ejects another electron with maximum kinetic energy.

peratures, there is a slight change in the energies and their distribution among the electrons having high energies, as shown in the distribution curve for the conductor at 1500°K.

For the purposes of this discussion we may consider the distribution of energy among the free electrons in a conductor at room temperature to be almost the same as one at absolute zero. Figure 4-11 is a schematic diagram of the possible energy values of a free electron near the surface of a conductor. Let $\mathcal{E}_s$ be the energy required to remove an electron of lowest energy from the metal. Let $\mathcal{E}_i$ be the energy of any one of the free electrons; $\mathcal{E}_i$ can have any value from zero to $\mathcal{E}_m$. Suppose that a photon of energy $h\nu$ is incident on this surface and causes the ejection of an electron. The electron will leave the surface of the metal with the amount of kinetic energy given by

$$\tfrac{1}{2}mv^2 = h\nu - (\mathcal{E}_s - \mathcal{E}_i). \tag{19}$$

Thus there can be a wide range of values for the kinetic energies of the electrons ejected by the action of photons of frequency ν. The electrons ejected with maximum kinetic energy are those which had energies $\mathcal{E}_i = \mathcal{E}_m$ inside the metal; thus

$$\tfrac{1}{2}mv^2_{\text{max}} = h\nu - (\mathcal{E}_s - \mathcal{E}_m). \tag{20}$$

A comparison of equations (17) and (20) shows that

$$p = \mathcal{E}_s - \mathcal{E}_m = h\nu_0. \tag{21}$$

The quantity p is usually called the work function of the metal; its numerical value is of the order of a few electron volts for most conductors and is the same as the work function for thermionic emission from these metals. At higher termperatures the distribution of energies among the free electrons does not have a sharp maximum; hence the curve for the stopping potential should not cut the V axis at V_0, but should approach this axis asymptotically. This has been observed in careful measurements on the photoelectric effect.

4-7. Phototubes

The simple photoelectric tube, consisting of a photosensitive surface used as a cathode and a metal in the form of a wire or other geometrical shape acting as the anode to collect the electrons emitted by the cathode, has come into common use for a great variety of purposes. The photoelectric current may be amplified with the aid of appropriate circuits utilizing thermionic tubes, so that very weak light signals can produce measurable effects. Within the past few years special phototubes, known as *photomultiplier tubes*, have been developed in which the amplification takes place within the phototube itself. The design of a photomultiplier tube is shown schematically in Figure 4-12 in which P is the photosensitive cathode. Light striking P causes the ejection of photoelectrons from it; these electrons are then attracted to a metal surface called a *dynode* and labeled 1 in the figure. It is known that an electron striking a metal surface with sufficient velocity can cause the ejection of one or more electrons from the surface. This process is called *secondary emission*.

Suppose that a photoelectron striking dynode 1 produces R electrons by secondary emission; these secondary electrons are then directed toward a second dynode 2, by making its potential higher than that of dynode 1. Suppose that R electrons are again ejected by secondary emission for each incident electron; then for each electron emitted by the photosensitive surface there are now R^2 electrons. If the tube consists of n dynodes, each

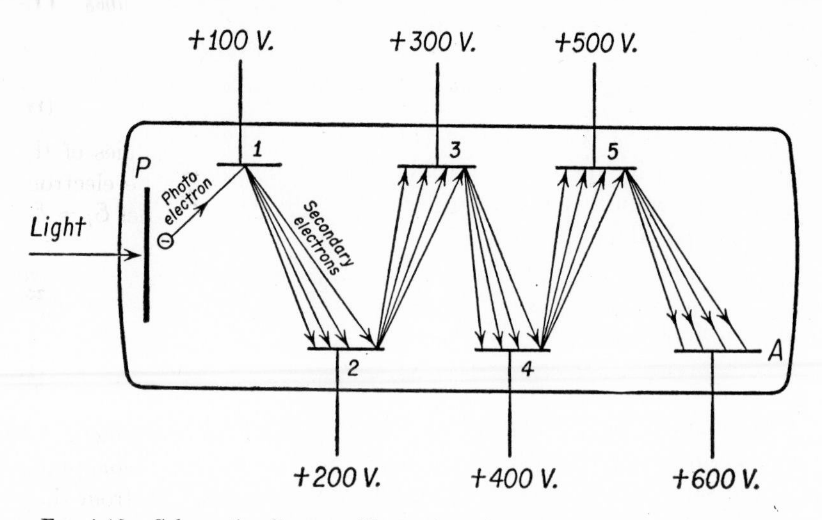

Fig. 4-12. Schematic diagram illustrating the operation of a photomultiplier tube. Four secondary electrons are assumed to be emitted for each electron striking a dynode.

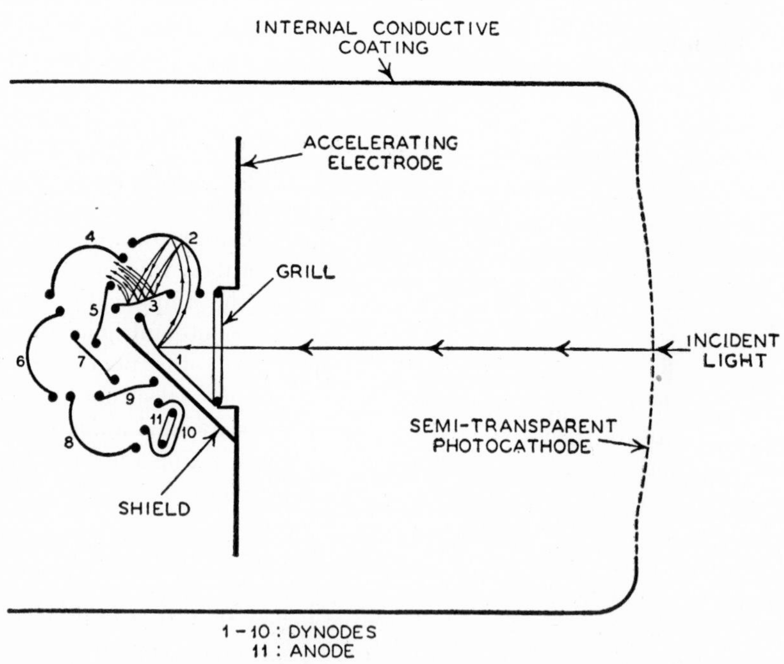

Fig. 4-13. Schematic diagram showing the arrangement of the electrode structure of a photomultiplier tube. (Courtesy of RCA, Victor Division.)

successive dynode at a suitably higher potential than the preceding one, the multiplication factor of the tube will be R^n. Modern photomultiplier tubes have from 10 to 16 dynodes. The electrons coming from the nth dynode go to the anode A, from which they go to some detecting circuit. An idea of the magnification produced by a photomultiplier tube can be obtained by setting $R = 4$ and the number of dynodes $n = 10$. Then the multiplication factor is 4^{10} or 10^6. The photomultiplier tube is thus capable of detecting single electrons emitted by the photocathode, since with a multiplication factor of 10^6, a measurable charge is produced. Some high-gain tubes have been developed with multiplication factors up to 10^9; details of such a tube are shown in Figure 4-13.

4-8. Scintillation Counters

Photomultipliers, used in conjunction with suitable fluorescent materials, called *phosphors*, are now being widely used for the detection and counting of particles emitted by radioactive substances and other particles of importance in nuclear physics. It will be recalled that one of the early methods used for the detection and counting of alpha particles was to allow them to strike a zinc sulfide screen and then observe the scintillations on the screen through a microscope. In the modern method the zinc sulfide screen is placed in close contact with the photomultiplier tube. The light coming from the scintillation produced by the incidence of an alpha particle on the phosphor strikes the photocathode and produces one or more photoelectrons. The action of the photomultiplier then increases the total charge by a factor of 10^6 or greater; this charge, when fed to a capacitor, will build up a potential difference whose value can be measured with a suitable circuit. The circuits used are such as to produce a pulse of a given amplitude or "height" when the capacitor is charged by the electrons from the photomultiplier. An oscilloscope is usually incorporated in the circuit for viewing the pulses produced as a result of the scintillations of the phosphor. These pulses are also fed into a counting circuit and scalar so that the number of scintillations can be counted; hence the name *scintillation counter*. The height of the pulse produced by a scintillation counter is proportional to the energy of the incident particles and, in any given case, is usually calibrated with particles of known energy.

Although a thin zinc sulfide screen is suitable for alpha-particle counting, phosphors having a large volume must be used for the more penetrating particles and radiation, such as beta rays, gamma rays, high energy protons, and so forth. Furthermore, these phosphors must be transparent so that the scintillations can reach the photomultiplier. Since the light produced in the phosphor can travel in all directions, the phosphor is frequently covered with a thin layer of aluminum, except for the face near the photocathode. The incident radiation will penetrate the aluminum very readily, while the visible radiation produced in the phosphor will be reflected from it one or more times until it reaches the photocathode, as illustrated in Figure 4-14.

A wide variety of organic materials, some solid and others in liquid form, has been found suitable as phosphors. Among them are anthracene, naphthalene, and stilbene. Some inorganic substances have also been found to be suitable as phosphors. In addition to zinc sulfide, sodium iodide

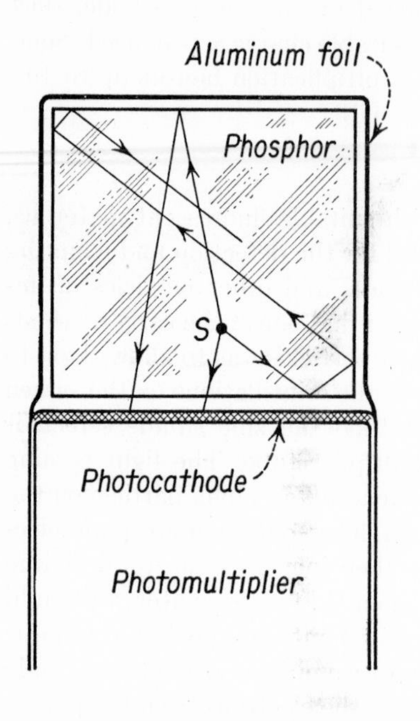

FIG. 4-14. Light coming from a scintillation S may be reflected many times to reach the photocathode of the photomultiplier tube.

crystals activated with thallium, NaI (Tl), and potassium iodide crystals with thallium, KI (Tl), have found wide application in scintillation counters. The usefulness of a phosphor as a scintillation counter depends upon the short duration of the light pulse, of the order of 10^{-8} second, produced by an incident particle so that many scintillations can be counted in a short time. Counting rates of several thousands per second are quite common. Suitable circuits have been designed to sort out particles within a given energy range so that the distribution in energy of the incident radiation may be measured. W. H. Jordan and P. R. Bell, who incorporated a pulse-sorter circuit in their scintillation counter, call the arrangement a *scintillation spectrometer*.

Scintillation counters are rapidly superseding Geiger counters in the study of the many different types of particles that have been discovered in work in nuclear physics. We shall refer to them at appropriate places in the book.

4-9. Cerenkov Radiation

A new method of producing visible radiation was discovered by P. A. Cerenkov in 1934. He observed that a beam of fast electrons, such as beta particles from radioactive substances, when moving in a transparent medium caused the emission of visible radiation, provided that the velocity of the electrons was greater than the velocity of light in the same medium. The theory developed by I. M. Frank and I. E. Tamm predicts that the light should be propagated at an angle θ to the direction of motion of the electron given by

$$\boxed{\cos\theta = \frac{c}{\mu v}} \tag{22}$$

where μ is the index of refraction of light and v the velocity of the electron in this medium. An electron moving through a substance loses most of its energy in ionization and excitation of the atoms. In these processes the electron itself experiences small accelerations and hence radiates energy in the form of electromagnetic waves. Since these waves originate at different points along the path of the electron, radiant energy will be observed only if the waves from the different points reinforce each other. The condition for reinforcement of the waves by interference can readily be derived with the aid of Figure 4-15. The electron beam enters the transparent medium at M and continues along the path MAB. The electron radiates energy in all directions from the points along this path. Using the Huygens construction, we obtain the wave front BD, where the distance AD is ct/μ and $AB = vt$ where t is the time taken by the electron to reach point B. From the figure it follows that the radiation will travel in a direction such that $\cos\theta = \dfrac{c}{\mu v}\cdot$

The Cerenkov radiation was investigated by G. B. Collins and V. G. Reiling (1938), using a beam of electrons of 1.9 Mev energy incident upon a series of thin films of various transparent substances such as glass, water, mica, and cellophane. They photographed the pattern of the emitted light and found the intensity to be a maximum in the direction given by the above equation. They also examined the emitted light spectroscopically and found the spectrum of the Cerenkov radiation to be continuous and to extend from the long wavelength limit of the apparatus usually > 5000 angstroms, down to the ultraviolet absorption limit of the medium in which it was produced. H. O. Wyckoff and J. E. Henderson (1943) extended the work of Collins and Reiling to slower electrons, with energies ranging from 240 kev to 815 kev. Using mica as the transparent medium, they obtained results in agreement with the predictions of Frank and Tamm concerning the direction of emission of the Cerenkov radiation.

Cerenkov radiation is becoming increasingly useful as a detector of high energy charged particles. The only condition imposed upon these

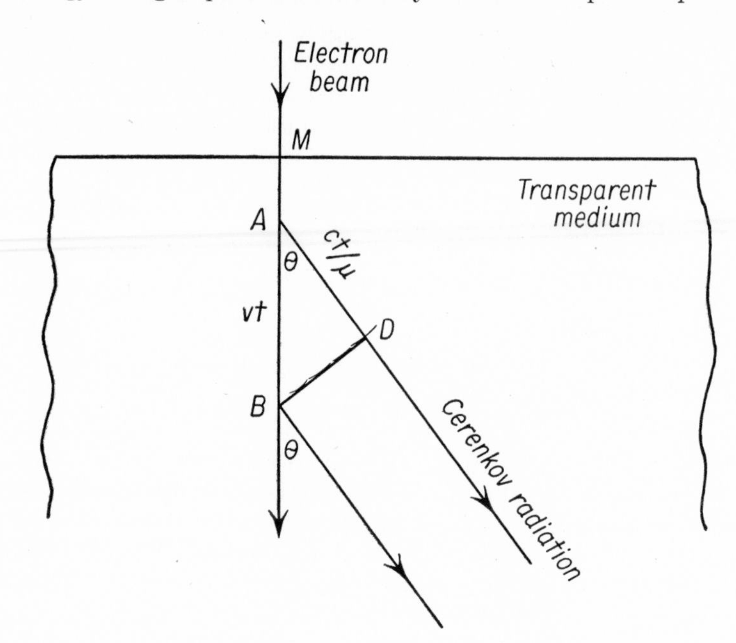

Fig. 4-15. Direction of propagation of Cerenkov radiation relative to the direction of motion of the electrons in a transparent medium.

particles is that their speeds be greater than the speed of light in the same medium. In any given medium the angle of emission θ is determined only by the velocity of the particle; hence the detection of the Cerenkov radiation is a convenient method for measuring the velocities of high energy charged particles.

Problems

4-1. An x-ray tube is operated at a difference of potential of 50 kv. Electrons striking the silver target with maximum kinetic energy are completely stopped in 10^{-5} cm of silver. Assuming that the acceleration is uniform, calculate the rate at which electromagnetic energy is radiated from the electron.

Ans. 0.44 erg/sec.

4-2. A calcium arc is placed between the poles of an electromagnet. The line $\lambda = 4226.7\text{A}$ is found to exhibit the normal Zeeman pattern in a field of 30,000 gausses. Calculate (**a**) the difference in frequencies between the displaced and undisplaced components, and (**b**) the difference in wavelengths between these components.

Ans. (**a**) 4.2×10^{10} sec^{-1}.
(**b**) 0.25A.

4-3. When a copper surface is illuminated by the radiation of wavelength $\lambda = 2537$A from a mercury arc, the value of the stopping potential is found to be 0.24 volts.

(**a**) Calculate the wavelength of the threshold value for copper.

(**b**) On the assumption that there are two free electrons per atom of copper, calculate the value of $\mathcal{E}_m$.

(**c**) Using the above values, calculate the work done in taking an electron through the surface of the copper.

Ans. (**a**) 2665A.
(**b**) 11.2 ev.
(**c**) 15.8 ev.

4-4. The photoelectric threshold of tungsten is 2300A. Determine the energy of the electrons ejected from the surface by ultraviolet light of wavelength 1800A.

Ans. 1.5 ev.

4-5. (**a**) Calculate the minimum velocity that electrons must possess in order to produce visible radiation when passing through glass whose index of refraction is 1.5. (**b**) Determine the kinetic energy of such electrons. (**c**) If a beam of electrons of this energy goes through a thin sheet of such glass, at what angle will the light be emitted relative to the direction of the beam?

Ans. (**a**) 2×10^{10} cm/sec.
(**b**) 0.17 Mev.
(**c**) 0°.

4-6. A beam of electrons of kinetic energy 0.8 Mev travels through a transparent substance whose index of refraction is 1.40. Calculate the angle at which Cerenkov radiation will be observed relative to the direction of the beam.

Ans. 39° 10′.

4-7. A beam of electrons traveling through a glass of index of refraction 1.50 is observed to emit Cerenkov radiation at an angle of 40° to the electron beam. Determine the kinetic energy of the electrons.

Ans. 0.53 Mev.

4-8. A stream of protons of 200 Mev kinetic energy is traveling through a transparent crystal whose index of refraction is 1.80. (**a**) Calculate the velocities of the protons. (**b**) Determine the angle that the beam of Cerenkov radiation will make with the proton beam.

Ans. (**a**) 0.566c.
(**b**) 11.0°.

4-9. A stream of protons is sent through a transparent crystal whose index of refraction for light of 5000A is 1.85. Cerenkov radiation of this wavelength is observed at an angle of 14° to the proton beam. Determine (**a**) the velocity of the protons, and (**b**) their kinetic energy.

Ans. (**a**) 0.557c.
(**b**) 192 Mev.

4-10. A stream of protons traverses a piece of glass whose index of refraction for light of 5000A is 1.70. Cerenkov radiation of this wavelength is observed at an angle of 25° to the proton beam. Determine the kinetic energy of the protons.

Ans. 295 Mev.

References

On polarized light

Wood, R. W., *Physical Optics.* New York: The Macmillan Company, 1934, Chap. IX.

Zeeman effect

Wood, R. W., *Physical Optics.* New York: The Macmillan Company, 1934, Chap. XXI.

Electromagnetic theory of light

Frank, N. H., *Introduction to Electricity and Optics.* New York: McGraw-Hill Book Company, Inc., 1950, Chaps. X, XI, XVIII, XIX.

Houston, R. A., *A Treatise on Light.* New York: Longmans, Green & Co., 1927, Chap. XXII.

Starling, S. G., *Electricity and Magnetism.* New York: Longmans, Green & Co., 1942, Chap. XIV.

Photoelectric effect

Hughes, A. L., and L. Du Bridge, *Photoelectric Phenomena.* New York: McGraw-Hill Book Company, Inc., 1932, Chap. II.

Zworykin, V. M., and E. G. Ramberg, *Photoelectricity and Its Applications.* New York: John Wiley & Sons, Inc., 1949.

X-Rays

5-1. Discovery of X-Rays

X-rays were discovered by Roentgen in 1895. He found that the operation of a cathode-ray tube produced fluorescence in a platinum-barium-cyanide screen placed at some distance from the tube. The source of the rays causing this fluorescence was traced to the walls of the cathode-ray tube. In further experiments he found that the interposition of various thicknesses of different substances between the screen and the tube reduced the intensity of the fluorescence but did not obliterate it completely. This showed that these x-rays, as Roentgen called them, had very great penetrating power. It was also found that these rays could blacken a photographic plate and could ionize a gas.

The x-rays, or Roentgen rays, traveled in straight lines from the source and were not deflected in passing through electric or magnetic fields. They were thus not charged particles. Roentgen tried to reflect and refract them but without success. Haga and Wind, in 1899, sent a beam of x-rays through a narrow aperture; they actually succeeded in getting a diffraction pattern, but the effect was so small that their results were not generally accepted as conclusive. It was not until 1912 that the wave nature of x-rays was definitely established by Laue's experiments on the diffraction of x-rays by crystals. Barkla's experiments on the polarization of x-rays established the fact that these rays were transverse waves similar to light waves.

5-2. Production of X-Rays

X-rays are produced whenever fast-moving electrons strike a substance. In Roentgen's experiment the cathode rays struck the walls of the tube so that the glass wall became the source of the x-rays. The gas-filled type of x-ray tube is a modification of the cathode-ray tube. Instead of allowing the cathode rays to strike the walls of the tube, the cup-shaped cathode C focuses them onto a metal target T, as shown in Figure 5-1. The gas pressure in the tube is of the order of 0.001 mm of Hg, and the difference of potential between the cathode and target is usually of the order of 30,000 to 50,000 volts. The electrons from the cathode are stopped by the target, which then becomes the source of x-rays. These x-rays proceed in all directions from the target.

The Coolidge type of x-ray tube is a thermionic tube in which the cathode is a tungsten filament; one modern design of a Coolidge tube is shown in Figure 5-2. When the filament is heated to incandescence by means

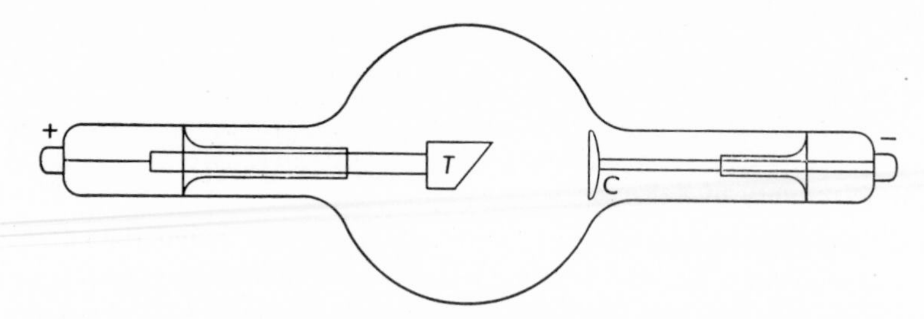

FIG. 5-1. Gas-filled type of x-ray tube; C is the cathode and T is the target.

of a current supplied either by a storage battery or by a step-down transformer, electrons are emitted by the filament. These electrons are accelerated to the target by a difference of potential maintained between them. The filament is placed inside a metallic cup in order to focus the electrons

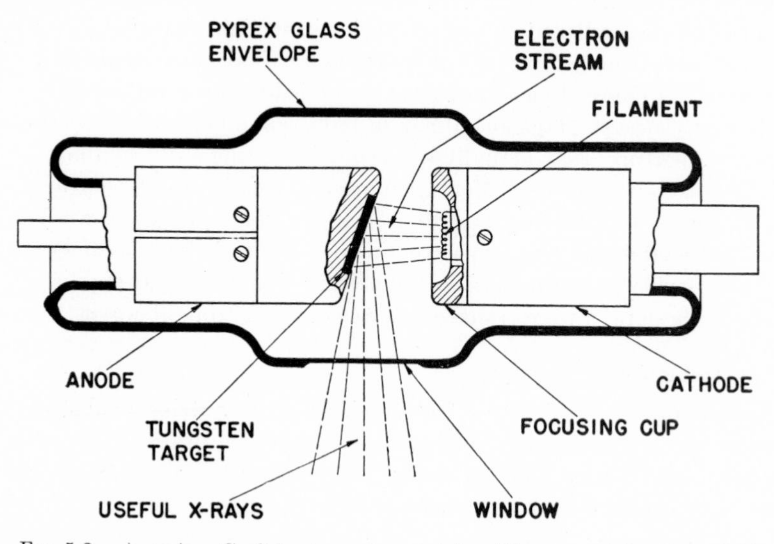

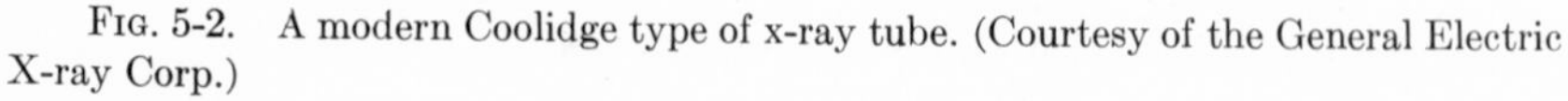

FIG. 5-2. A modern Coolidge type of x-ray tube. (Courtesy of the General Electric X-ray Corp.)

onto the target. The tube must be highly evacuated so that no electric discharge can take place in the residual gas under normal operating conditions. One great advantage of the Coolidge type of tube is that the emission, and hence the current in the tube, can be controlled by varying the temperature of the filament. In general, the Coolidge tube is more stable in operation than the gas type of tube.

Coolidge x-ray tubes have been designed to operate at voltages which range from a few hundred volts to about one million volts. Various types of high-voltage sources are used in operating x-ray tubes. In special cases small lead storage cells have been connected in series to supply voltages from a few hundred volts up to one hundred thousand volts. The most common type of high-voltage source is the step-up transformer with its secondary coil well insulated from the primary coil. If the ac voltage from the secondary is applied directly across the cathode and the target of the x-ray tube, the tube acts as its own rectifier, that is, current flows in the tube only during that half of the cycle in which the target is positive with respect to the cathode. In those experiments in which it is necessary to have a constant direct current through the tube, the transformer terminals are connected to a rectifier circuit consisting of two or more high-voltage rectifiers together with a large capacitor and inductance coils. The rectified, constant dc voltage is then applied to the x-ray tube.

When an x-ray tube is to be operated continuously with comparatively large amounts of power, special arrangements must be made for cooling the target. One common method of doing this is to mount the target material on a hollow copper tube and to circulate water through this tube. Almost any substance can be used as the target of an x-ray tube, depending upon the problem under investigation. The targets of general-purpose x-ray tubes usually are made of tungsten or molybdenum because these metals have high melting points.

An entirely new type of x-ray tube has recently been developed by D. W. Kerst (1941); this tube is called a *betatron*. In the older type of x-ray tubes, the electrons which strike the target acquire their energy by the application of a high voltage between the filament and the target. In the betatron, the electrons acquire their energy by the action of the force exerted on them by the electric field which accompanies a changing magnetic field. Some betatrons now in operation (1954) accelerate electrons so that they have energies up to 100 Mev when they strike the target and produce x-rays. These x-rays have been used in nuclear experiments as described in Chapter 11. The mode of operation of the betatron will be described in greater detail in Chapter 16 on particle accelerators.

5-3. Measurement of the Intensity of X-Rays

The intensity of a beam of x-rays may be measured by any one of its effects, such as the blackening of a photographic plate, the rise in the temperature of a piece of lead which absorbs these rays, or by the ionization produced in a gas or vapor.

The *ionization chamber* is commonly used for measuring the intensity of x-rays; it makes use of the ionization produced in a gas or vapor by the passage of x-rays through it. A typical ionization chamber is shown in Figure 5-3. It consists of a metal cylinder C containing some convenient gas or vapor such as air or methyl bromide, at about atmospheric pressure. A metal rod R, insulated from the cylinder, runs parallel to the axis of the cylinder. The x-ray beam enters the chamber through a thin window W, usually made of mica or thin aluminum, and ionizes the gas in the chamber. A battery B maintains a difference of potential between R and C so that the ions are set in motion toward C and R just as soon as they are formed. This ionization current is measured by the electrometer E.

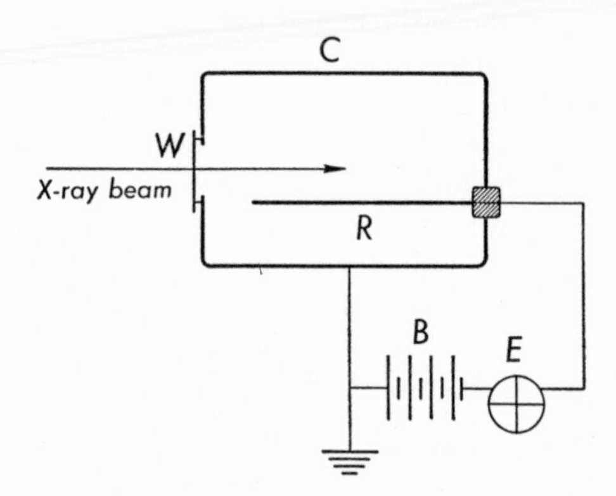

FIG. 5-3. Ionization chamber and electrometer for measuring the intensity of x-rays.

Experiment shows that the ionization current is directly proportional to the intensity of the x-ray beam.

The intensity of the x-rays coming from any tube has been found to depend upon the element used as the target, the power supplied to the tube, and the difference of potential between the target and cathode.

The Geiger counter tube, originally developed for the counting of alpha particles (§3-4), has also been adapted for measuring the intensity of x-rays. Another device which is coming into great use, particularly for the measurement of x-rays from high-voltage sources, is the *scintillation counter* (§4-8). In this device, the x-rays are allowed to penetrate a transparent crystal or liquid in which the energy of the x-radiation is transformed into visible fluorescent radiation. This radiation is then incident on the sensitive surface of a photomultiplier tube. The photoelectric current thus produced can be amplified and measured with appropriate circuits.

5-4. Diffraction of X-Rays

The explanation of the origin of x-rays on the basis of classical electrodynamics is that x-rays are emitted in the form of electromagnetic pulses or groups of waves when the electrons are stopped by the target of an x-ray tube. The existence of a wave motion can be definitely established only by diffraction and interference phenomena. The conditions under which these phenomena occur are well known for waves in the visible region of the spectrum. For example, if yellow light is allowed to pass through a diffraction grating having about 6000 lines to the centimeter, a diffraction pattern is obtained consisting of a central image or undeviated line, then a first-order image which is deviated by about 20° from the original direction, and farther on a second-order image, and so on. An analysis of the action of the grating shows that the spacing between the lines ruled on the grating should be of the order of magnitude of the wavelength of the light used. The results of the early experiments on the dif-

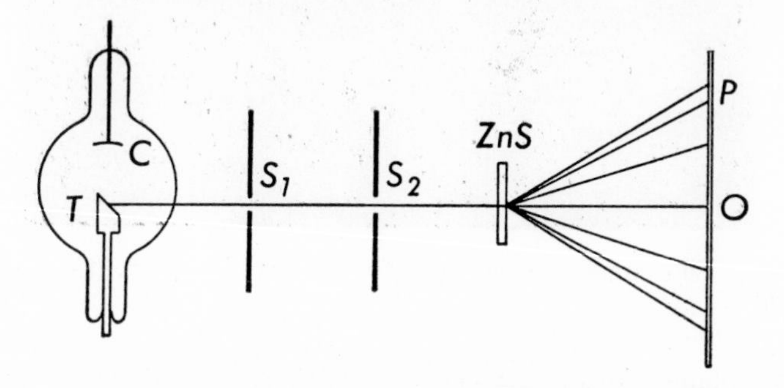

FIG. 5-4. Arrangement of apparatus for producing a Laue diffraction pattern.

fraction of x-rays indicated that their wavelengths were of the order of 10^{-8} or 10^{-9} cm. It occurred to M. von Laue (1912) that the ordered arrangement of atoms or molecules in crystals fulfilled all the conditions essential for the diffraction of such short wavelengths. The spacing between these atoms or molecules was known to be of the order of 10^{-8} cm. A crystal differs from an ordinary diffraction grating in that the diffracting centers in the crystal are not all in one plane; the crystal acts as a space grating rather than as a plane grating.

Following Laue's suggestion, Friedrich and Knipping carried out the following experiment. A narrow pencil of x-rays was allowed to pass through a thin crystal of zinc blende (ZnS). The emergent beam fell on a photographic plate P, as shown in Figure 5-4. The diffraction pattern obtained consisted of the central spot at O and a series of spots arranged in a definite pattern about O.

Figure 5-5 is a photograph of the Laue diffraction pattern obtained by passing a narrow pencil of x-rays through a thin crystal of rock salt perpendicular to its *cleavage* planes; these cleavage planes are parallel to a surface along which a crystal can be readily split or broken. From a knowledge of the structure of the crystal, some of the wavelengths in the incident radiation could be computed. A simple interpretation of the diffraction pattern was given by W. L. Bragg. He assumed that the diffraction spots were produced by x-rays which were scattered from certain sets

FIG. 5-5. Photograph of Laue diffraction pattern of rocksalt. (From photograph by J. G. Dash.)

of parallel planes within the crystal, which contained large numbers of atoms. That some planes are richer in atoms than others can be seen by considering a two-dimensional array of points, and drawing lines through these points, as in Figure 5-6. These lines correspond to planes in a three-dimensional crystal.

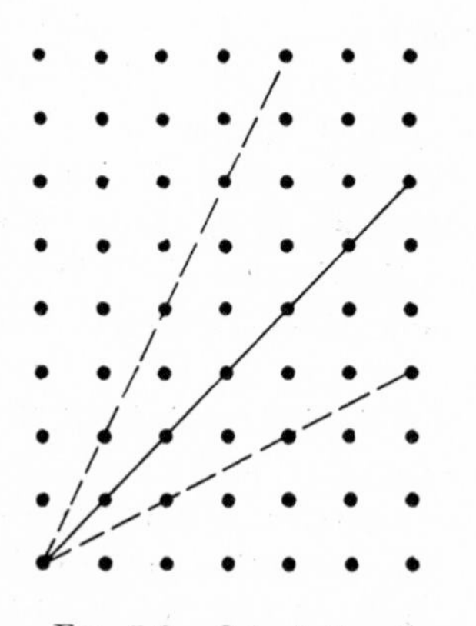

FIG. 5-6. Orientation in a crystal of some planes which are rich in atoms.

It is easy to derive the condition under which the x-rays scattered from a series of atomic planes will produce an intense spot. Consider a series of parallel atomic planes spaced a distance d apart. Suppose a narrow beam of x-rays from some source is incident upon these planes at an angle θ, as shown in Figure 5-7. The beam will be scattered in all directions by the atoms in the various atomic planes. Let us first consider the x-rays scattered by any one plane. Following the usual Huygens construction, it can be seen that the scattered beam will have a maximum intensity at an angle θ to this plane which is equal to the angle of incidence. Figure 5-8 shows a portion MN of the incident wave front advancing to PQ, thus causing the atoms between M and Q to send out wavelets in all directions. These wavelets produce a wave front QR, the reflected wave, which ad-

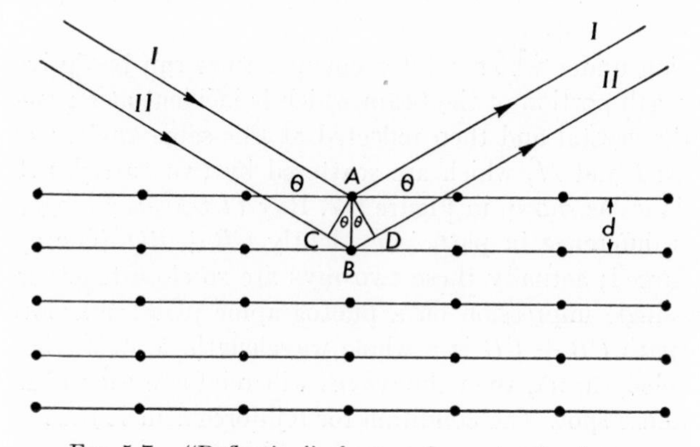

FIG. 5-7. "Reflection" of x-rays from atomic planes.

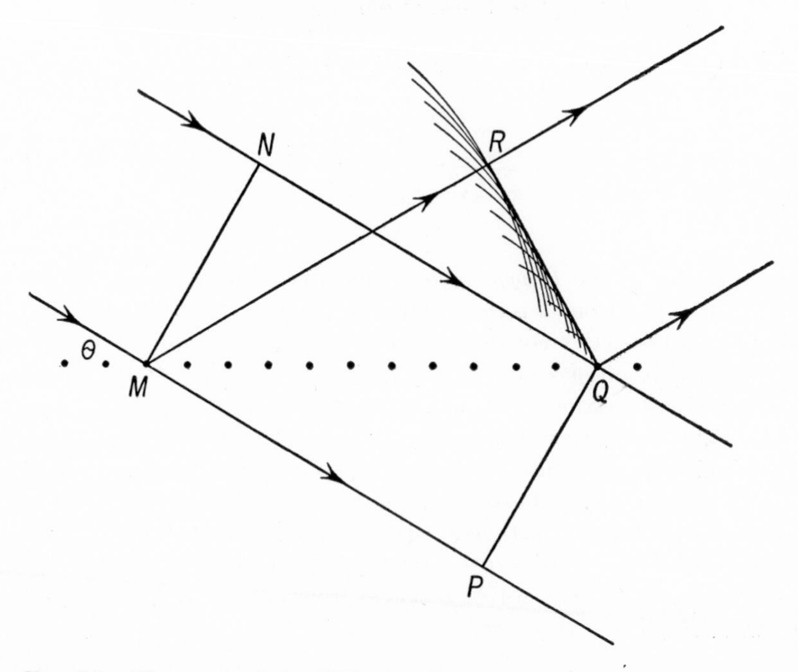

FIG. 5-8. Plane wave front MN advancing toward PQ is reflected by atoms between M and Q to form the reflected wave front RQ—Huygens construction. The angle of incidence and the angle of reflection are equal.

vances along the direction MR. This is identical with ordinary optical reflection and is independent of the wavelength of the x-rays or of the spacings of the atoms in the plane. However, if we now consider the effect of the reflections from a set of parallel planes spaced a distance d apart, then the wavelets from the atoms in the different planes will reinforce each other and produce maximum intensity only if they meet in phase. The condition under which reinforcement occurs can be derived by considering a small portion of the beam which is incident at an angle θ to the planes of the crystal and then reflected at this same angle. Consider two rays such as I and II, which are scattered by two particles A and B in adjacent planes as shown in Figure 5-7. Ray II travels a longer path than ray I; this difference in path is evidently $CB + BD$. The spacings are greatly enlarged; actually these two rays are so close together that they produce a single impression on a photographic plate. Whenever the difference in path $CB + BD$ is a whole wavelength, λ, or a whole multiple of the wavelength, $n\lambda$, then the waves will reinforce each other and produce an intense spot. The condition for reinforcement is thus

$$CB + BD = n\lambda,$$

and from the figure

$$CB = d \sin \theta$$

and

$$BD = d \sin \theta;$$

hence

$$\boxed{n\lambda = 2d \sin \theta.} \tag{1}$$

This is known as the *Bragg equation* and gives the condition for the *reflection* of x-rays from a series of atomic planes. The Bragg equation is essentially a restrictive condition on the appearance of intense maxima in the scattered beam of x-rays. A more extensive analysis would show that no other intense maxima exist than those predicted by the Bragg equation. If the distance between atomic planes is known, the wavelength of the x-rays which produce intense maxima upon reflection by the crystal can be calculated by using the Bragg equation; or the converse, using x-rays of known wavelengths, distances between atomic planes can be computed.

In the Bragg equation n is always an integer. When $n = 1$, the difference in path between waves reflected from any two adjacent planes is one wavelength. For this case,

$$\lambda = 2d \sin \theta_1$$

gives the condition for the first-order reflection of wavelength λ from the crystal. For $n = 2$, the equation becomes

$$2\lambda = 2d \sin \theta_2;$$

that is, the second-order reflection of the same wavelength will occur at a larger angle of incidence and reflection, θ_2.

The analysis used in deriving the Bragg equation can now be used to explain the Laue diffraction pattern. The x-rays which penetrate the crystal are scattered from the different atomic diffraction centers. We can construct sets of parallel atomic planes inside the crystal as shown in Figure 5-9

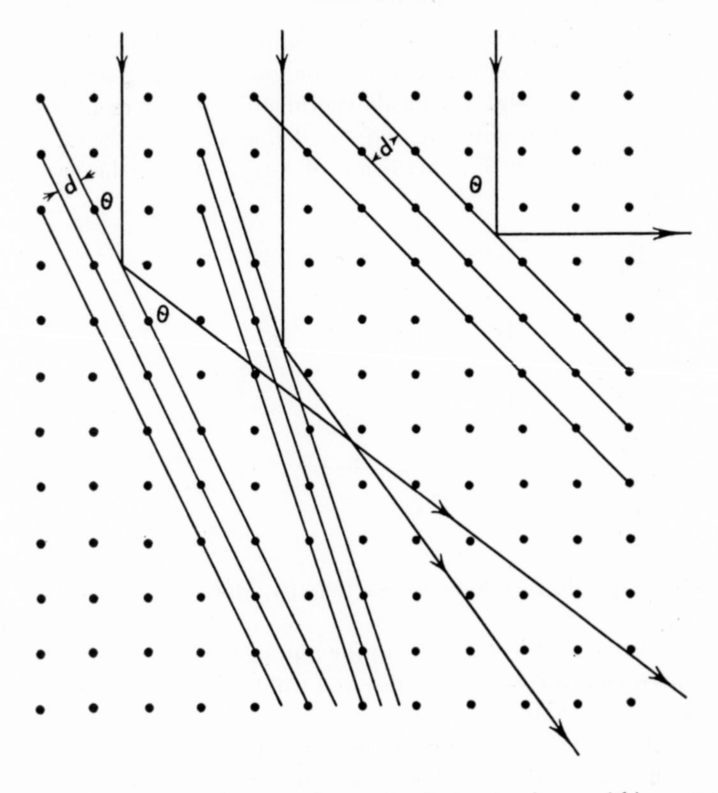

FIG. 5-9. Reflection of x-rays from sets of atomic planes within a crystal to produce the Laue diffraction pattern.

and apply the Bragg equation to each set of parallel planes. The value of the incident angle will be different for each set of planes, and each set of parallel planes will have its own particular value for the distance d, but these distances will be related in a simple way to the distance between planes which are parallel to the cleavage face because of the geometry of the crystal. The x-rays scattered from any set of parallel planes will reinforce each other only if the particular wavelength which will satisfy the Bragg equation is present in the incident beam. Furthermore, an examination of Figure 5-9 will show that there are comparatively few sets of parallel planes which are sufficiently rich in atoms to produce intense diffraction spots. Hence, even if the incident radiation contains a wide range of wavelengths, which is the most common method of producing a Laue pattern, the number of intense diffraction spots produced will be small in spite of the large number of atomic diffraction centers in the crystal.

5-5. Single Crystal X-Ray Spectrometer

The Laue diffraction patterns are very complex and difficult to interpret. Instead of using a crystal as a transmission grating, Bragg set up the crystal as a reflection grating. A typical experimental arrangement is shown in Figure 5-10. Two lead slits, S_1 and S_2, define a narrow beam of x-rays coming from the target T. This beam of x-rays strikes the crystal C at

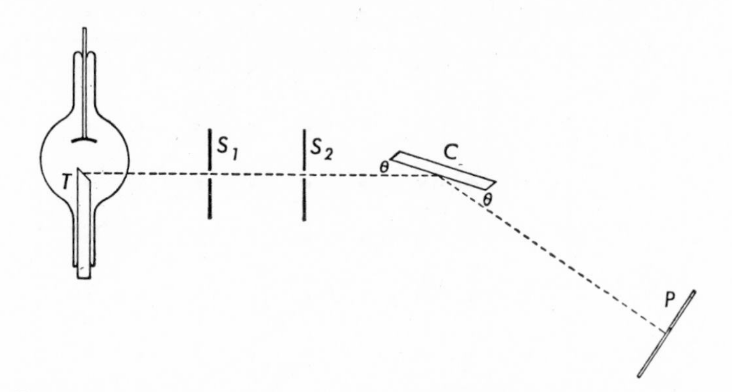

FIG. 5-10. Single crystal x-ray spectrometer, with photographic plate.

some angle θ, and is reflected by it to the photographic plate P. The crystal C is mounted on a spectrometer table and can be rotated so that the glancing angle θ may be varied.

At each particular setting of the crystal only the particular wavelength λ which satisfies the Bragg equation

$$n\lambda = 2d \sin \theta$$

will be reflected to the photographic plate. As the crystal is rotated, other wavelengths will be reflected by the crystal. In this way a spectrum of the incident beam is obtained. The spectrum may consist of several orders. If, in the Bragg equation, $n\lambda = 2d \sin \theta$, n has the value unity, the spectrum is said to be a first-order spectrum; if $n = 2$, a second-order spectrum is obtained, and so on.

In many experiments, the photographic plate is replaced by an ionization chamber, a Geiger counter, or a scintillation counter, which can be rotated about the same axis as the crystal.

The choice of crystal to be used in an x-ray spectrometer is determined by several factors, such as the range of wavelengths to be examined, the ease with which a good surface can be obtained, and the reflecting power of the crystal. Crystals most commonly used are calcite, quartz, and rocksalt. It is obvious that for use in measuring x-ray wavelengths, the distance d between atomic planes in the crystals must be known from other data. Sufficient data can be obtained from crystallographic studies for some of the simpler crystals, such as rocksalt and calcite, for an independent determination of the spacing between atomic planes.

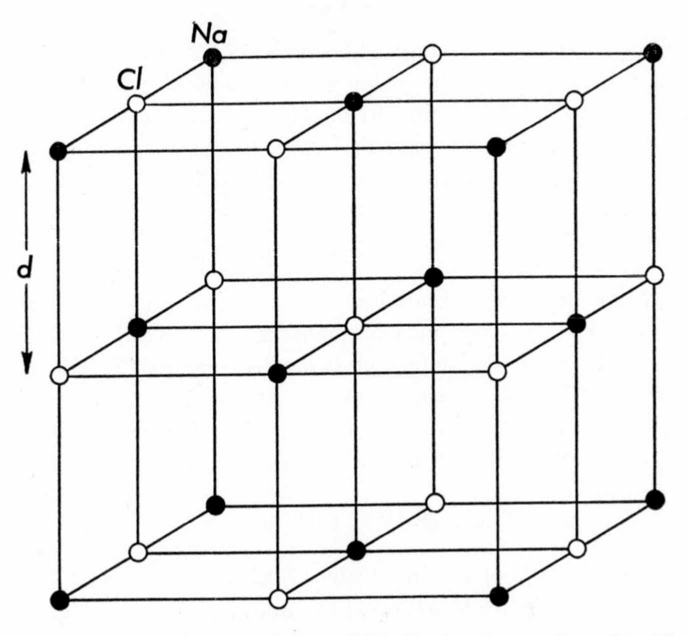

FIG. 5-11. Arrangement of sodium ions and chlorine ions in a sodium chloride crystal.

5-6. The Grating Space of Rocksalt Crystals

The distance between atomic planes, or the *grating space* of a crystal, can be calculated when the structure of the crystal is known. Rocksalt, one of the best known and one of the simplest of crystals, has the geometrical structure of a simple cube, with ions of sodium and chlorine arranged alternately at the corners of a cube, as shown in Figure 5-11. The distance between atomic planes can be found by determining the volume of one of these elementary cubes. If M is the molecular weight of NaCl and ρ is its density, then the volume of one mole of NaCl is

$$v = \frac{M}{\rho}.$$

Since there are $2N$ ions or diffracting centers in a mole, the volume associated with each ion will be

$$V = \frac{M}{2\rho N_0},$$

where N_0 is the Avogadro number. The distance d between ions will therefore be

$$d = \sqrt[3]{\frac{M}{2\rho N_0}}. \tag{2}$$

The molecular weight of sodium chloride is 58.45 and its density is 2.164 gm/cm^3. Substitution of the value of N_0 yields $d = 2.814 \times 10^{-8}$ cm. This was the value known in 1913. The measurements of x-ray wavelengths soon achieved very high precision. Siegbahn, from whose laboratory came a great many of the precise determinations of x-ray wavelengths, adopted the value

$$d = 2.81400 \times 10^{-8} \text{ cm at } 18°\text{C}$$

for the grating space of rocksalt. Large, good, single crystals of rocksalt of the type needed for x-ray measurements are not readily available and, when available, have the defect of being hygroscopic; calcite is a much better crystal for such measurements and is more readily obtainable as good, large, single crystals. Careful comparisons between calcite and rocksalt crystals made with monochromatic x-rays led to the adoption of the value

$$d = 3.02945 \times 10^{-8} \text{ cm at } 18°\text{C}$$

for the grating space of calcite. Unless otherwise noted, all x-ray wavelength measurements are based upon the above value for the grating space of calcite. (See §5-12.)

5-7. Typical X-Ray Spectra

With a knowledge of the grating space of a crystal and the use of the Bragg equation, it is possible to measure the wavelengths of the x-rays emitted by the target of an x-ray tube. When resolved by means of a crystal spectrometer, the heterogeneous beam of x-rays from a target is found to consist of two distinct types of spectra:

1. A continuous spectrum
2. A sharp line spectrum superposed on the continuous spectrum

Typical x-ray spectra, obtained by Ulrey, are shown in the curves in Figure 5-12, in which the intensity of a given wavelength is plotted against the wavelength in angstrom units. The curve for tungsten shows the continuous spectrum of the x-rays coming from the tungsten target of an x-ray tube operated at a voltage of 35 kilovolts. The curve for molybdenum was obtained under similar conditions and shows two sharp lines characteristic of the element molybdenum superposed on the continuous spectrum. These

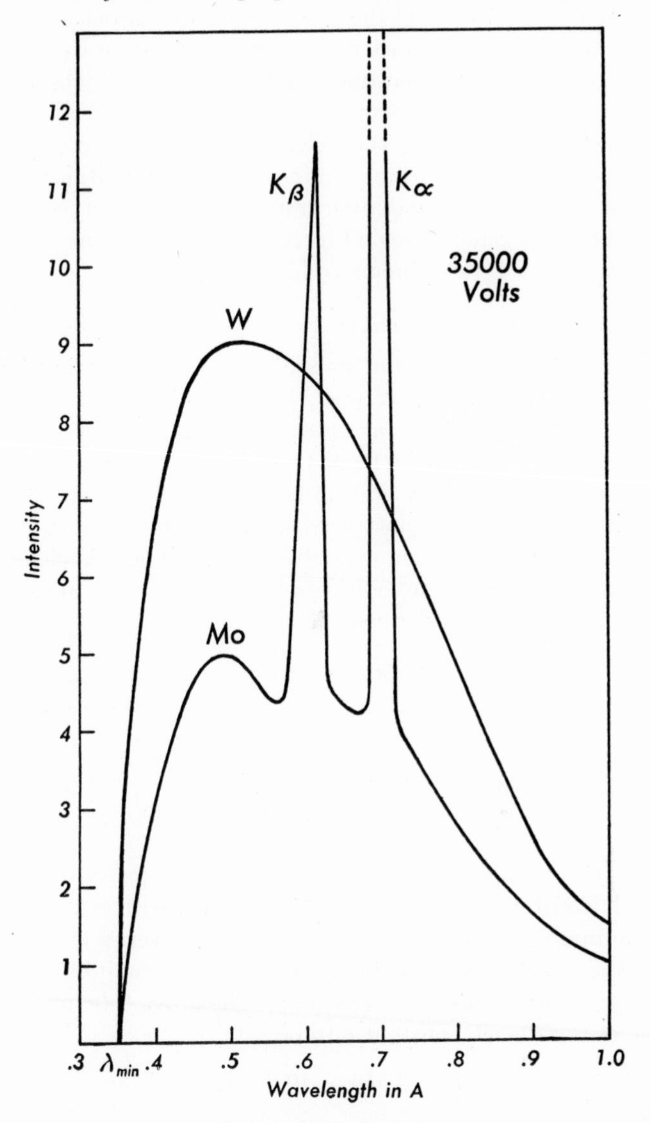

FIG. 5-12. Typical x-ray spectra from tungsten and molybdenum targets, respectively.

lines are known as the K_α and K_β lines of molybdenum. To get the K_α and K_β lines of tungsten, the tube would have to be operated at about 70 kilovolts (§9-3).

The two distinctively different types of spectra from the same target must have different origins. It will be shown in Chapter 8 that the sharp line spectrum is produced by the energy changes which take place as a result of the rearrangement of the electrons in the various electronic levels of the atom following the transfer of energy to the atom by the impinging electron. The continuous spectrum, on the other hand, results from the radiation emitted by the electrons which are accelerated in the Coulomb field of force of the nuclei of the target atoms. The term *bremsstrahlung* (from the German: *bremse*—brake, and *strahlung*—radiation) has come to be accepted to describe the radiation emitted by a charged particle which is accelerated in the Coulomb field of force of a nucleus. Thus the continuous x-ray spectrum is a type of bremsstrahlung.

5-8. Continuous X-Ray Spectrum

The continuous x-ray spectrum presents several interesting features. It will be noted from Figure 5-12 that there is a definite short wavelength limit λ_{min} to the continuous x-ray spectrum independent of the material of the target. Figure 5-13 shows the distribution of intensity with respect to wavelength for different accelerating potentials. When the voltage across the tube is increased, the short wavelength limit λ_{min} is shifted toward smaller values. Duane and Hunt showed that the short wavelength limit of the continuous spectrum varies inversely as the voltage across the tube. Put in terms of frequencies,

$$\nu_{max} = \frac{c}{\lambda_{min}}, \tag{3}$$

and

$$\boxed{Ve = h\nu_{max} = \frac{hc}{\lambda_{min}},} \tag{4}$$

where V is the voltage across the tube, e is the electronic charge, and h is the Planck constant. Ve represents the energy with which an electron strikes the target. Duane and Hunt carried out a series of careful experiments on the determination of the short wavelength limit of the continuous x-ray spectrum for various voltages across the x-ray tube and determined the value of the Planck constant h to be

$$h = 6.556 \times 10^{-27} \text{ erg sec.}$$

This is in good agreement with the value of h determined by means of the photoelectric effect. One may look at this phenomenon as the inverse of the photoelectric effect, since the maximum kinetic energy of an electron striking the target is

$$\tfrac{1}{2}mv_{max}^2 = Ve = h\nu_{max}. \tag{5}$$

Another method of determining h by means of x-rays is to keep the crystal fixed at some arbitrary angle θ, and to increase the voltage across the tube until the wavelength corresponding to this angle first appears. The

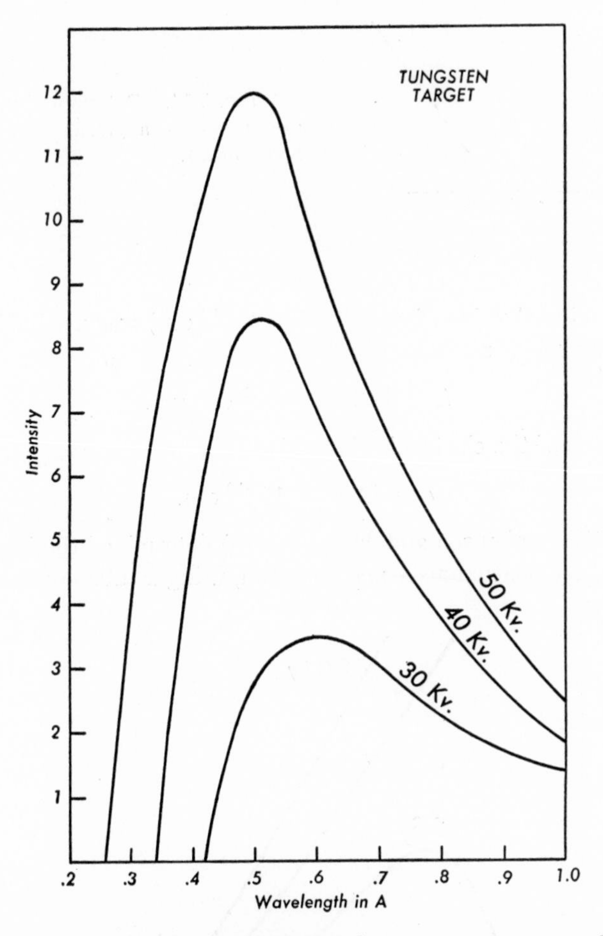

FIG. 5-13. The continuous x-ray spectrum from a tungsten target showing the dependence of the short wavelength limit on the voltage across the tube.

wavelength is then determined from the Bragg equation. A typical curve of this type, obtained by Feder, using a rocksalt crystal set at $\theta = 14° \, 00.5'$, is shown in Figure 5-14. The voltage at which the wavelength first appeared was 9045 volts. From a series of such experiments Feder obtained the value

$$h = 6.5465 \times 10^{-27} \text{ erg sec.}$$

This x-ray method provides one of the most accurate ways of determining h, but it must be remembered that the value of the electronic charge e must be known in order to calculate h. In the above determinations of h,

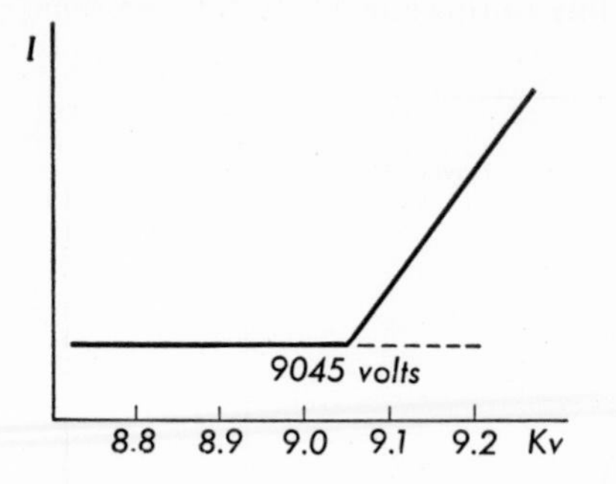

FIG. 5-14. Determination of the voltage at which a given x-ray wavelength first appears.

Millikan's original value of e ($= 4.77 \times 10^{-10}$ esu) was used. The present accepted value of the Planck constant is

$$h = 6.625 \times 10^{-27} \text{ erg sec},$$

and the value of the electronic charge is

$$e = 4.803 \times 10^{-10} \text{ esu}.$$

Recently Stephenson and Mason (1949) determined the intensity distribution of the continuous x-ray spectrum, using a tube operated at com-

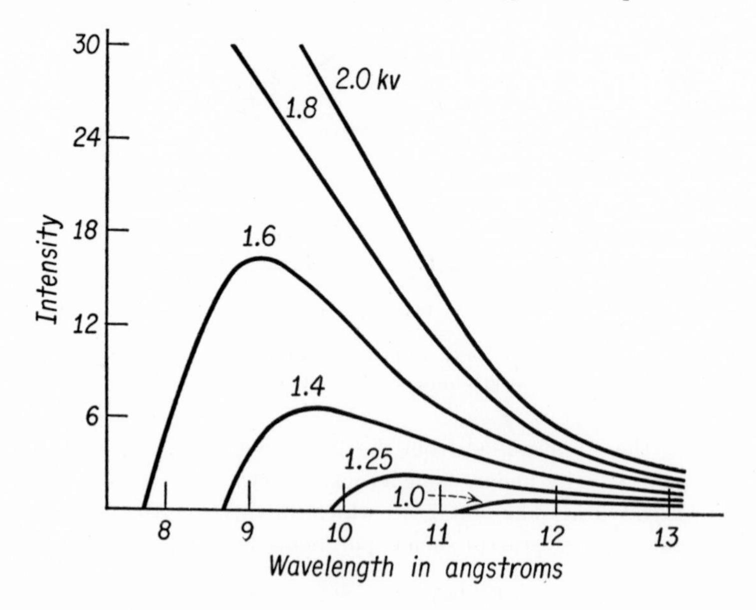

FIG. 5-15. Intensity of the continuous x-ray spectrum as a function of wavelength at comparatively low voltages. (Stephenson and Mason, *Phys. Rev.*, 75, 1713, 1949.)

paratively low voltages, from 1 to 2.0 kv. They used a single crystal spectrometer placed under an evacuated bell jar and detected the x-rays with a Geiger counter. The distribution in intensities at a fixed voltage, as a function of the wavelength, is essentially similar to that obtained at higher operating voltages, as shown in Figure 5-15. They also compared the relative intensities of the x-rays emitted by three different targets, Al, Cu, and W, when operated under similar conditions. They found that the total intensity of the x-rays was proportional to the atomic number of the target element.

5-9. Wavelengths of Gamma Rays

In examining the radiations from radioactive materials, it was found that gamma rays were not affected by electric and magnetic fields. It is now known that gamma rays are short electromagnetic waves of the same nature as x-rays, except that they are emitted from the nucleus of the atom. The wavelengths of some of the gamma rays have been measured by x-ray crystal diffraction methods.

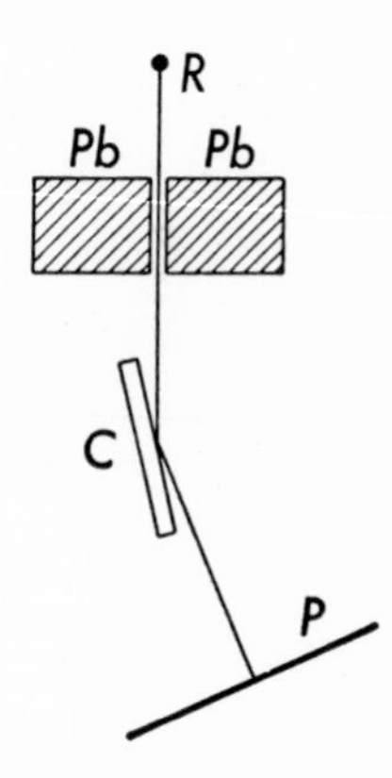

FIG. 5-16. Bragg-type crystal reflection method of determining gamma-ray wavelengths.

Rutherford and Andrade (1914) made use of the Bragg spectrometer for determining the wavelengths of gamma rays from radium B. A narrow beam of gamma rays from the radioactive preparation, *R*, after passing through a fine slit in a lead block, was reflected by the rocksalt crystal, *C*, onto the photographic plate, *P*, as shown in Figure 5-16. By rotating the crystal from 0° to about 15°, a series of sharp lines was obtained corresponding to the gamma-ray wavelengths emitted by radium B. This method has been used for measuring the wavelengths of the gamma rays from many other radioactive substances. The smallest gamma-ray wavelength measured with the Bragg type of crystal spectrometer is $\lambda = 0.016$A, one of the lines emitted by radium C. In order to produce x-rays of the same wavelength, the x-ray tube would have to be operated at a difference of potential of 770,000 volts.

The very small angles involved in the measurement of very short wavelengths limit the accuracy of the Bragg type of single crystal spectrometer. A new design, suggested by Du Mond (1927) and first constructed by Mlle Cauchois (1932) using a curved crystal, has since been developed into an instrument of high precision for the measurement of gamma rays

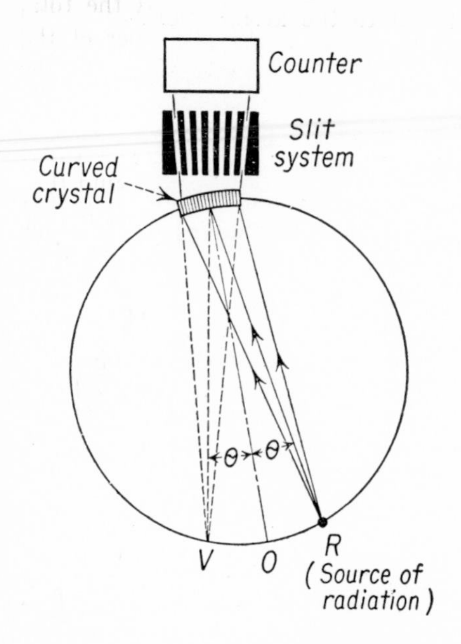

Fig. 5-17. Schematic diagram of the Du Mond curved crystal spectrometer used in measuring short wavelength gamma rays and x-rays. R is the source of radiation, V is its virtual image, and θ is the Bragg angle.

and x-rays of very short wavelength. Figure 5-17 is a schematic diagram of one design used by Du Mond in some recent experiments. The crystal, originally a flat lamina of quartz, 2 mm thick and 50 mm wide, is curved by placing it between two cylindrical steel surfaces which have windows in them to permit the radiation to pass through the crystal. The radius of curvature of the crystal is 2 meters. The atomic planes, which are perpendicular to the curved surface, converge when produced toward the point O. A circle through O and through the curved crystal, with a diameter equal to the radius of curvature of the crystal, is called the *focal circle*. A small source of gamma rays placed at point R on this focal circle sends a narrow beam of radiation at an angle θ to the crystal planes; it is reflected from these planes and transmitted through the crystal in such a manner as to form a virtual image on the focal circle at V. A sufficiently large Geiger counter or a scintillation counter is placed behind the crystal to receive this beam. A lead collimator is placed between the counter and the crystal to stop the direct transmitted beam but allows the reflected beam to pass through it. The Bragg angle θ is determined from the position of the source S on the focal circle. Du Mond and his co-workers have measured wavelengths smaller than 0.01 angstrom with an accuracy of 10^{-5}A with the curved crystal spectrometer.

5-10. X-Ray Powder Crystal Diffraction

Comparatively few substances are available in the form of large single crystals for use in the Bragg type of spectrometer. Most substances exist as aggregates of very small crystals. Methods have been developed for studying the crystal structure of a substance even though these crystals may be very minute. If the substance is made into a very fine powder, it may be considered as made up of a multitude of very small crystals. Suppose a very

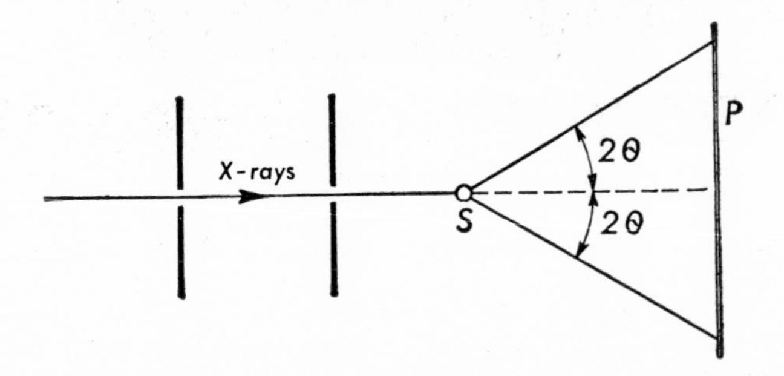

FIG. 5-18. Method of obtaining x-ray diffraction patterns from a substance in powder form.

narrow pencil of monochromatic x-rays of wavelength λ is incident on this powder at S, as in Figure 5-18. Since these small crystals are oriented at random, there undoubtedly will be some crystal oriented at just the right angle to satisfy the Bragg equation $n\lambda = 2d \sin \theta$ for this particular wavelength λ. The scattered beam will have maximum intensity at an angle 2θ with respect to the incident beam of x-rays, and because of the random orientations of the crystals, these maxima will lie on a cone of central angle 4θ. If the x-rays scattered by the powder are incident on a photographic plate placed perpendicular to the incident beam, concentric circles will be registered on it corresponding to the different orders of reflection. Another method is to bend a thin strip of photographic film in the form of a circle with the powder at the center of this circle. Small holes are cut in this film to permit the direct beam of x-rays to enter and leave the camera without blackening the photographic film.

Frequently, instead of a monochromatic beam, x-rays from a target which emits a few intense characteristic lines are used for these powder photographs. Since the relative intensities of these characteristic lines are known, it is not difficult to determine which circles correspond to the dif-

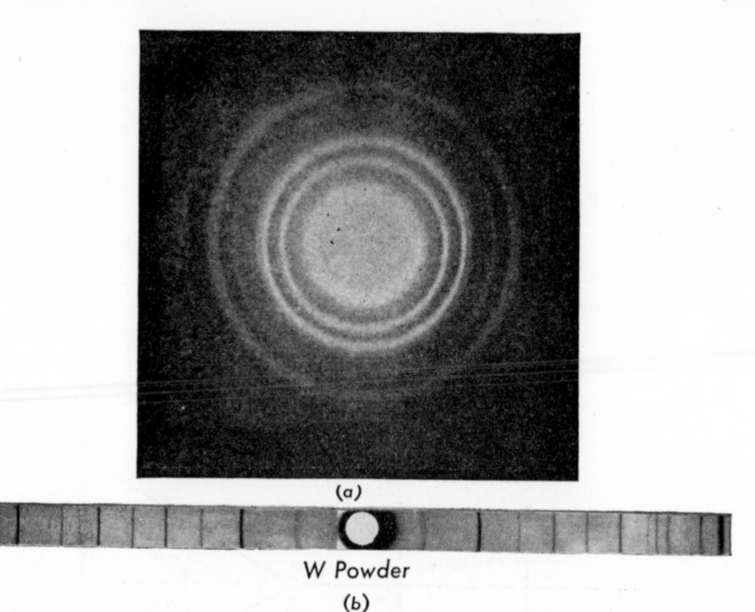

FIG. 5-19. (a) X-ray powder diffraction pattern of aluminum. (Reproduced with the permission of A. W. Hull.)
(b) X-ray powder diffraction pattern of tungsten obtained with a photographic film bent in the form of a circular cylinder. Radiation from a copper target was used in making this pattern. (From a photograph by L. L. Wyman and supplied by A. W. Hull.)

ferent wavelengths. Typical powder crystal diffraction patterns are shown in Figure 5-19. This method of crystal analysis was first developed by Debye and Scherrer and by Hull, and is one of the most valuable aids in studying crystal structure.

5-11. Refraction of X-Rays

Several of the early experimenters, including Roentgen and Barkla, tried to find out whether x-rays are refracted when they enter a material medium. The phenomenon of refraction, however, was not discovered until 1919, when Stenström observed that Bragg's law $n\lambda = 2d \sin \theta$ did not yield the same value for λ in the different orders of reflection of a monochromatic beam from a crystal. The explanation of this apparent failure of Bragg's law is that the x-rays are refracted when they penetrate the crystal. Because of refraction, the wavelength in the crystal is different from that outside. If μ is the index of refraction, λ the wavelength in a vacuum, and λ' the wavelength in the crystal, then

$$\mu = \frac{\lambda}{\lambda'}. \tag{6}$$

Further, the angle of incidence upon the inner crystal planes is not the angle between the incident beam and the surface of the crystal, but is the angle between the refracted ray and the atomic planes in the crystal. The deviations from Bragg's law show that the angle of refraction θ' is less than the grazing angle of incidence θ; that is, that the x-rays are bent away from the normal upon penetrating into the crystal. This means that the index of

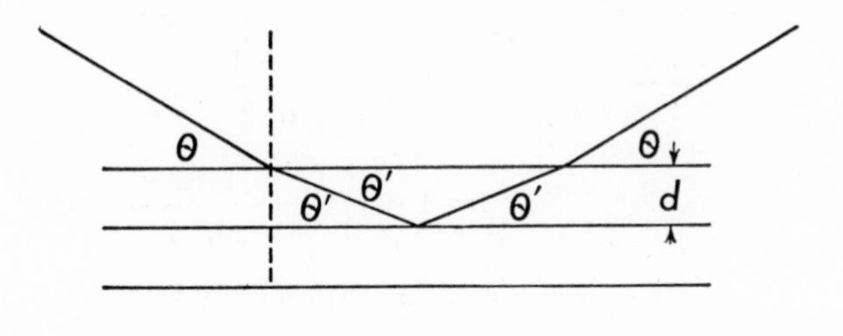

FIG. 5-20. Refraction of x-rays on penetrating a crystal.

refraction for x-rays is less than unity. In Figure 5-20, if θ is the angle between the incident ray and the surface of the crystal, and θ' the angle of refraction, then Snell's law of refraction takes the form

$$\mu = \frac{\cos\theta}{\cos\theta'}. \tag{7}$$

The angle θ' is not only the angle of refraction, but also the angle that the ray makes with the atomic planes, so that inside the crystal Bragg's law is

$$n\lambda' = 2d\sin\theta'. \tag{8}$$

However, the angle that is actually measured is the angle θ, and the wavelength usually desired is the wavelength λ in a vacuum. A modified form of Bragg's law containing λ, θ, and μ can be obtained by combining equations (6) and (7) with (8). Remembering that

$$\sin\theta' = (1 - \cos^2\theta')^{1/2}$$

and substituting the values of $\cos\theta'$ and λ' from equations (6) and (7), we find that equation (8) becomes

$$\frac{n\lambda}{\mu} = 2d\left(1 - \frac{\cos^2\theta}{\mu^2}\right)^{1/2}$$

$$n\lambda = 2d(\mu^2 - \cos^2\theta)^{1/2},$$

or

$$n\lambda = 2d(\mu^2 - 1 + \sin^2\theta)^{1/2};$$

and by factoring out $\sin\theta$, we have

$$n\lambda = 2d\sin\theta\left[1 + \frac{\mu^2 - 1}{\sin^2\theta}\right]^{1/2} \tag{9}$$

Equation (9) is a modified form of Bragg's law. For purposes of calculation, this equation can be simplified by expanding the quantity in the bracket by means of the binomial theorem; thus

$$\begin{aligned}\left[1 + \frac{\mu^2 - 1}{\sin^2\theta}\right]^{1/2} &= 1 + \frac{1}{2}\,\frac{\mu^2 - 1}{\sin^2\theta} + \cdots \\ &= 1 + \frac{1}{2}\,\frac{(\mu + 1)(\mu - 1)}{\sin^2\theta}.\end{aligned}$$

Experiment shows that μ does not differ appreciably from unity, and to a

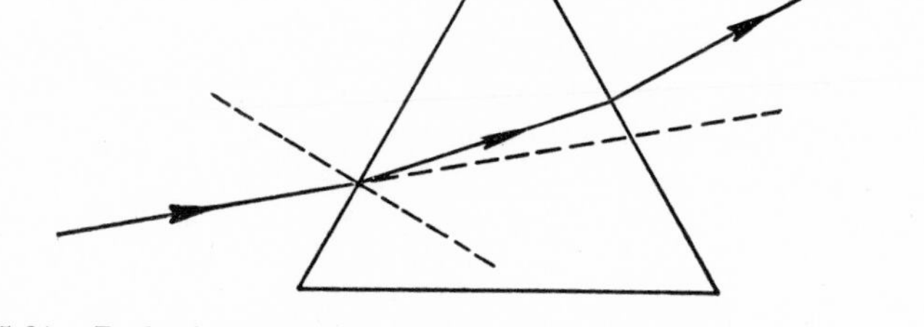

Fig. 5-21. Path of a beam of x-rays refracted through a prism. The beam is bent away from the normal on entering the prism.

very close approximation $\mu + 1 = 2$, so that the bracket can be written as

$$\left[1 + \frac{\mu^2 - 1}{\sin^2\theta}\right]^{1/2} = 1 - \frac{1 - \mu}{\sin^2\theta},$$

and the modified form of Bragg's law is then

$$\boxed{n\lambda = 2d\left[1 - \frac{1 - \mu}{\sin^2\theta}\right]\sin\theta.} \tag{10}$$

The more common method of expressing the results is to give the quantity $\delta = 1 - \mu$, which shows how the index of refraction differs from unity. For example, the index of refraction of calcite for the wavelength $\lambda = 0.708$A differs from unity by the amount

$$\delta = 1 - \mu = 1.85 \times 10^{-6}.$$

Two interesting conclusions can be drawn from the fact that the index of refraction of x-rays in material media is less than unity. One is that when x-rays pass through a prism, the beam will be deviated in a direction opposite to that for ordinary light. The path of an x-ray beam through a prism is shown in Figure 5-21. The other conclusion is that at a certain critical angle θ_c, the x-ray beam should not be refracted into the medium at all but should be totally reflected. At this critical angle of incidence, $\cos \theta' = 1$ and

$$\boxed{\mu = \cos \theta_c.} \tag{11}$$

For all angles smaller than θ_c, there should be no refraction at all; only total reflection of the x-ray beam.

An experimental method for the determination of this critical angle is shown in Figure 5-22. A narrow beam is obtained by passing the x-rays from

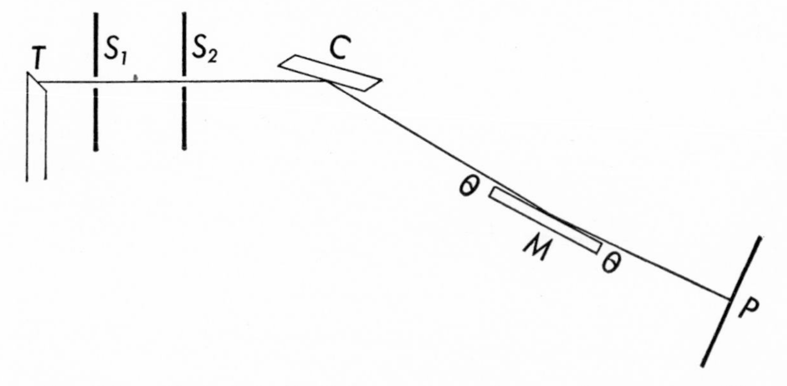

FIG. 5-22. Method of reflecting monochromatic x-rays from a mirror M.

the target T through two slits, S_1 and S_2. The crystal C reflects a particular wavelength λ onto the plane surface M of the material. If the grazing angle of incidence θ is less than the critical angle θ_c, the beam will be totally reflected to the photographic plate P, and the surface M will act as a mirror. As the angle of incidence is increased, the beam continues to be reflected until $\theta = \theta_c$, after which the beam is refracted into the material medium and the intensity of the reflected beam becomes practically zero. A photograph of a beam of x-rays reflected from a palladium surface is shown in Figure 5-23.

According to the classical theory of dispersion, when an electromagnetic wave of frequency ν passes through a substance containing n electrons per unit volume, the index of refraction of the substance is given by

$$\mu = 1 - \frac{ne^2}{2\pi m\nu^2}, \tag{12}$$

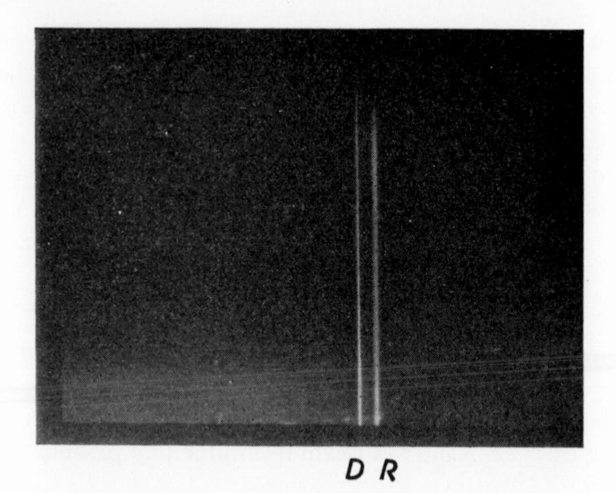

FIG. 5-23. Reflection of monochromatic x-rays (AgK_γ line) from a palladium mirror near the critical angle. D is the direct beam and R is the reflected beam. (From photograph by the author.)

provided that the natural frequency of the electrons is small in comparison with ν, and that absorption is negligible. Equation (12) can be rewritten as

$$1 - \mu = \delta = \frac{ne^2}{2\pi m\nu^2}.$$

Setting

$$\nu = \frac{c}{\lambda},$$

we get

$$\delta = \frac{ne^2\lambda^2}{2\pi mc^2}. \tag{13}$$

Now

$$\mu = \cos\theta_c.$$

Since θ_c is small, $\cos\theta_c$ can be expanded in terms of θ_c, yielding

$$\cos\theta_c = 1 - \frac{\theta_c^2}{2} + \cdots,$$

so that

$$\delta = 1 - \mu = \frac{\theta_c^2}{2}$$

or

$$\theta_c = \sqrt{2\delta} = \sqrt{\frac{ne^2}{\pi mc^2}}\,\lambda. \tag{14}$$

Measurements of the critical angle show that it is directly proportional to the wavelength of the x-rays and to the square root of the density of the material except in the neighborhood of an absorption limit (§9-3). This is in good agreement with equation (14). However, the classical theory is inadequate to explain refraction in the neighborhood of an x-ray absorption limit. A quantum theory of dispersion has been developed which predicts results in fair agreement with experimental data. A discussion of the quantum theory of dispersion is beyond the scope of this book.

The index of refraction of a medium for an electromagnetic wave is defined as

$$\mu = \frac{c}{w}, \tag{15}$$

where c ($=3 \times 10^{10}$ cm/sec) is its velocity in a vacuum, and w is the velocity of the wave in the medium. Since the index of refraction for x-rays is less than unity, its velocity w in a material medium is greater than c. At first sight this may appear to be in contradiction to the fundamental postulate of the special theory of relativity which states that electromagnetic waves are always propagated with the same velocity c. Actually there is no contradiction. On the microscopic point of view, a material body is not a continuous medium but consists of nuclei and electrons separated by distances which are large relative to their sizes. These particles may be imagined to be situated in empty space. The incident wave, in traversing this space, sets the charges into vibration, causing them to emit electromagnetic waves. Two sets of waves, therefore, travel through this space: the incident wave, and the waves produced by the forced vibrations of the electrons. These elementary waves travel through the space with velocity c. But, through superposition of the elementary waves, a new wave form is produced, which, on the macroscopic (large-scale) point of view, consists of a train of waves traveling through the material body with a wave velocity w which may be greater or smaller than c (see §6-8). But the energy carried by the incident wave and the energy radiated by the forced vibrations of the electrons always travel with velocity c.

The refracted wave thus consists of a train of waves traveling with a velocity w whose magnitude depends upon the binding forces acting on the electrons. The dielectric constant k of the material medium is determined by the magnitude of these binding forces, and it can be shown, on the basis of Maxwell's electromagnetic theory of light, that the index of refraction, μ, is given by the equation

$$\mu = \sqrt{k} = \frac{c}{w}. \tag{16}$$

It is this equation which is used in deriving the expression for the index of refraction given by equation (12).

5-12. Measurement of X-Ray Wavelengths by Ruled Gratings

An extremely important application of the total reflection of x-rays is the measurement of x-ray wavelengths by using a ruled grating with a known number of lines per millimeter. As long as the grazing angle of incidence θ is less than the critical angle $\theta_c = \sqrt{2\delta}$, the x-ray beam will be totally reflected from a polished surface. This surface can be made into a diffraction grating by ruling a series of uniformly spaced lines a distance d apart. The spaces between the rulings will act as diffracting centers producing vari-

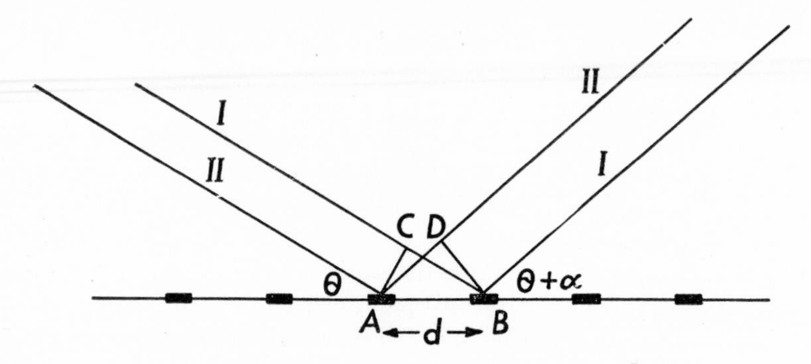

FIG. 5-24. Reflection of x-rays from a ruled grating.

ous orders of diffraction on either side of the regularly reflected line. In Figure 5-24, if the rays are incident at an angle θ to the surface of the ruled grating, an intense maximum will be produced at some other angle $(\theta + \alpha)$, provided the difference in path between two adjacent rays is a whole number of wavelengths. The difference in paths between rays I and II is

$$CB - AD = d \cos \theta - d \cos (\theta + \alpha),$$

so that the condition for an intense maximum at this angle of reflection is

$$\boxed{d[\cos \theta - \cos (\theta + \alpha)] = n\lambda,} \quad (17)$$

where n is an integer and may be either positive or negative. The regular reflection at the angle θ is called the zero order; the other orders of reflection are called positive if α is positive and negative if α is negative.

Diffraction gratings for x-rays have been made of glass, speculum metal, silver, and gold, and the number of lines per millimeter has ranged from 50 to 600. Since the grating space d is accurately known and the angles θ and $(\theta + \alpha)$ can be measured with a high degree of precision, this method can be used as a check on the wavelengths measured with crystal gratings. A comparison of some wavelengths measured by ruled gratings and by crystals is shown in Table 5-1.

Table 5-1

Comparison of Wavelengths Measured by Ruled Gratings and by Crystals

Line	λ_g by Grating	λ_c by Crystal	$\lambda_g - \lambda_c$ in Per Cent	Observer
Mo L_α	5.4116A	5.3950A	+0.31	Cork
Mo L_β	5.1832	5.1665	+0.33	"
Cu K_α	1.54172	1.5387	+0.20	Bearden
Cu $K_{\beta 1}$	1.39225	1.3894	+0.20	"
Cr K_α	2.29097	2.2859	+0.22	"
Cr $K_{\beta 1}$	2.08478	2.0806	+0.22	"

In every case the wavelength measured with a ruled grating is greater than that measured with a crystal grating. The possible sources of error in the ruled grating measurements were investigated by many physicists, but in no case could they account for this large discrepancy—about $\frac{1}{4}$ of 1 per cent. This led to a reexamination of the basis on which crystal grating wavelength measurements depend, namely, the grating space d. It will be recalled that this distance, for rocksalt, is given by the equation

$$d = \sqrt[3]{\frac{M}{2\rho N_0}}; \tag{2}$$

and for crystals which are not simple cubes, such as calcite and quartz, this equation becomes

$$d = \sqrt[3]{\frac{M}{2\rho N_0 \phi(\beta)}}, \tag{2a}$$

where $\phi(\beta)$ is a function of the angles of the crystal lattice. The least accurately known constant entering in the computation of d is the Avogadro number N_0. The Avogadro number is computed from the relationship

$$F = N_0 e,$$

where F is the Faraday constant and e is the electronic charge. F is very accurately known from many experiments extending over a long period of time. To get agreement between the ruled grating and the crystal grating measurements of x-ray wavelengths, it is necessary to increase the value of e from Millikan's value 4.77×10^{-10} esu to about 4.803×10^{-10} esu. As stated in §2-4, redeterminations of the value of the electronic charge have led to the adoption of the value

$$e = 4.803 \times 10^{-10} \text{ esu.}$$

Within recent years improved methods have increased the accuracy of the determinations of the densities of crystals. Chemically pure crystals of NaCl, KCl, and LiF have been prepared artificially, and the grating spaces of these crystals have been determined by measuring the Bragg angle for monochromatic x-rays whose wavelengths are known from ruled grating measurements. Using the known molecular weights of these crystals, we can determine values of the Avogadro number with the aid of equation (2). Birge has stated that the Avogadro number determined in this manner, together with the known value of the Faraday constant, leads to the most reliable determination of the electronic charge.

5-13. Absorption of X-Rays

When a parallel beam of x-rays passes through any material, the intensity of the emergent beam is less than that of the incident beam. The decrease in

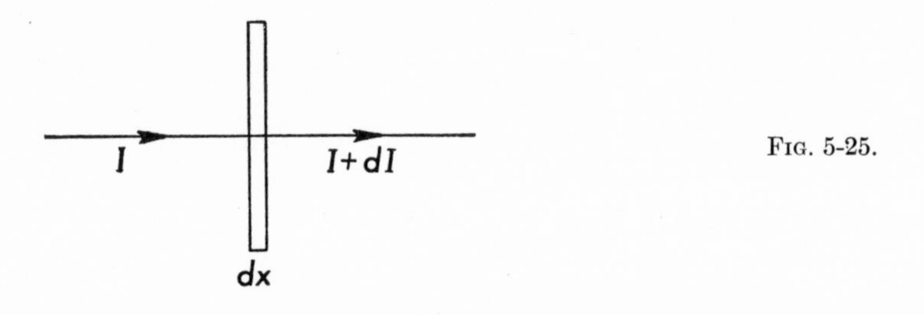

FIG. 5-25.

intensity of the beam when it traverses a small thickness dx of the material, Figure 5-25, depends upon the thickness and upon the intensity I of the beam, or

$$-dI = \mu I dx$$

where $-dI$ represents the decrease in intensity of the beam, and μ is a factor of proportionality called the *absorption coefficient*. It represents the fraction of the energy removed from the beam per centimeter of path, and is sometimes referred to as the total absorption coefficient of the material.

The above equation can be written as

$$\frac{dI}{I} = -\mu dx,$$

and upon integration becomes

$$\boxed{I = I_0 \epsilon^{-\mu x},} \tag{18}$$

where I_0 is the initial intensity of the beam, and I is its intensity after it has traversed a thickness x of the material.

There are two ways in which the atoms of a substance can remove the energy from the incident beam. One process is that of *scattering* in which the electrons of the atoms are set into forced vibrations and then radiate this energy in all directions. The second process is the absorption of some of the energy by the atom, which then radiates a new type of x-ray characteristic of the atom. This radiation is called *fluorescent radiation* and is also emitted in all directions.

The total absorption coefficient μ can be written as the sum of two terms

$$\mu = \sigma + \tau, \tag{19}$$

where σ is the *scattering coefficient* and τ is the *fluorescent transformation coefficient*. These coefficients can be interpreted in a slightly different way by referring to a beam whose cross-sectional area is 1 cm^2. In this case, μ represents the total fraction of the energy removed from the beam by 1 cm^3 of the material, σ represents the fraction of the energy scattered by 1 cm^3, and τ represents the fraction of the energy transformed into fluorescent radiation by this unit volume.

The *mass absorption coefficient* is defined as μ/ρ where ρ is the density of the material. Also

$$\frac{\mu}{\rho} = \frac{\sigma}{\rho} + \frac{\tau}{\rho}. \tag{20}$$

The mass absorption coefficient μ/ρ is characteristic of the material and represents the fraction of the energy removed from a beam of unit cross section by one gram of the substance. Similar interpretations hold for the mass scattering coefficient σ/ρ and the mass transformation coefficient τ/ρ.

5-14. Atomic Absorption Coefficient

From the microscopic point of view, an *atomic absorption coefficient*, μ_a, is of greater interest than a mass absorption coefficient. The former can be defined in terms of the latter by the equation

$$\boxed{\mu_a = \frac{\mu}{\rho}\frac{M}{N_0},} \tag{21}$$

where N_0 is the Avogadro number and M is the atomic mass of the isotope of the element under discussion. The dimensions of μ_a are those of an area/atom. For example, μ/ρ for copper, for x-rays of 0.70A, is about 50 cm^2/gm. Taking $M = 63$ gm/gm-at wt and $N_0 = 6 \times 10^{23}$ atoms per gm-at wt, equation (21) yields

$$\mu_a = 50 \times 10^{-21} \text{ cm}^2/\text{atom}.$$

If we imagine the atom to be a sphere of radius of about 2×10^{-8} cm, then we can think of this atom as having a geometrical cross section of approximately 12×10^{-16} cm^2. The absorption cross section is thus very much smaller than the geometrical cross section.

The atomic absorption coefficient, and hence the cross section for absorption, varies with the wavelength of the incident x-rays for any one substance. We can interpret the atomic absorption coefficient as a measure of the probability of the absorption of the given radiation by the atoms of the substance irradiated. As has already been shown, absorption of radiation by the atoms may result in its scattering, which will be represented by an *atomic scattering coefficient* σ_a, or it may result in the transformation of its energy into fluorescent radiation which will be represented by an *atomic fluorescent transformation coefficient* τ_a. The value of each of these coefficients is a measure of the probability for the occurrence of the given type of process and is expressed in units of cm^2/atom.

5-15. Scattering of X-Rays

When a beam of x-rays passes through a substance, the electrons in this substance are set into vibration and radiate x-rays in all directions. The radiation emitted by these electrons is called *scattered* or *secondary radiation.* If E is the electric intensity of the incident wave, the acceleration of the electron will be

$$a = \frac{Ee}{m},$$

where e is the charge of the electron and m is its mass. If the speed of the electron is small in comparison with the speed of light c, then the electric intensity E_ϕ of the scattered wave at a distance r from this electron is

$$E_\phi = \frac{ea \sin \phi}{rc^2}, \qquad \text{(Chap. 4, Eq. [1])}$$

where ϕ is the angle between E and r, as shown in Figure 5-26. Substituting the value for the acceleration in the above equation, we get

$$E_\phi = \frac{Ee^2}{rmc^2} \sin \phi. \tag{22}$$

Since the intensity of the wave is proportional to the square of the electric vector, the ratio of the intensity I of the incident radiation to the intensity

I_ϕ of the wave sent out along r is

$$\frac{I_\phi}{I} = \frac{E_\phi^2}{E^2} = \frac{e^4}{r^2m^2c^4}\sin^2\phi. \quad (23)$$

Choose a set of axes so that the incident or primary beam is propagated parallel to the x axis. The electric intensity E will then be in a plane parallel

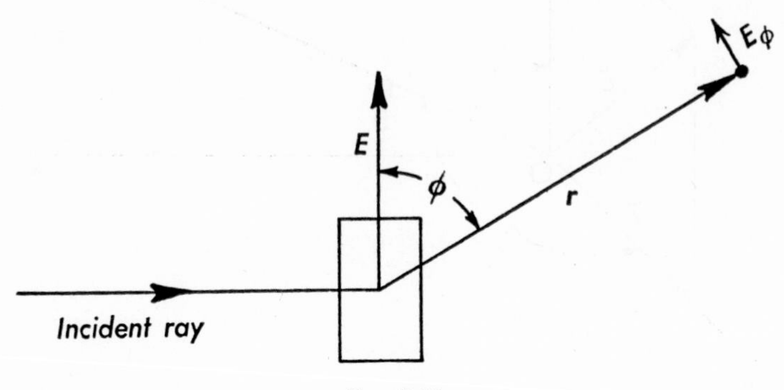

FIG. 5-26.

to the y-z plane. Since the position of the y and z axes can be chosen arbitrarily in this plane, let the y axis be taken in the plane determined by the direction of the scattered ray OP and the primary ray (Figure 5-27), and let the electron be at the origin of coordinates. The electric vector E may be resolved into two perpendicular components, Y and Z, such that

$$E^2 = Y^2 + Z^2.$$

Since the intensity of the wave is proportional to the square of the electric field intensity, we can write

$$I = I_y + I_z,$$

where I_y is the intensity of the y component of the incident wave and I_z is the intensity of its z component. Since the primary ray is unpolarized, the average values of Y^2 and Z^2 are equal; hence the intensities of the y and z components are equal, yielding

$$I_y = I_z = \frac{I}{2}\cdot$$

Now the intensity, I_1, of the scattered beam at the point P due to the y component of the incident wave is, from equation (23),

$$I_1 = I_y\frac{e^4\sin^2\phi_1}{r^2m^2c^4} = \tfrac{1}{2}I\frac{e^4\cos^2\theta}{r^2m^2c^4}, \quad (24)$$

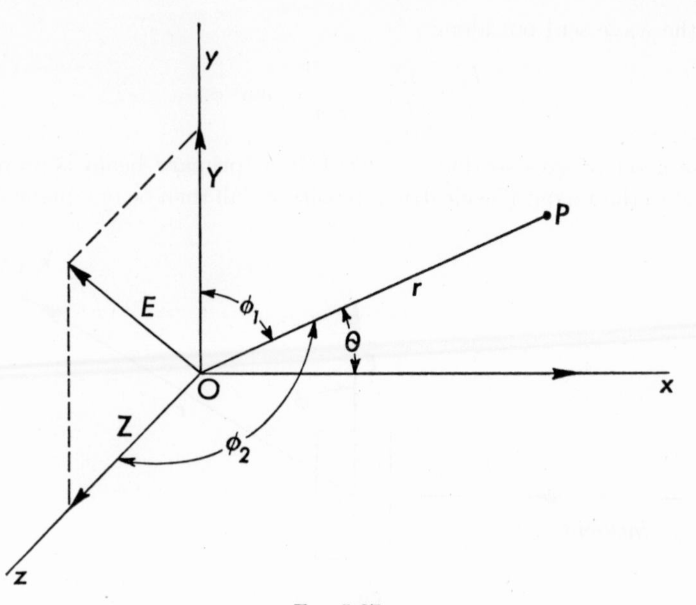

FIG. 5-27.

where ϕ_1 is the angle between OP and Y, and $\theta = \pi/2 - \phi_1$. Similarly, the intensity, I_2, of the scattered beam at the point P due to the z component of the incident wave is

$$I_2 = I_z \frac{e^4 \sin^2 \phi_2}{r^2 m^2 c^4} = \tfrac{1}{2} I \frac{e^4}{r^2 m^2 c^4}, \tag{25}$$

where ϕ_2 is the angle between OP and Z, and is always $\pi/2$. The total intensity, I_e, of the scattered wave at P due to the energy radiated by a single electron is thus

$$I_e = I_1 + I_2 = I \frac{e^4}{2r^2 m^2 c^4} (1 + \cos^2 \theta). \tag{26}$$

If there are n electrons per unit volume of material, and if we make the assumption that each electron is effective in scattering the x-rays independently of all the other electrons, then the intensity of the scattered wave at point P, coming from a unit volume of the scatterer, will be given by

$$\boxed{I_s = nI_e = I \frac{ne^4}{2r^2 m^2 c^4} (1 + \cos^2 \theta).} \tag{27}$$

This analysis of the intensity of the scattered x-ray beam leads to three conclusions, each of which can be investigated experimentally. One is that a measurement of the total energy scattered should yield the number of electrons per unit volume effective in scattering, and hence the number of electrons per atom effective in scattering. Another is that when the scattering angle is 90°, the scattered beam should be linearly polarized with the direction of vibration of the electric vector parallel to the z axis. The third is that equation (27) predicts a definite distribution of intensity of the scattered beam as a function of the angle of scattering with a minimum intensity at 90°.

5-16. Determination of the Number of Electrons per Atom

The rate at which energy is scattered by the electrons in a cubic centimeter of matter can be calculated by integrating I_s over a large sphere of radius r

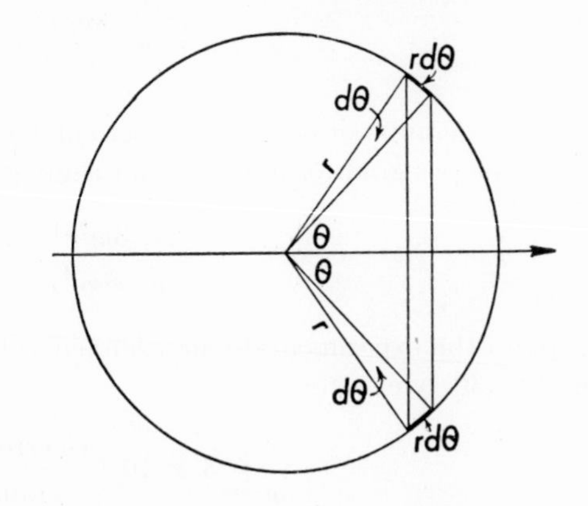

Fig. 5-28.

with its center at the scatterer. A convenient element of surface area is one over which I_s has a constant value and is, from Figure 5-28,

$$dA = 2\pi r \sin\theta \cdot r d\theta.$$

The amount of energy, W_s, which is scattered by unit volume in one second is therefore

$$\begin{aligned} W_s &= \int_0^A I_s dA \\ &= \frac{\pi I n e^4}{m^2 c^4} \int_0^\pi (1 + \cos^2\theta) \sin\theta d\theta \\ &= \frac{8\pi}{3} \frac{ne^4}{m^2c^4} I. \end{aligned} \tag{28}$$

Let

$$\boxed{\sigma = \frac{W_s}{I} = \frac{8\pi}{3} \frac{ne^4}{m^2c^4}.} \tag{29}$$

The quantity σ is called the scattering coefficient of the substance and represents the fraction of the energy removed from the incident beam by the process of scattering when traversing one centimeter of the material. A measurement of σ would make possible an evaluation of the number of electrons effective in scattering. One of the earliest determinations of the scattering coefficient was made by Barkla (1911), and later repeated with greater accuracy by Hewlett, using carbon as the scattering element. Hewlett measured the intensity of the scattered beam over a range of angles θ from about 0 to π, thus performing the integration experimentally. The wavelength of the incident beam was 0.71A. The result obtained for the mass scattering coefficient is $\sigma/\rho = 0.2$, where ρ is the density of carbon. Solving equation (29) for n, we get

$$n = \sigma \cdot \frac{3m^2c^4}{8\pi e^4}.$$

Since n is the number of electrons per cubic centimeter, n/ρ is the number of electrons per gram of material and is given by

$$\frac{n}{\rho} = \frac{\sigma}{\rho} \cdot \frac{3m^2c^4}{8\pi e^4}. \tag{30}$$

Putting in the experimentally determined values on the right-hand side of equation (30) yields

$$\frac{n}{\rho} = 3 \times 10^{23} \frac{\text{electrons}}{\text{gram}}.$$

There are $\dfrac{6.02 \times 10^{23}}{12} = 5.01 \times 10^{22}$ atoms per gram of carbon. Therefore the number of electrons per atom effective in scattering is

$$\frac{3 \times 10^{23}}{5 \times 10^{22}} = 6,$$

which is the atomic number of carbon. Hence the number of electrons effective in scattering is equal to the atomic number of the scattering element. This is in excellent agreement with the results of the experiments on the scattering of alpha particles, and is a direct determination of the number of electrons outside the nucleus of the atom.

It must be remarked that such good agreement between the results of the experiments on the scattering of x-rays and Thomson's theory has been obtained only with scattering substances of low atomic number and then only with x-rays of wavelengths greater than 0.1A. The theory of the scattering of x-rays will be discussed further in §5-19.

5-17. Polarization of X-Rays

This classical theory of scattering predicts that the beam scattered at an angle of 90° should be linearly polarized. This can be seen by a glance at equations (24) and (25). For $\theta = 90°$, the intensity due to the y component

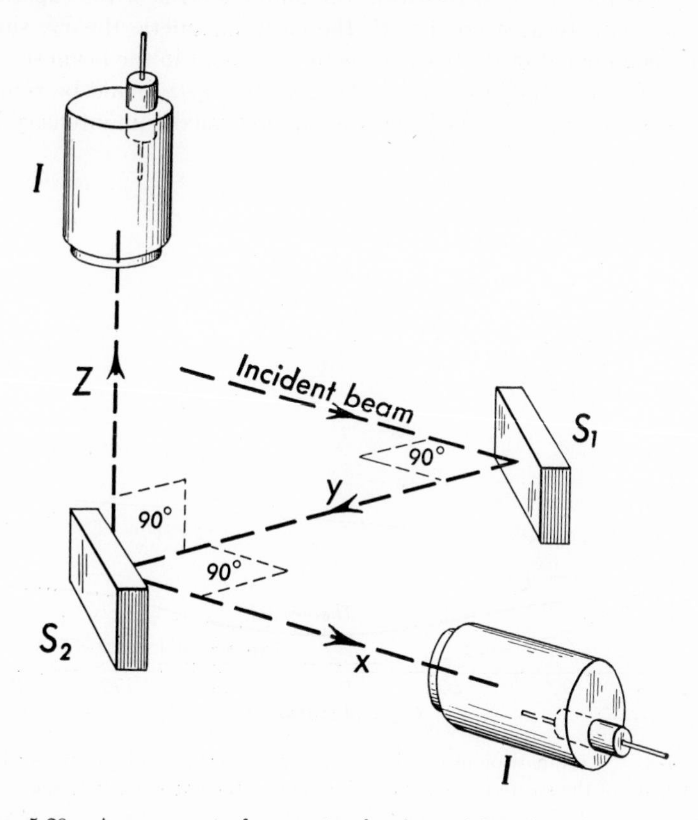

FIG. 5-29. Arrangement of apparatus for determining the polarization of x-rays scattered through 90°.

of the electric vector will be zero, while the intensity at any point in the X-Y plane due to the z component of the electric vector is independent of the angle. Thus in the y direction the scattered beam will be linearly polarized with the direction of vibration parallel to the z axis. To detect this polarization another scatterer is used as an analyzer. Barkla was the first to show the polarization of the beam scattered at an angle of 90°. Compton and Hagenow (1924) repeated this experiment with improved apparatus. Figure 5-29 shows a diagram of their apparatus. A narrow beam of x-rays from a tungsten target was scattered by S_1 to a second scatterer placed at S_2 so that the scattered beam made an angle of 90° with the original beam.

The scattering materials were blocks of paper, carbon, aluminum, and sulfur. The beam scattered by S_2 was examined in two directions at right angles to one another and perpendicular to the direction S_1S_2. The intensity in the direction S_2–x was found to be a maximum, while that in the direction S_2–z was practically zero within the limits of error of the experiment. This is in complete agreement with the electromagnetic theory, since, if only the z component of the electric vector is present in the beam scattered from S_1 to S_2, then the intensity in the direction S_2–z should be zero for a transverse wave; similarly the beam should have maximum intensity in the direction S_2–x.

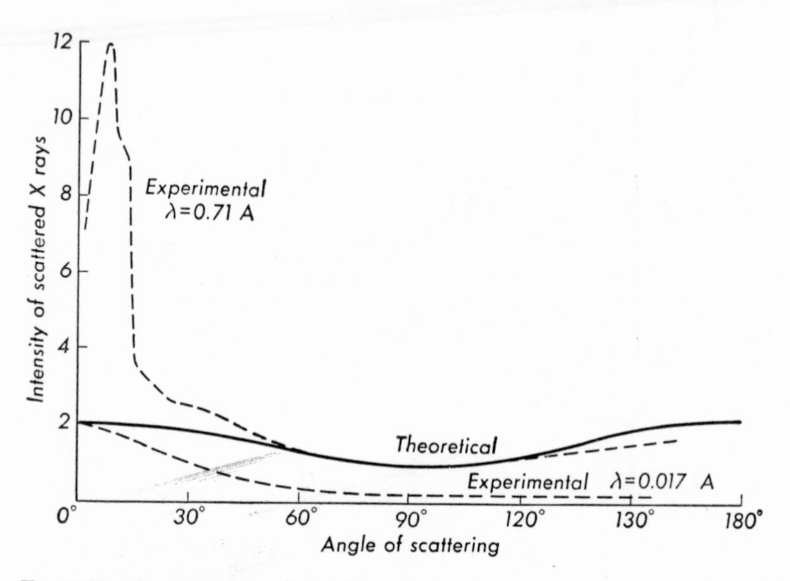

FIG. 5-30. A comparison of the theoretical and experimentally determined values of the intensity of the scattered x-rays as a function of the angle of scattering.

5-18. Intensity of the Scattered X-Rays

Many measurements have been made on the distribution of intensity in the scattered x-ray beam as a function of the angle of scattering. For x-ray wavelengths greater than 0.2A the distribution follows the $(1 + \cos^2 \theta)$ law fairly well except for small angles of scattering, in which cases the intensity of the scattered beam is much greater than that predicted by equation (27) (see Figure 5-30). This large intensity of the scattered beam at small angles can be explained on the assumption that the phase differences of the rays scattered at these angles are small so that the waves scattered by neighboring electrons reinforce each other.

However, for wavelengths much smaller than 0.2A, the intensity falls off rapidly at large angles; the scattering coefficient is much smaller than that predicted by the classical theory. The lowest curve in Figure 5-30 shows the intensity of the rays scattered by iron; the incident rays were hard gamma rays of wavelength 0.017A.

Evidently the classical theory of scattering is not completely satisfactory. To account for the small intensity of the beam at large angles of scattering, A. H. Compton proposed a quantum theory of scattering, in which the x-rays, considered as photons, cause the ejection of electrons from the atom as a result of the scattering process. As will be shown in the next section, the greater the angle of scattering, the greater is the amount of energy removed from the beam by these ejected or *recoil* electrons.

5-19. The Compton Effect

In the experiments on the scattering of x-rays by matter, it was noted that for wavelengths of the order of 1A, the experimental results were in good agreement with the classical theory of scattering, but for shorter wavelengths there was great divergence between the classical theory and experimental results. In working with scattered radiation, A. H. Compton (1923) observed that the wavelength of the radiation scattered by a block of

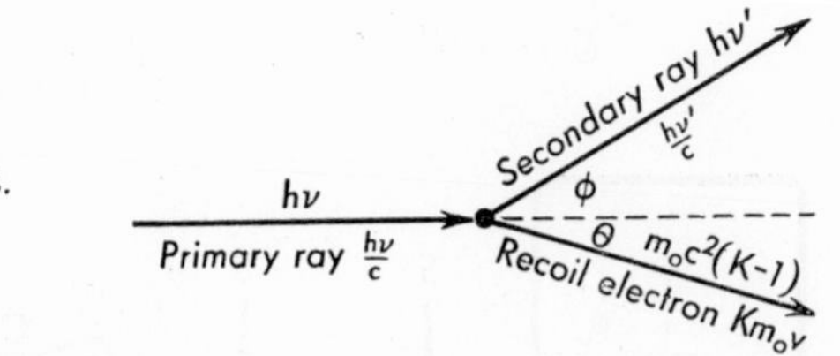

FIG. 5-31. The Compton effect.

paraffin, in a direction at right angles to the incident beam, was greater than the wavelength of the incident beam. The theory of this effect was given by Compton and also by Debye at about the same time.

Consider the incident radiation as consisting of photons, or quanta, of energy $h\nu$ traveling in the direction of the primary ray with velocity c. From the relationship between mass and energy derived from the theory of relativity, a photon of energy $h\nu$ has a mass given by $h\nu/c^2$. Since the momentum of a particle is the product of its mass by its velocity, the momentum of the photon becomes $h\nu/c$. Suppose that this photon strikes a comparatively free electron at rest. If we assume that the principles of conservation of energy and conservation of momentum hold during this process, then as a result of this collision, the electron will acquire a velocity v in a direction making an angle θ with the direction of motion of the incident photon, and a photon of energy $h\nu'$ will be scattered at an angle ϕ with the original direction as shown in Figure 5-31. From the principle of conservation of energy we get

$$h\nu = h\nu' + m_0c^2(K - 1), \tag{31}$$

where $m_0c^2(K - 1)$ is the kinetic energy of the electron as derived on the basis of the special theory of relativity, and K is $(1 - v^2/c^2)^{-1/2}$.

Resolving the momentum vectors into two rectangular components, along and at right angles to the direction of the incident photon, and using the principle of conservation of momentum, we get

$$\frac{h\nu}{c} = \frac{h\nu'}{c}\cos\phi + Km_0v\cos\theta; \tag{32}$$

$$0 = \frac{h\nu'}{c}\sin\phi - Km_0v\sin\theta. \tag{33}$$

The solution of these equations (Appendix VII) yields the following results:

$$\lambda' - \lambda = \frac{h}{m_0c}(1 - \cos\phi), \tag{34}$$

$$\cot\frac{\phi}{2} = (1 + \alpha)\tan\theta, \tag{35}$$

$$\mathcal{E} = m_0c^2(K - 1) = h\nu\frac{2\alpha\cos^2\theta}{(1 + \alpha)^2 - \alpha^2\cos^2\theta}, \tag{36}$$

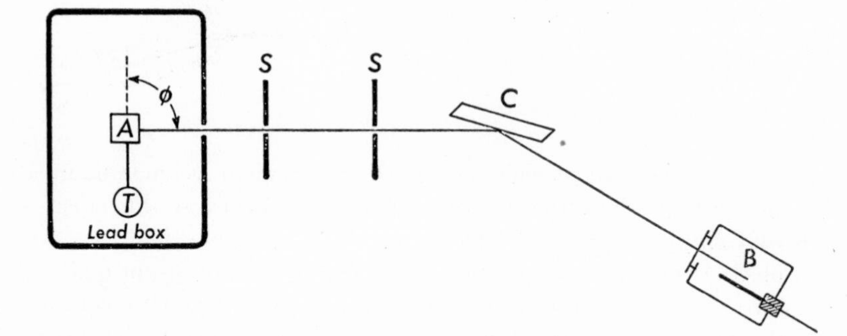

FIG. 5-32. Method of determining the wavelength of the scattered x-rays.

where $\alpha = h\nu/m_0c^2$, $\mathcal{E}$ is the kinetic energy of the recoil electron, and the wavelengths λ' and λ corresponding to the frequencies ν' and ν have been introduced.

Equation (34) states that the wavelength of the ray scattered at any angle ϕ should always be greater than the wavelength of the incident radiation. Furthermore, this difference in wavelength should not depend upon the nature of the scattering material but should depend only on the angle of scattering.

Equation (35) gives the relationship between the direction of motion of the recoil electron and the scattered photon, while equation (36) gives the kinetic energy of the recoil electron in terms of the energy of the incident photon and the angle θ.

A typical experimental arrangement for studying the Compton effect is shown in Figure 5-32. X-rays from some target T, giving out strong characteristic radiation, are scattered in all directions by the body A. The radiation scattered in some direction ϕ is then allowed to fall on the crystal C of an x-ray spectrometer, which analyzes the beam into its component wavelengths. This radiation may be measured with aid of an ionization chamber B, or with a photographic plate in place of B.

The results of a typical set of measurements are shown in Figure 5-33. In this case the K_α line of molybdenum was scattered by graphite, and measurements were made at scattering angles of 45°, 90°, and 135°. Each scattered beam is seen to consist of two distinct lines. One line, P, has a wavelength corresponding to the wavelength of the incident radiation. The second line, M, has a longer wavelength, λ', which depends upon the angle of scattering. The wavelength λ' of this *modified* line is in good agreement with that calculated from equation (34). Similar results were obtained when other substances were used as scatterers. In all cases, the wavelength of the modified line was found to depend only upon the angle of scattering and not upon the nature of the scattering substance.

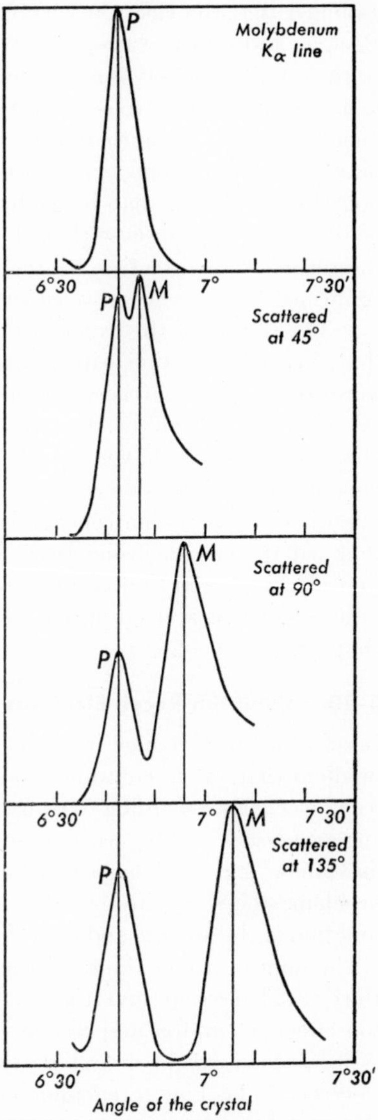

FIG. 5-33. Curves showing the displacement of the "modified" line in the Compton effect for three different angles of scattering.

The presence of a line with the same wavelength as the incident radiation is not predicted by equation (34). In deriving this equation it was assumed that the electron which took part in the scattering was a "free" electron and that it was ejected from the atom. The unmodified line is due to the interaction between the incident quanta and bound electrons. In this case the bound electrons do not receive energy or momentum from the incident quantum and there is no change in the wavelength of the scattered photon. In light atoms, such as Be, C, and Al, the electrons are probably bound more loosely than in the heavier elements. The modified line should be relatively more intense than the unmodified line for light elements, while the reverse should be true for the heavier elements. This has actually been confirmed by the scattering experiments.

The results of the experiments on the Compton effect leave no doubt that, in its interaction with matter, radiant energy behaves as though it were composed of particles. A similar behavior was observed in the photoelectric effect. It will be shown later that in the processes of emission and absorption light behaves as though it consisted of corpuscles. But the phenomena of interference and diffraction can be explained only on the hypothesis that radiant energy is propagated as a wave motion. We are thus led to the conclusion that radiant energy exhibits a dual character, that of a wave and that of a corpuscle. The relationship between these two concepts, wave and corpuscle, will be examined more fully in the next chapter.

5-20. Compton Recoil Electrons

In addition to a change in wavelength, the theory of the Compton effect predicts that every collision should be accompanied by the ejection of a recoil electron. According to equation (35), these electrons will be ejected at angles θ less than 90°, with those ejected in the forward direction having maximum energy. There are two different modes of approach to the problem: one is the investigation of the energy of the recoil electron as a function of the angle θ, and the other is the investigation of the simultaneity of the appearance of the recoil electron with that of the scattered photon. Both problems were investigated shortly after the discovery of the Compton effect. Compton and Simon (1925) sent a beam of x-rays through a Wilson cloud chamber and measured the maximum range of the recoil electrons. The kinetic energies calculated from the range measurements agreed within about 20 per cent with those predicted by theory. The problem of simultaneity was investigated by Bothe and Geiger; they sent a beam of x-rays through hydrogen and detected the recoil electrons and scattered photons in two adjacent Geiger counters. The Geiger counter pulses were recorded on moving photographic film. They observed a reasonable number of coincidences between the scattering of a photon and the ejection of a recoil electron. No great accuracy can be claimed for these experiments since photons are not directly detected by Geiger counters, but are detected only by the recoil electrons produced in the gas in the Geiger counter chamber.

The development of fast-counting crystal scintillation counters and the great improvement in electronic circuits have led to a reinvestigation of both problems recently. In one experiment by Cross and Ramsey (1950) a collimated beam of gamma-ray photons from a RaTh source was allowed

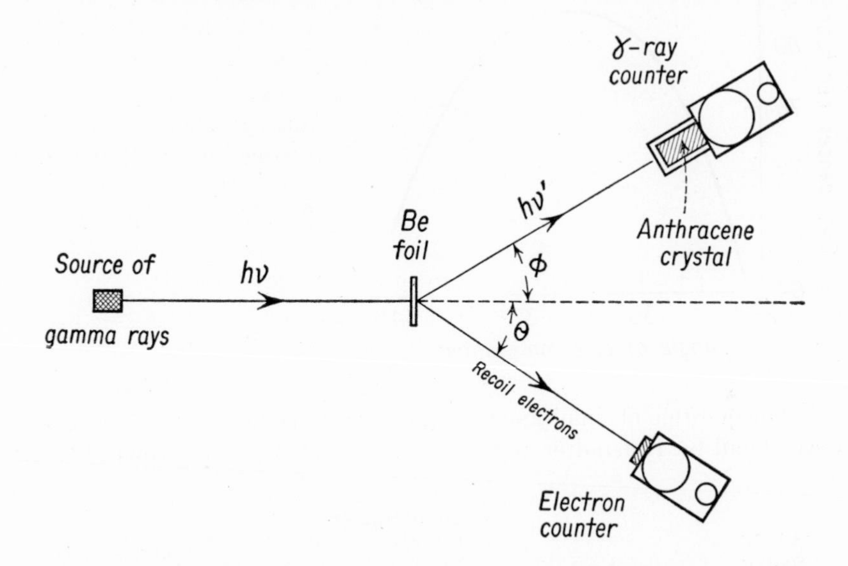

FIG. 5-34. Schematic diagram of the apparatus of Cross and Ramsey for investigating the Compton effect.

to strike a foil of beryllium (see Figure 5-34). The scattered photons were detected by one scintillation counter and the recoil electrons detected in a second scintillation counter. The pulses from these two counters were fed into a coincidence circuit; that is, only coincidences of the two counters were registered. In the experiment, the gamma-ray counter was kept at a fixed angle $\theta = 30°$. The energy of the gamma-ray photons was 2.62 Mev. The electron recoil scattering angle for this case can be calculated from equation (35) and shown to be $\theta = 31.3°$. In one part of the experiment, both counters remained fixed at the appropriate angles while the beryllium scatterer was moved. The coincidence rate showed a maximum at the proper position of the scatterer, that is, the position for which $\phi = 30°$ and $\theta = 31.3°$. In another part of the experiment, the beryllium foil and the gamma-ray detector were kept fixed in position, while the electron detector was moved about 2° on either side of the correct position. The curve of coincidence counts against angle (see Figure 5-35) showed a maximum at 31.3°. The resolving time of the circuits used was 0.3 microsecond; the above results thus confirm the fundamental assumptions of the Compton effect and also show that the scattered photon and recoil electron are emitted simultaneously within the above time interval.

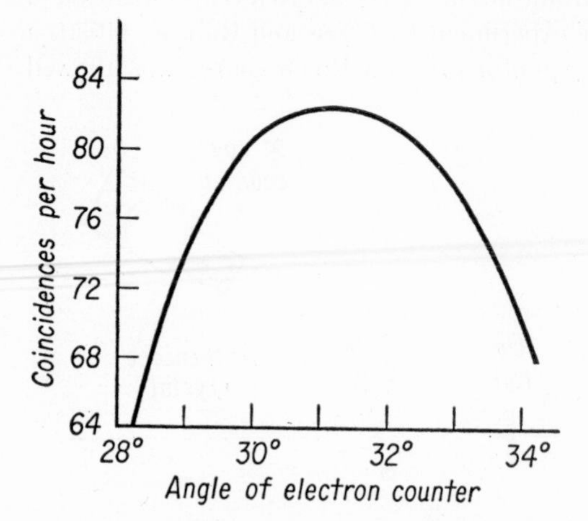

Fig. 5-35. Graph of coincidences against angle of the electron counter with gamma-ray counter held at 30°. (After *Phys. Rev.*, 80, 933, 1950.)

The question of simultaneity in the Compton effect was investigated in great detail by Hofstadter and McIntyre (1950) using the somewhat dif-

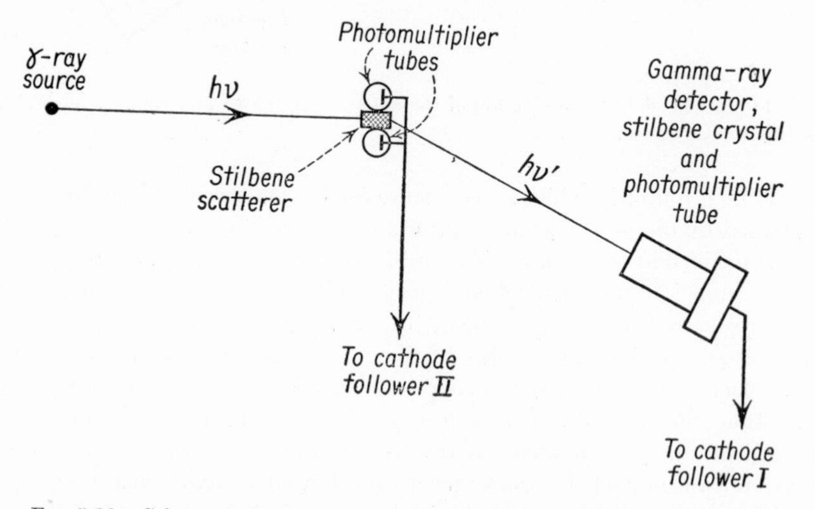

Fig. 5-36. Schematic diagram of the apparatus used by Hofstadter and McIntyre to investigate simultaneity in the Compton effect.

ferent arrangement shown in Figure 5-36. Gamma-ray photons from a small rod of radioactive Co^{60} were collimated by means of a thick lead shield and allowed to strike a crystal of stilbene. This stilbene crystal has two functions: (a) it scatters a photon $h\nu'$ which then travels to another larger stilbene crystal mounted on a photomultiplier tube; (b) the first stilbene crystal also acts as the detector of the recoil electron released in it, by converting its energy into light which is detected by two adjacent photomultiplier tubes connected in parallel. The pulses from the gamma-ray detector and electron detector are fed to opposite plates of a cathode-ray tube and the pulses produced are photographed. The timing of the cathode-ray pulses is checked by impressing two known simultaneous pulses on the two detecting circuits.

In the above experiment, the gamma-ray detector was set at scattering angles of 30°, 50°, 70°, and 90°, and simultaneous pulses observed from the recoil electron and scattered photon detectors. The accuracy of the experiment was such that the pulses were considered to be simultaneous within 1.5×10^{-8} second.

Problems

5-1. The mass absorption coefficient of silver is 38 cm^2/gm for x-rays of wavelength 0.4A, and is 11 cm^2/gm for a wavelength of 0.5A. (**a**) Determine the atomic absorption coefficients of silver for these wavelengths. (**b**) Compare these values with the geometrical cross section of silver atoms.

Ans. (**a**) 6.83×10^{-21} cm^2/atom,
1.97×10^{-21} cm^2/atom.

5-2. The mass absorption coefficient of lead for x-rays of wavelength 0.5A is 60 cm^2/gm; for 2.25A, 500 cm^2/gm. (**a**) Determine the atomic absorption coefficients of lead for these wavelengths. (**b**) Compare these values with the geometrical cross section of lead atoms.

Ans. (**a**) 2.06×10^{-20} cm^2/atom,
17.3×10^{-20} cm^2/atom.

5-3. The absorption coefficient of aluminum is 0.73 per cm for x-rays of wavelength 0.20A. Determine (**a**) the mass absorption coefficient, and (**b**) the atomic absorption coefficient. Compare the latter with the geometrical cross section of aluminum atoms.

Ans. (**a**) 0.27 cm^2/gm.
(**b**) 1.16×10^{-23} cm^2/atom.

5-4. The mass absorption coefficient of x-rays of wavelength $\lambda = 0.7$A is 5 per gram per cm^2 for aluminum, and 50 per gram per cm^2 for copper. The density of aluminum is 2.7 grams per cm^3 and that of copper is 8.93 grams per cm^3. What thickness, in cm, of each of these substances is needed to reduce the intensity of the x-ray beam passing through it to one-half its initial value?

Ans. Al—0.051 cm.
Cu—0.0016 cm.

5-5. Calculate the grating space d of calcite from the following data: molecular weight $M = 100.091$, density $\rho = 2.71029$ gm/cm³, and $\phi\ (\beta) = 1.09594$.

Ans. 3.0357×10^{-8} cm.

5-6. The radiation from an x-ray tube operated at 40 kv is analyzed with a Bragg x-ray spectrometer using a calcite crystal cut along its cleavage plane. (**a**) Calculate the short wavelength limit of the x-ray spectrum coming from this tube. (**b**) What is the smallest angle between the crystal planes and the x-ray beam at which this wavelength can be detected?

Ans. (**a**) $\lambda = 0.309$A.
(**b**) $\theta = 2° 55.4'$.

5-7. Monochromatic x-rays are reflected in the first order from a calcite crystal set with its cleavage planes at an angle of 13° with respect to the x-ray beam. These x-rays are allowed to fall on a silver mirror at a very small angle to the plane of the mirror. The mirror is then rotated until the critical angle is reached. (**a**) Calculate the wavelength of the x-rays incident on the mirror. (**b**) Calculate the index of refraction of silver for this x-ray beam. (**c**) Determine the critical angle. The density of silver is 10.5 gm per cm³.

Ans. (**a**) 1.363A.
(**b**) $\delta = 1 - \mu = 24 \times 10^{-6}$.
(**c**) $\theta_c = 23.8'$.

5-8. A ruled glass surface covered with a thin layer of gold forms a diffraction grating with 200 lines per mm. A very narrow beam of the copper K_α radiation, $\lambda = 1.541$A, is incident upon the grating at an angle of 20 minutes to its surface.

(**a**) Show that for small angles equation (17) can be put in the form

$$n\lambda = d\left(\alpha\theta + \frac{\alpha^2}{2}\right)$$

by expanding the cosine functions.

(**b**) Calculate the angle between the first-order and the zero-order beams.

Ans. $\alpha = 13.5'$.

5-9. The K_α radiation from a molybdenum target, $\lambda = 0.708$A, is scattered from a block of carbon, and the radiation scattered through an angle of 90° is analyzed with a calcite crystal spectrometer. (**a**) Calculate the change in wavelength produced in the scattering process. (**b**) Determine the angular separation in the first order between the modified and unmodified lines produced by rotating the crystal through the required angle.

Ans. (**a**) $\lambda' - \lambda = 0.024$A.
(**b**) 27.9 min.

5-10. (**a**) Calculate the angle between the direction of motion of the recoil electron and the incident photon in problem 5-9.

(**b**) Determine the energy of the recoil electron.

Ans. (**a**) $\theta = -44° 2'$.
(**b**) 9.37×10^{-10} erg $= 586$ ev.

5-11. Monochromatic x-rays of wavelength $\lambda = 0.124A$ are scattered from a carbon block. (**a**) Determine the wavelength of the x-rays scattered through 180°. (**b**) Determine the maximum kinetic energy of the recoil electrons produced in this scattering process.

Ans. (**a**) $\lambda' = 0.172A$.
(**b**) 2.813×10^4 ev.

5-12. The value σ/n obtained from equation (29) is the scattering cross section per electron. Show that the "radius" of the electron calculated from the above value is $\left(\frac{8}{3}\right)^{1/2} a_e$, where a_e is the classical electron radius.

References

Bragg, W. H., and W. L. Bragg, *X-Rays and Crystal Structure*. London: George Bell & Sons, Ltd., 1925, Chaps. II, III, IV, X.

Clark, G. L., *Applied X-Rays*. New York: McGraw-Hill Book Company, Inc., 1940, Chaps. I–X.

Compton, A. H., and S. K. Allison, *X-Rays in Theory and Experiment*. New York: D. Van Nostrand Company, Inc., 1935, Chaps. I–III, IX.

Richtmyer, F. K., and E. H. Kennard, *Introduction to Modern Physics*. New York: McGraw-Hill Book Company, Inc., 1947, Chap. X.

Siegbahn, M., *The Spectroscopy of X-Rays*. New York: Oxford University Press, 1925, Chaps. I–III, VII.

Worsnop, B. L., *X-Rays*. New York: John Wiley & Sons, Inc., 1950.

chapter **6**

Waves and Particles

6-1. Refraction of Particles and Waves on Newtonian Mechanics

In the explanation of the photoelectric effect and the Compton effect, it was found necessary to assume that radiant energy, in its interaction with matter, behaves as though it consists of corpuscles. Newton had also assumed that light consisted of a stream of particles; but on the basis of Newtonian mechanics, it is possible to distinguish between the behavior of particles and waves. As an example, consider the phenomenon of refraction, which occurs whenever a beam, either of waves or of particles, suffers a change in velocity when it goes obliquely from one medium to another. Snell's law of refraction, which is an empirical law, states that

$$\boxed{\mu = \frac{\sin i}{\sin r},} \tag{1}$$

where μ is the relative index of refraction of medium II with respect to medium I, i is the angle of incidence, and r is the angle of refraction. Suppose that a beam of particles goes from the medium I in which the velocity of a particle v_1 is characteristic of the medium, into medium II in which it has a new velocity v_2 characteristic of this second medium. To account for the abrupt change in velocity at the boundary of the two media it is necessary to assume the existence of forces which act through very small distances, of the order of magnitude of atomic dimensions. If we resolve the velocity of a particle into two components, one parallel and the other normal to the boundary surface, only the normal component of the velocity will change because of the action of these short-range forces. This will produce a change in direction of the beam of particles as it crosses the boundary.

Referring to Figure 6-1, let AO be the direction of the incident beam and OD that of the refracted beam. Let OC be a continuation of AO drawn so that its length is proportional to v_1. OE and EC are then proportional respectively to the normal and parallel components of the velocity v_1. When the beam goes into the second medium, only the normal component of the velocity is changed. Draw OD so that its component parallel to the surface, FD, is equal to EC. Then

$$\mu = \frac{\sin i}{\sin r} = \frac{\dfrac{EC}{OC}}{\dfrac{FD}{OD}} = \frac{OD}{OC};$$

hence

$$\boxed{\mu = \frac{v_2}{v_1}.} \qquad (2)$$

As the beam of particles crosses the boundary between the two media, the short-range forces produce a change in the normal component of the

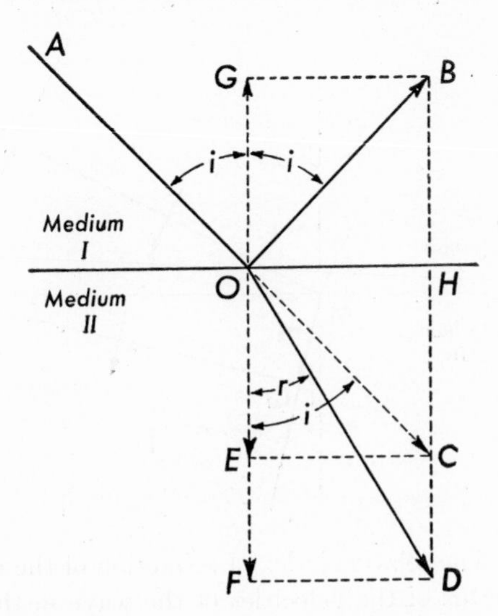

Fig. 6-1.

velocity of each particle and hence a change in the energy of each particle. If we assume the principle of conservation of energy to hold in this case, we can write

$$U_1 + \tfrac{1}{2}mv_1^2 = U_2 + \tfrac{1}{2}mv_2^2, \qquad (3)$$

where U_1 is the potential energy of a particle in the first medium and U_2 is the potential energy of the particle in the second medium. Setting

$$U = U_1 - U_2,$$

we can write

$$U + \tfrac{1}{2}mv_1^2 = \tfrac{1}{2}mv_2^2; \qquad (4)$$

and solving for v_2, we get

$$v_2 = \sqrt{v_1^2 + \frac{2U}{m}}. \tag{5}$$

The relative index of refraction μ of the two media can therefore be written as

$$\boxed{\mu = \frac{v_2}{v_1} = \sqrt{1 + \frac{U}{\frac{1}{2}mv_1^2}}.} \tag{6}$$

If the relative index of refraction of the two media is measured for a beam of particles and if the kinetic energy of the particles in the first medium is known, then equation (6) can be used to determine the difference in potential energy U as the particle goes from one medium into the other.

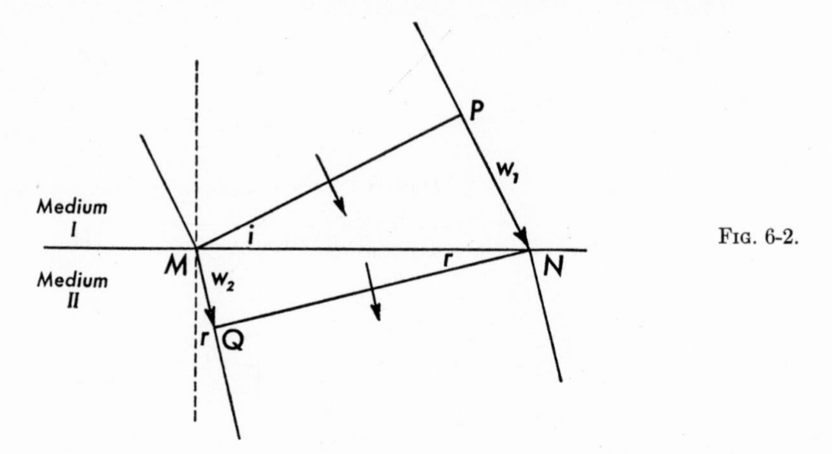

Fig. 6-2.

The relative index of refraction of the two media can also be expressed in terms of the velocities of the wave in the two media. Referring to Figure 6-2, let MP represent a wave front traveling with velocity w_1 in medium I, and let PN be the distance traversed by this wave in unit time. QN represents the refracted wave front and MQ the distance traveled in the second medium during the same unit of time. Evidently

$$\frac{PN}{MQ} = \frac{w_1}{w_2}. \tag{7}$$

Hence

$$\mu = \frac{\sin i}{\sin r} = \frac{\frac{PN}{MN}}{\frac{MQ}{MN}} = \frac{PN}{MQ},$$

from which

$$\boxed{\mu = \frac{w_1}{w_2}.} \tag{8}$$

A comparison of equations (6) and (8) shows that there is a marked difference between the refraction of waves and the refraction of particles; one equation is the reciprocal of the other. It will be recalled that Fizeau and Foucault measured the velocity of light in water and showed it to be less than that in air. Since the index of refraction was known to be greater than unity, the results of these experiments could only be explained on the hypothesis that light is propagated in the form of a wave motion.

6-2. De Broglie's Hypothesis

In order to explain the results of some of the experiments involving the interaction between radiant energy and matter, such as the photoelectric effect and the Compton effect, it was necessary to assign to radiant energy some properties characteristic of particles rather than waves. The amount of energy assigned to such a particle of radiant energy, or photon, is given by

$$\mathcal{E} = h\nu, \tag{9}$$

where h is the Planck constant and ν is the frequency of the radiation. The frequency ν is not a directly measurable quantity but is computed from measurements of the wavelength λ of the radiation using the relationship

$$\nu = \frac{c}{\lambda}, \tag{10}$$

where c is the velocity of light. The wavelength λ can be measured only by some experiment which involves interference or diffraction, phenomena characteristic of wave motion. In spite of the fact that radiation possesses this dual character, it never exhibits both characteristics in any one experiment. In a given experiment it behaves either as a wave or as a corpuscle.

According to a hypothesis introduced by L. de Broglie (1924), this dual character, wave and particle, should not be confined to radiation alone, but should also be exhibited by all the fundamental entities of physics. On this hypothesis, electrons, protons, atoms, and molecules should have some type of wave motion associated with them. De Broglie was led to this hypothesis by considerations based upon the special theory of relativity and upon the quantum theory.

Returning for a moment to a consideration of light of wavelength λ, we find that the energy of a photon can be written as

$$\mathcal{E} = \frac{hc}{\lambda} \tag{11}$$

by combining equations (9) and (10). If m is the mass of the photon, then, on the basis of the special theory of relativity,

$$m = \frac{\mathcal{E}}{c^2} = \frac{h\nu}{c^2}. \tag{12}$$

The momentum p of this photon is

$$p = mc = \frac{h\nu}{c} = \frac{h}{\lambda}. \tag{13}$$

The quantity $1/\lambda$ is commonly used by spectroscopists and is known as the *wave number* or the number of waves per centimeter in the monochromatic beam of light. If we let

$$k = \frac{1}{\lambda}, \tag{14}$$

then

$$p = hk. \tag{15}$$

Since momentum is a vector quantity whose magnitude is given by p, and h is a scalar quantity, k may be interpreted as the magnitude of a vector quantity whose direction is that of the direction of propagation of the light waves of length λ.

De Broglie carried these considerations over into the dynamics of a particle. On De Broglie's hypothesis a wavelength λ is associated with each particle and is related to the momentum p of the particle by the equation

$$\boxed{p = \frac{h}{\lambda}.} \tag{13}$$

If m is the total mass of the particle and v its velocity, then

$$p = mv, \tag{16}$$

so that

$$\boxed{\lambda = \frac{h}{mv}.} \tag{17}$$

Equation (17) gives the relationship between the wavelength λ associated with a particle and the mass m and velocity v of the particle. The existence of these waves was demonstrated experimentally by Davisson and Germer (1927) and G. P. Thomson (1928).

6-3. Electron Diffraction Experiments of Davisson and Germer

De Broglie's hypothesis that material particles should exhibit a dual character, that of a wave and that of a corpuscle, has led to many interesting and far-reaching consequences. The wavelength associated with any particle of mass m moving with velocity v is

$$\lambda = \frac{h}{mv}, \tag{17}$$

where h is the Planck constant. If the particle is an electron which has acquired its velocity v under the action of a difference of potential V, its kinetic energy, if v is small in comparison with c, is

$$\tfrac{1}{2}mv^2 = Ve, \tag{18}$$

and the wavelength associated with it can be expressed as

$$\boxed{\lambda = \frac{h}{\sqrt{2mVe}}.} \tag{19}$$

For a difference of potential of 100 volts, for example,

$$\lambda = 1.22 \times 10^{-8} \text{ cm} = 1.22\text{A}.$$

This wavelength is of the order of magnitude of the distances between atomic planes in crystals. This fact immediately suggests the possibility of showing the existence of these waves by using crystals as diffraction gratings for electrons in a manner analogous to their use with x-rays. Such a series of experiments was first carried out by Davisson and Germer (1927).

The experimental arrangement used by Davisson and Germer is shown in Figure 6-3. Electrons from a hot tungsten filament are accelerated by a difference of potential V between the filament F and the plate P. Some of these electrons emerge from a small opening in the plate P and strike the surface of a nickel crystal at normal incidence. The electrons are scattered in all directions by the atoms in the crystal. The intensity of the electron beam scattered in any given direction is determined by allowing the electrons to enter a chamber or bucket, B, set in the appropriate position, and then measuring the deflection produced by a galvanometer connected to the bucket. By rotating the bucket B about a line in the face of the crystal through the point of incidence as an axis, the intensity of the scattered beam can be measured as a function of the angle of scattering. The results of one such set of measurements are shown in the set of curves of Figure 6-4. These curves are plotted in polar coordinates; the length of the radius vector is proportional to the intensity of the scattered beam and the angle between the radius vector and the y axis is the angle of scattering. The crystal is held in a fixed position throughout this set of measurements.

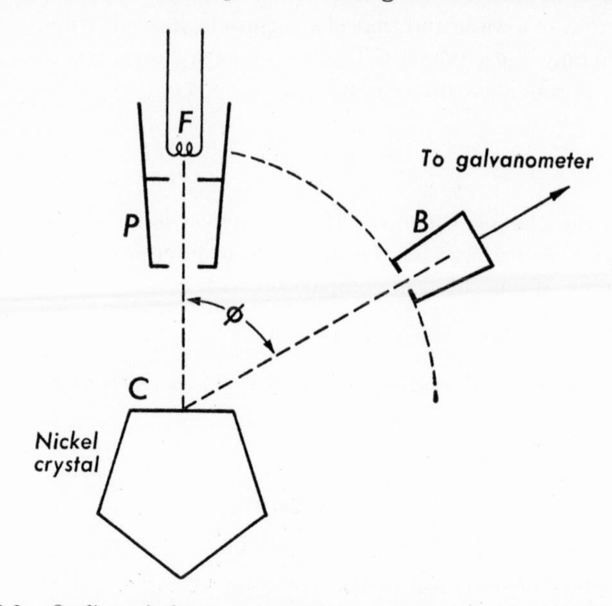

FIG. 6-3. Outline of the experimental arrangement in the electron diffraction experiments of Davisson and Germer.

When the difference of potential between F and P is 40 volts, the curve is fairly smooth. At 44 volts, a distinct spur appears on the curve at an angle

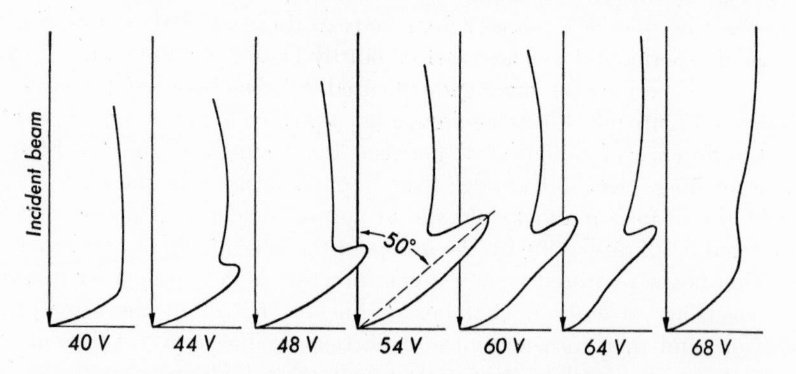

FIG. 6-4. Curves, plotted in polar coordinates, showing the intensity of the scattered beam at different angles of scattering. The incident beam in each case is perpendicular to the face of the nickel crystal.

of about 60°. The measurement of the distribution of intensity in the scattered beam is repeated at higher voltages. The length of the spur increases until it reaches a maximum at 54 volts at an angle of 50°, then decreases and disappears completely at 68 volts at an angle of about 40°.

The selective reflection of the "54-volt" electrons at an angle of 50° can be explained as due to the constructive interference, that is, reinforcement, of the electron waves from the regularly spaced atoms of the nickel crystal. Consider a regular array of atoms such as that shown in Figure 6-5. Several sets of parallel planes rich in atoms can be drawn through this

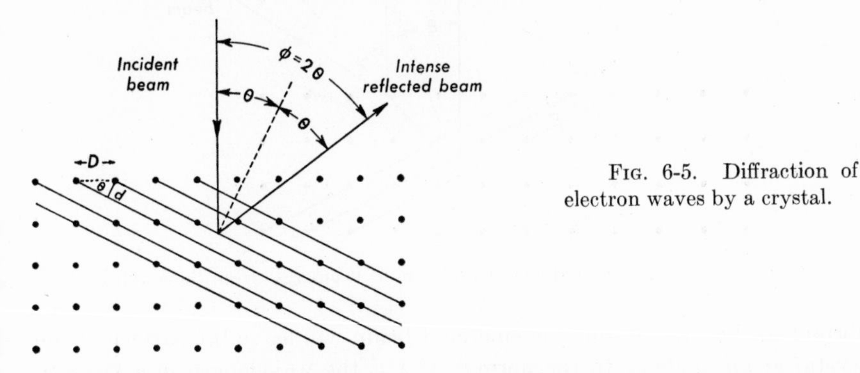

FIG. 6-5. Diffraction of electron waves by a crystal.

array in a manner identical with that used in the explanation of the Laue x-ray diffraction patterns. The parallel lines drawn in the figure represent the traces of one such set of planes perpendicular to the plane of the figure. A beam of electrons incident on the crystal will make some angle θ with the normal to these planes. If the wavelength of the De Broglie waves associated with these electrons is such as to satisfy Bragg's law

$$n\lambda = 2d \cos \theta, \tag{20}$$

then the waves scattered from these planes will have the correct phase relationships to reinforce one another and will produce an intense beam reflected at an equal angle θ to the normal. The Bragg equation can be put in a more useful form by noting that the distance d between atomic planes is related to the distance D between atoms in the surface layer by the simple equation

$$d = D \sin \theta.$$

Substitution of this value of d in equation (20) yields

$$n\lambda = 2D \sin \theta \cos \theta = D \sin 2\theta,$$

from which

$$n\lambda = D \sin \phi, \tag{21}$$

where

$$\phi = 2\theta.$$

The angle ϕ would represent the angle between the incident beam and the direction of the most intense part of the scattered beam, provided the beam was not refracted. But, just as in the case of light and x-rays, we should expect the beam of electron waves to be refracted. Referring to Figure 6-6, we find that the incident beam is not deviated since it enters the crystal

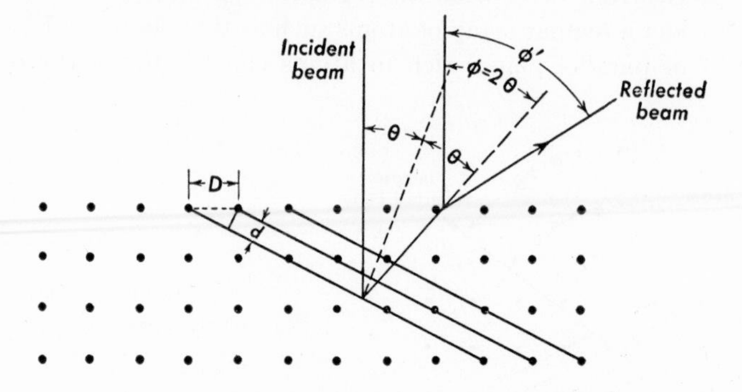

FIG. 6-6. Refraction of the electron beam as it emerges from the crystal.

normal to the surface, but the emergent beam will leave the surface of the crystal at an angle ϕ' to the normal. If λ is the wavelength in a vacuum and λ' the wavelength in the crystal, then the index of refraction μ is

$$\mu = \frac{\lambda}{\lambda'} = \frac{\sin \phi'}{\sin \phi} = \frac{\sin \phi'}{\sin 2\theta},$$

from which
$$\lambda = \frac{\lambda' \sin \phi'}{\sin 2\theta}.$$

Now, in the crystal
$$n\lambda' = 2d \cos \theta;$$

therefore
$$\lambda = \frac{2d \cos \theta}{n \sin 2\theta} \cdot \sin \phi'$$

or
$$n\lambda = \frac{2d \cos \theta}{2 \sin \theta \cos \theta} \cdot \sin \phi';$$

and since
$$D = \frac{d}{\sin \theta},$$

we have
$$n\lambda = D \sin \phi'. \tag{22}$$

The angle ϕ' represents the angle between incident beam and the direction of the most intense part of the scattered beam, that is, the angle that the spur on the curves of Figure 6-4 makes with the incident beam. It will be noticed that equation (22) has the same form as the equation for a plane diffraction grating using light at normal incidence, with n an integer representing the order of the diffraction pattern.

The above equation can be applied directly to the measurements made by Davisson and Germer. For the case of the "54-volt" electron beam, $\phi' = 50°$ and $n = 1$; from x-ray data D is known to be 2.15A; hence

$$\lambda = 2.15\text{A} \times \sin 50° = 1.65\text{A}.$$

This wavelength can be compared with the value obtained by substituting $V = 54$ volts into equation (19). The latter yields $\lambda = 1.66$A. Similar measurements were made with higher energy electrons, and comparable results were obtained in each case. The results of these experiments are in good agreement with De Broglie's hypothesis.

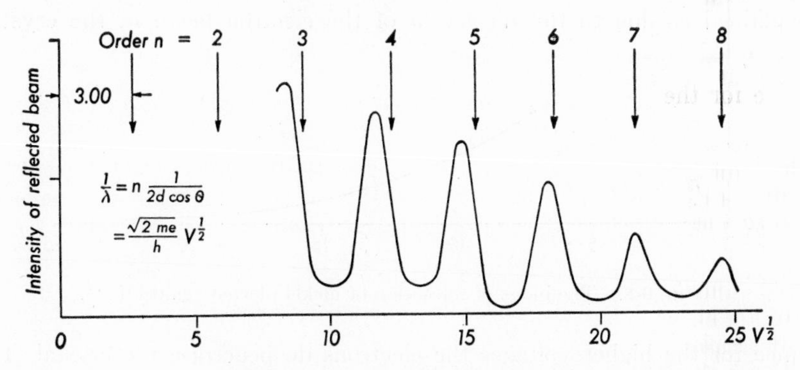

FIG. 6-7. Curve obtained when the angle of incidence and the angle of reflection of the electron beam were each kept at 10°, while the energy of the electrons was increased.

In one variation of this experiment, an oblique angle of incidence was used. An examination of the intensity of the scattered beam showed that there was an intense maximum at an angle of "reflection" equal to the angle of incidence, in accord with Bragg's law of reflection from a crystal grating. In this case the atomic planes producing the diffraction pattern are parallel to the surface.

With the angle of incidence kept fixed, measurements were made of the intensity of the beam reflected at this angle when the energy of the incident electrons was varied. Figure 6-7, in which the intensity of the reflected beam is plotted against the square root of the voltage between filament and plate, shows a series of maxima almost equally spaced. Each maximum represents a different order of diffraction. The existence of these maxima follows directly from an application of Bragg's law

$$n\lambda = 2d \cos \theta, \tag{20}$$

where θ is now the angle between the incident beam and the normal to the atomic planes. Combining this with equation (19), we have

$$\frac{1}{\lambda} = \frac{\sqrt{2me}}{h} V^{1/2} = \frac{n}{2d \cos \theta}. \tag{23}$$

Whenever the wavelength is such as to satisfy Bragg's law, there will be an intense maximum at an angle of reflection equal to the angle of incidence. Since θ is kept constant, $2d \cos \theta$ is also constant; there will therefore be an intense maximum for each new value of n, the order of diffraction, as V is changed. From equation (23), the spacings between maxima should all be the same and proportional to $1/2d \cos \theta$. Actually the positions of the maxima differ slightly from the calculated positions as shown by the positions of the arrows in Figure 6-7. This discrepancy can be explained as due to the refraction of the electron beam in the crystal,

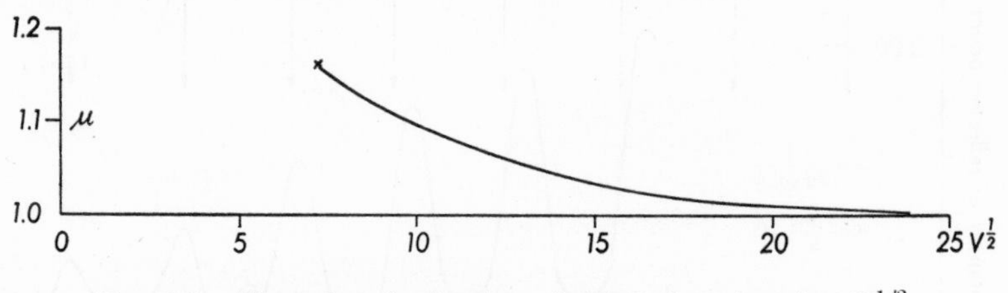

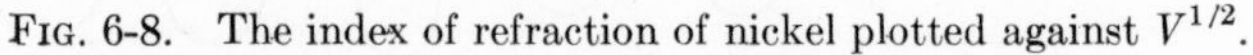

FIG. 6-8. The index of refraction of nickel plotted against $V^{1/2}$.

since for the higher voltages the electrons do penetrate the crystal. The index of refraction μ can be calculated with the aid of the modified form of Bragg's law, which is

$$n\lambda = 2d(\mu^2 - \sin^2 \theta)^{1/2}. \tag{24}$$

Values of the index of refraction are plotted against $V^{1/2}$ in Figure 6-8. For low energy electrons μ is large and greater than unity; at higher energies μ decreases and approaches unity. This is in agreement with the equation (6) for the index of refraction of a medium for a beam of particles. By substituting the measured values of μ into this equation, we can determine the energy, U, of the electrons in the nickel crystal. For example, the index of refraction of a 100 ev electron beam, as obtained from Figure 6-8, is 1.1. Substituting this value in equation (6), we get

$$1.1 = \sqrt{1 + \frac{U}{100 \text{ ev}}},$$

from which

$$U = 21 \text{ ev}.$$

This large value for the potential energy of an electron inside a metal is in agreement with the modern electron theory of metals.

6-4. Electron Diffraction Experiments of G. P. Thomson

G. P. Thomson (1928) was able to secure electron diffraction patterns by passing a narrow beam of cathode rays through very thin films of matter. The cathode rays were produced in a gas-discharge tube operated at

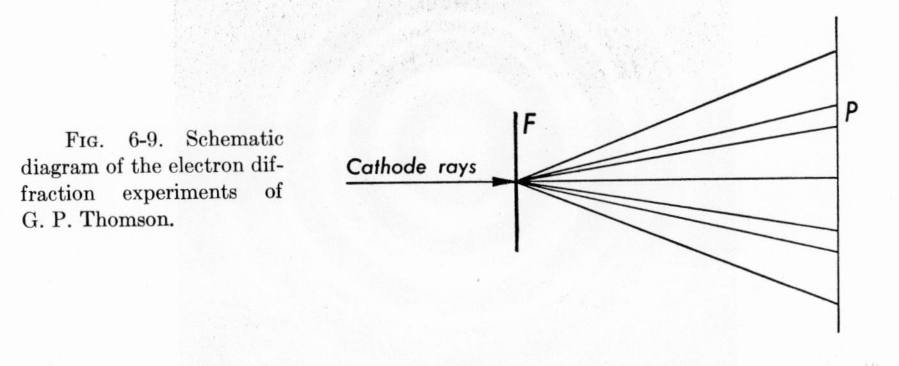

FIG. 6-9. Schematic diagram of the electron diffraction experiments of G. P. Thomson.

potentials varying from 10,000 to 60,000 volts. The cathode rays, after passing through the thin film F, were received on a photographic plate at P, as shown in Figure 6-9. The pattern on the photographic plate consisted

FIG. 6-10. Diffraction pattern obtained by passing a beam of electrons through gold foil. (Reproduced from Thomson, *Wave Mechanics of Free Electrons*, Cornell University Press.)

of a series of well-defined concentric rings about a central spot, as shown in Figure 6-10. This pattern is very similar in appearance to x-ray powder diffraction patterns.

Ordinary metals, such as gold, silver, aluminum, are microcrystalline in structure, i.e., they consist of a large number of very small crystals oriented at random. If any wave of length λ is incident upon a thin film of such a microcrystalline substance, a definite circular diffraction pattern will be obtained; the wavelength λ can be determined if the lattice constant, d, of the microcrystals is known. In Thomson's experiments, a beam of electrons moving with speed v was used instead of the x-ray beam, and a circular diffraction pattern was obtained. The wavelength λ associated with the electron can be calculated with the aid of Bragg's formula, using

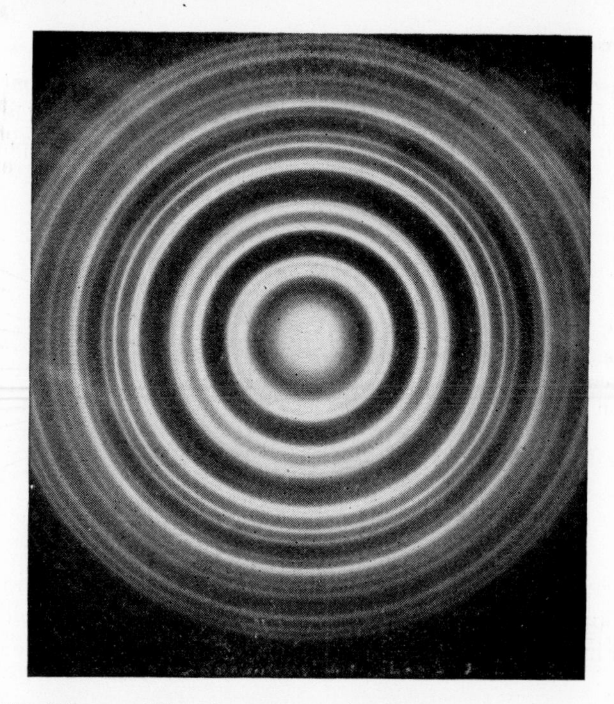

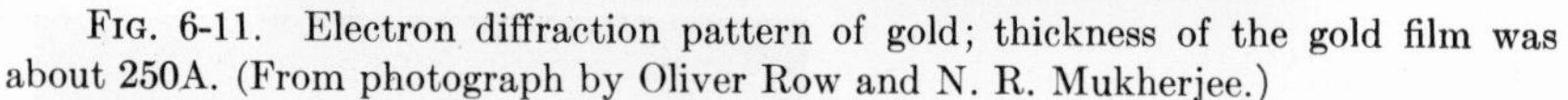

FIG. 6-11. Electron diffraction pattern of gold; thickness of the gold film was about 250A. (From photograph by Oliver Row and N. R. Mukherjee.)

the value of d from x-ray data. Actually, Thomson determined the wavelength of the electrons from the De Broglie formula

$$\lambda = \frac{h}{mv},$$

and then calculated the spacing d between atomic planes, and compared it with x-ray determinations. The following table gives a few of the results of Thomson's experiments:

Table 6-1

Values of d in A			
Metal	X-Rays	Cathode Rays	
Aluminum	4.05	4.06	4.00
Gold	4.06	4.18	3.99
Platinum	3.91	3.88	
Lead	4.92	4.99	

The results of these experiments confirm De Broglie's hypothesis that there is a wave motion associated with every moving electron.

The electron diffraction camera has since been developed into an instrument of great precision and utility, particularly for the study of surface phenomena such as corrosion and other chemical changes, and for the determination of crystal grating spaces of microcrystals. Figure 6-11 is a recent photograph taken by Oliver Row and N. R. Mukherjee showing an electron diffraction pattern of gold; the thickness of the gold foil was about 250A.

6-5. Waves Associated with Atoms and Molecules

Since De Broglie's formula applies to any mass particle moving with speed v, it should be possible to secure diffraction and interference effects with atoms and molecules as well as with electrons. The diffraction of atoms and molecules by crystals was first clearly demonstrated by Stern and his co-

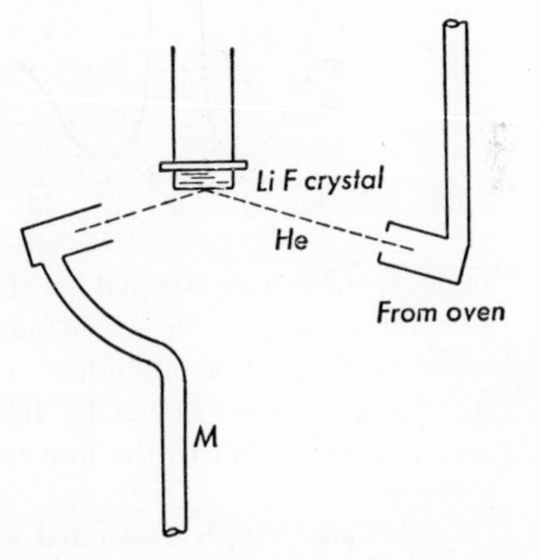

FIG. 6-12. Schematic diagram showing the arrangement of apparatus used in the diffraction of atoms and molecules

workers. In these experiments they investigated the diffraction of hydrogen and helium molecules, using crystals of lithium fluoride and sodium chloride. A stream of molecules from an oven at a known temperature T was directed against the surface of the crystal at some angle θ. The surface of the lithium fluoride crystal in this case behaves in very much the same manner as a "crossed" diffraction grating does in optical experiments, that is, the diffracting centers are at the corners of squares. The incident beam is scattered in all directions, and intensity maxima for any given wavelength occur only at those points where the waves from the different diffracting centers meet in phase.

In the case of the molecular beam scattered by the crystal, the points of maximum intensity correspond to regions of maximum pressure of the gas. Hence Stern used a very sensitive manometer, M (see Figure 6-12), to locate the diffraction pattern produced by the crystal. This manometer could be rotated about an axis at right angles to the face of the crystal and could thus measure the intensity of the scattered molecular beam at various points. Figure 6-13 is a typical curve showing the diffraction pattern obtained by reflecting helium from the LiF crystal. The intensity maximum at 0° corresponds to the regularly reflected beam in which the

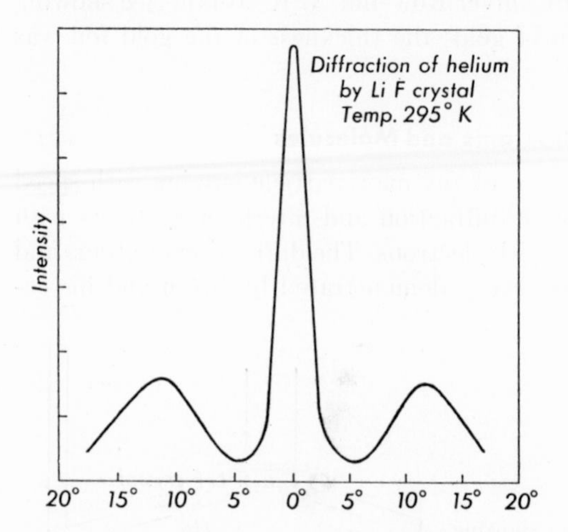

Fig. 6-13. The diffraction pattern obtained with helium reflected from a lithium fluoride crystal.

angle of reflection is equal to the angle of incidence. Then, as the manometer is rotated on either side of the reflected beam, the pressure is found to drop to a minimum value at about 5° and to rise again to a maximum on either side at 10° from the directly reflected beam. These two maxima correspond to the first-order diffraction patterns obtained with a grating.

The wavelength associated with the helium atoms can be calculated, using the known spacing of the atoms in the lithium fluoride crystal and the positions of the first-order diffraction patterns. The wavelengths calculated in this manner are in excellent agreement with those predicted by the De Broglie formula

$$\lambda = \frac{h}{mv},$$

where m is the mass of the helium atom and v is the average velocity of the helium atoms calculated from a knowledge of the temperature of the helium in the oven. Many experiments were performed using temperatures varying from 100° abs to 650° abs. Diffraction patterns were obtained in all cases. Similar experiments were performed with hydrogen molecules, H_2, and the wavelengths obtained were found to be in agreement with De Broglie's hypothesis.

A similar experiment was performed by T. H. Johnson in which a beam of hydrogen atoms was reflected from a lithium fluoride crystal and allowed to strike a plate coated with molybdenum oxide. The oxide was reduced to metallic molybdenum wherever the hydrogen struck the plate, and the pattern thus formed was then photographed. The diffraction patterns obtained agreed with the predictions based upon De Broglie's hypothesis and with the results obtained by Stern.

6-6. Diffraction of Neutrons

The existence of De Broglie waves having been definitely established, we have one more powerful tool for studying the interaction between different types of particles. The neutron is unique among these particles in that it has no charge; hence it will not be influenced by the electrostatic fields of electrons and nuclei, and will penetrate most substances very readily. In the majority of cases the interaction of neutrons with matter takes the form of elastic collisions with nuclei. The neutron loses a fraction of its energy in each such collision, and if the substance occupies a sufficient volume, the neutrons will finally reach an equilibrium velocity depending upon the temperature of the substance.

Another type of interaction between neutrons and nuclei is one in which the neutron is captured by the nucleus. We shall consider the subject of neutron capture in greater detail in Chapter 11. Here we shall merely make use of the fact that the capture of a neutron by a nucleus results in an unstable isotope; the latter then usually disintegrates with the emission of some particle such as a beta particle, or a proton, or an alpha particle. The detection of the emitted particle is one of the simplest methods of showing that the neutron has been captured.

When neutrons are in equilibrium with a mass of material at absolute temperature T, their average kinetic energies will be proportional to this temperature, or

$$\boxed{\mathcal{E}_k = kT,} \qquad (25)$$

where k is the Boltzmann constant whose value is $k = 1.38 \times 10^{-16}$ erg/deg. Thus if neutrons come to equilibrium in a block of graphite or paraffin at room temperature, which we can take as approximately 300° abs, then the average kinetic energy of these neutrons will be

$$\mathcal{E}_{300} = 1.38 \times 10^{-16} \times 300$$

$$= 4.14 \times 10^{-14} \text{ erg.}$$

The average velocity of a neutron of this energy is about 2.2×10^5 cm/sec. Since 1.6×10^{-12} erg $= 1$ ev, a neutron in equilibrium with matter at

300° abs has an energy of about 1/40 ev. Neutrons of such low energy are usually referred to as *slow* neutrons, or *thermal* neutrons.

The De Broglie wavelength of thermal neutrons can thus readily be evaluated, yielding

$$\lambda = 1.82\text{A},$$

which is about the same order of magnitude as x-rays. Hence the experimental techniques developed for x-rays can be applied, with suitable modifications, to the study of the interactions of slow neutrons with

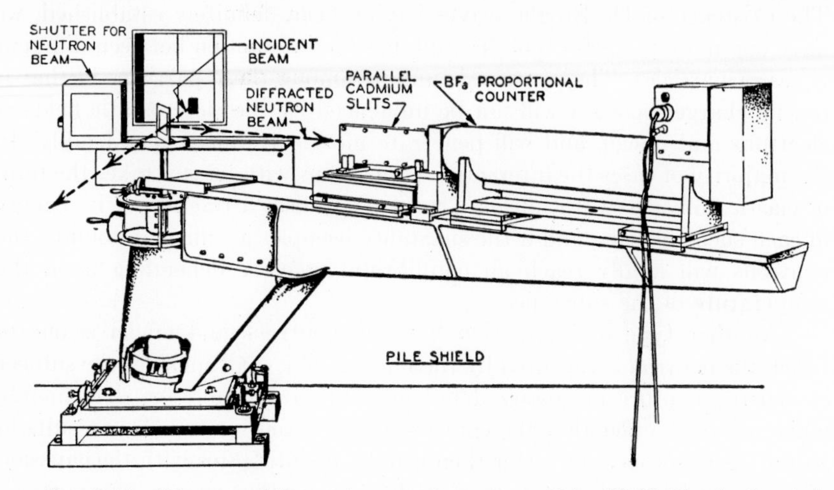

FIG. 6-14. Diagram of the neutron spectrometer used by W. H. Zinn in the study of neutron diffraction. (Courtesy of W. H. Zinn, Argonne National Laboratory.)

matter. Powerful sources of slow neutrons are now available from *nuclear reactors*, sometimes called chain-reacting piles. W. H. Zinn (1947) studied the distribution of wavelengths, and hence energies, of a neutron beam from a chain-reacting pile which had been slowed down to room temperature by passing through a large block of graphite. The neutrons were reflected from a calcite crystal, and the intensity of the reflected beam at a given crystal angle θ was measured by allowing the neutrons to enter a proportional counter filled to a pressure of 40 cm of Hg with boron trifluoride gas enriched with the B^{10} isotope, as shown in Figure 6-14. Slow neutrons are easily captured by B^{10} nuclei, which then emit alpha particles. These alpha particles ionize the gas in the chamber, producing a pulse whose amplitude is proportional to the energy of the alpha particle. The graph of Figure 6-15 shows the distribution of energy among the neutrons in the thermal column.

E. O. Wollan and C. G. Shull have studied the structure of crystalline substances, using the Laue diffraction technique and the powder crystal method. In the latter case they first monochromatized a narrow beam from the Oak Ridge graphite reactor by reflecting it from a NaCl crystal at an angle of about 6.5°. The monochromatic beam of neutrons was scattered by the powdered crystals under investigation; the intensity of the beam scattered at a given angle enters a proportional counter filled with BF_3 gas enriched with the B^{10} isotope. The counter rotates about an axis through

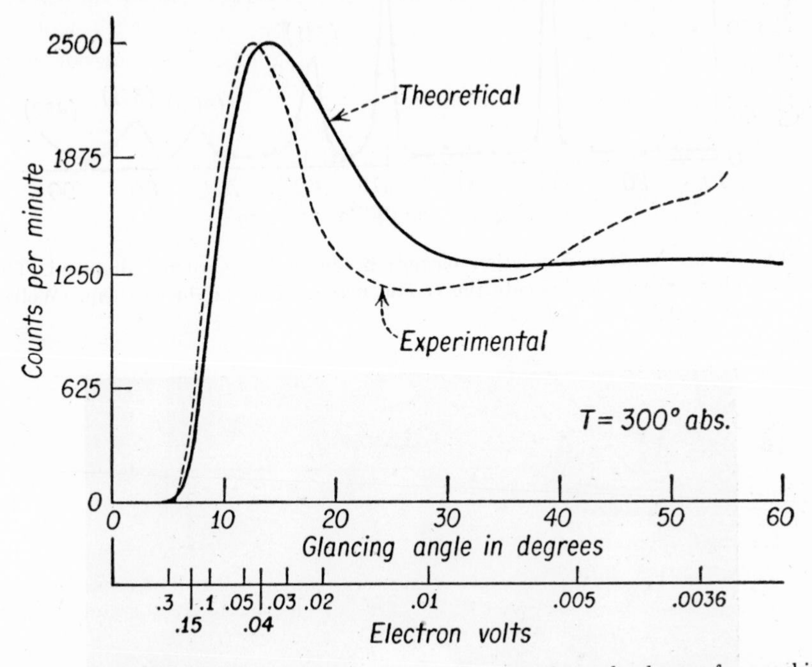

FIG. 6-15. Energy distribution among neutrons in thermal column of a graphite reactor as determined with a calcite crystal neutron spectrometer. (Zinn, *Phys. Rev.*, 71, 755, 1947.)

the center of the spectrometer table on which the powder is mounted. The counter readings are recorded automatically. A typical powder diffraction pattern obtained with powdered diamond is shown in Figure 6-16. The numbers above the peaks designate the planes in the diamond effective in producing these intense maxima.

In producing Laue diffraction patterns, such as that shown in Figure 6-17, Wollan, Shull, and Marney sent a narrow beam of neutrons possessing a continuous wavelength distribution of from 0.5A to 3.0A through a sodium chloride crystal 0.35 cm thick, with the incident beam parallel to one of the axes of the cube. The photographic film was placed 6.4 cm from the crystal. However, since neutrons do not affect a photographic film to any extent, the film was covered with a sheet of indium, 0.5 mm thick.

Neutrons are readily captured by indium, and the unstable nuclei thus formed disintegrate with the emission of beta particles. The latter do

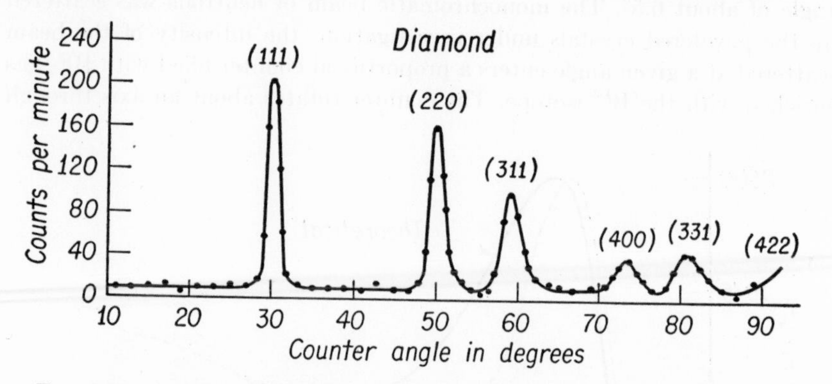

FIG. 6-16. Neutron diffraction pattern produced by powdered diamond. The numbers above the peaks indicate the crystal planes which produced them. (Wollan and Shull, *Phys. Rev.*, 73, 834, 1948.)

FIG. 6-17. Neutron Laue diffraction pattern produced by a crystal of rocksalt. (Photograph supplied by E. O. Wollan and C. G. Shull.)

affect the photographic plate. A hole was cut in the center of the indium plate to reduce the blackening due to the undeflected neutron beam.

Laue patterns of a variety of crystals have been obtained in this way, utilizing the De Broglie waves associated with neutrons.

6-7. Velocity of De Broglie Waves

The velocity of the De Broglie waves associated with a particle is not necessarily the same as that of the particle. The relationship between the two velocities can be found very readily. If λ is the length of the De Broglie wave and ν is its frequency, then the velocity w of this wave is given by the usual equation

$$\boxed{w = \nu\lambda.} \tag{26}$$

The momentum p of the particle is related to the wavelength by the fundamental equation

$$p = \frac{h}{\lambda}\cdot \tag{13}$$

Let us now assume that the relationship between the total energy $\mathcal{E}$ of the particle and the frequency ν of the associated wave is given by the usual equation from quantum theory

$$\mathcal{E} = h\nu, \tag{9}$$

and that the total energy $\mathcal{E}$ and the total mass m, including the rest mass, are given by the Einstein relativity equation

$$\mathcal{E} = mc^2, \tag{27}$$

and that the momentum p is given by

$$\boxed{p = mv} \tag{28}$$

where v is the velocity of the particle. It then follows that

$$w = \mathcal{E}\frac{\lambda}{h},$$

or

$$w = \frac{\mathcal{E}}{p} = \frac{mc^2}{mv},$$

from which

$$\boxed{w = \frac{c^2}{v}\cdot} \tag{29}$$

Since the velocity v of a material particle is always less than the velocity of light c, the velocity of the De Broglie wave associated with it is always greater than c. There is no contradiction between this fact and the postulate of the theory of relativity that no signal, that is, energy, can be transmitted with a speed greater than c. We have already encountered velocities of waves greater than c, for example, the velocity of x-rays in material media. R. W. Wood has shown that the index of refraction of visible light passing through media in which anomalous dispersion is produced is less than unity—for example, yellow light passing through a prism of sodium. This means that its wave velocity in sodium is greater than c.

The fact that the wave velocity is greater than the particle velocity does not mean that the De Broglie waves get away from the particle. Instead we can think of the particle inside a *wave packet* or group of waves, with the entire group or packet traveling with the particle velocity v, while the individual waves composing the group travel with the wave velocity w. In our discussion of wave and group velocity in the next section we shall prove that the group velocity of the De Broglie waves is equal to the particle velocity.

The wave velocity of the De Broglie waves differs from the velocity of light in one important aspect: even in free space, the wave velocity is a function of the wavelength. To show this, let us write for the momentum

$$p = mv,$$

and for the total energy

$$\mathcal{E} = mc^2,$$

so that

$$p = \frac{\mathcal{E}}{c^2} v.$$

Using the relativistic expression for the mass of a particle, the equation for its momentum becomes

$$p = \frac{m_0}{\left(1 - \frac{v^2}{c^2}\right)^{1/2}} v,$$

where m_0 is the rest mass of the particle. Eliminating v between the last two equations yields

$$\boxed{m_0^2 = \frac{\mathcal{E}^2}{c^4} - \frac{p^2}{c^2}.} \qquad (30)$$

Now, since

$$p = \frac{h}{\lambda},$$

and $\mathcal{E} = h\nu,$

we can write $m_0 = \frac{h}{c}\sqrt{\frac{\nu^2}{c^2} - \frac{1}{\lambda^2}}.$

For De Broglie waves $w = \nu\lambda;$

hence

$$m_0 = \frac{h}{c}\sqrt{\frac{w^2}{c^2\lambda^2} - \frac{1}{\lambda^2}}, \qquad (31)$$

from which

$$w = c\sqrt{1 + \frac{m_0^2c^2}{h^2}\lambda^2}. \qquad (32)$$

This equation shows that for a particle of rest mass $m_0 > 0$, the wave velocity w is always greater than c; furthermore, the wave velocity of the De Broglie waves is a function of the wavelength even in free space.

As a special case of De Broglie waves, consider those waves which are propagated with a wave velocity $w = c$. This corresponds to the propagation of electromagnetic waves. The velocity of the associated particle, the photon, is therefore also equal to c. If the value $w = c$ is substituted in equation (31), we find that the rest mass of the photon $m_0 = 0$; that is, there is no such thing as a photon at rest. Photons always move with the velocity c.

6-8. Wave and Group Velocities

In any dispersive medium, that is, one in which the velocity w of a wave depends upon its wavelength, waves of different wavelengths are propagated through the medium as a group with a velocity u which is different from w. To derive the relationship between these two velocities, let us consider two waves of slightly different wavelengths traveling together through a dispersive medium. In Figure 6-18 the upper wave ABC has a wavelength λ and a wave velocity w, while the wave $A'B'C'$ drawn just below it has a wavelength $\lambda + d\lambda$ and is moving with a velocity $w + dw$ in the same direction as the upper wave.

The two waves, although drawn separately, are traveling together through the same space. Let us choose an instant when two crests, say B and B', coincide at time $t = 0$. The amplitude of the combined wave will be a maximum at this position. After a certain time t, B' will have moved ahead of B by an amount $d\lambda$ so that now A' coincides with A. The position of maximum amplitude has thus shifted in this time to the place where A and A' coincide. Let us call this distance s, and define the group velocity u

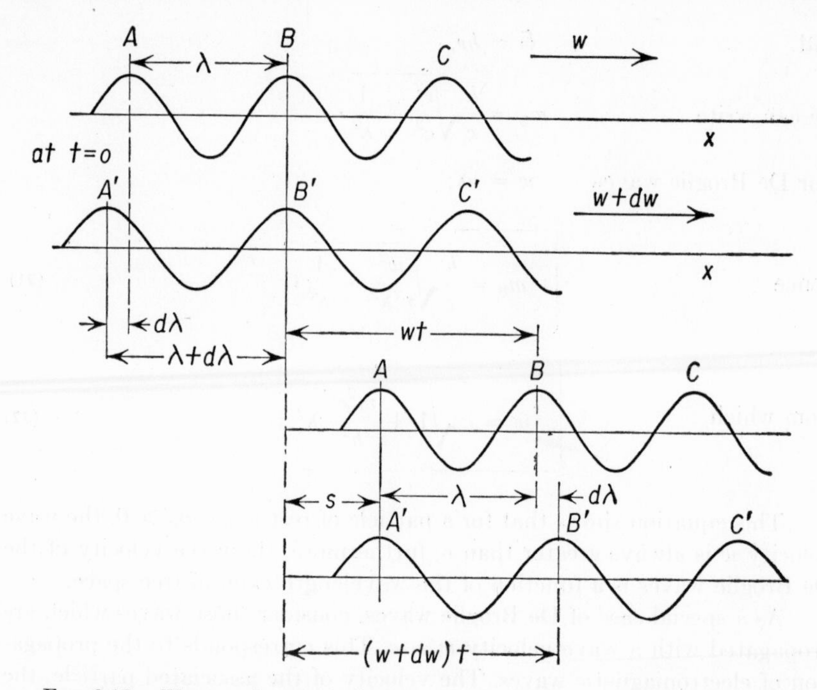

FIG. 6-18. Wave and group velocities: t is the time required for A' to get into phase with A; in this time B has traveled a distance wt while the position of maximum amplitude has advanced a distance s with the group velocity u.

by the equation

$$u = \frac{s}{t}\cdot \tag{33}$$

From the figure it can be seen that

$$s = wt - \lambda,$$

so that

$$u = w - \frac{\lambda}{t}\cdot \tag{34}$$

It can also be seen from the figure that the distance $d\lambda$ that B' has moved from B in the same time t is

$$d\lambda = (w + dw)t - wt = t dw$$

from which

$$t = \frac{d\lambda}{dw}\cdot$$

Substituting this value of t in equation (34) yields

$$\boxed{u = w - \lambda \frac{dw}{d\lambda}}\cdot \tag{35}$$

Equation (35) gives the relationship between the velocity u of a group of waves and the wave velocity w of the individual waves of the group. If there is no dispersion, for example, light traveling in a vacuum, then $dw/d\lambda = 0$ and $u = w$; that is, the group velocity and wave velocity are the same.

6-9. Group Velocity and Particle Velocity

It is a comparatively simple matter to show that the group velocity of the De Broglie waves is the same as the velocity of the particle. It has been shown that the wave velocity of the De Broglie waves is given by

$$w = c\sqrt{1 + \frac{m_0^2c^2}{h^2}\lambda^2}. \tag{32}$$

Now
$$\frac{dw}{d\lambda} = \frac{c}{\sqrt{1 + \frac{m_0^2c^2}{h^2}\lambda^2}} \times \frac{m_0^2c^2}{h^2}\lambda.$$

Substituting this value of $dw/d\lambda$ into equation (35) and using equation (32) for w, we obtain

$$u = \frac{c^2}{w}\cdot$$

But we have shown that
$$v = \frac{c^2}{w}; \tag{29}$$

hence
$$u = v;$$

that is, the group velocity of the De Broglie waves is the same as that of the particle. Or, stated in another way, the De Broglie waves move with the particle.

6-10. Heisenberg's "Uncertainty Principle"

An interesting interpretation of the duality, wave and particle, of both matter and radiant energy has been given by Heisenberg. The concepts of a particle and of a wave have been built up on the basis of experiments performed on a comparatively large scale; these concepts are mental pictures formed on the basis of such experiments. When applied to experiments involving quantities of the order of magnitude of atomic dimensions, these concepts can have the validity of analogies only. The concept of the electron as a particle, for example, was derived from the results of experiments on the motion of the electron through electric and magnetic fields. The problem of particle dynamics is to predict the position and velocity of the particle at any time t when its initial position and velocity are known. But the experiments on electron diffraction show that this is not always possible.

Electrons starting with the same initial conditions are not all scattered through the same angle by the crystals; the result is a diffraction pattern showing a definite distribution of these electrons with respect to both position and momentum. But a diffraction pattern is the best evidence that we are dealing with a wave phenomenon. To apply the wave concept to a single electron, the electron may be pictured as a small bundle or packet of waves extending over some small region of space Δs. The association of a wave packet with an electron means that the position of the electron at any instant of time t cannot be specified with any desired degree of accuracy; all that can be said of the electron is that it is somewhere within this group of waves which extends over a small region of space Δs.

Heisenberg's *uncertainty principle* refers to the *simultaneous* determination of the position and the momentum of the particle and states that *the uncertainty, Δx, involved in the measurement of the coordinate of the particle and the uncertainty Δp_x involved in the simultaneous measurement of its momentum are governed by the relationship*

$$\Delta x \cdot \Delta p_x \geqslant h, \tag{36}$$

where h is the Planck constant.

An examination of a few idealized experiments will serve to show how the wave concept acts as a limitation on the particle concept, giving rise to the uncertainty principle. One such idealized experiment was given by Bohr. Suppose it is desired to determine the position of an electron, using some instrument such as a microscope of very high resolving power. It can be shown that the resolving power of a microscope is given by

$$\Delta x = \frac{\lambda}{\sin \alpha},$$

where Δx represents the distance between two points which can just be resolved by the microscope, λ is the wavelength of the light used, and α is the semivertical angle of the cone of light coming from the illuminated object. The uncertainty in the determination of the x coordinate of the position of the electron is represented by Δx. To make Δx as small as possible, light of very short wavelength must be used, either x-rays or gamma rays. The minimum amount of light that can be used is a single quantum $h\nu$. When the electron scatters this quantum into the microscope, as shown in Figure 6-19, the electron will receive some

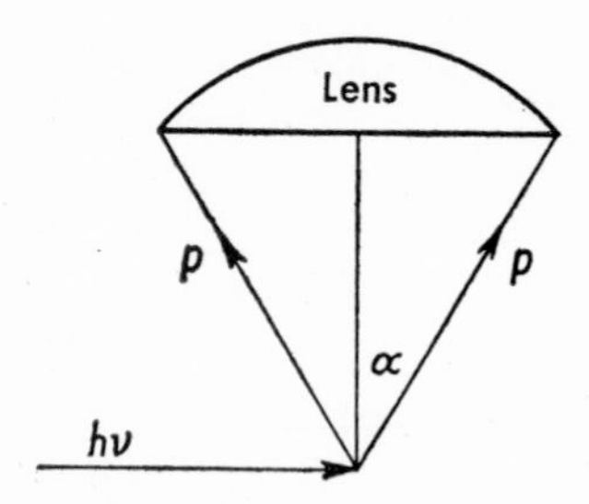

Fig. 6-19. Schematic diagram of the gamma-ray microscope experiment.

momentum from the quantum (Compton effect). Since the scattered quantum can enter the microscope anywhere within the semivertical angle α, its contribution to the x component of the momentum of the electron is unknown by an amount

$$\Delta p_x = p \sin \alpha = \frac{h}{\lambda} \sin \alpha,$$

where h/λ is the momentum of the quantum. The product of the uncertainties in the determination of the simultaneous values of the position and momentum of the electron is therefore

$$\Delta x \cdot \Delta p_x = \frac{\lambda}{\sin \alpha} \cdot \frac{h}{\lambda} \sin \alpha = h.$$

Another illustration of the uncertainty principle is supplied by an experiment in which a beam of electrons passes through a narrow slit, and

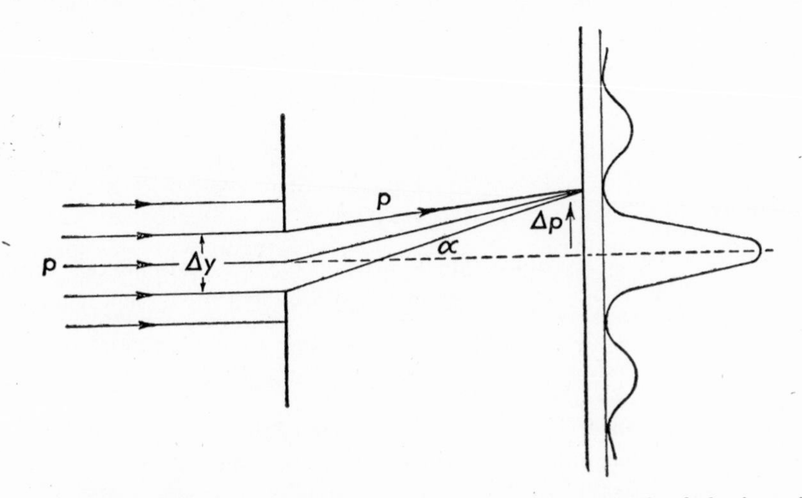

FIG. 6-20. Diffraction of electrons by a narrow slit. A graph of the intensity pattern obtained is shown on the right.

is then recorded on a photographic plate placed some distance away, as sketched in Figure 6-20. Every electron which is registered on the photographic plate must have passed through the slit, and if its width is Δy, then the y coordinate of the electron is indeterminate by an amount Δy. Making this width smaller increases the accuracy in the knowledge of the y coordinate of the electron at the instant it passes through the slit. But with a very narrow slit a very definite diffraction pattern is observed on the photographic plate. This diffraction pattern is interpreted to mean that the electron receives additional momentum parallel to the slit at the instant that it passes through the slit. If p is the momentum of the electron, the component in the y direction is $p \sin \theta$, where θ is the angle of deviation. The electron may be anywhere within the diffraction pattern, so that if α is the angular width of the pattern, the uncertainty in the knowledge of the y component of the momentum of the electron is

$$\Delta p_y = p \sin \alpha.$$

The angular width of the diffraction pattern is determined by the slit width Δy and is given by the equation

$$\Delta y \sin \alpha = \lambda.$$

Hence the product of the uncertainties in the simultaneous determination of the y coordinate and y momentum of the electron in its passage through the slit is

$$\Delta y \cdot \Delta p_y = p \sin \alpha \cdot \frac{\lambda}{\sin \alpha} = p\lambda.$$

From De Broglie's hypothesis

$$p = \frac{h}{\lambda};$$

therefore

$$\Delta y \cdot \Delta p_y = h.$$

Another set of variables can be used to express Heisenberg's uncertainty principle. If $\mathcal{E}$ is the energy of the system at time t, then it may be shown that

$$\Delta\mathcal{E} \cdot \Delta t \geqslant h, \tag{37}$$

where $\Delta\mathcal{E}$ is the uncertainty in our knowledge of the value of the energy $\mathcal{E}$ and Δt is the uncertainty in the knowledge of the time.

6-11. Probability Concept

The wave-particle parallelism must be extended to include an interpretation of the intensity of light and also the intensity of the electron beam. According to the wave theory of light, the intensity is determined by the square of the amplitude of the electric vector at the point under consideration. On the corpuscular theory the intensity of the beam of light must be determined by the number of photons per second which pass through a unit area perpendicular to their direction of motion, or

$$N \sim Y_0^2, \tag{38}$$

where Y_0 is the amplitude of the electric vector and N is the number of photons per unit volume of the beam; also, Nc is the number of photons passing through unit area in unit time. The intensity relationship $N \backsim Y_0^2$, while adequate for intense beams, is no longer satisfactory when dealing with very weak beams for which N is a very small number ($N \ll 1$). In this case it becomes difficult to determine the exact location of each particle in the continuous wave; that is, the expression $N \sim Y_0^2$ involves an indeterminacy with respect to the position of these photons in space.

An alternative approach to the problem is through a statistical interpretation. The square of the amplitude, Y_0^2, can be thought of as proportional to the *probability* of a photon's crossing unit area perpendicular to the direction of motion in unit time at the point under consideration. For example, if a beam of light passes through a narrow slit and is incident upon a photographic plate, a definite diffraction pattern will be obtained showing regions of great intensity alternating with regions of very small intensity. On the statistical interpretation, the probability of a photon's striking the photographic plate is very great where the intensity is great and is very small where the intensity is small. In the case of a very weak beam of light, say, one in which a single photon passes through the slit every minute, it is impossible to predict just where any individual photon will strike the photographic plate. All that can be said is that the probability of the photon's striking a certain portion of the plate is large just where the wave theory predicts large intensity and the probability is small just where the wave theory predicts small intensity. If only a few photons strike the photographic plate, their arrangement will undoubtedly be haphazard. But if a sufficient time is allowed to elapse so that a large number of photons reach the photographic plate, the result will be the diffraction pattern predicted by the wave theory.

The above mode of description can be applied to the diffraction of an electron beam by a narrow slit. The wave associated with the electron is the De Broglie wave. There is a certain probability that an electron, after passing through the slit, will strike a given point on the photographic plate; this probability is proportional to the square of the amplitude of the associated De Broglie wave. It is impossible to predict just where any one electron will strike the plate; yet, after an interval of time sufficient to allow a large number of electrons to strike the plate, a definite diffraction pattern will be observed, and the intensities at the different points will correspond to the amplitudes of the diffracted waves at those points.

The phenomena of transmission and reflection at a plane surface can be explained in a similar manner. If a system of waves is incident on a plane surface, part of it will be reflected and part transmitted, and their intensities will be proportional to the squares of the amplitudes of the reflected and transmitted waves respectively. According to the corpuscular theory, the particle associated with the incident wave has a certain probability of being reflected and a certain probability of being transmitted, these probabilities being proportional to the squares of the amplitudes of the corresponding waves.

From the discussion of the last two sections it can be asserted that while there is an indeterminacy in the description of phenomena from the corpuscular point of view, there is no lack of determinacy from the point of view of the wave theory. The wave functions necessary to describe these phenomena are continuous functions of the coordinates and the time. These wave functions are obtained from the solutions of the appropriate wave equations: in general, second-order partial differential equations involving the coordinates and the time. For the case of light, these wave functions are obtained from the solutions of the differential equations which form the basis of the electromagnetic theory of light. For the case of material particles, these wave functions are obtained from the solutions of a wave equation first formulated by Schroedinger and forming the basis of a new division of physics called *wave mechanics*.

6-12. Schroedinger's Equation for a Single Particle

A typical wave equation in Cartesian coordinates is

$$\frac{\partial^2 U}{\partial x^2} + \frac{\partial^2 U}{\partial y^2} + \frac{\partial^2 U}{\partial z^2} = \frac{1}{w^2}\frac{\partial^2 U}{\partial t^2}, \tag{39}$$

where U is the wave function which is propagated with the wave velocity w. For example, in the case of electromagnetic waves, U may represent any one of the components of the electric vector or of the magnetic vector which is propagated through space. Schroedinger's contribution was the incorporation of De Broglie's waves associated with material particles into the above equation.

For the case of a single particle of mass m, velocity v, and total energy $\mathcal{E}$, the following equations have been shown to apply:

$$\mathcal{E} = h\nu, \tag{9}$$

$$p = \frac{h}{\lambda}, \tag{13}$$

$$w = \lambda\nu = \frac{\mathcal{E}}{p} = \frac{h\nu}{p}. \tag{26}$$

Since the kinetic energy of the particle is the difference between the total energy $\mathcal{E}$ and the potential energy V, we can write

$$mv^2 = 2(\mathcal{E} - V),$$

assuming that $v \ll c$ so that the relativity expressions need not be used.

Now
$$p = mv = \sqrt{2m(\mathcal{E} - V)}, \tag{16}$$

so that
$$w = \frac{h\nu}{\sqrt{2m(\mathcal{E} - V)}}\cdot \tag{40}$$

In general, only those wave functions U which are harmonic functions of the time are of physical significance. Such wave functions can be expressed as sin $2\pi\nu t$ or cos $2\pi\nu t$, or combinations of sine and cosine functions represented by the exponential function $\epsilon^{2\pi\nu i t}$, where $i = \sqrt{-1}$. Suppose

$$U = u\epsilon^{2\pi\nu i t}$$

represents the wave function where u is a function of the coordinates only. Two successive differentiations of the function with respect to the time only yield

$$\frac{\partial^2 U}{\partial t^2} = -4\pi^2\nu^2 u\epsilon^{2\pi\nu i t}$$
$$= -4\pi^2\nu^2 U. \tag{41}$$

Substitution of the values from equations (40) and (41) into the wave equation yields

$$\frac{\partial^2 U}{\partial x^2} + \frac{\partial^2 U}{\partial y^2} + \frac{\partial^2 U}{\partial z^2} = -\frac{8\pi^2 m}{h^2}(\mathcal{E} - V)U, \tag{42}$$

which is one form of Schroedinger's wave equation for a single particle. By canceling the exponential factor from each term of the wave equation, a similar equation is obtained for the amplitude u, which is

$$\frac{\partial^2 u}{\partial x^2} + \frac{\partial^2 u}{\partial y^2} + \frac{\partial^2 u}{\partial z^2} = -\frac{8\pi^2 m}{h^2}(\mathcal{E} - V)u. \tag{43}$$

It will be noticed that the time does not enter explicitly into this amplitude equation; in the wave mechanics of a particle, the function u is usually referred to as the *wave function*. The potential energy V is, in general, a function of the coordinates. The problem in wave mechanics is to put in the appropriate value for V and seek solutions of Schroedinger's equation. It is beyond the scope of this book to solve these partial differential equations, but the results of such solutions will be made use of wherever necessary in the discussion of atomic physics.

The interpretation of the wave function has already been indicated in the previous section in the discussion of the De Broglie waves associated with matter. Solutions of Schroedinger's equation will give u as a continuous function of the coordinates, and hence its value will be determined for every point in space. The square of this wave function or amplitude, u^2, is proportional to the probability of finding the particle at any given point in space. Or if the product u^2dv is formed, it can be considered as a measure of the probability of finding the particle in this volume element dv. Summing up these products over all space, and equating this sum to unity, or expressing it mathematically,

$$\int_{\text{space}} u^2dv = 1, \tag{44}$$

is equivalent to saying that it is certain that the particle is somewhere in space. If the wave function u is chosen to satisfy the above integral equation, the function is said to be *normalized* and the product u^2dv now measures the absolute value of the probability of finding the particle in the particular volume element dv. While the above discussion has been limited to a single particle, the effect produced by a large number of particles is simply the sum of the elementary effects produced by the individual particles. Thus, in wave mechanics, the problem of determining the motion of a single particle is reduced to that of determining the probability of finding the particle in any particular place at a given time.

6-13. Electron Optics

Nearly all the phenomena that are usually associated with light and x-rays, and which form the subject of optics, can also be observed with electrons. Electrons can be reflected and refracted; interference and diffraction phenomena can be produced at will; electrons from a point source may be focused by passing them through properly shaped electric or magnetic fields; such fields play the role of lenses. A completely new branch of science, known as *electron optics*, has been developed within recent years, and investigations in this subject not only have led to a better understanding of physical phenomena but have also produced several important instruments which have wide applications. One of these is the *electron microscope.*

A microscope is used to provide an enlarged image of a small object as well as to show greater detail in its structure. The latter property is determined by the resolving power of the microscope. We have already seen that the limit of the resolving power of a microscope is determined by the wavelength of the incident radiation. In the case of optical microscopes, the limit of the resolving power of the optical microscope is of the order of magnitude of the wavelength of visible light, which we may take as 5000A. But, since the wavelengths associated with electrons are determined by the relation

$$\lambda = \frac{h}{mv},$$

it is possible to get much smaller wavelengths by using appropriate accel-

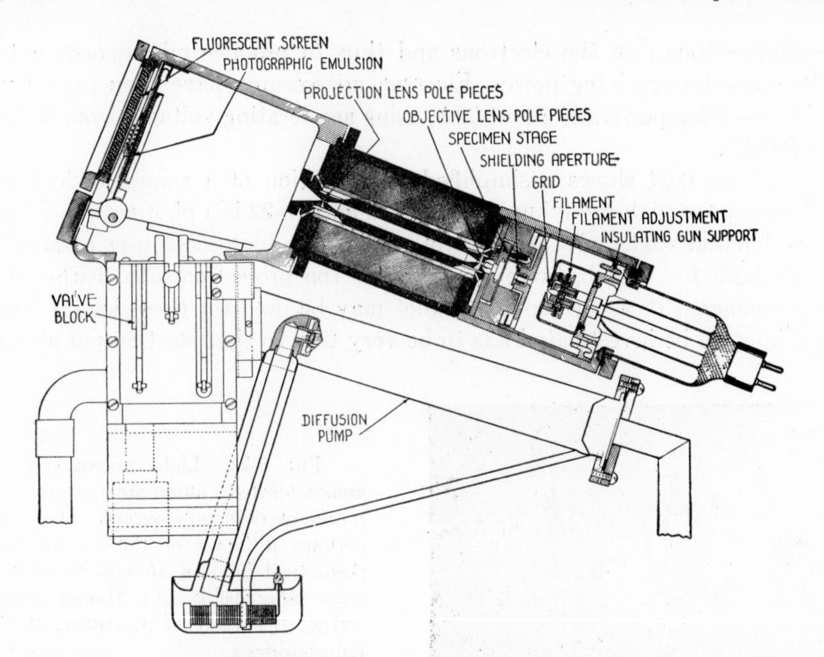

Fig. 6-21. A simplified cross section of a small electron microscope. (Courtesy of RCA Laboratories.)

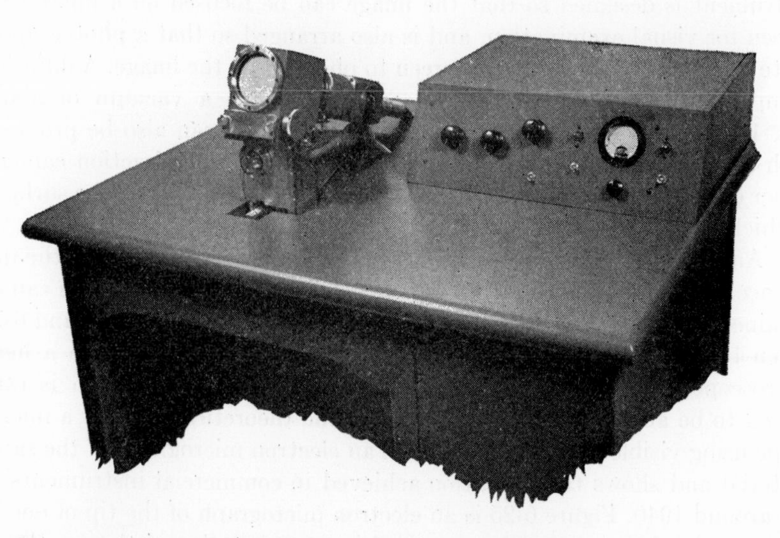

Fig. 6-22. A photograph of the experimental model of the small electron microscope with the control panel. (Courtesy of RCA Laboratories.)

erating voltages on the electrons and thus to produce microscopes with much greater resolving power. Electron microscopes have been produced with resolving powers of about 20A, using accelerating voltages from 30 kv to 100 kv.

Figure 6-21 shows a simplified cross section of a compact electron microscope of high resolving power, and Figure 6-22 is a photograph of the experimental model with the control panel. This microscope uses magnetic fields both for the objective lens and for the projection lens. Either an electromagnet or a permanent magnet may be used for these lenses. The specimen to be investigated has to be very thin so that electrons of about

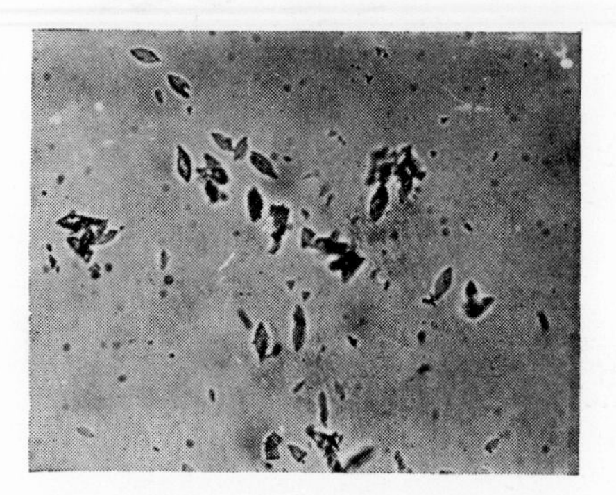

FIG. 6-23. Light micrograph of monohydrated aluminum oxide. A representative micrograph that is perhaps a factor of three from the theoretical limit of an optical microscope using visible light. Magnification 500 ×. (Courtesy of J. Hillier, RCA Laboratories.)

30 kev energy can be transmitted through it without loss of energy. The instrument is designed so that the image can be focused on a fluorescent screen for visual examination, and is also arranged so that a photographic plate can be put in front of the screen to photograph the image. A diffusion pump is connected to the microscope to provide a vacuum of about 5×10^{-5} mm of mercury pressure. This instrument can also be provided with an adapter so that it can be used as an electron diffraction camera. Other electron microscopes have been designed for the study of the surfaces of thick specimens by the reflection of electrons from the surface.

An idea of the meaning of the term *resolving power* as well as the difference in resolving powers between light and electron microscopes can be obtained from the three photographs shown in Figures 6-23, 6-24, and 6-25 taken by James Hillier. Figure 6-23 is a photograph taken with a light microscope of monohydrated aluminum oxide. This micrograph is estimated to be about a factor of three from the theoretical limit of a microscope using visible light. Figure 6-24 is an electron micrograph of the same material and shows the resolution achieved in commercial instruments in use around 1940. Figure 6-25 is an electron micrograph of the tip of one of the crystals of the same substance and is representative of the resolution that could be achieved in 1950. It is estimated that this micrograph is also

FIG. 6-24. FIG. 6-25.

FIG. 6-24. Electron micrograph of monohydrated oxide. Representative of the resolution achieved with commercial electron microscopes in 1940. Magnification 13,600 ×. (Courtesy of J. Hillier, RCA Laboratories.)

FIG. 6-25. Electron micrograph of the tip of one of the plates of the same monohydrated aluminum oxide as in Fig. 6-24. Representative of the resolution achieved in 1950. The resolving power is about a factor of three from the theoretical limit of the electron microscopes of about 1950. Magnification 90,000 ×. Compare with Figure 6-23. (Courtesy of J. Hillier, RCA Laboratories.)

about a factor of three from the theoretical limit of resolution of present-day electron microscopes.

The development of the electron microscope has provided a powerful tool for the study of the structure of large molecules and the structure of bacteria as well as for the photography of viruses and other very small objects. Further developments in this field will undoubtedly increase the resolving power to better values.

Problems

6-1. Calculate the length of the wave associated with a particle of one gram mass moving with a velocity of 2×10^5 cm/sec. Discuss the probability of performing a successful diffraction experiment with a stream of such particles.

Ans. 3.3×10^{-32} cm.

6-2. Calculate the wavelength associated with an alpha particle emitted by the nucleus of an atom of radon. Compare this wavelength with the diameter of the nucleus.

Ans. 6.13×10^{-13} cm.

6-3. It can be shown that the rate at which a gas at absolute temperature T moves out of an orifice in an oven is the same as that of a gas moving out of the aperture with a uniform velocity equal to $\frac{1}{4}\bar{c}$ where $\bar{c}$ is the average velocity of the molecules. Further, the average kinetic energy of the molecules of a gas is given by

$$\tfrac{1}{2}MC^2 = \tfrac{3}{2}kT,$$

where

$$C^2 = \frac{3\pi}{8}\bar{c}^2.$$

k is Boltzmann's constant and is equal to 1.37×10^{-16} erg/molecule/deg. (**a**) Derive an expression for the length of the waves associated with a stream of molecules of a gas at temperature T. (**b**) Calculate the wavelength associated with a stream of helium molecules issuing from an oven at 300° abs. (**c**) Devise an experiment for showing the existence of these waves, giving approximate dimensions of the essential parts of the apparatus.

Ans. (**a**) $\lambda = h\sqrt{\dfrac{2\pi}{MkT}}$.
(**b**) $\lambda = 3.14$A.

6-4. Electrons from a heated filament are accelerated by a difference of potential between the filament and the anode of 30 kv; a narrow stream of electrons coming through a hole in the anode is transmitted through a thin sheet of aluminum. (**a**) Assuming Bragg's law to hold, calculate the angle of deviation of the first-order diffraction pattern. (**b**) Determine the velocity of these waves in the aluminum foil.

Ans. (**a**) $\phi = 2\theta = 55$ min.
(**b**) $w = 9.04 \times 10^{10}$ cm/sec.

6-5. A stream of electrons of 240 ev energy is incident upon the surface of platinum at an angle of 30° to the normal. The electron energy U in platinum is known to be about 12 ev. (**a**) Calculate the index of refraction of platinum for these electrons. (**b**) Determine the angle of refraction. (**c**) Determine the wave velocity of the electron waves in platinum. (**d**) Determine the velocity of the electrons in platinum.

Ans. (**a**) $\mu = 1.025$.
(**b**) 29°.
(**c**) 9.5×10^{11} cm/sec.
(**d**) 9.48×10^8 cm/sec.

6-6. Deep-water waves travel with a wave velocity $w = (g\lambda/2\pi)^{1/2}$, where g is the gravitational acceleration. Show that the group velocity of such waves is $u = w/2$.

6-7. Ripples on the surface of a liquid travel with a wave velocity $w = (2\pi S/\lambda\rho)^{1/2}$ in which S is the surface tension and ρ is the density of the liquid. Show that the group velocity of the ripples is $u = \frac{3}{2}w$.

6-8. (**a**) Light of wavelength λ travels through a medium of index of refraction μ with a wave velocity w given by $\mu = c/w$. Show that the group velocity is given by

$$u = w\left(1 + \frac{\lambda}{\mu}\frac{d\mu}{d\lambda}\right).$$

(**b**) Determine the ratio of the group velocity to the wave velocity of light of wavelength 6000A, in a glass, from the following data: when $\lambda = 5890$, $\mu = 1.5682$; when $\lambda = 6235$, $\mu = 1.5663$.

References

Bacon, G. E., and K. Lonsdale, "Neutron Diffraction," in *Reports on Progress in Physics*. London: The Physical Society of London, 1953, XVI, 1–61.

Bohm, D., *Quantum Theory*. New York: Prentice-Hall, Inc., 1951, Parts I, II, and III.

Born, M., *Atomic Physics*. New York: G. E. Stechert & Company, 1951, Chap. IV.

Heisenberg, W., *The Physical Principles of the Quantum Theory*. Chicago: The University of Chicago Press, 1930, Chaps. I–IV.

Jacob, L., *An Introduction to Electron Optics*. New York: John Wiley & Sons, Inc., 1951.

Richtmyer, F. K., and E. H. Kennard, *Introduction to Modern Physics*. New York: McGraw-Hill Book Company, Inc., 1947, Chap. VII.

Rojansky, V., *Introductory Quantum Mechanics*. New York: Prentice-Hall, Inc., 1938, Chaps. I–IV.

Thomson, G. P., *Wave Mechanics of Free Electrons*. New York: McGraw-Hill Book Company, Inc., 1930, Chap. IV.

The EXTRANUCLEAR STRUCTURE of the ATOM

chapter **7**

The Hydrogen Atom

7-1. Spectrum of Hydrogen

Hydrogen, the simplest of all the elements, has been investigated most extensively both experimentally and theoretically. The knowledge obtained from this study has acted as a guide to the study of the more complex elements. One of the greatest aids in determining the structure of the atoms of any one element has been the study of the radiation emitted and absorbed by the element. When the light from an element in the gas or vapor phase is analyzed with the aid of a spectroscope, it is found to consist of a series of very sharp lines of definite wavelengths characteristic of the element emitting the radiation. Most of the atomic spectra are very complex, and their analysis involves exceedingly careful and painstaking measurements of the wavelengths and their relative intensities. As a result of this work many of the spectral lines of each element were found to be related in a simple manner expressed by means of a simple equation suggested by Rydberg (1889) in which the reciprocal of the wavelength, that is, the wave number, of a line is given as the difference between two numbers, or two terms. In this chapter we shall limit our considerations to the hydrogen atom.

As long ago as 1885, Balmer succeeded in obtaining a simple relationship among the wave numbers of the lines in the visible region of the hydrogen spectrum. Balmer's equation expressed in modern notation is

$$\boxed{\frac{1}{\lambda} = \bar{\nu} = R_{\text{H}}\left(\frac{1}{2^2} - \frac{1}{n^2}\right), \qquad (n = 3, 4, 5 \cdots),} \tag{1}$$

where λ is the wavelength and $\bar{\nu}$ is the wave number of the spectral line. R_{H} is a constant known as Rydberg's constant for hydrogen and n is an integer greater than 2. The empirical value of Rydberg's constant for hydrogen is

$$R_{\text{H}} = 109{,}677.581 \text{ cm}^{-1}.$$

By substituting for n in equation (1) the successive values 3, 4, 5, 6, $\cdots$, we obtain the wave numbers of the lines in the Balmer series. Figure 7-1 is a photograph of the lines of the Balmer series. The relative positions of these lines on a wave number scale are shown in Figure 7-2. It is obvious

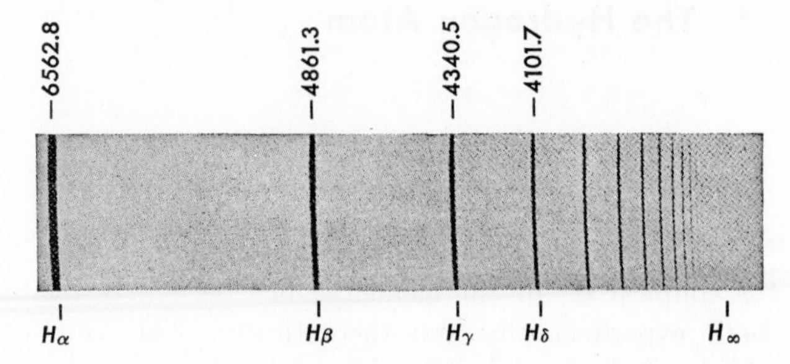

FIG. 7-1. Photograph of the emission spectrum of hydrogen showing the Balmer series lines in the visible and near ultraviolet region. H∞ shows the theoretical position of the series limit. (Reprinted by permission from *Atomic Spectra and Atomic Structure*, by G. Herzberg, Dover Publications.)

from the equation that as n approaches infinity, the lines crowd together and approach a limit known as the *series limit*. The value of the limit of the Balmer series is $R_H/2^2 = 27{,}419.40 \text{ cm}^{-1}$.

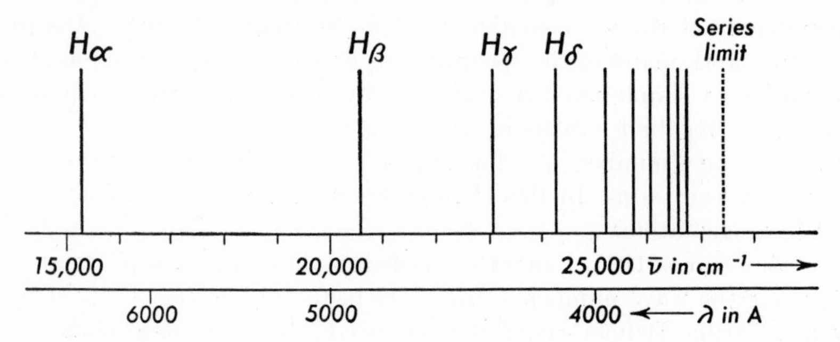

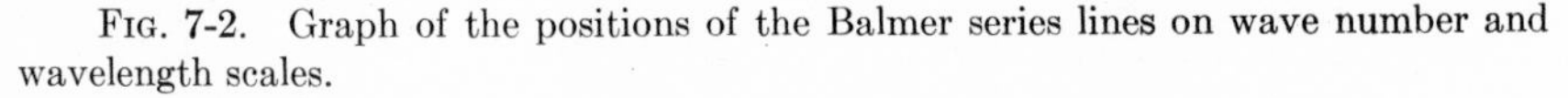

FIG. 7-2. Graph of the positions of the Balmer series lines on wave number and wavelength scales.

Another way of expressing the Balmer formula is by writing the wave number of each line as the difference between two terms

$$\bar{\nu} = T_l - T, \tag{2}$$

where $T_l = R_H/2^2$ is the value of the series limit, and $T = R_H/n^2$ is the variable term. This mode of expressing the series relationship will be found very useful for more complex spectra.

7-2. Bohr's Theory of the Hydrogen Atom

The first quantitatively correct derivation of the Balmer formula on the basis of an atomic model was given by Bohr (1913), in his theory of the hydrogen atom. This theory has played such an important role in the development of atomic physics that, even though it has been modified and extended by the later developments in quantum mechanics, it will be worth while to present the original simplified theory. Bohr adopted Rutherford's nuclear model of the atom; on this basis the hydrogen atom should consist of a singly charged positive nucleus and an electron outside the nucleus, since the atomic number is equal to unity. Assuming Coulomb's law of force and Newton's laws of motion to be applicable in the atomic domain, the path of the electron around the nucleus should be a conic section. As a first approximation assume that this conic section is a circle of radius r with the nucleus fixed at the center of the circle. If E is the charge on the nucleus and e the charge on the electron, then from Coulomb's law, the force of attraction between the nucleus and the electron is

$$F = \frac{Ee}{r^2} = -\frac{e^2}{r^2}, \tag{3}$$

since the atomic number $Z = 1$ and $E = -Ze = -e$. From Newton's second law of motion

$$F = ma = -\frac{mv^2}{r}, \tag{4}$$

where m is the mass of the electron, a is its centripetal acceleration, and v is its velocity. The minus sign indicates that the acceleration is directed toward the center of the circle. Equating (3) and (4), we get

$$\frac{e^2}{r^2} = \frac{mv^2}{r},$$

from which

$$mv^2 = \frac{e^2}{r}. \tag{5}$$

The potential at any point distant r from the charge E is E/r so that the potential energy of the electron is

$$\frac{Ee}{r} = -\frac{e^2}{r}. \tag{6}$$

The kinetic energy of the electron is $\frac{1}{2}mv^2$. Therefore the total energy $\mathcal{E}$, which is the sum of the potential and kinetic energies, is

$$\mathcal{E} = \tfrac{1}{2}mv^2 - \frac{e^2}{r}, \tag{7}$$

which, upon the substitution of equation (5), becomes

$$\boxed{\mathcal{E} = -\frac{e^2}{2r}.} \tag{8}$$

Since in this discussion the nucleus has been considered stationary, equation (8) represents the total energy of the atom excluding the rest mass energy of the two particles. It will be noticed that $\mathcal{E} = 0$ when $r = \infty$; that is, the zero level of energy is taken as that of the ionized atom. The minus sign shows that the energy of the atom is decreased as the electron comes closer to the nucleus. It is reasonable to assume that this decrease in energy is given out in the form of light.

On the basis of classical electrodynamics, the atom should radiate energy continuously at a rate proportional to the square of the acceleration of the electron. The frequency of the radiation should be the same as the mechanical frequency of the electron. The mechanical frequency is proportional to the angular velocity ω of the electron. The value of the angular velocity can be obtained from equation (5),

$$mv^2 = \frac{e^2}{r}. \tag{5}$$

Since

$$v = \omega r,$$

we get

$$\omega^2 = \frac{e^2}{mr^3}.$$

Now equation (8) shows that the energy of the atom is $-e^2/2r$; therefore, as the atom radiates energy, the radius of the orbit should decrease continually. This would produce a continuous increase in the mechanical frequency of the electron and should result in a continuous increase of the frequency of the radiation emitted and hence produce a continuous spectrum.

To explain the observed sharp line spectrum of hydrogen, Bohr introduced two fundamental postulates. *The first postulate is that of all the electron orbits, only those orbits are permissible for which the angular momentum of the electron is a whole multiple of $h/2\pi$, and that no energy is radiated while the electron remains in any one of these permissible orbits.* Since the angular momentum of the electron in any orbit is mvr, only those orbits are permissible which satisfy Bohr's postulate, which may be stated as

$$\boxed{mvr = \frac{nh}{2\pi},} \tag{9}$$

where n is an integer. These orbits are sometimes called *stationary* orbits.

The second postulate states that whenever radiant energy is emitted or absorbed by an atom, this energy is emitted or absorbed in whole quanta of amount hν, and that the energy of the atom is changed by this amount; thus

$$\mathcal{E}_i - \mathcal{E}_f = h\nu, \tag{10}$$

where $\mathcal{E}_i$ represents the initial value of the energy of the atom, $\mathcal{E}_f$ represents the final value of this energy, ν is the frequency of the radiation emitted or absorbed by the atom, and h is the Planck constant. If $\mathcal{E}_i$ is greater than $\mathcal{E}_f$, energy is radiated, and if $\mathcal{E}_i$ is less than $\mathcal{E}_f$, energy is absorbed by the atom. Thus on Bohr's theory, the atom radiates energy only when an electron jumps from a stationary orbit of higher energy to one of lower energy.

The radii of these permissible orbits can be calculated by eliminating v from equations (5) and (9), yielding

$$r = n^2 \frac{h^2}{4\pi^2 me^2}. \tag{11}$$

The smallest orbit will be that for which $n = 1$; its radius r_1 can be determined by substituting the empirically determined values of the constants h, m, and e. This yields

$$r_1 = 0.529 \times 10^{-8} \text{ cm} = 0.529\text{A}.$$

It will be noticed that this numerical value is of the same order of magnitude as that obtained on the basis of the kinetic theory of gases.

The radius r_n of any other orbit of quantum number n is given by

$$r_n = n^2 r_1,$$

so that radii of successive orbits increase as the square of n.

The energy $\mathcal{E}_n$ of the atom when the electron is in the stationary orbit characterized by the quantum number n can now be determined by eliminating r from equations (8) and (11), yielding

$$\mathcal{E}_n = -\frac{2\pi^2 me^4}{n^2 h^2}. \tag{12}$$

According to Bohr's second postulate, the frequency ν of the energy radiated when an electron goes from orbit n_i to orbit n_f is

$$\nu = \frac{\mathcal{E}_i - \mathcal{E}_f}{h}, \tag{13}$$

so that

$$\nu = \frac{2\pi^2 me^4}{h^3}\left(\frac{1}{n_f^2} - \frac{1}{n_i^2}\right). \tag{14}$$

Equation (14) has exactly the same mathematical form as Balmer's formula. To compare this equation with spectroscopic data, it will be more convenient to write it in terms of wave numbers where

$$\bar{\nu} = \frac{1}{\lambda} = \frac{\nu}{c}, \tag{15}$$

yielding

$$\bar{\nu} = \frac{2\pi^2 me^4}{ch^3}\left(\frac{1}{n_f^2} - \frac{1}{n_i^2}\right). \tag{16}$$

The identity of equation (16) with Balmer's formula can only be established by comparing the numerical value of R_{H} obtained spectroscopically with the numerical value of the factor

$$\frac{2\pi^2 me^4}{ch^3},$$

using the values of m, e, c, and h determined by independent experiments. Putting in the values of these constants yields

$$\frac{2\pi^2 me^4}{ch^3} = 109{,}740 \text{ cm}^{-1},$$

in excellent agreement with the value of R_{H} within the limits of error of the experiments. The numerical value of the above factor may be changed slightly by better determinations of e and h, but the impetus given to atomic physics by Bohr's original theory cannot be diminished.

In this simple model of the hydrogen atom the nucleus is at the center of the atom, while the electron may be in any one of the circular orbits characterized by the quantum numbers $n = 1, 2, 3, 4, \ldots$. As long as the electron remains in its orbit no energy is radiated, but whenever an electron jumps from an outer orbit to an inner orbit, energy is radiated in the form of light. A line of the Balmer series corresponds to a jump of the electron from an initial orbit of quantum number n greater than 2 to the final orbit for which $n = 2$ (see Figure 7-3). The red line or H_α line of the Balmer series corresponds to a transition from orbit of quantum number $n_i = 3$ to orbit of quantum number $n_f = 2$. Any one atom at any instant can emit only one photon of frequency ν, but since there are always many atoms in any quantity of hydrogen which is examined spectroscopically, there are always other atoms which emit photons of different frequencies

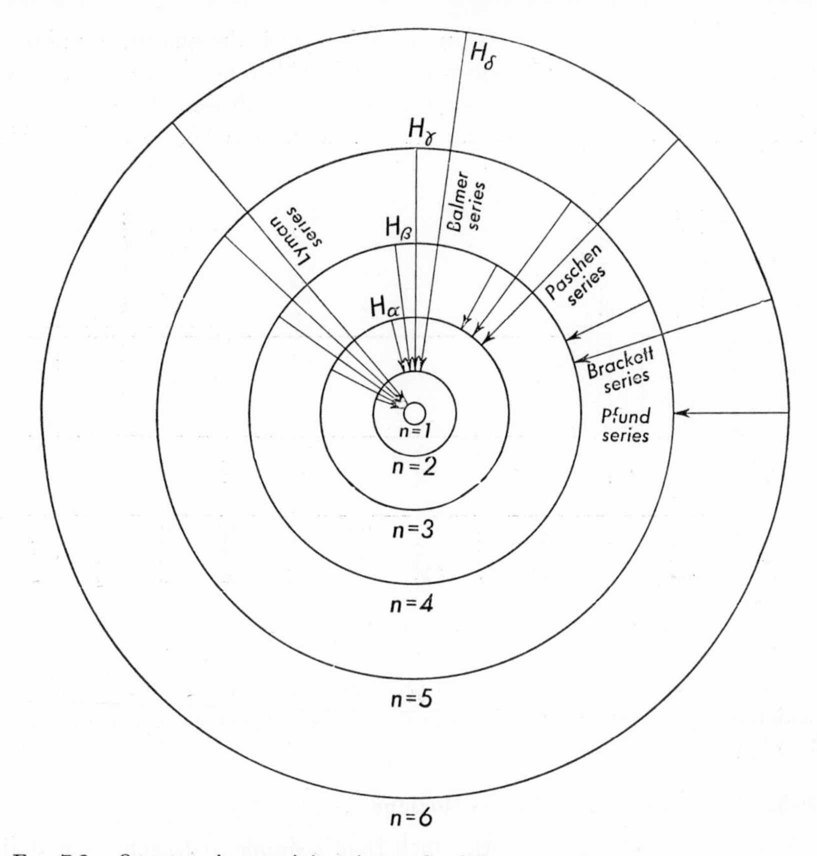

FIG. 7-3. Quantum jumps giving rise to the different spectral series of hydrogen.

so that the result is the series of lines actually observed. The relative number of atoms in which the electrons go from a given initial state to a given final state determines the relative intensity of the particular spectral line corresponding to this electron transition.

In addition to the Balmer series, other groups or series of spectral lines of hydrogen have been discovered. The Lyman series lies entirely in the ultraviolet region; the wave numbers of the lines of the Lyman series are given by

$$\bar{\nu} = \frac{2\pi^2 me^4}{ch^3}\left(\frac{1}{1^2} - \frac{1}{n_i^2}\right), \qquad (n_i = 2, 3, 4, \cdots),$$

that is, an electronic jump from any outer orbit to the innermost orbit ($n_f = 1$) gives rise to a line of the Lyman series. When the electron is in the lowest orbit, $n = 1$, the hydrogen atom is said to be in its *normal* state. When the electron is in any orbit for which the quantum number n is greater than unity, the hydrogen atom is said to be in an *excited* state.

Three other series of lines are known for hydrogen; these series are all in the infrared region and are known as the Paschen series for which

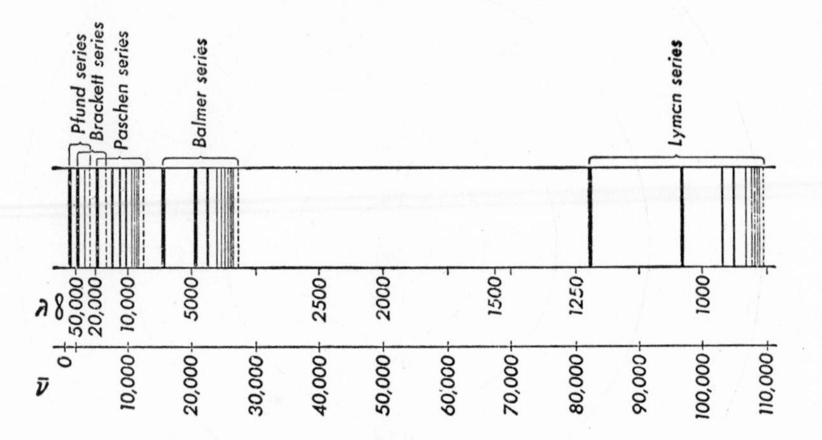

FIG. 7-4. Relative positions of the lines of the different spectral series of hydrogen.

$n_f = 3$, the Brackett series for which $n_f = 4$, and the Pfund series for which $n_f = 5$. The relative positions of these spectral series are shown in Figure 7-4.

7-3. Motion of the Hydrogen Nucleus

The extraordinary success with which Bohr's simple hydrogen atom model not only explains quantitatively the Balmer series but also predicts the

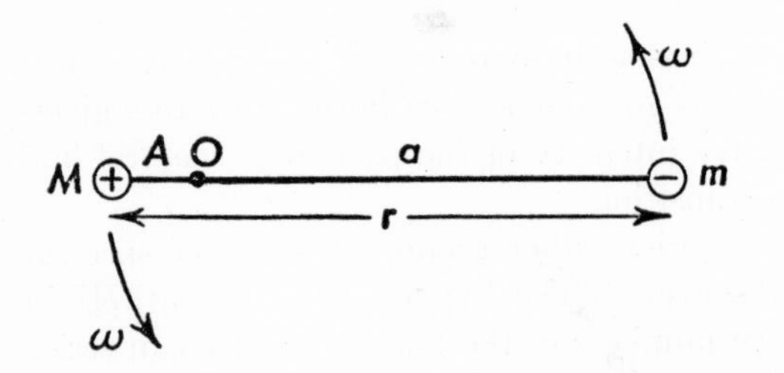

FIG. 7-5. Rotation of the nucleus and electron about a common axis through O.

existence of the other spectral series encourages us to proceed with further refinements of the theory. The simplest method is to remove some of the restrictions imposed upon the original model. One such restriction was that the nucleus remained fixed at the center of the circular orbits. This can be true only if the nucleus has infinitely large mass. But if the mass of the nucleus is M, then both the nucleus and the electron will rotate about a common center of mass with a common angular velocity ω. The new axis of rotation is on the line joining the nucleus and the electron, and divides this line in the inverse ratio of their masses. If a is the distance of the electron from the axis of rotation and A the distance of the nucleus from the same axis, as shown in Figure 7-5, then

$$\frac{a}{A} = \frac{M}{m} \tag{17}$$

and

$$r = a + A, \tag{18}$$

from which

$$a = r\frac{M}{M+m} \tag{19}$$

and

$$A = r\frac{m}{M+m}\cdot \tag{20}$$

Further, if v is the linear velocity of the electron and V is the linear velocity of the nucleus, then

$$v = a\omega \tag{21}$$

and

$$V = A\omega. \tag{22}$$

The kinetic energy of the system is the sum of the kinetic energies of the electron and the nucleus, or

$$\begin{aligned}\mathcal{E}_k &= \tfrac{1}{2}MV^2 + \tfrac{1}{2}mv^2 \\ &= \tfrac{1}{2}MA^2\omega^2 + \tfrac{1}{2}ma^2\omega^2.\end{aligned} \tag{23}$$

Substituting the values for a and A from equations (19) and (20), we reduce the expression for the kinetic energy of the system to

$$\mathcal{E}_k = \frac{1}{2}\frac{mM}{M+m}r^2\omega^2$$

or

$$\boxed{\mathcal{E}_k = \tfrac{1}{2}\mu r^2\omega^2,} \tag{24}$$

where

$$\boxed{\mu = \frac{mM}{M+m} = \frac{m}{1+\dfrac{m}{M}}\cdot} \tag{25}$$

The expression for the kinetic energy of this system differs from that in which the nucleus was considered at rest in that the quantity μ replaces the mass m of the electron. An examination of equation (25) shows that when $M = \infty$, μ is equal to m; μ is usually referred to as the *reduced* electronic mass.

In a similar manner, it can be shown that the potential energy of the system, $\mathcal{E}_p = -e^2/r$, is given by

$$\mathcal{E}_p = -\frac{e^2}{r} = -\mu\omega^2 r^2, \tag{26}$$

so that the total energy $\mathcal{E}$ is

$$\mathcal{E} = \mathcal{E}_k + \mathcal{E}_p = \tfrac{1}{2}\mu\omega^2 r^2 - \mu\omega^2 r^2$$

or

$$\mathcal{E} = -\tfrac{1}{2}\mu\omega^2 r^2. \tag{27}$$

From equations (26) and (27) we get, for the total energy of the atom,

$$\mathcal{E} = -\frac{e^2}{2r}, \tag{28}$$

which is identical in form with equation (8).

Bohr's first postulate applied to this atomic system is that the angular momentum of this system is a whole multiple of $h/2\pi$. The angular momentum of this system is the sum of the angular momenta of the proton and electron, that is,

$$MA^2\omega + ma^2\omega,$$

which, with the aid of equations (19) and (20), becomes $\mu r^2\omega$. Hence Bohr's first postulate now becomes

$$\mu r^2\omega = \frac{nh}{2\pi}. \tag{29}$$

Eliminating ω from equations (26) and (29), we get

$$r = \frac{n^2 h^2}{4\pi^2\mu e^2}. \tag{30}$$

Substituting this value of r into equation (29), we get for the total energy of the hydrogen atom in a state of quantum number n

$$\boxed{\mathcal{E} = -\frac{2\pi^2\mu e^4}{n^2h^2}.} \tag{31}$$

Making use of Bohr's second postulate as given by equation (10) and changing from frequency to wave number, we get, for the wave numbers of the spectral lines,

$$\bar{\nu} = \frac{2\pi^2 me^4}{ch^3}\,\frac{1}{1+\dfrac{m}{M}}\left(\frac{1}{n_f^2} - \frac{1}{n_i^2}\right) \tag{32}$$

or

$$\boxed{\bar{\nu} = R\left(\frac{1}{n_f^2} - \frac{1}{n_i^2}\right),} \tag{33}$$

where

$$R = \frac{2\pi^2 me^4}{ch^3} \cdot \frac{1}{1 + \dfrac{m}{M}} = R_\infty \frac{1}{1 + \dfrac{m}{M}} \tag{34}$$

and

$$\boxed{R_\infty = \frac{2\pi^2 me^4}{ch^3}.} \tag{35}$$

Equation (34) shows that the Rydberg constant is dependent upon the mass of the nucleus. The difference between equations (32) and (16) lies in the correction factor $1\Big/\left(1 + \dfrac{m}{M}\right)$, which, though small, is not outside the limits of accuracy of spectroscopic experiments. It will be more instructive to rewrite equation (32) to include the atomic number Z explicitly. Remembering that in equation (3) the nuclear charge E was replaced by $-Ze$, the factor e^4 should be $(-Ze)^2e^2$ or Z^2e^4, so that equation (32) should read

$$\bar{\nu} = Z^2 \cdot \frac{2\pi^2 me^4}{ch^3} \cdot \frac{1}{1 + \dfrac{m}{M}}\left(\frac{1}{n_f^2} - \frac{1}{n_i^2}\right)$$

or

$$\boxed{\bar{\nu} = Z^2R\left(\frac{1}{n_f^2} - \frac{1}{n_i^2}\right).} \tag{36}$$

An examination of equation (36) leads to three very interesting conclusions. In the first place, spectral series similar to those of hydrogen should exist for ions which have a hydrogenlike structure, i.e., a nucleus of charge $-Ze$ and a single external electron. For example, singly ionized helium, He^+, of nuclear charge $-2e$ should give a series of spectral lines whose wave numbers are given by the equation

$$\bar{\nu} = 4R\left(\frac{1}{n_f^2} - \frac{1}{n_i^2}\right).$$

Except for the small change in the value of the Rydberg constant due to the difference in the nuclear masses, these wave numbers are four times as large as the wave numbers of the lines in the corresponding series of hydrogen. Such lines have actually been observed in the spectrum of helium.

Other hydrogenlike spectra have been observed for doubly ionized lithium, triply ionized beryllium on up to multiply ionized oxygen. The following table lists the values of the Rydberg constant for hydrogen and hydrogenlike ions and shows its dependence on the mass of the nucleus.

Table 7-1

Dependence of the Rydberg Constant on the Mass of the Nucleus*

Nucleus	Rydberg constant in cm^{-1}
${}_1H^1$	109,677.581
${}_1H^2$	109,707.419
${}_1H^3$	109,717.348
${}_2He^3$	109,717.344
${}_2He^4$	109,722.264
${}_3Li^6$	109,727.295
${}_3Li^7$	109,728.723
${}_4Be^9$	109,730.623
${}_5B^{11}$	109,731.835
${}_6C^{12}$	109,732.286
${}_7N^{14}$	109,733.004
${}_8O^{16}$	109,733.539

* Values taken from *Atomic Energy States*, edited by Charlotte E. Moore, Bureau of Standards, Circular 467.

A second interesting conclusion that follows from equation (36) is that a knowledge of the Rydberg constant for hydrogen and ionized helium can be used to calculate the ratio of the mass of the proton to the mass of the electron. Using the subscripts H and He for the quantities characteristic of hydrogen and ionized helium, we get

$$\frac{R_{\mathrm{H}}}{R_{\mathrm{He}}} = \frac{1 + \dfrac{m}{M_{\mathrm{He}}}}{1 + \dfrac{m}{M_{\mathrm{H}}}}.$$

By substituting the value

$$M_{\mathrm{He}} = 3.9717 M_{\mathrm{H}}$$

obtained from mass spectroscopic data into the above equation as well as the values of R_H and R_{He}, we get

$$\frac{M_H}{m} = 1840,$$

in excellent agreement with values determined by other methods (see §2-6).

A third and extremely important conclusion that can be drawn from equation (36) is that even for the same value of Z, that is, for the same type of atom, there should be lines of slightly different wave numbers for nuclei of different masses. This has led directly to the discovery of the hydrogen isotope of mass number 2, now called *deuterium*. The history of the discovery of deuterium is very interesting. As a result of Aston's very precise measurements of the masses of many isotopes, the relative chemical atomic weights could be computed, taking into consideration the fact that oxygen consisted not only of the isotope of mass number 16 but also of small quantities of mass numbers 17 and 18. The relative chemical atomic weights of hydrogen and oxygen computed by Aston differed by about 2 parts in 10,000 from that determined by direct physical and chemical methods. Birge and Menzel (1931) suggested that this discrepancy could be explained by assuming the existence of two isotopes of hydrogen, H^1 and H^2, in the ratio of 4500 : 1.

Urey, Murphy, and Brickwedde (1932) performed a series of experiments on the spectrum of hydrogen to find the isotope H^2. They used a 21-foot concave diffraction grating and photographed the lines of the Balmer series. The dispersion of the instrument was 1.3A per mm. They first used ordinary tank hydrogen in the discharge tube and obtained a faint trace of a line slightly displaced from the regular H_β line. On the assumption that this faint line was due to the presence of a small quantity of deuterium in the hydrogen, they decided to prepare samples of hydrogen containing larger concentrations of deuterium and thus increase the relative intensity of this line. To accomplish this, they took liquid hydrogen, allowed most of it to evaporate, and used the small part that remained. In the process of evaporation, the lighter constituent evaporates at a greater rate, leaving the residue with a greater concentration of the heavier constituent. Two different samples were used: (1) the part that remained after the liquid hydrogen evaporated at atmospheric pressure, and (2) the part that remained after the liquid hydrogen evaporated at a pressure slightly higher than the triple point pressure. With these samples, the intensity of the displaced line was greatly enhanced, showing that they were now much richer in the isotope H^2. The results of their experiment on four lines of the Balmer series are given in Table 7-2.

The discovery of deuterium led rapidly to methods for isolating it in comparatively large quantities, enabling scientists to use it in many

Table 7-2

Separation of the Balmer Lines Due to the Two Isotopes of Hydrogen

Spectrum Lines	$H^1_\alpha - H^2_\alpha$	$H^1_\beta - H^2_\beta$	$H^1_\gamma - H^2_\gamma$	$H^1_\delta - H^2_\delta$
Calculated	1.793A	1.326A	1.185A	1.119A
Observed using ord. H		1.346	1.206	1.145
Observed using evap. H (1)		1.330	1.199	1.103
Observed using evap. H (2)	1.791	1.313	1.176	1.088

different fields of investigation in chemistry and biology as well as in physics. In physics, deuterium and the ionized atom known as the *deuteron* have been of inestimable value in the study of atomic nuclei.

7-4. Elliptic Orbits for Hydrogen

Bohr's original theory, which dealt only with circular orbits, was extended by Sommerfeld to include elliptic orbits. To accomplish this, Sommerfeld generalized Bohr's first postulate for the determination of the permissible orbits to read

$$\oint p_i dq_i = n_i h, \tag{37}$$

where q_i is a coordinate which varies periodically, p_i is the corresponding value of the momentum, and n_i is an integer. The symbol $\oint$ means that the integration is taken over a whole period of motion. In the case of circular orbits there is only one coordinate which varies periodically, namely, the angle ϕ which the radius vector makes with the x axis. In the case of elliptic motion, not only does the angle ϕ vary, but the length of the radius vector r also varies periodically, as shown in Figure 7-6. The elliptic orbits will therefore be determined by the two quantum conditions

$$\oint p_\phi d\phi = n_\phi h \tag{38}$$

$$\oint p_r dr = n_r h, \tag{39}$$

where n_ϕ is called the *angular* or *azimuthal* quantum number and n_r is called the *radial* quantum number. Let the origin of coordinates be taken at the nucleus which will be considered fixed, and let the mass of the electron be constant, that is, neglect the relativity variation of mass with velocity.

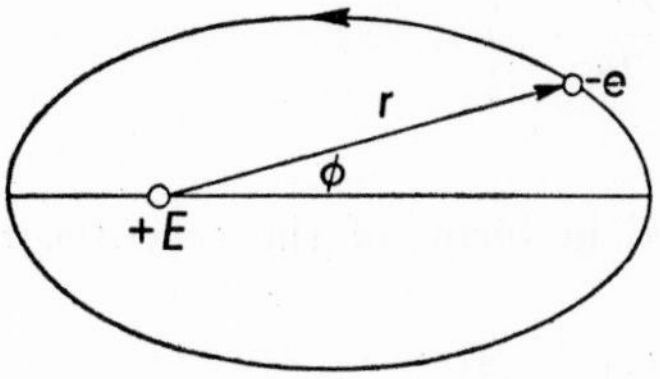

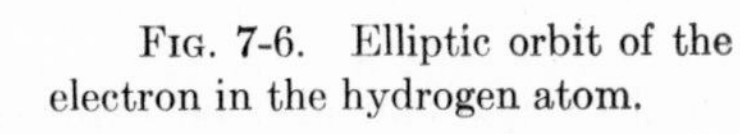

Fig. 7-6. Elliptic orbit of the electron in the hydrogen atom.

The first integral can be evaluated very easily since the momentum p_ϕ corresponding to the coordinate ϕ is merely the angular momentum, p, of the electron in the elliptic orbit, and this, from Kepler's law, is a constant (see Appendix VI, equation [6]). Integrating equation (38) over one period, from 0 to 2π, yields

$$\int_0^{2\pi} p_\phi d\phi = n_\phi h$$

or

$$p_\phi = p = \frac{n_\phi h}{2\pi} = \frac{kh}{2\pi}; \tag{40}$$

that is, the angular momentum is always an integral multiple of $h/2\pi$; n_ϕ is now replaced by the letter k since the latter is more commonly used to denote the azimuthal quantum number.

The second integral, when evaluated (see Appendix VIII), yields the equation

$$n_r h = \frac{2\pi p}{(1 - \epsilon^2)^{1/2}} - 2\pi p, \tag{41}$$

where ϵ is the eccentricity of the ellipse. Substituting the value for p from equation (40) yields

$$n_r h = \frac{kh}{(1 - \epsilon^2)^{1/2}} - kh$$

or

$$n_r + k = \frac{k}{(1 - \epsilon^2)^{1/2}}.$$

If we set

$$n = n_r + k, \tag{42}$$

then

$$1 - \epsilon^2 = \frac{k^2}{n^2}. \tag{43}$$

n is called the *principal* quantum number. The total energy of the electron in the elliptic orbit depends only on the length of its semimajor axis (see Appendix VIII) and is given by

$$\boxed{\mathcal{E} = -\frac{Ze^2}{2a}.} \tag{44}$$

The total energy can also be expressed in terms of the eccentricity (see Appendix VIII), as follows:

$$\mathcal{E} = -\frac{mZ^2e^4(1 - \epsilon^2)}{2p^2}. \tag{45}$$

Substituting the values for ϵ and p from equations (43) and (40), respectively, we get

$$\boxed{\mathcal{E} = -\frac{2\pi^2me^4Z^2}{n^2h^2},} \tag{46}$$

which is identical with the expression for the energy of the electron in a circular orbit of quantum number n. The introduction of elliptic orbits does not result in the production of new energy terms; hence no new spectral lines are to be expected because of this *multiplicity* of orbits. However, since the spectral lines of hydrogen do show fine structure when examined with instruments of high resolving power, its explanation must lie elsewhere. It was not satisfactorily explained until the introduction of the concept of *electron spin* in 1925. (See §8-4.)

It is interesting to determine the possible electronic orbits for any given principal quantum number n. The length of the semimajor axis a is obtained from equations (44) and (46):

$$a = n^2\frac{h^2}{4\pi^2me^2Z} = n^2\frac{a_0}{Z}; \tag{47}$$

while the semiminor axis is given by

$$b = a(1 - \epsilon^2)^{1/2}, \tag{48}$$

so that

$$b = nk\frac{a_0}{Z}, \tag{49}$$

where

$$a_0 = \frac{h^2}{4\pi^2me^2} = 0.529 \times 10^{-8}\text{ cm}$$

is the radius of the first Bohr orbit. These equations show that the length of the semimajor axis is determined solely by the principal quantum number n, while the length of the semiminor axis depends upon the azimuthal quantum number k. For the first orbit corresponding to the lowest energy level or the normal state of hydrogen, the principal quantum number $n = 1$. Since the sum of n_r and k must be unity, and each must be an integer, when $n_r = 0$, $k = 1$, and when $n_r = 1$, $k = 0$. On the basis of this theory of the

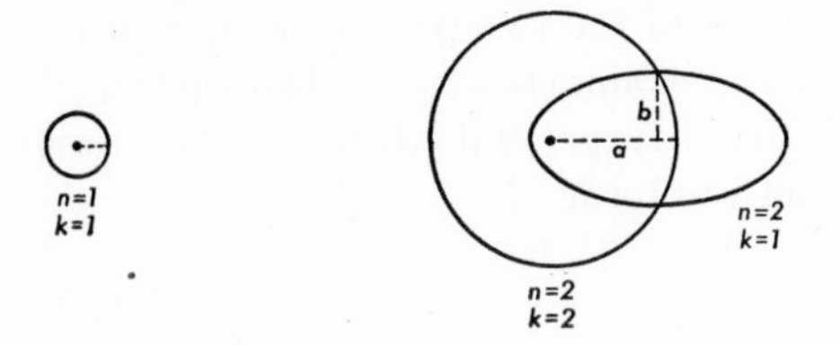

FIG. 7-7. Possible electronic orbits for a given total quantum number n.

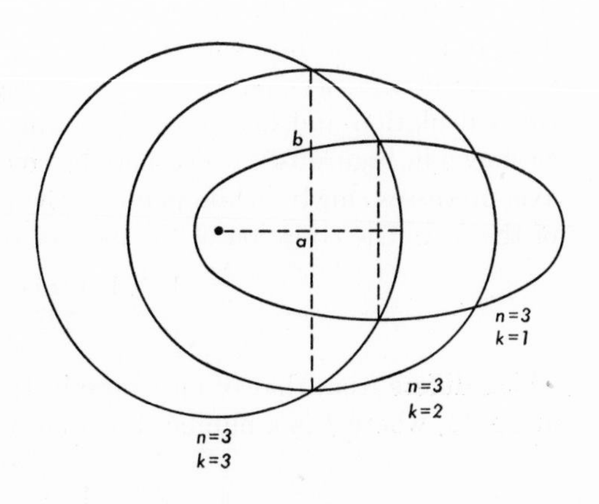

structure of the atom, it was decided that k can never be zero since that would mean that the ellipse would be reduced to a straight line and that the electron would have to pass through the nucleus twice during every period. The smallest possible value for k is thus always unity. With $n = k = 1$, the first orbit is a circle identical with the first Bohr orbit. With $n = 2$, k may have the values 1 or 2, so that there are two possible orbits for $n = 2$, a circle and an ellipse. Similarly there are three possible orbits for $n = 3$, a circle and two ellipses, as shown in Figure 7-7. For ionized helium, $Z = 2$, the orbits are similar but the radius of the first orbit is $a_0/2$. The orbits for the other hydrogenlike atoms can be constructed in the same manner.

It may at first sight appear strange that with the introduction of two quantizing conditions instead of one, no new energy levels and no new spectral lines are predicted. An examination of these two conditions shows, however, that both of them have exactly the same periodicity; that is, as the angle ϕ goes from 0 to 2π, the radius vector r goes from its maximum value through the minimum value and back to its maximum value. A mathematical examination of multiply periodic systems shows that whenever the ratio of two of the periods of such a system is a rational number, the two quantum conditions degenerate into a single quantum condition. But if the ratio of the two periods is an irrational number, that is, if the two periods are incommensurable, then there will be two independent quantum conditions. In general, there will be as many independent quantum conditions of the form

$$\oint p_i dq_i = n_i h \tag{37}$$

as there are incommensurable periods in the motion. In such cases the system is referred to as a *nondegenerate system.* One method for removing this degeneracy, in the case of the elliptic motion of the electron in hydrogen, is to take into consideration the relativity change of mass as the velocity of the electron in its orbit changes. Sommerfeld has carried out this calculation and has shown that the path of an electron is a rosette, as shown in Figure 7-8, which may be considered as an ellipse whose major axis precesses slowly in the plane of the ellipse about an axis through one of the foci. The equation of the path of the electron is

$$\frac{1}{r} = \frac{1 + \epsilon \cos \psi\phi}{a(1 - \epsilon^2)},$$

which differs from that of an ellipse in that the angle ϕ is replaced by the angle $\psi\phi$, where ψ is a number less than unity and is given by

$$\psi^2 = 1 - \frac{Z^2 e^4}{c^2 p^2}$$

When the angle ϕ is increased by 2π, r does not return to its original value but reaches it only after the angle $\psi\phi$ has been increased by 2π, or when ϕ has been increased by the angle $2\pi/\psi$. Hence the radius vector r returns to its original value only after the axis of the ellipse has precessed through an angle

$$\Delta\phi = \frac{2\pi}{\psi} - 2\pi.$$

The effect of the relativity correction on the expression for the total energy of the orbit is to introduce an additional term in equation (46). This additional term is

$$\Delta\mathcal{E} = -\frac{2\pi^2 m e^4}{h^2} Z^4 \alpha^2 \left(\frac{n}{k} - \frac{3}{4}\right) \frac{1}{n^4}, \tag{50}$$

where

$$\alpha = \frac{2\pi e^2}{ch} = 7.297 \times 10^{-3} \doteq \frac{1}{137} \tag{51}$$

is known as the Sommerfeld *fine structure* constant. This term shows that the energy does depend upon the azimuthal quantum number k which has the effect of splitting up the energy level into n terms very close together.

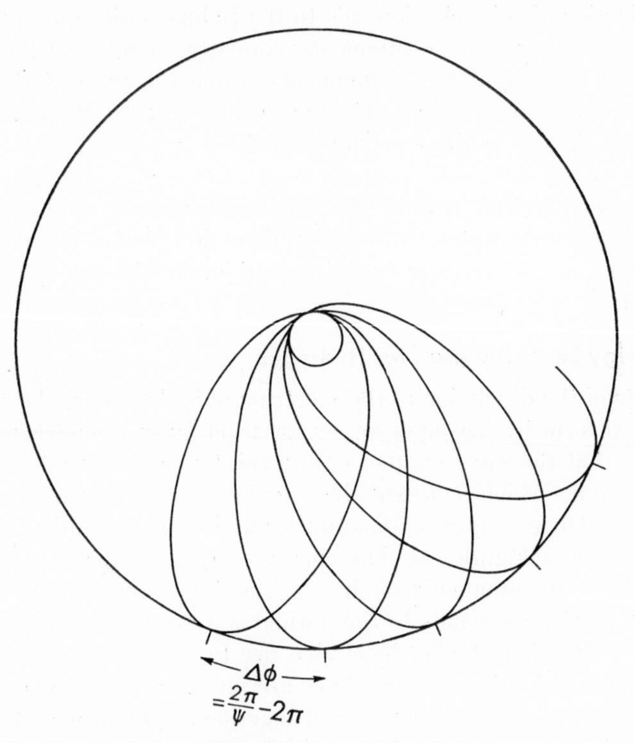

FIG. 7-8. Rosette figure of the path of an electron in hydrogen when the relativity correction is taken into consideration.

The energy of the first orbit, $n = 1$, can have only one possible value since $k = 1$, or there is only one energy level for $n = 1$. For principal quantum number $n = 2$, the energy can have two possible values corresponding to the two values of k, 1 and 2; that is, there are two energy levels for $n = 2$. Similarly there are three possible energy values or energy levels for $n = 3$, and so on. For the first line of the Balmer series, corresponding to the change in the principal quantum numbers $n_i = 3$ to $n_f = 2$, there are six possible transitions for the different values of k. This means that, with a spectroscope of very high resolving power, the H_α line should appear to consist of six lines very close together. Actually the H_α line has fewer components. To make experiment and theory agree, some of the transitions have to be ruled out by some *selection* principle. The selection principle chosen is that the azimuthal quantum number k can change only by $+1$ or -1 or, expressed in mathematical form,

$$\boxed{\Delta k = \pm 1.} \tag{52}$$

The application of this selection rule to the Balmer series shows that each line should consist of three components; similarly, each line of the Paschen series should consist of five components, while the lines of the Lyman series should all be single lines. The fine structure of the Balmer lines and some of the lines of ionized helium have been carefully studied but the agreement with the theoretical predictions is not very good. Most of these discrepancies were later removed by the introduction of the hypothesis of electron spin (see Chapter 8). Further discussion of the fine structure of spectral lines will be postponed until the subject of electron spin has been considered.

7-5. Energy Level Diagram for Hydrogen

The results of the discussion of the spectrum of hydrogen can be presented in graphical form by means of an energy level diagram which makes use of the fact that the wave number of any spectral line is the difference between two terms which represent the energies of the initial and final states of the atom. The energy level diagram for hydrogen, neglecting fine structure, is shown in Figure 7-9. The energy levels are drawn as horizontal lines and the wave number scale, in cm^{-1}, is shown in the figure. The lowest energy level corresponds to the normal state of hydrogen. Transitions to this level from any higher level give rise to the Lyman series of lines. The origins of the other spectral lines are indicated in the figure. It will be noted that the energy levels crowd together as the principal quantum numbers get large, since each term is of the form

$$T = \frac{R}{n^2} \cdot \tag{53}$$

From this it follows that the lines of a spectral series will converge toward the series limit.

Transitions from higher to lower energy levels can occur spontaneously. In order to get into one of these higher energy states, the atom must be *excited* by some external agency. Such excitation may take place because of the transfer of energy during collisions between atoms in a gas at high temperature. Atoms may also be raised from the normal to the excited states by impact with electrons having the right amount of kinetic energy.

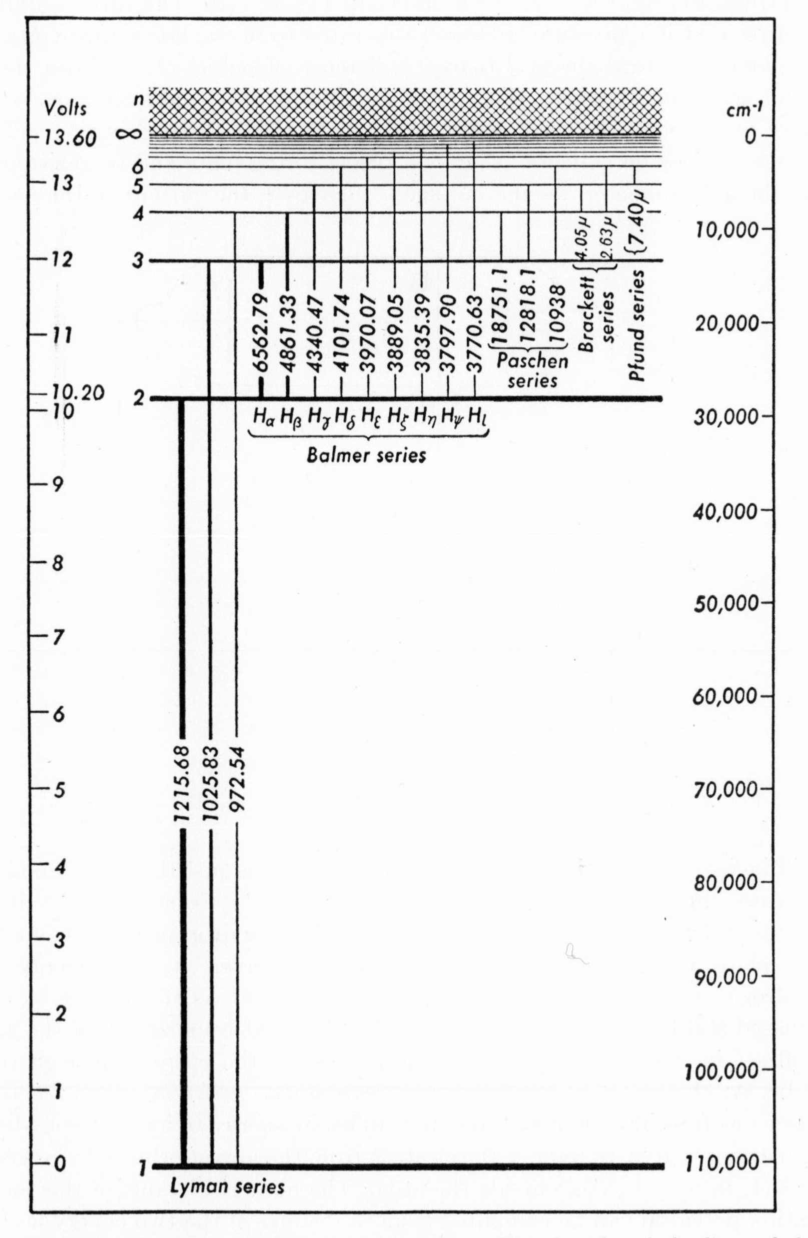

Fig. 7-9. Energy level diagram for hydrogen. Wavelengths of the lines of the Lyman, Balmer, and Paschen series are in angstroms.

A simplified experimental arrangement for producing collisions between electrons and hydrogen atoms is shown in Figure 7-10. The tube contains hydrogen at low pressure. Electrons liberated from the hot filament F are accelerated toward the grid G by a difference of potential V. When they enter the region between the grid G and the plate P, these electrons will have an amount of energy equal to $Ve = \frac{1}{2}mv^2$. If these electrons suffer no energy loss on collision, they will travel to the plate and be registered by the galvanometer. As the voltage is increased, the current to the plate

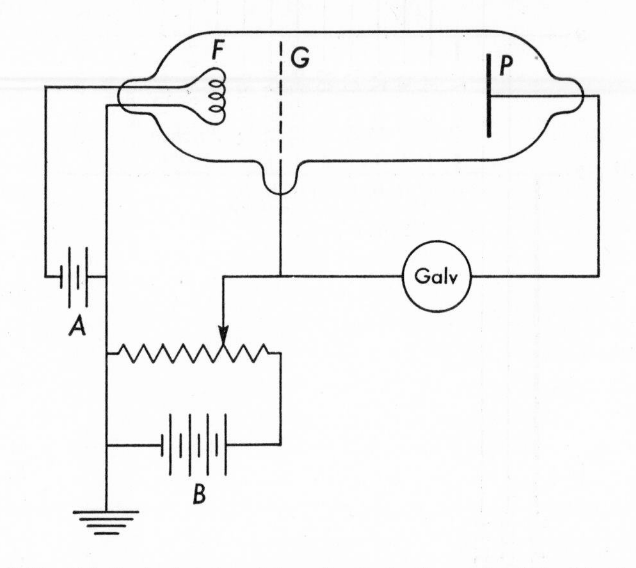

FIG. 7-10. Method of determining the ionization potential of hydrogen.

will be increased until the energy of the electrons is just the right amount to raise the hydrogen atom from the normal state to one of its excited states. When this value is reached there will be a drop in the current to the plate, indicating that many electrons have given up their energy to hydrogen atoms to raise them to an excited state. As the voltage is increased still further, a point will be reached at which ionization of the gas will set in, resulting in a very large increase in the current through the tube. At this value of the voltage, known as the *ionization potential*, the electrons from the filament have just sufficient energy to ionize the hydrogen atom; that is, to remove the electron from the lowest orbit of hydrogen, $n = 1$, to $n = \infty$, i.e., outside the atom. The numerical value of this ionization potential can be computed from the values of the two energy levels $\mathcal{E}_\infty$ and $\mathcal{E}_1$, and is

$$V = 13.595 \text{ volts.} \tag{54}$$

The value of the ionization potential determined empirically is 13.54 volts, in good agreement with the Bohr theory.

In the energy level diagram a shaded region of continuous energy values is shown extending beyond the last quantized orbit, $n = \infty$. This corresponds to the fact that the electrons which are knocked out of the hydrogen atom have kinetic energies representing the differences between the ionization energy and the energies of the incident electrons. The electrons outside the hydrogen orbits are not subject to quantum conditions since their motion is not periodic. The kinetic energies of these electrons may have any values whatever. When an electron in the neighborhood of a hydrogen ion falls into one of its orbits, the system will radiate energy. If the initial kinetic energy of the electron is zero, and it falls into orbit $n = 2$, the system will radiate an amount of energy corresponding to the limit of the Balmer series. If the initial kinetic energy of the electron is greater than zero, then when it falls into orbit $n = 2$, the system will radiate a greater amount of energy. The frequency of this radiation will be greater than the frequency of the series limit. Since the initial kinetic energy can have any value whatever, a *continuous* spectrum should appear at the end of the Balmer series beginning at the position of the series limit. The continuous spectrum at the end of the Balmer series has actually been observed.

Another important method of raising the hydrogen atom from the normal to one of its excited states is through the absorption of light. If the incident light contains one of the wavelengths of the Lyman series, say 1025.8A, then those atoms which absorb this light will be raised from energy level $n = 1$ to the higher energy level $n = 3$. The atoms in this higher state can return to the normal state by the emission of radiation either in a single step with the emission of the same wavelength, or in two successive stages, from $n = 3$ to $n = 2$, and then from $n = 2$ to $n = 1$. In the latter case two lines will be emitted, the H_α line of the Balmer series and the first line of the Lyman series, $\lambda = 1215.7\text{A}$. *Fluorescent radiation* is the name given to the light emitted by atoms which have been excited by the absorption of light.

The hydrogen atom may be ionized by the absorption of light of frequency greater than that of the Lyman series limit, i.e., of wave number greater than R_H. The kinetic energy of the electron knocked out of the hydrogen atom will then be the difference between the energy of the incident radiation and the energy of the hydrogen atom in the normal state, or

$$\tfrac{1}{2}mv^2 = h\nu - h\nu_\text{L}. \tag{55}$$

But this is Einstein's photoelectric equation in which ν_L is the frequency of the Lyman series limit, and ν is the frequency of the incident radiation.

The energy level diagram of hydrogen can be used in the discussion of hydrogenlike atoms by merely changing the scale, since the energy terms differ only by the factor Z^2, neglecting relativity terms.

7-6. De Broglie's Hypothesis and the Quantization of Orbits

The older quantum theory sketched in the preceding sections, while very successful when applied to the hydrogen problem, could only be applied either in a semiempirical or in a qualitative manner to other problems in atomic physics. Schroedinger's wave mechanics, based upon De Broglie's hypothesis, has been much more successful in obtaining rigorous mathematical solutions for many of these problems. It is interesting to see how Bohr's quantization hypothesis comes out of this new theory and what the modern picture of the hydrogen atom is.

On De Broglie's hypothesis, the wavelength associated with an electron is given by

$$\lambda = \frac{h}{mv}. \tag{56}$$

Instead of an electron moving in a stationary orbit, we must now think of a series of waves moving in this orbit. In order that the waves should not cancel one another by interference, they must move in such a manner as to produce a stationary or standing wave in the orbit. The necessary condition that must be fulfilled is that the length of path should be a whole multiple of the wavelength. Or stated mathematically,

$$2\pi r = n\lambda \tag{57}$$

where n is a whole number and r is the radius of the orbit. Substituting the value for λ, we get

$$2\pi r = \frac{nh}{mv}$$

or

$$mvr = \frac{nh}{2\pi},$$

which is identical with Bohr's quantization hypothesis.

7-7. Application of Wave Mechanics to the Hydrogen Problem

In wave mechanics, Schroedinger's equation is used as the basic dynamical equation and in the case of the hydrogen problem, this equation and the appropriate restrictive conditions replace all of Bohr's postulates. In this problem an electron of charge e is at a distance r from a nucleus of charge $E = -Ze$ so that the potential energy of the electron with respect to the nucleus is

$$V = -\frac{Ze^2}{r}. \tag{58}$$

With this value of the potential energy substituted in Schroedinger's equation (§6-12), it becomes more convenient to use spherical coordinates (r, θ, ϕ) instead of Cartesian coordinates (x, y, z). There is a regular formal procedure for solving such second-order partial differential equations (see the references at the end of the chapter). In the solution of this equation, wave functions u are sought subject to the restrictive conditions that they must be everywhere finite, single-valued, and continuous, with continuous first derivatives. It is found that solutions satisfying the above conditions exist for all positive values of the total energy $\mathcal{E}$, and for those negative values of the total energy which satisfy the condition that

$$\mathcal{E} = -\frac{2\pi^2 me^4 Z^2}{n^2 h^2} \tag{59}$$

where n is a positive integer. The above equation is identical with the expression for the energy of a stationary state characterized by the principal quantum number n in the Bohr theory. It must be remarked that no additional hypotheses or assumptions are introduced in the solution of Schroedinger's equation. The fact that certain quantities restricted to integral values appear as the result of solutions of partial differential equations is not new in mathematical physics. The solutions of the differential equations governing the vibrations of strings and membranes, particularly those involving stationary modes of vibration, are solutions in which integers play a very important part. For example, a string fixed at both ends can have stationary modes of vibration set up in it only when the length of the string is an integral multiple of $\lambda/2$, where λ is the length of the wave traveling along the string. Thus, in the new wave mechanics, the quantum number n appears naturally as the result of the solution of a fundamental equation, although Bohr introduced it without any apparent reason, except that it did predict the correct values for the frequencies of the spectral lines of hydrogen.

The complete solution of Schroedinger's equation introduces not just the single integer n, but three integers usually denoted by the letters n, l, and m. (The letter m is not to be confused with the mass of the electron.) While the quantum number n may have any integral value, the quantum numbers l and m are restricted in values by the conditions of the problem. The quantum number l may have the values

$$l = 0, 1, 2, \cdots (n - 1). \tag{60}$$

By comparing these values with the values of the azimuthal quantum number k of the older theory, it is seen that l may be identified with $k - 1$. The quantum number m may take all integral values from $-l$ through 0, to $+l$; that is, it can have $2l + 1$ values. For example, for $l = 2$, m may have the values $-2, -1, 0, +1, +2$. The quantum number m

is usually called the magnetic quantum number; it will be considered in greater detail in the next chapter.

The wave function u is, of course, dependent upon the values assigned to the quantum numbers n, l, and m. The functions which satisfy Schroedinger's equation for the discrete energy states are usually called proper functions or eigen functions. While no immediate physical significance can be attached to these proper functions, it will be recalled that u^2dv can be

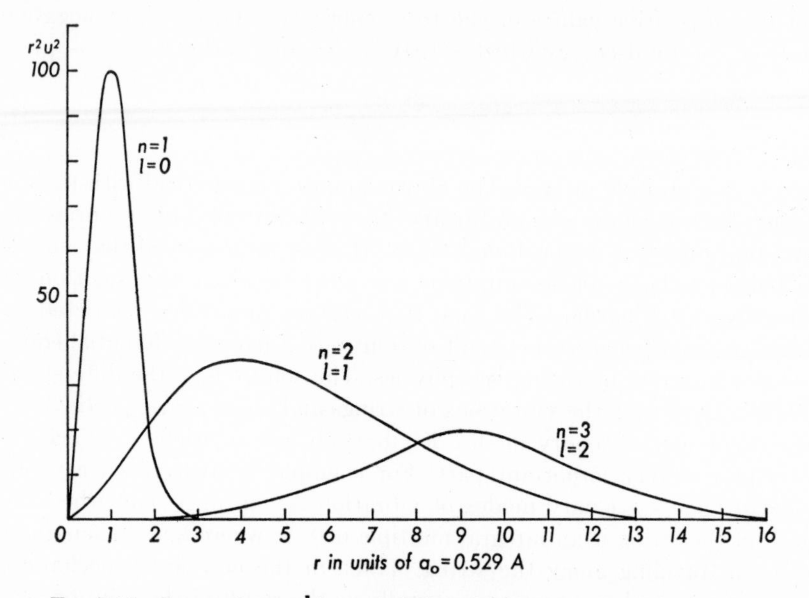

FIG. 7-11. Curves showing the probability of finding the electron in the hydrogen atom within a spherical shell of radius r and thickness dr for some values of n and l.

interpreted as the probability of finding the electron in the volume element dv. Of greater interest is the probability of finding the electron at a given distance r from the nucleus. If u^2 is multiplied by the surface area of a sphere, $4\pi r^2$, then the term $4\pi r^2u^2dr$ represents the probability of finding the electron within a spherical shell of radius r and thickness dr. In Figure 7-11, r^2u^2 is plotted against the distance r for quantum numbers $n = 1$, $l = 0$; $n = 2$, $l = 1$; $n = 3$, $l = 2$. These quantum numbers correspond to those representing the circular orbits in Bohr's theory. From the figure, it is seen that the probability of finding the electron at any distance from the nucleus has a maximum at the distance equal to the radius of the corresponding Bohr orbit.

The picture of the hydrogen atom from the standpoint of wave mechanics can be presented in another manner. The term eu^2dv, where e is the electronic charge, represents the probability of finding the electric charge in the volume element dv. This is sometimes called the density distribution of the electric charge in the atom or the *electronic cloud* around the nucleus. It must not be assumed that the electronic charge is smeared out over the atom, although calculations based on this assumption lead to correct results. The density at any point in the electronic cloud represents the probability of finding the electron in the particular volume element in the neighborhood of that point.

It may be argued that Bohr's simple picture of the hydrogen atom has been given up for a somewhat nebulous picture of the atom without gaining anything thereby. However, many things which were inexplicable on Bohr's theory come naturally out of further refinements of wave mechanics. For example, Bohr had to postulate that an atom in a stationary state should not radiate, contrary to classical electrodynamics. In the wave mechanical theory of radiation, it is shown, in a manner analogous to the classical theory, that an atom in a stationary state will not radiate energy because the radiations from the different parts of the electronic cloud will cancel each other by interference. Further, it is shown that only those frequencies will occur in the spectrum of the atom which are formed by the differences in the frequencies of two atomic states. This leads directly to Bohr's frequency condition,

$$\nu = \frac{\mathcal{E}_i - \mathcal{E}_f}{h} \cdot$$

Another important contribution is the calculation of the intensity of a spectral line. A surprising result of this calculation is the prediction that the most intense lines will be those for which the changes in the quantum numbers l and m obey the rules that

$$\Delta l = \pm 1 \tag{61}$$

and

$$\Delta m = 0, \quad \text{or} \quad \pm 1. \tag{62}$$

These selection rules apply not only to the hydrogen type of atom but to other atoms in which a single electron is responsible for the changes in the atomic energy states. There are no selection rules for the quantum number n.

Problems

7-1. Discuss the relationship between the frequency of rotation of the electron in the circular Bohr orbits and the frequency of the radiation emitted when the quantum number changes by unity. Show that for very large quantum numbers, the frequency of rotation of the electron and the frequency of the radiation emitted when the quantum number changes by unity approaches the value $\nu = 2cR/n^3$.

7-2. Using the data from Table 7-1, plot a curve showing the dependence of Rydberg's constant on the nuclear mass. Determine the value of R_∞ from this curve.

7-3. Hydrogen of mass number 3 sufficient for spectroscopic examination is put into a tube containing ordinary hydrogen. Determine the separation of the H_α lines that should be observed.

Ans. $\Delta\lambda = 2.38$A.

7-4. (a) Draw an energy level diagram for the energy levels characterized by the principal quantum numbers $n = 2$ and $n = 3$, taking the relativity corrections into consideration. Show the transitions permitted by the selection rule. (b) Draw a diagram showing the positions of these lines relative to the position of the line predicted without relativity correction.

7-5. Ultraviolet light of 800A is incident upon hydrogen in a quartz tube. Calculate the kinetic energies with which electrons will be ejected from the hydrogen atoms. Express the results in ev.

Ans. 1.94 ev; 12.14 ev.

7-6. Calculate the limit of the Paschen series in wave numbers, angstrom units, and ev.

7-7. In an electron tube containing hydrogen, such as that shown in Figure 7-10, the maximum kinetic energy of the electron is 13.0 ev. Determine which lines of the hydrogen spectrum will be emitted by the gas.

References

Born, M., *Atomic Physics.* New York: G. E. Stechert & Company, 1951, Chap. V.

Herzberg, G., *Atomic Spectra and Atomic Structure.* New York: Dover Publications, Inc., 1944, Chap. I.

Richtmyer, F. K., and E. H. Kennard, *Introduction to Atomic Physics.* New York: McGraw-Hill Book Company, Inc., 1947, Chap. VI.

Solutions of Schroedinger's equation

Born, M., *Atomic Physics.* New York: G. E. Stechert & Company, 1951, Appendix XVII.

Condon, E. U., and P. M. Morse, *Quantum Mechanics.* New York: McGraw-Hill Book Company, Inc., 1929, §§ 16–20.

Rojansky, V., *Introductory Quantum Mechanics.* New York: Prentice-Hall, Inc., 1938, Chaps. V, VI.

chapter **8**

Optical Spectra and Electron Distribution

8-1. Introduction

The study of atomic spectra has yielded invaluable information concerning the arrangement and distribution of the electrons within the atom. Most of the principles and rules used in spectroscopy have been obtained empirically, but within the past few years, with the development of wave mechanics, many of them have been placed on a good theoretical foundation. One of the most important of these principles is Bohr's frequency condition, which states that the frequency of any line of the spectrum is proportional to the difference between the values of the energies of two states of the atom emitting the radiation; that is

$$\boxed{\nu = \frac{\mathcal{E}_i - \mathcal{E}_f}{h},} \tag{1}$$

where ν is the frequency of the emitted radiation, $\mathcal{E}_i$ is the energy of the initial state of the atom, $\mathcal{E}_f$ is the energy of the final state of the atom, and h is the Planck constant. Expressed in terms of the corresponding wave number $\bar{\nu}$, this equation becomes

$$\bar{\nu} = \frac{\mathcal{E}_i}{ch} - \frac{\mathcal{E}_f}{ch}, \tag{2}$$

where c is the velocity of light. Equation (2) shows that the wave number of any spectral line can be expressed as the difference between two terms:

$$\bar{\nu} = T_i - T_f, \tag{3}$$

where each term, T, expressed in wave numbers, represents an atomic energy state or energy level.

Atomic spectra can be grouped in two general classifications: (1) optical spectra, and (2) x-ray spectra. For any given element, the wave numbers of the lines in the x-ray spectra are much greater than those in the optical spectra. From this it can be inferred that the difference in energies between two states of an atom which emits an x-ray spectral line is very large and that the energy values of these atomic states are also very large. The wave numbers of the lines of the optical spectra are comparatively small. It will be shown not only that the difference between two atomic energy states is small, but that the energies of the atomic states giving rise to these optical lines are also small. In general, the optical spectrum of any given element is much more complex than the x-ray spectrum of the same element. In this chapter, a few typical optical spectra will be considered, together with the relationship of these spectra to the extranuclear structure of the atom. X-ray spectra will be discussed in the next chapter.

8-2. Optical Spectral Series

A great deal of work had been done in analyzing optical spectra in the century preceding the publication of Bohr's theory of hydrogen. The spectral lines of an element had been arranged in several *series*, and as aids in selecting lines belonging to the same series, various types of evidence were used such as (1) the physical appearance of the lines, whether "sharp" or "diffuse," (2) the methods used in producing the spectra, whether with the aid of an arc or a spark, and (3) the behavior of the lines when the emitting atoms were subjected to external electric and magnetic fields, e.g., the Zeeman effect.

Rydberg (1889) suggested that the optical series then known could be arranged in such a way that the wave number of any line in the series would be given by the difference between two terms as follows

$$\bar{\nu} = \bar{\nu}_{\infty} - \frac{RZ^2}{(n + \phi)^2}, \tag{4}$$

in which R is Rydberg's constant, n is an integer, and ϕ is a fraction less than unity which is practically constant for all lines of the series. The series approaches a limit for very large values of n; the term $\bar{\nu}_{\infty}$ is the wave number approached by the series in the limit as n approaches infinity. Z has the value unity for series due to neutral atoms, the value two for singly charged ions, three for doubly charged ions, and so on. The similarity between Rydberg's formula and Bohr's frequency condition is obvious. In each case the wave number of a line of a spectral series is given as the difference between a fixed term and a variable term. The fixed term is the wave number of the series limit represented by either $\bar{\nu}_{\infty}$ or T_l. The variable term is a wave number associated with an atomic state described by a specific value of the integer n and the constant ϕ.

Of the several series of spectral lines from any one element, the most intense are the principal series, the sharp series, the diffuse series, and the fundamental or Bergmann series. In terms of Rydberg's formula, these series are represented by the following equations:

principal series

$$\bar{\nu} = P_\infty - \frac{R}{(n+P)^2} \qquad (n = 2, 3, 4, \cdots);$$

sharp series

$$\bar{\nu} = S_\infty - \frac{R}{(n+S)^2} \qquad (n = 2, 3, 4, \cdots);$$

diffuse series (5)

$$\bar{\nu} = D_\infty - \frac{R}{(n+D)^2} \qquad (n = 3, 4, 5, \cdots);$$

fundamental series

$$\bar{\nu} = F_\infty - \frac{R}{(n+F)^2} \qquad (n = 4, 5, 6, \cdots).$$

The fixed term $\bar{\nu}_\infty$ is replaced by P_∞, S_∞, D_∞, or F_∞, and the constant ϕ in the variable term is replaced by P, S, D, or F in Rydberg's formula. The constants P, S, D, and F all have different values. It has been found empirically that the fixed terms have the following values:

$$P_\infty = \frac{R}{(1+S)^2};$$

$$S_\infty = \frac{R}{(2+P)^2};$$

$$D_\infty = \frac{R}{(2+P)^2};$$

and

$$F_\infty = \frac{R}{(3+D)^2}.$$

It will be noticed that the sharp and diffuse series both have the same series limit. A shorthand notation is frequently used in writing the equations for the different series. This is done by using the letters which appear in the denominator of the particular term to represent the term. Thus nP is written as an abbreviation of the term $R/(n+P)^2$, nS for $R/(n+S)^2$, nD for $R/(n+D)^2$, and so on. In this notation, the lines of the different series are written as follows:

principal series

$$\bar{\nu} = 1S - nP \qquad (n = 2, 3, 4, 5, \cdots);$$

sharp series (6)

$$\bar{\nu} = 2P - nS \qquad (n = 2, 3, 4, 5, \cdots);$$

diffuse series

$$\bar{\nu} = 2P - nD \qquad (n = 3, 4, 5, 6, \cdots);$$

fundamental series

$$\bar{\nu} = 3D - nF \qquad (n = 4, 5, 6, 7, \cdots). \tag{6}$$

From the analyses of their spectra, term values have been computed for many of the energy states of all the elements. While the wave number of any line can be expressed as the difference between two terms, the converse is not always true; that is, not all the differences that can be formed between the term values of an atom represent spectral lines. In order to account for the nonappearance of certain lines, selection rules are necessary. Such selection rules, originally formulated empirically, can be derived by means of wave mechanics. They are best stated in terms of possible changes in quantum numbers intimately related to the structure of the atom. The simplest formulation is in terms of an atom model, the so-called *vector model* of the atom. Many other points, such as the fine structure of some spectral lines, and the Zeeman effect, are best explained with the aid of this vector model.

8-3. Vector Model of the Atom: Orbital Angular Momentum

It will be recalled that in Bohr's theory of the hydrogen atom, the electron was assumed to be moving in a circular orbit with angular velocity ω. Angular velocity is a vector quantity and is represented by a vector along the axis of rotation, perpendicular to the plane of the orbit. Because of this angular velocity, the electron has a definite angular momentum, p_ϕ, which, on Bohr's theory, was a whole multiple of $h/2\pi$ represented by $k(h/2\pi)$, where k is the azimuthal quantum number. In the vector model of the atom, the quantum number k is replaced by the quantum number l, and the electron is assigned the orbital angular momentum

$$\boxed{p_\phi = l\frac{h}{2\pi}.} \tag{7}$$

Angular momentum is also a vector quantity and is represented by a vector along the axis of rotation. If the unit of angular momentum is chosen as $h/2\pi$, then the angular momentum vector will be l units long. It will be convenient to use l to represent the orbital angular momentum. It must be remarked here, however, that wave mechanics shows that the magnitude of the angular momentum of an electron has the value

$$\boxed{p_\phi = \sqrt{l(l+1)}\,\frac{h}{2\pi}.} \tag{8}$$

While it will be more convenient in the discussion of the vector model of the atom to use the vector $\boldsymbol{l}$, in any calculations that have to be made, its magnitude l will be replaced by the correct value $\sqrt{l(l+1)}$. It will be recalled that l can have the values 0, 1, 2, $\cdots$, $(n-1)$, where n is the principal quantum number.

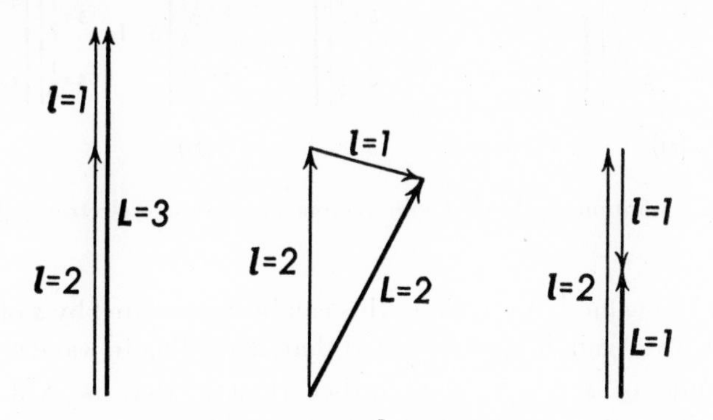

FIG. 8-1. Method of addition of angular momentum vectors.

In considering the more complex atoms, each electron outside the nucleus is assigned an orbital angular momentum as well as a principal quantum number n. The total orbital angular momentum of the atom, denoted by the letter $\boldsymbol{L}$, is the vector sum of the orbital angular momenta of the individual electrons. However, this vector sum, $\boldsymbol{L}$, is restricted by quantum conditions to integral values. For example, in the case of two electrons for which $l = 2$ and $l = 1$, the sum $\boldsymbol{L}$ may have any one of the three values 3, 2, or 1. The method of adding these vectors is shown in Figure 8-1.

The quantity $h/2\pi$ is so widely used as a unit of angular momentum, and occurs so often in atomic and nuclear physics, that it is now commonly represented by the single symbol $\hbar$ (read h bar); thus

$$\hbar = \frac{h}{2\pi}.$$

8-4. Electron Spin

In order to account for the fine structure of the lines in the spectral series of some of the elements and also to account for the anomalous Zeeman effect, Uhlenbeck and Goudsmit (1925) introduced the hypothesis that the electron rotates or spins about an axis just like a top. The angular momentum of the electron due to its spin, p_s, is assigned the value

$$\boxed{p_s = s\frac{h}{2\pi},} \tag{9}$$

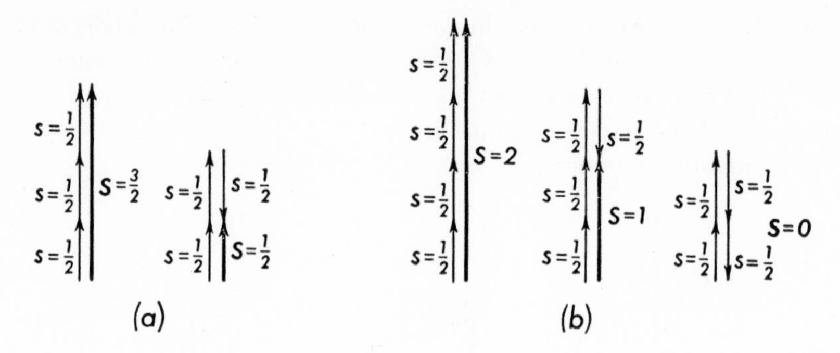

FIG. 8-2. Addition of electron spin vectors (a) for three electrons, (b) for four electrons.

where s has the value $\frac{1}{2}$. Vectorially this can be represented by $\boldsymbol{s}$ of length $\frac{1}{2}$ in units of $h/2\pi$. Again it must be noted that, according to wave mechanics, the magnitude of $\boldsymbol{s}$ is $\sqrt{s(s+1)}$ rather than s; that is, $\sqrt{3}/2$ rather than $\frac{1}{2}$. In the vector treatment of the atom, the *spin quantum number s* will be used, but in actual calculation its wave mechanics value will be substituted.

The vector sum, $\boldsymbol{S}$, of the angular momenta of several electrons is subject to the following restrictions: for an odd number of electrons, $\boldsymbol{S}$ must be an odd multiple of $\frac{1}{2}$; for an even number of electrons, $\boldsymbol{S}$ must be an integer. This means that the vectors representing the spin must always be parallel or antiparallel, i.e., oppositely directed. This is shown in two typical cases in Figure 8-2, one for three electrons for which $\boldsymbol{S}$ can have the values $\frac{1}{2}$ or $\frac{3}{2}$, the other for four electrons for which $\boldsymbol{S}$ can have the values 0, 1, or 2.

8-5. Total Angular Momentum Vector

In many cases, for example in the alkali elements, the changes in the atomic configuration giving rise to the optical spectrum are produced by the motion of a single electron. The total angular momentum of a single electron is the vector sum of the orbital and spin angular momenta of the single electron. The total angular momentum is given by $j(h/2\pi)$ where j is the total angular momentum quantum number. The vector $\boldsymbol{j}$, representing the total angular momentum, is defined by the equation

$$\boxed{\boldsymbol{j} = \boldsymbol{l} + \boldsymbol{s},} \qquad (10)$$

with the restriction that the vector sum must always be an odd multiple of $\frac{1}{2}$. Since s is always equal to $\frac{1}{2}$, j can have only two values for a given value of l, namely, $l + \frac{1}{2}$ and $l - \frac{1}{2}$ except when $l = 0$, in which case j can

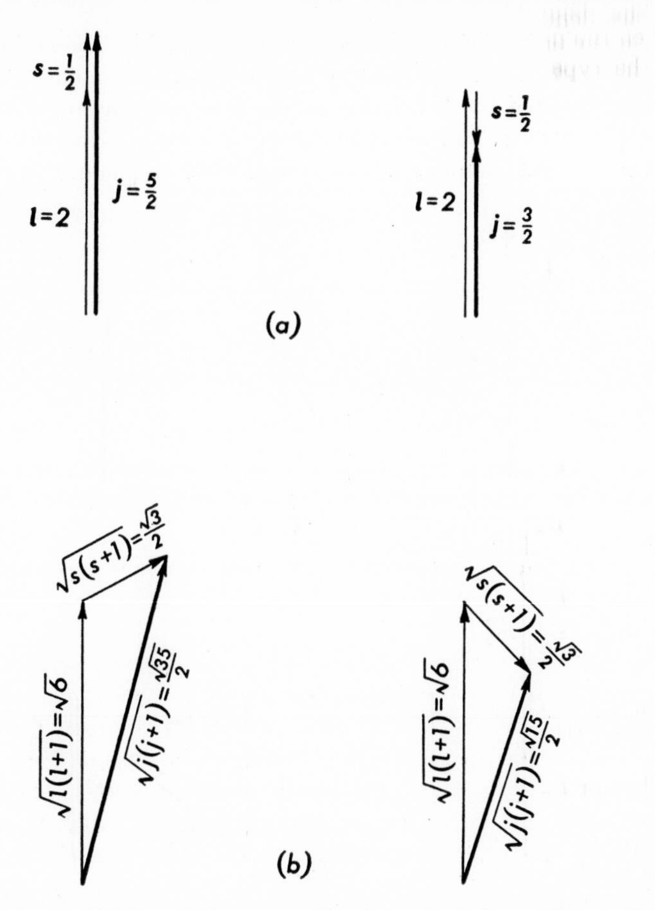

Fig. 8-3. (a) Addition of the vectors $\boldsymbol{l}$ and $\boldsymbol{s}$ to form $\boldsymbol{j}$ according to the vector model. (b) Addition of the vectors $\boldsymbol{l}$ and $\boldsymbol{s}$ to form $\boldsymbol{j}$ according to wave mechanics.

have the value $\frac{1}{2}$ only. Thus for $l = 2$ and $s = \frac{1}{2}$, see Figure 8-3(a), j can have the values $\frac{5}{2}$ and $\frac{3}{2}$.

Again it must be remarked that, from wave mechanical considerations, the magnitude of the vector $\boldsymbol{j}$ should be $\sqrt{j(j+1)}$. In the addition of vectors $\boldsymbol{l}$ and $\boldsymbol{s}$ to form the vector $\boldsymbol{j}$, the magnitude of $\boldsymbol{l}$ is taken as $\sqrt{l(l+1)}$, and that of $\boldsymbol{s}$ is taken as $\sqrt{s(s+1)}$. The numerical values of l, s, and j, which are needed for determining the wave mechanical values of the corresponding vectors, are the values obtained from the vector model of the atom. The angle between the vectors $\boldsymbol{l}$ and $\boldsymbol{s}$ in Figure 8-3(b) can be obtained from the figure with the aid of the cosine law, yielding

$$\cos(s, l) = \frac{j(j+1) - l(l+1) - s(s+1)}{2\sqrt{s(s+1)}\,\sqrt{l(l+1)}}\,. \tag{11}$$

If the changes in atomic states are produced by the action of two or more electrons, then the value of the total angular momentum of these electrons, denoted by J, will depend upon the interaction or the coupling between the orbital and the spin angular momenta. Experience has shown that the type of coupling which occurs most frequently is the Russell-

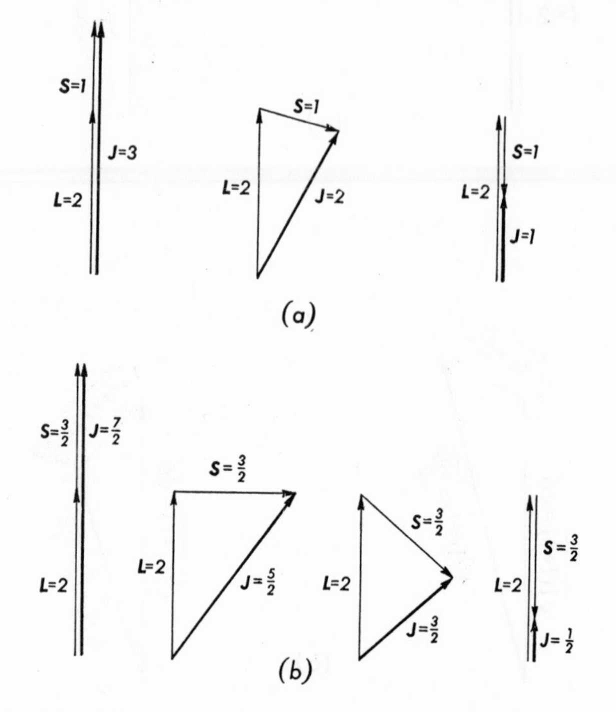

FIG. 8-4. (a) Addition of the vectors $\boldsymbol{L}$ and $\boldsymbol{S}$ to yield integral values of $\boldsymbol{J}$. (b) Addition of the vectors $\boldsymbol{L}$ and $\boldsymbol{S}$ to yield odd half-integral values of $\boldsymbol{J}$.

Saunders or $\boldsymbol{L}$-$\boldsymbol{S}$ type of coupling. In this type of coupling all the orbital angular momentum vectors of the electrons combine to form a resultant $\boldsymbol{L}$, and independently all their spin angular momentum vectors combine to form a resultant $\boldsymbol{S}$. The total angular momentum of the atom is then given by the relation

$$\boxed{\boldsymbol{J} = \boldsymbol{L} + \boldsymbol{S},} \tag{12}$$

with the restriction that J must be an integer if S is an integer, and J must be an odd multiple of $\frac{1}{2}$ if S is an odd multiple of $\frac{1}{2}$. This type of coupling is illustrated in Figure 8-4 for $L = 2$, $S = 1$, and $L = 2$, $S = \frac{3}{2}$. It can be seen from the figure that the number of possible values of J, for $L > S$, is

$2S + 1$. The reader can construct similar figures for other values of L and S and show that when $L < S$, J can have $2L + 1$ values. In particular, if $L = 0$, J can have only one value, namely $J = S$.

8-6. Magnetic Moment of an Orbital Electron

An electron moving in a plane orbit of area A is equivalent to a current i given by

$$i = \frac{e}{cT}, \tag{13}$$

where T is the period of the electron in its orbit, i the current in em units, e the charge of the electron in es units, and c the ratio of the em to the es unit of charge. A plane circuit carrying current (see §1-13) has a magnetic moment μ given by

$$\mu = iA,$$

so that the magnetic moment of the orbital electron is

$$\mu = \frac{eA}{cT}. \tag{14}$$

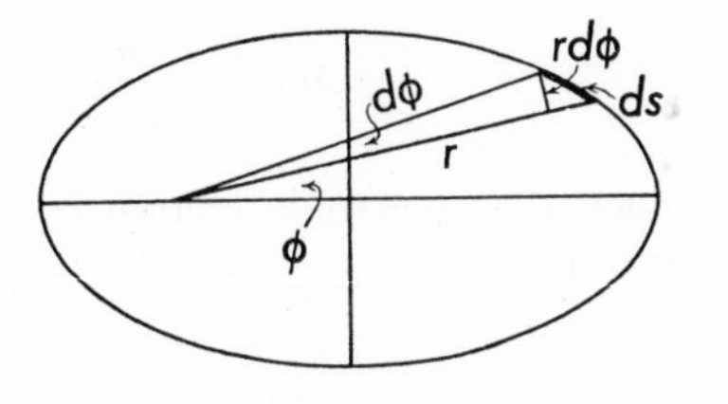

Fig. 8-5. Elliptic orbit of an electron.

To evaluate this magnetic moment, assume that the electron is moving in an elliptic orbit. With polar coordinates r and ϕ, as shown in Figure 8-5, the area can be expressed as

$$A = \tfrac{1}{2}\int_0^{2\pi} r^2 d\phi.$$

Now the angular momentum of the electron p_ϕ is constant and can be expressed as

$$p_\phi = mr^2 \frac{d\phi}{dt}.$$

The elimination of r^2 between the last two equations yields

$$A = \tfrac{1}{2}\int_0^T \frac{p_\phi}{m} dt = \tfrac{1}{2}\frac{p_\phi}{m} T. \tag{15}$$

The magnetic moment μ is therefore

$$\boxed{\mu = \frac{e}{2mc} p_\phi.} \tag{16}$$

The angular momentum p_ϕ can also be expressed in terms of the orbital quantum number l as

$$p_\phi = \frac{lh}{2\pi},$$

from which

$$\mu = l\,\frac{eh}{4\pi mc}. \tag{17}$$

The magnetic moment of the orbital electron is therefore an integral multiple of the quantity $eh/4\pi mc$. This quantity is known as the magnetic moment of a *Bohr magneton* and will be represented by the symbol M_B. Substitution of the numerical values for the constants yields

$$M_B = \frac{eh}{4\pi mc} = 9.27 \times 10^{-21} \text{ erg gauss}^{-1}.$$

Since the electronic charge is negative, the magnetic moment due to its orbital motion,

$$\boldsymbol{\mu} = \boldsymbol{l} M_B,$$

can be represented by a vector opposite to that of $\boldsymbol{l}$.

8-7. Magnetic Moment Due to Spin

An electron spinning about its axis should also behave as a tiny magnet and possess a magnetic moment due to this spin. However, nothing is known about the shape of an electron or the manner in which its charge is distributed. Lacking this information, it is impossible to calculate its spin magnetic moment in a manner analogous to that used for the orbital motion. In order to obtain agreement with experimental results, it is necessary to assign to the spin magnetic moment the value

$$\mu_s = 2 \cdot \frac{e}{2mc}\, p_s, \tag{18}$$

where

$$p_s = s\,\frac{h}{2\pi};$$

so that

$$\mu_s = 2s\,\frac{eh}{4\pi mc}. \tag{19}$$

On the basis of the vector model of the atom, s is always $\frac{1}{2}$, so that the magnetic moment due to spin would have the value of one Bohr magneton. According to wave mechanics this value of s should be replaced by $\sqrt{s(s+1)} = \sqrt{3}/2$. In this case

$$\boxed{\mu_s = \sqrt{3}\,\frac{eh}{4\pi mc}}$$

$$= 1.62 \times 10^{-20} \text{ erg gauss}^{-1}.$$

8-8. Magnetic Quantum Numbers

When the atoms of an element are placed in a very strong magnetic field of intensity H, the electrons, because of their magnetic moments, will experience torques tending to orient them. One of the effects of the introduction of this external magnetic field is that there now exists a definite

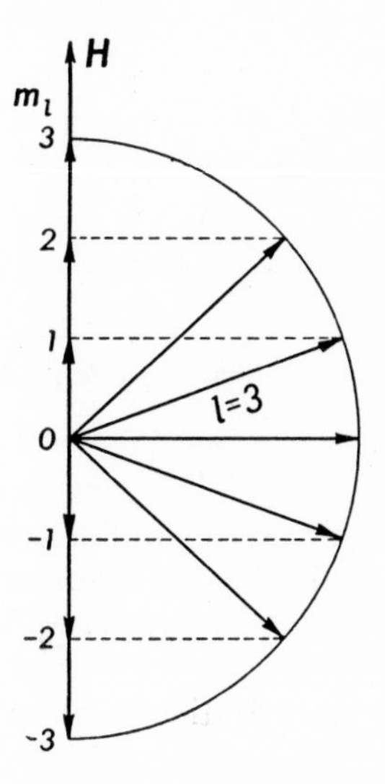

FIG. 8-6. Projection of $\boldsymbol{l}$ in the direction of the magnetic field $\boldsymbol{H}$ determines the magnetic orbital quantum number $\boldsymbol{m_l}$.

direction in space to which the vector quantities may be referred. If the magnetic field is strong enough to break down the coupling between the electrons so that each electron acts independently, then the spin and angular momentum vectors will take up definite positions in space with respect to the magnetic field. These vectors, however, may be oriented only in certain definite directions with respect to the magnetic field. According to wave mechanics, the directions that the vector $\boldsymbol{l}$ may assume are such that its projection in the direction of the magnetic field must always have an integral value.

The projection of $\boldsymbol{l}$ on the magnetic field direction is denoted by $\boldsymbol{m_l}$, and is called the *magnetic orbital quantum number*. The possible values of

m_l are $l, l-1, l-2, \cdots 0, \cdots -l$, that is, there are $2l+1$ possible values of m_l. This is illustrated in Figure 8-6 for $l = 3$. The angle θ between $\boldsymbol{l}$ and $\boldsymbol{H}$ is given by

$$\cos\theta = \frac{m_l}{l}. \tag{20}$$

The torque due to the magnetic field causes the angular momentum vector $\boldsymbol{l}$ to precess about the direction of the magnetic field as an axis,

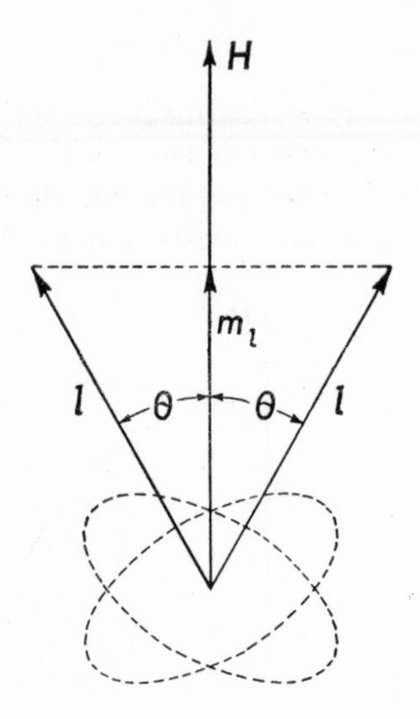

Fig. 8-7. Precession of the angular momentum vector $\boldsymbol{l}$ about $\boldsymbol{H}$ as an axis.

always maintaining the same inclination θ, as shown in Figure 8-7. The additional energy $\Delta\mathcal{E}$ due to the action of the magnetic field is given by

$$\Delta\mathcal{E} = \mu H \cos\theta. \qquad \text{(Chap. 1, Eq. [21])}$$

Substitution of the values of μ and $\cos\theta$ from equations (17) and (20) yields

$$\boxed{\Delta\mathcal{E} = \frac{eh}{4\pi mc} H m_l.} \tag{21}$$

This equation will be useful in the discussion of the Zeeman effect.

The vector $\boldsymbol{s}$ representing the spin angular momentum can assume only two possible positions with respect to the magnetic field: it may be parallel to it or antiparallel; that is, oppositely directed to it. Its projection along the direction of the magnetic field is denoted by $\boldsymbol{m_s}$, which is called the magnetic spin quantum number, and can have only two values, $+\frac{1}{2}$ or $-\frac{1}{2}$, as illustrated in Figure 8-8.

There are similar restrictions on the positions that the total angular momentum vector j can assume in the presence of a magnetic field. Since we are dealing with only a single electron, j can have only odd half-integral

FIG. 8-8. Projection of the spin vector $\boldsymbol{s}$ in the direction of the magnetic field showing the two possible values of $\boldsymbol{m_s}$.

values; the restriction on the positions of j is that m_j, the projection of j on the direction of the magnetic field, must have odd half-integral values. Figure 8-9(a) shows the possible values of m_j for $j = \frac{3}{2}$.

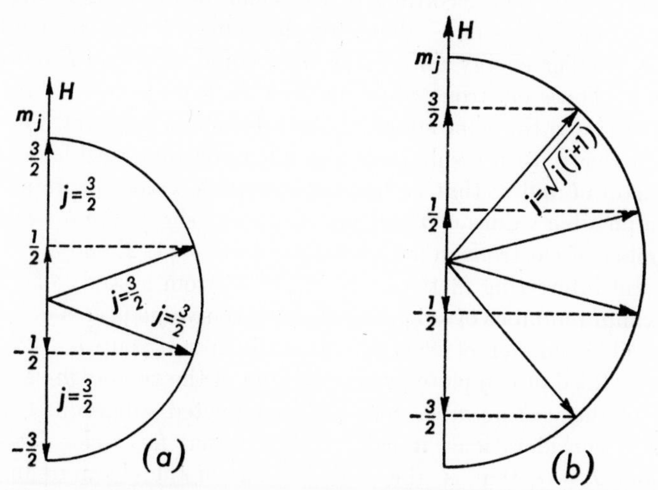

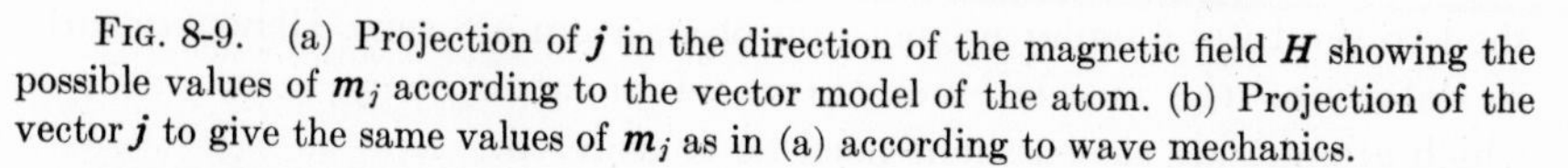
FIG. 8-9. (a) Projection of j in the direction of the magnetic field $\boldsymbol{H}$ showing the possible values of $\boldsymbol{m_j}$ according to the vector model of the atom. (b) Projection of the vector j to give the same values of $\boldsymbol{m_j}$ as in (a) according to wave mechanics.

On the basis of wave mechanics, m_j remains a half-integer for the corresponding values of j even though the magnitude of j is $\sqrt{j(j+1)}$. The orientations of j with respect to the magnetic field are, however, slightly different, as illustrated in Figure 8-9(b). It will be noted that there are $2j + 1$ values for $\boldsymbol{m}_j$ in both methods of projection. The term *space quantization* is usually applied to the above restrictions imposed on the orientation of the vectors $\boldsymbol{l}$, $\boldsymbol{s}$, and $\boldsymbol{j}$ in the presence of a magnetic field.

8-9. Pauli's Exclusion Principle

All these quantum numbers having been introduced, the problem now is to assign the appropriate set of quantum numbers to each electron in the atom in order to specify the *state* of the electron. Wave mechanics does not offer any guiding principle for the assignment of these quantum numbers. However, Pauli (1925) introduced a principle, known as *Pauli's exclusion principle*, for the assignment of quantum numbers to the electrons in the atom. *Pauli's exclusion principle states that no two electrons in an atom can exist in the same state.* Now, the state of any one electron can be completely specified by a group of four quantum numbers, such as n, l, m_l, m_s or n, l, j, m_j. Hence Pauli's exclusion principle states that the group of values assigned to the four quantum numbers must be different for different electrons.

Electrons having the same value for the principal quantum number n form a definite *group*, or *shell*, or *energy level*. Electrons with the same n are further subdivided according to the value of the orbital angular momentum l. Differences in l values, for the same value of n, denote comparatively smaller energy differences than equal values of l and different values of n. Those electrons which possess the same value of l for a given n are said to be in the same subgroup, or subshell, or sublevel. The possible number of electrons in a subgroup depends upon the possible orientations of the vectors $\boldsymbol{l}$ and $\boldsymbol{s}$; that is, upon the possible values of $\boldsymbol{m}_l$ and $\boldsymbol{m}_s$, or upon the possible values of $\boldsymbol{j}$ and $\boldsymbol{m}_j$. Table 8-1 shows the maximum possible number of electrons in a given group for $n = 1, 2,$ and 3.

Several interesting facts can be obtained from a study of Table 8-1. The maximum number of subgroups for a given value of n is n. The maximum possible number of electrons in a given subgroup is $2(2l + 1)$. A subgroup is filled or completed when the sum of the vectors $\boldsymbol{m}_l$ is zero. Also the sum of the vectors $\boldsymbol{m}_s$ is zero for a completed subgroup. From wave mechanical considerations, it can be shown that *for a closed shell* $\boldsymbol{S}=0$, $\boldsymbol{L} = 0$, *and* $\boldsymbol{J} = 0$; that is, the contributions of the electrons in a closed shell to the total angular momentum of an atom are zero. Hence, in order to determine the angular momentum of an atom, only those electrons which are outside closed shells need be considered.

8-10. Distribution of Electrons in an Atom

In assigning electrons to the different groups and subgroups in an atom, we must have recourse not only to optical and x-ray spectra, but also to

Table 8-1

Possible Number of Electrons in a Given Group

n	l	m_l	m_s	No. of Electrons in Subgroup	No. of Electrons in Completed Group
1	0	0	$+\frac{1}{2}$	2	2
1	0	0	$-\frac{1}{2}$		
2	0	0	$+\frac{1}{2}$	2	8
2	0	0	$-\frac{1}{2}$		
2	1	-1	$+\frac{1}{2}$	6	
2	1	-1	$-\frac{1}{2}$		
2	1	0	$+\frac{1}{2}$		
2	1	0	$-\frac{1}{2}$		
2	1	1	$+\frac{1}{2}$		
2	1	1	$-\frac{1}{2}$		
3	0	0	$+\frac{1}{2}$	2	18
3	0	0	$-\frac{1}{2}$		
3	1	-1	$+\frac{1}{2}$	6	
3	1	-1	$-\frac{1}{2}$		
3	1	0	$+\frac{1}{2}$		
3	1	0	$-\frac{1}{2}$		
3	1	1	$+\frac{1}{2}$		
3	1	1	$-\frac{1}{2}$		
3	2	-2	$+\frac{1}{2}$	10	
3	2	-2	$-\frac{1}{2}$		
3	2	-1	$+\frac{1}{2}$		
3	2	-1	$-\frac{1}{2}$		
3	2	0	$+\frac{1}{2}$		
3	2	0	$-\frac{1}{2}$		
3	2	1	$+\frac{1}{2}$		
3	2	1	$-\frac{1}{2}$		
3	2	2	$+\frac{1}{2}$		
3	2	2	$-\frac{1}{2}$		

Table 8-2

Distribution of Electrons in the Atoms

X-Ray Notation			K	L		M			N				
Values of n, l			1,0	2,0	2,1	3,0	3,1	3,2	4,0	4,1	4,2	4,3	
Spectral Notation			1s	2s	2p	3s	3p	3d	4s	4p	4d	4f	
Element	Atomic Number Z	First Ionization Potential in Volts											Lowest Spectral Term
H	1	13.595	1										$^2S_{1/2}$
He	2	24.580	2										$^1S_0$
Li	3	5.390	2	1									$^2S_{1/2}$
Be	4	9.320	2	2									$^1S_0$
B	5	8.296	2	2	1								$^2P_{1/2}$
C	6	11.264	2	2	2								$^3P_0$
N	7	14.54	2	2	3								$^4S_{3/2}$
O	8	13.614	2	2	4								$^3P_2$
F	9	17.418	2	2	5								$^2P_{3/2}$
Ne	10	21.559	2	2	6								$^1S_0$
Na	11	5.138	Neon Configuration 10 Electron Core			1							$^2S_{1/2}$
Mg	12	7.644				2							$^1S_0$
Al	13	5.984				2	1						$^2P_{1/2}$
Si	14	8.149				2	2						$^3P_0$
P	15	10.55				2	3						$^4S_{3/2}$
S	16	10.357				2	4						$^3P_2$
Cl	17	13.01				2	5						$^2P_{3/2}$
A	18	15.755				2	6						$^1S_0$
K	19	4.339	Argon Configuration 18 Electron Core						1				$^2S_{1/2}$
Ca	20	6.111							2				$^1S_0$
Sc	21	6.538						1	2				$^2D_{3/2}$
Ti	22	6.818						2	2				$^3F_2$
V	23	6.743						3	2				$^4F_{3/2}$
Cr	24	6.764						5	1				$^7S_3$
Mn	25	7.432						5	2				$^6S_{5/2}$
Fe	26	7.868						6	2				$^5D_4$
Co	27	7.862						7	2				$^4F_{9/2}$
Ni	28	7.633						8	2				$^3F_4$
Cu	29	7.724						10	1				$^2S_{1/2}$
Zn	30	9.391						10	2				$^1S_0$
Ga	31	6.00						10	2	1			$^2P_{1/2}$
Ge	32	7.88						10	2	2			$^3P_0$
As	33	9.81						10	2	3			$^4S_{3/2}$
Se	34	9.75						10	2	4			$^3P_2$
Br	35	11.84						10	2	5			$^2P_{3/2}$
Kr	36	13.996						10	2	6			$^1S_0$

Table 8-2 (*Continued*)

Distribution of Electrons in the Atoms

X-Ray Notation			K	L	M	N				O					P						
Values of n, l			1 1,0	2 0,1	3 0,1,2	4,0	4,1	4,2	4,3	5,0	5,1	5,2	5,3	5,4	6,0	6,1	6,2	6,3	6,4	6,5	
Spectral Notation			$1s$	$s.p$	s,p,d	$4s$	$4p$	$4d$	$4f$	$5s$	$5p$	$5d$	$5f$	$5g$	$6s$	$6p$	$6d$	$6f$	$6g$	$6h$	
Element	Atomic Number Z	First Ionization Potential in Volts																			Lowest Spectral Term
Rb	37	4.176								1											$^2S_{1/2}$
Sr	38	5.692	Krypton Configuration							2											$^1S_0$
Y	39	6.38						1		2											$^2D_{3/2}$
Zr	40	6.835						2		2											$^3F_2$
Nb	41	6.88						4		1											$^6D_{1/2}$
Mo	42	7.13	36 Electron Core					5		1											$^7S_3$
Tc	43	7.23						6		1											$^6S_{5/2}$
Ru	44	7.36						7		1											$^5F_5$
Rh	45	7.46						8		1											$^4F_{9/2}$
Pd	46	8.334						10													$^1S_0$
Ag	47	7.574								1											$^2S_{1/2}$
Cd	48	8.991	Palladium Configuration							2											$^1S_0$
In	49	5.785								2	1										$^2P_{1/2}$
Sn	50	7.332								2	2										$^3P_0$
Sb	51	8.64								2	3										$^4S_{3/2}$
Te	52	9.01	46 Electron Core							2	4										$^3P_2$
I	53	10.44								2	5										$^2P_{3/2}$
Xe	54	12.127								2	6										$^1S_0$
Cs	55	3.893	Xenon Configuration 54 Electron Core												1						$^2S_{1/2}$
Ba	56	5.210													2						$^1S_0$
La	57	5.61	Shells $1s$ to $4d$ contain 46 electrons							2	6	1			2						$^2D_{3/2}$
Ce	58	6.91							1	2	6	1			2						
Pr	59	5.76							2	2	6	1			2						
Nd	60	6.31							3	2	6	1			2						$^5I_4$
Pm	61	—							4	2	6	1			2						
Sm	62	5.6							5	2	6	1			2						$^7F_0$
Eu	63	5.67							6	2	6	1			2						$^8S_{7/2}$
Gd	64	6.16							7	2	6	1			2						$^9D_2$
Tb	65	6.74							8	2	6	1			2						
Dy	66	6.82							9	2	6	1			2						
Ho	67	—							10	2	6	1			2						
Er	68	—							11	2	6	1			2						
Tm	69	—							13	2	6	0			2						$^2F_{7/2}$
Yb	70	6.2							14	2	6	0			2						$^1S_0$
Lu	71	5.0							14	2	6	1			2						$^3D_{5/2}$

Table 8-2 *(Concluded)*

Distribution of Electrons in the Atoms

X-Ray Notation			K	L	M	N	O					P						Q		
Values of n, l			1	2	3	4	5,0	5,1	5,2	5,3	5,4	6,0	6,1	6,2	6,3	6,4	6,5	7,0	7,1	
Spectral Notation							$5s$	$5p$	$5d$	$5f$	$5g$	$6s$	$6p$	$6d$	$6f$	$6g$	$6h$	$7s$	$7p$	
Element	Atomic Number Z	First Ionization Potential in Volts																		Lowest Spectral Term
Hf	72	5.5	Shells 1s to 5p contain 68 electrons						2			2								$^3F_2$
Ta	73	7.7							3			2								$^4F_{3/2}$
W	74	7.98							4			2								$^5D_0$
Re	75	7.87							5			2								$^6S_{5/2}$
Os	76	8.7							6			2								$^5D_4$
Ir	77	9.2							7			2								$^4F_{9/2}$
Pt	78	8.96							9			1								$^3D_3$
Au	79	9.223							10			1								$^2S_{1/2}$
Hg	80	10.434	Shells 1s to 5d contain 78 electrons									2								$^1S_0$
Tl	81	6.106										2	1							$^2P_{1/2}$
Pb	82	7.415										2	2							$^3P_0$
Bi	83	8.3										2	3							$^4S_{3/2}$
Po	84	8.4										2	4							
At	85	9.5										2	5							
Rn	86	10.745										2	6							$^1S_0$
Fr	87	4.0	Radon Configuration 86 Electron Core															1		
Ra	88	5.277																2		$^1S_0$
Ac	89											2	6	1				2		
Th	90									1		2	6	1				2		$^3F_2$
Pa	91									2		2	6	1				2		
U	92	4								3		2	6	1				2		$^5L_6$
Np	93									4		2	6	1				2		
Pu	94									5		2	6	1				2		
Am	95									6		2	6	1				2		
Cm	96									7		2	6	1				2		
Bk	97									8		2	6	1				2		
Cf	98									9		2	6	1				2		

NOTE: The lowest spectral term and the ionization potential for each element obtained from Table 23 of National Bureau of Standards, Circular 467, with corrections supplied by Charlotte E. Moore.

other phenomena, such as the magnetic and chemical behavior of the element. The normal state of an atom is one in which all the electrons are in the lowest possible energy levels. In the atom of the simplest element, hydrogen, $Z = 1$, the normal state is characterized by the quantum numbers $n = 1, l = 0$; m_l is, of course, zero, and m_s may be either $+\frac{1}{2}$ or $-\frac{1}{2}$. The atom of the next element, helium, $Z = 2$, has both its electrons in the shell $n = 1, l = 0$; m_s is $+\frac{1}{2}$ for one electron and $-\frac{1}{2}$ for the second electron. This shell is now completed or closed. It will be recalled that helium is one of the inert gases; therefore it may be expected to have a very stable electron configuration. This should also be true of all the other inert gases.

In the atom of the next element, lithium, $Z = 3$, two electrons can be put in the shell $n = 1, l = 0$, but the third electron must be put into a new shell $n = 2, l = 0$. Lithium is one of the alkali elements and has a valence of unity. This means that a single electron, in shell $n = 2$, can be detached easily from the atom to form the lithium ion, Li^+. This is indicated by the fact that its ionization potential is only 5.39 volts, whereas for He it is 24.58 volts (see Table 8-2). Another interesting point is that the lithium ion, Li^+, has the same configuration as neutral helium. One may expect the atoms of the other alkali elements, sodium, potassium, rubidium, and caesium, to be built up in a similar manner, that is, a single valence electron starting a new shell outside a closed configuration typical of an inert gas. This is shown in Table 8-2, which gives the distribution of electrons in the atoms of the elements.

It is convenient at this point to introduce the x-ray notation for the different groups. The group or shell for which $n = 1$ is called the K shell, $n = 2$ the L shell, $n = 3$ the M shell, and so on. Beryllium, for example, with $Z = 4$, has two electrons in the completed K shell, and two additional electrons in the L shell, thus completing the first subgroup in this shell. Beryllium is one of the alkaline earth elements with a valence of 2. The atoms of the other elements of this group, magnesium, calcium, strontium, barium, and radium, should have similar structures, that is, two electrons outside an inert gas or closed shell configuration. This can be verified from Table 8-2.

Boron, $Z = 5$, has two electrons in the completed K shell and three electrons in the L shell, and two in the completed subgroup $n = 2, l = 0$, the third electron starting the new subgroup $n = 2, l = 1$. The atoms of the other elements in this group, aluminum, gallium, indium, and thallium, similarly have three electrons outside a closed shell, two in a completed subgroup $l = 0$, and one in the next subgroup $l = 1$.

This process of atom building can be continued by the addition of an electron to the L shell subgroup $l = 1$, as the element of atomic number $Z + 1$ is formed from element of atomic number Z. In each case the positive charge on the nucleus must be increased by one. The L shell will be completed with the element neon, $Z = 10$, with two electrons in the K shell and eight electrons in the L shell. Neon is one of the inert gases and has a very stable configuration. Fluorine, $Z = 9$, has two electrons in the K shell and seven electrons in the L shell. In chemical action it is found that fluorine has a valence of -1, indicating that it very easily forms an ion F^- by adding an electron to the L shell, forming a stable configuration similar to that of neon.

The next eight elements, from sodium, $Z = 11$, to argon, $Z = 18$, are formed by adding the additional electrons to the M shell for which $n = 3$. Sodium has an electron ($n = 3, l = 0$) outside a closed shell; magnesium has two electrons outside this closed shell, both in the subgroup $l = 0$, thus completing it. The next subgroup with $l = 1$ is begun with aluminum, $Z = 13$, and completed with argon, $Z = 18$. It may be remarked here that the chemical properties of an element are determined mostly by the electrons in the outer shell of the atom.

Potassium, $Z = 19$, retains the argon configuration of the first eighteen electrons, but the nineteenth electron starts a new group, $n = 4$, belonging to the N shell. Calcium, $Z = 20$, has two electrons in the N shell $n = 4, l = 0$. It might have been expected that these electrons would have been placed in the still incomplete M shell $n = 3, l = 2$, but spectroscopic evidence is against this. However, the next group of atoms from scandium, $Z = 21$, to copper, $Z = 29$, have their additional electrons placed in the M shell $n = 3, l = 2$, which is then completed. From gallium, $Z = 31$, to krypton, $Z = 36$, an inert gas, the additional electrons are added to the N shell $n = 4, l = 1$. By examining Table 8-2, the reader will find the order in which electrons have been assigned to the various groups and subgroups. It will be of interest to check this assignment with the chemical properties of the elements, remembering that these properties are controlled essentially by the outer electrons.

8-11. Spectral Notation

In the course of the development of spectroscopy, several types of notation have been used. The following is the modern notation. In describing the electron configuration small letters are used to represent the values of l as follows:

$$\begin{aligned} l = {} & 0,\ 1,\ 2,\ 3,\ 4,\ 5,\ \cdots \\ & s,\ p,\ d,\ f,\ g,\ h,\ \cdots. \end{aligned}$$

That is, if an electron is in a shell for which $l = 0$, it is called an s electron, for $l = 1$, a p electron, and so on. The value of the total quantum number n is written as a prefix to the letter representing its l value. The number of electrons having the same n and l values is indicated by an index written at the upper right of the letter representing their l value. Thus the eleven electrons of sodium in the normal state are designated as follows:

$$1s^2\ 2s^2\ 2p^6\ 3s;$$

that is, there are two $1s$ electrons, two $2s$ electrons, six $2p$ electrons, and one $3s$ electron. One must be careful not to confuse the symbol s written for $l = 0$ with the same symbol used for the spin quantum number.

Capital letters are used to represent the total orbital angular momentum of an atom according to the following scheme:

$$\begin{aligned} L &= 0,\ 1,\ 2,\ 3,\ 4,\ 5,\ \cdots \\ &\ \ S,\ P,\ D,\ F,\ G,\ H,\ \cdots \end{aligned}$$

The value of the total angular momentum of the atom, J, is written as a subscript at the lower right of the letter representing the particular L value of the atomic state. *The number of possible values of J for a given value of L is written as a superscript at the upper left of the letter representing the L value.* Thus $^2P_{1/2}$, $^2P_{3/2}$, read "doublet P one half," etc., or $^3P_2$, $^3P_1$, $^3P_0$, read "triplet P two," . . . , and so on. For example, in the case of the alkali atoms, J has two values for each of the P, D, F terms, but can have only one value for the S term. But, by custom, to keep the notation symmetrical, S is allotted the superscript 2. As will be shown, this superscript is an indication of the multiplicity of the terms of the atomic configuration.

8-12. Spectrum of Sodium

The optical spectrum of sodium is typical of the spectra of all the alkali atoms. In its normal state, the sodium atom consists of a closed core of ten electrons and one additional electron in the $3s$ state. Since the closed core contributes nothing to the angular momentum of the atom, only the states of this eleventh or optical electron need be considered in discussing the spectrum of neutral sodium.

The atoms of sodium can be raised from the normal state to higher energy states by bombarding them with electrons, or by subjecting them to high temperatures in a flame or in an electric arc, or by allowing them to absorb radiant energy from an external source. The atom in one of the higher energy states is said to be in an *excited* state. When the atom returns to a state of lower energy, radiation is emitted in the form of a photon of very definite frequency given by Bohr's frequency condition. The spectrum of sodium, as shown in Figure 8-10, consists of several series of spectral lines, some of which were mentioned in §8-2. When these spectral lines are examined with instruments of high resolving power, it is found that many of the lines consist of doublets, that is, two lines very close together. Such lines are said to exhibit *fine structure*. For example, the well-known yellow line of sodium, frequently referred to as the sodium D line, consists of two lines close together of wavelengths 5889.96A and 5895.93A; that is, they are separated by about 6A. These lines form one of the doublets of the principal series. The other lines of the principal series are in the ultraviolet region. Lines of the principal series are due to transitions from a P state to the lowest S state. Since the smallest value of the principal quantum number for the optical electron of sodium is $n = 3$, the lowest state is designated as a $3S$ state. Since $l = 0$, the value of j for this state is $j = s = \frac{1}{2}$. For the P state $L = l = 1$, and since $J = L + \frac{1}{2}$ and $L - \frac{1}{2}$,

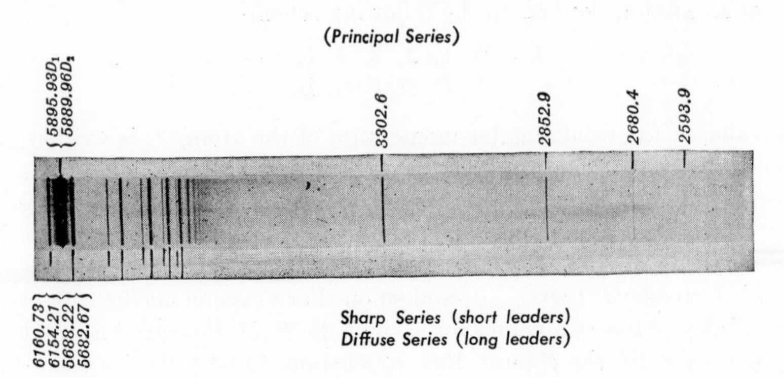

FIG. 8-10. The emission spectrum of sodium showing lines of three series. The upper numbers are wavelengths, in A, of the lines of the principal series. The short leaders below the spectrum indicate the lines of the sharp series, while the long leaders indicate the lines of the diffuse series. (Reprinted by permission from *Atomic Spectra and Atomic Structure*, by G. Herzberg, Dover Publications.)

the total angular momentum of the P state is $\frac{1}{2}$ or $\frac{3}{2}$. Since there are two values of J, the P state is a doublet state and is designated as

$$^2P_{1/2},\ ^2P_{3/2}.$$

Similarly for the D terms for which $L = l = 2$, $J = j = \frac{3}{2}$ or $\frac{5}{2}$, so that the D term is a doublet and is designated as

$$^2D_{3/2},\ ^2D_{5/2},$$

and the F term $L = l = 3$, $J = j = \frac{5}{2}$ or $\frac{7}{2}$, is designated as

$$^2F_{5/2},\ ^2F_{7/2}.$$

The S state is always a single state but since the other states of the atom are all doublets, the S state is also designated as

$$^2S_{1/2}.$$

The energy level diagram of sodium, Figure 8-11, shows the relative positions of these energy levels, drawn approximately to scale. The $^2P_{3/2}$ level is actually slightly above the $^2P_{1/2}$ level, but the separation is too small to be shown in the figure. For example, the separation of the ^2P levels giving rise to the yellow lines of sodium is only 17 cm^{-1}, whereas the term value is about 25,000 cm^{-1}. Similarly the ^2D and ^2F levels are drawn as single levels. The principal quantum number n is written for each term in the figure. It will be noticed that the large wave numbers are

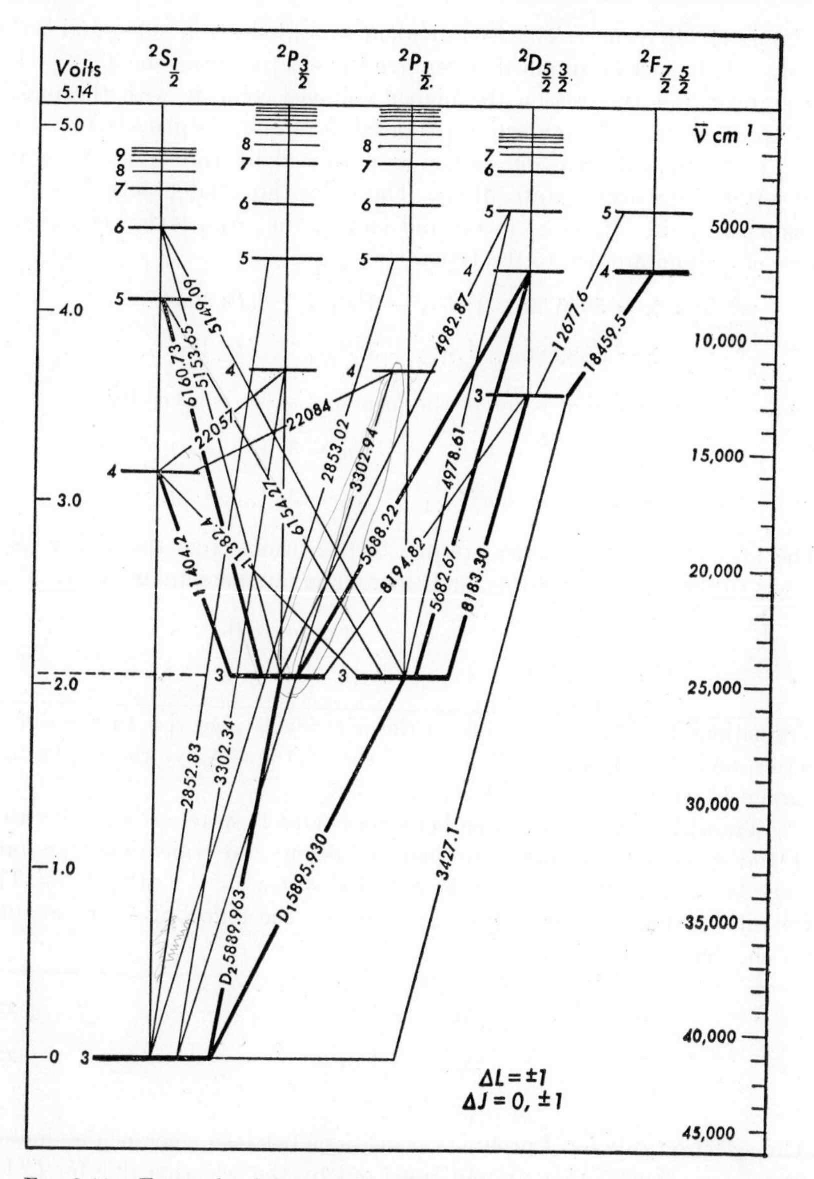

FIG. 8-11. Energy level diagram of sodium. The numbers along the lines are the wavelengths, in angstroms, emitted during the indicated transitions.

associated with the low energy terms. This is due to the fact that the zero level of energy is taken as the energy of ionized atom; the energy values are all negative, but the minus signs have been omitted as a matter of convenience. The lowest energy level is the $3^2S_{1/2}$ level and its numerical value is 41,449.0 cm^{-1}. This is equivalent to 5.14 electron volts, and is the energy that must be supplied to remove the electron from the $3^2S_{1/2}$ level to infinity. For this reason the higher voltages coincide with the higher energy levels, and the ionization potential, 5.14 volts, is placed at $n = \infty$.

The principal series of sodium is produced by transitions from the ^2P states to the lowest state, $3^2S_{1/2}$. These lines are all doublets since they originate in the $^2P_{1/2,\ 3/2}$ levels and end in the $^2S_{1/2}$ level. The yellow lines of sodium are due to the transitions

$$\lambda = 5895.93\text{A},\ 3^2S_{1/2} - 3^2P_{1/2} \qquad (D_1 \text{ line})$$

$$\lambda = 5889.96\text{A},\ 3^2S_{1/2} - 3^2P_{3/2} \qquad (D_2 \text{ line}).$$

The wave number of any line of the principal series is given by

$$\bar{\nu} = 3^2S_{1/2} - n^2P_{1/2}, \qquad (n = 3, 4, 5, \cdots)$$

or

$$\bar{\nu} = 3^2S_{1/2} - n^2P_{3/2} \qquad (n = 3, 4, 5, \cdots).$$

The lines of the sharp series are due to transitions from the higher $^2S_{1/2}$ levels to the $3^2P_{1/2,\ 3/2}$ levels, and their wave numbers are given by

$$\bar{\nu} = 3^2P_{1/2} - n^2S_{1/2} \qquad (n = 4, 5, 6, \cdots)$$

$$\bar{\nu} = 3^2P_{3/2} - n^2S_{1/2} \qquad (n = 4, 5, 6, \cdots).$$

Transitions from the ^2D levels to the 3^2P levels give rise to the diffuse series, and those from the ^2F levels to the 3^2D levels give rise to the fundamental series.

Transitions can take place between S and P states, P and D states, D and F states, but under normal conditions, no transitions can take place between S and D states, or S and F states, or P and F states. The transitions that can take place are given by the following selection rules for the vectors $\boldsymbol{L}$ and $\boldsymbol{J}$:

$$\Delta L = \pm 1 \qquad \textbf{(22a)}$$

$$\Delta J = \pm 1 \text{ or } 0. \qquad \textbf{(22b)}$$

The selection rule for J prohibits transitions between some of the doublet levels even though they are not ruled out by the selection rule for $\boldsymbol{L}$. For example, in the diffuse series, the transition $^2P_{1/2} - {}^2D_{5/2}$ is forbidden, while the other three transitions are permitted.

The doublet character of the energy levels is typical not only of sodium and the other alkali elements, but also of the singly ionized alkaline earth elements such as Be^+, Mg^+, Ca^+, and so on. A glance at Table 8-2 will show that the singly ionized atoms of the alkaline earths have exactly the same electronic structure as the neutral alkali atoms, that is, a single electron outside a closed core typical of the configuration of the atoms of the inert elements. It should be emphasized that the doublet character of the energy levels is satisfactorily accounted for by the hypothesis that the electron possesses a spin.

8-13. Absorption of Energy

If white light is sent through sodium vapor and then examined with a reflection grating, it is found that those wavelengths which correspond to the lines of the principal series of sodium are missing. Such a spectrum is called an *absorption* spectrum. R. W. Wood and his collaborators performed a series of experiments on the absorption spectrum of sodium. In one such experiment the vapor was obtained by heating metallic sodium

FIG. 8-12. Photograph of the absorption spectrum of sodium showing some of the lines in the ultraviolet region. The numbers are the wavelengths of the lines in angstroms. (Reprinted by permission from *Atomic Spectra and Atomic Structure* by H. Herzberg, Dover Publications.)

in a steel tube faced with quartz windows. It was necessary to use quartz windows in this experiment since most of the lines of the principal series of sodium are in the ultraviolet region. As many as sixty lines were observed in this absorption spectrum. That only lines of the principal series appear in the absorption spectrum is due to the fact that most of the atoms in the tube are in the lowest state, $3^2S_{1/2}$. A photograph of the absorption spectrum of sodium is shown in Figure 8-12. In emission, the lines of the principal series correspond to transitions from the $^2P_{1/2,\ 3/2}$ levels to the ground state, $3^2S_{1/2}$; in absorption, the transitions are from the lowest state, $3^2S_{1/2}$ to the $^2P_{1/2,\ 3/2}$ levels.

An interesting experiment would be to send monochromatic light of wavelength equal to that of the sodium D lines into a tube containing sodium vapor. R. W. Wood performed such an experiment, using the yellow light from an oxyhydrogen flame containing sodium. The yellow light was focused on the axis of an evacuated test tube containing sodium vapor. On looking down into the test tube it was found that the sodium vapor, near the wall of the tube where the incident beam entered, emitted yellow fluorescent radiation. Other investigations showed that the fluorescent radiation consisted only of the yellow lines of sodium. By referring to the energy level diagram, it can be seen that the atoms in the normal state, $3^2S_{1/2}$, were raised to the next higher states, $3^2P_{1/2,\ 3/2}$, by the absorption of the yellow D lines. On returning to the normal state these atoms emitted radiation of the same wavelength. This type of fluorescent radiation is called *resonance radiation.*

An entirely different method of raising the atoms from their normal to excited states is to utilize the kinetic energy of an electron beam. A simplified schematic diagram for accomplishing this is shown in Figure 8-13. The electrodes are in an evacuated tube containing a small amount of

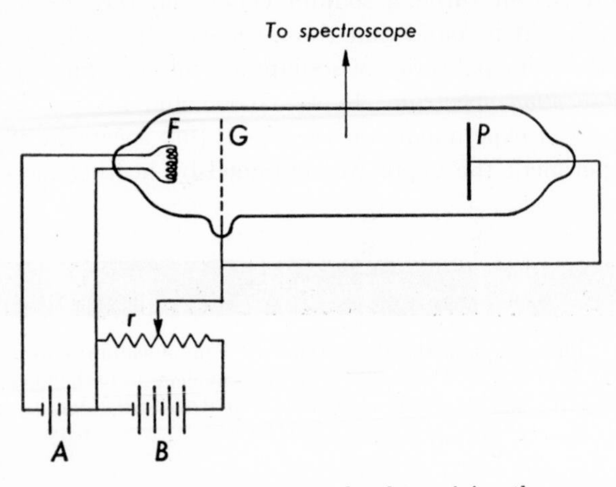

FIG. 8-13. A diagram of the apparatus for determining the resonance and ionization potentials of sodium.

sodium vapor. Electrons from the heated filament F are accelerated by a difference of potential V to the grid G. The plate P is at the same potential as G, so that in the space between P and G the electrons are moving with a kinetic energy given by

$$\tfrac{1}{2}mv^2 = Ve.$$

Although electrons undoubtedly collide with some of the sodium atoms, no radiation is observed when the voltage between F and G is below 2.1 volts. When this voltage is reached, the sodium vapor in the region between G and P is observed to emit yellow light. An examination of this light with a spectrograph shows that it consists of the sodium resonance lines only. The interpretation of this phenomenon is that an electron, on colliding with a sodium atom, loses an amount of energy, equivalent to 2.1 ev, to the sodium atom, thereby raising it from the normal to the next higher state, $3^2P_{1/2,\,3/2}$. On returning to its normal state, the sodium atom then emits the resonance radiation. This means that the energy of the incident electron must be at least equal to the quantum of energy corresponding to the sodium D lines. This can be checked by substituting the appropriate values in the formula

$$Ve = h\nu = \frac{hc}{\lambda},$$

and calculating λ. This yields $\lambda = 5898\text{A}$, in good agreement, within the limits of experimental error, with the wavelengths of the D lines of sodium. This potential, at which the resonance lines appear, is called the *resonance potential.*

When the voltage between the filament and grid in the above apparatus is increased to about 4 volts, the color of the light emitted by the sodium vapor changes, indicating that additional spectral lines are being emitted. At this voltage, the spectrogram shows in addition to the D lines the presence of the doublet $3^2S_{1/2} - 4^2P_{1/2,\,3/2}$ of wavelengths 3302A and 3303A of the principal series, and the doublet $3^2P_{1/2,\,3/2} - 5^2S_{1/2}$ of wavelengths 6154A and 6161A of the sharp series. Other lines appear at 4.4 and 4.6 volts. At 5.14 volts, ionization of the sodium vapor occurs as indicated by the very large increase in current from the filament to the plate, and, at the same time, the spectrograph records the appearance of the entire optical spectrum of sodium.

The emission of the entire optical spectrum when the voltage reaches the value of the ionization potential, 5.14 volts, can readily be explained by the fact that the electrons from the filament which have an amount of energy equal to 5.14 electron volts are capable of ionizing the sodium atoms. In this process electrons are removed from the normal state, $3s3^2S_{1/2}$, of the sodium atoms. An electron returning to an ionized atom may enter any one of the excited states and finally reach the normal state by a series of successive quantum jumps. Corresponding to each quantum jump there is an emission of radiation of appropriate frequency, giving rise to the lines observed in the optical spectrum. The intensity of a spectral line is determined by the number of atoms in which identical transitions take place simultaneously. The transitions giving rise to the intense spectral lines must have a greater probability of occurrence than those producing the weaker lines. The most probable transitions are those permitted by the selection rules. The probability that transitions will occur which are not permitted by the selection rules is vanishingly small under ordinary conditions.

8-14. Normal Zeeman Effect and the Vector Model

In our previous discussion of the Zeeman effect (Chapter 4), we found that the classical theory was adequate to explain the normal Zeeman effect but was totally inadequate to explain the anomalous Zeeman effect such as that exhibited by the sodium D lines. Let us now examine the treatment of the Zeeman effect on the basis of the vector model of the atom.

It was remarked earlier in this chapter that one of the reasons for the introduction of an electron spin was to explain the anomalous Zeeman effect. If the spin of the electron is left out of consideration, then the only angular momentum possessed by the electron is that due to its orbital motion of amount

$$l\frac{h}{2\pi}.$$

In the presence of a magnetic field of intensity H, the vector $\boldsymbol{l}$ precesses around the direction of the magnetic field as axis. The angular velocity of precession may be obtained by direct calculation or from a famous theorem due to Larmor, which states that the effect of a magnetic field on an electron moving in an orbit is to superimpose on the orbital motion a precessional motion of the entire orbit about the direction of the magnetic field with angular velocity o given by

$$\boxed{o = \frac{e}{2mc}H,} \tag{23}$$

in which e is in es units. Figure 8-7 shows two positions of the vector $\boldsymbol{l}$ as it precesses about the magnetic field at constant inclination, and the corresponding positions of the electronic orbit. The additional energy of the electron due to this precessional motion was shown to be given by

$$\begin{aligned} \Delta\mathcal{E} &= \mu H \cos\theta \\ &= \boldsymbol{m}_l \frac{eh}{4\pi mc} H, \end{aligned} \tag{21}$$

where $\boldsymbol{m}_l$ is the projection of $\boldsymbol{l}$ on H. In terms of the Larmor precession, the expression for the additional energy can be written as

$$\Delta\mathcal{E} = m_l o \frac{h}{2\pi}. \tag{24}$$

Since $\boldsymbol{m}_l$ is restricted to the $(2l + 1)$ integral values $l, l - 1, \cdots, 0, \cdots, -l$, the effect of the magnetic field is to split up each energy level into $2l + 1$ components spaced an amount $(eh/4\pi mc)H$ apart. This is illustrated in Figure 8-14 for two energy levels, one for which $l = 2$, the other, $l = 1$. If $\mathcal{E}_0'$ represents the energy of the level $l = 1$ in the absence of a magnetic field, and $\mathcal{E}_H'$ represents the energy of this level in the presence of the magnetic field of intensity H, then

$$\mathcal{E}_H' = \mathcal{E}_0' + \Delta\mathcal{E}' = \mathcal{E}_0' + m_l' \frac{eh}{4\pi mc} H.$$

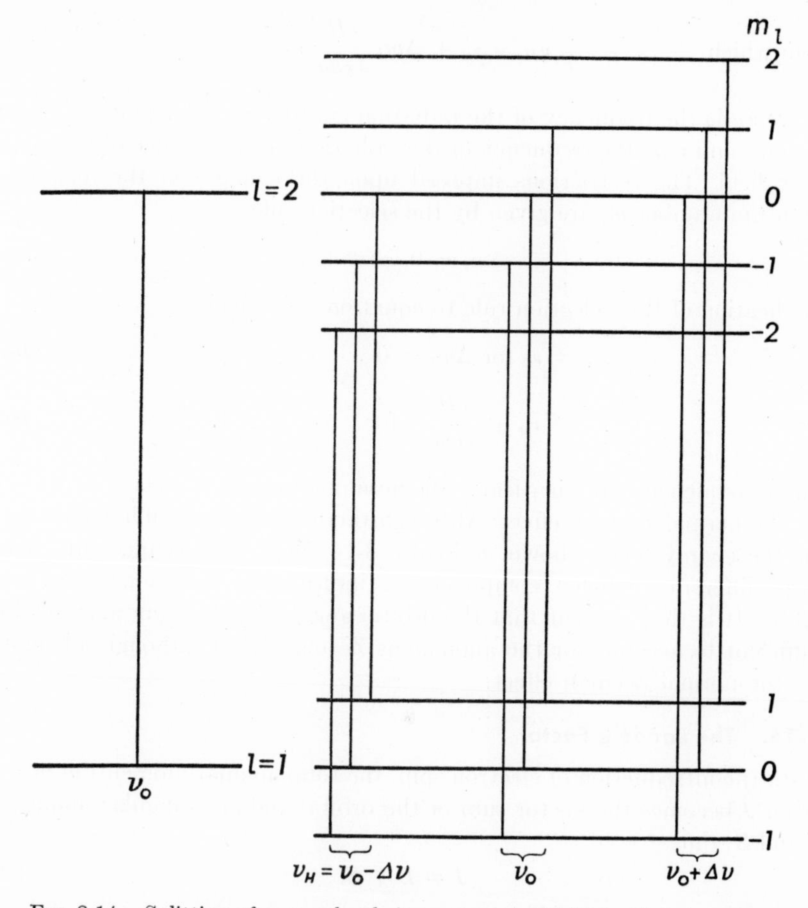

FIG. 8-14. Splitting of energy levels in a magnetic field into $2l + 1$ components. Section on the left represents the single transition in the absence of a magnetic field, while that at the right represents the splitting of these two energy levels in a magnetic field and the possible transitions yielding the normal Zeeman effect.
Selection rule: $\Delta m_l = 0, \pm 1$.

Similarly, if $\mathcal{E}_0''$ and $\mathcal{E}_H''$ represent the energies of the level $l = 2$ without and with the magnetic field respectively, then

$$\mathcal{E}_H'' = \mathcal{E}_0'' + \Delta\mathcal{E}'' = \mathcal{E}_0'' + m_l'' \frac{eh}{4\pi mc} H.$$

The quantity of energy radiated in the presence of the magnetic field is given by

$$h\nu_H = \mathcal{E}_H'' - \mathcal{E}_H' = \mathcal{E}_0'' - \mathcal{E}_0' + (m_l'' - m_l') \frac{eh}{4\pi mc} H$$

$$= h\nu_0 + \Delta m_l \frac{eh}{4\pi mc} H, \tag{25}$$

from which
$$\nu_H = \nu_0 + \Delta m_l \frac{eH}{4\pi mc}, \tag{26}$$

where ν_H is the frequency of the radiation emitted with the magnetic field present, and ν_0 is the frequency of the radiation in the absence of the magnetic field. The restrictions imposed upon the changes in the magnetic quantum number m_l are given by the selection rule

$$\Delta m_l = 0, \text{ or } \pm 1. \tag{27}$$

Application of this selection rule to equation (26) yields

$$\nu_H = \nu_0 \text{ for } \Delta m_l = 0 \tag{28a}$$

and
$$\nu_H = \nu_0 \pm \frac{eH}{4\pi mc} \quad \text{for} \quad \Delta m_l = \pm 1. \tag{28b}$$

These frequencies are identical with those obtained on the classical theory for the normal Zeeman effect. Although there are nine possible transitions for the energy levels shown in Figure 8-14, these are grouped into only three different frequency components as indicated by equations (28a) and (28b). It is thus evident that the orbital angular momentum alone is not sufficient to account for the anomalous Zeeman effect although adequate for the normal Zeeman effect.

8-15. The Landé g Factor

With the introduction of electron spin, the total angular momentum of the atom J becomes the vector sum of the orbital and spin angular momenta L and S; thus

$$J = L + S. \tag{12}$$

Because of the interaction between these two angular momenta, the vectors $\boldsymbol{L}$ and $\boldsymbol{S}$, while maintaining their relative orientations, precess about their resultant J. The magnetic moment due to the orbital motion, $\boldsymbol{\mu}_L$, is given by

$$\boldsymbol{\mu}_L = \boldsymbol{L} \frac{eh}{4\pi mc}. \tag{17}$$

Because of the negative charge, $\boldsymbol{\mu}_L$ is directed oppositely to $\boldsymbol{L}$. The magnetic moment due to the spin of the electron is given by

$$\boldsymbol{\mu}_S = 2S \frac{eh}{4\pi mc}. \tag{19}$$

Again $\boldsymbol{\mu}_S$ is directed oppositely to $\boldsymbol{S}$ because of the negative charge of the electron. The relationships between the magnetic moments and the angular momenta are shown in Figure 8-15. In the scale chosen, $\boldsymbol{\mu}_L$ is drawn twice the length of L; hence μ_S must be drawn four times the length of S. The resultant magnetic moment μ is therefore not along J. Because the vectors L and S precess about J, μ_L and μ_S must also precess about J. If each of

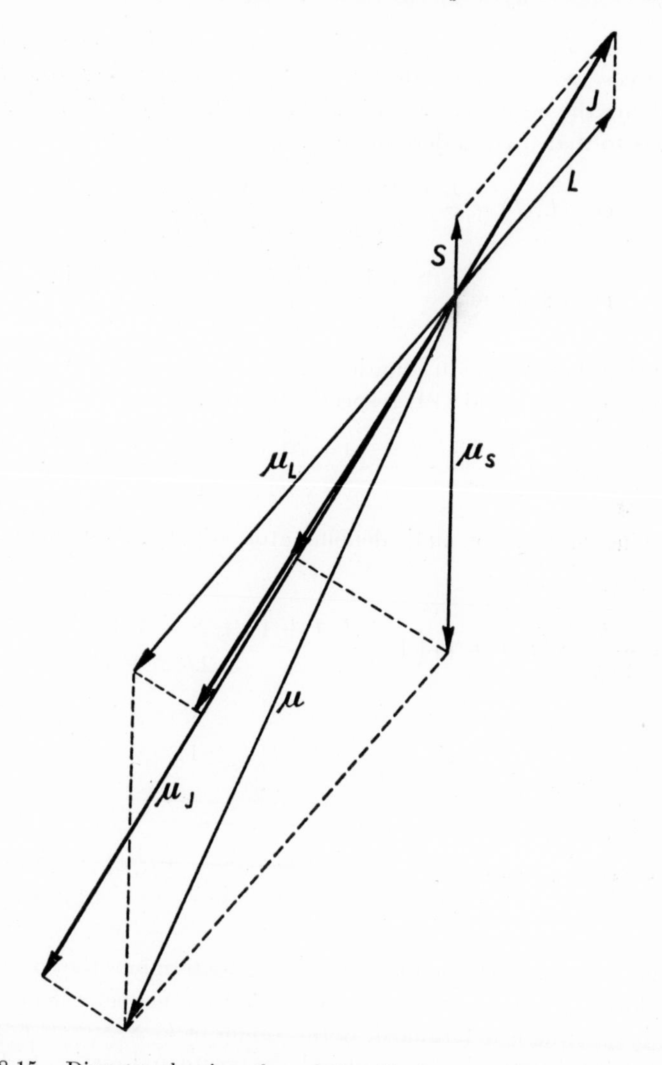

FIG. 8-15. Diagram showing the relationship between the magnetic moment vectors and the angular momentum vectors.

these vectors is resolved into two components, one parallel to J and the other perpendicular to it, then the value of the perpendicular component of each vector, averaged over a period of the motion, will be zero, since it is constantly changing direction. The effective magnetic moment of the atom will therefore be μ_J, the sum of the components of μ_L and μ_S along J. This is given by

$$\mu_J = \mu_L \cos(L, J) + \mu_S \cos(S, J) \tag{29}$$

where $\cos(L, J)$ represents the cosine of the angle between $\boldsymbol{L}$ and J, and similarly $\cos(S, J)$ represents the cosine of the angle between $\boldsymbol{S}$ and J. By applying the cosine law to the triangle formed by $\boldsymbol{L}$, $\boldsymbol{S}$, $\boldsymbol{J}$ in a manner analogous to that used in deriving equation (11), we get

$$\cos(L, J) = \frac{L(L+1) + J(J+1) - S(S+1)}{2\sqrt{L(L+1)}\sqrt{J(J+1)}}$$

and

$$\cos(S, J) = \frac{S(S+1) + J(J+1) - L(L+1)}{2\sqrt{S(S+1)}\sqrt{J(J+1)}}.$$

Substituting these values in equation (29) as well as the values of μ_L and μ_S from equations (17) and (19) respectively, we get

$$\mu_J = \frac{eh}{4\pi mc}\,\frac{3J(J+1) + S(S+1) - L(L+1)}{2\sqrt{J(J+1)}}.$$

Multiplying numerator and denominator of the above equation by $\sqrt{J(J+1)}$, we get

$$\mu_J = \frac{eh}{4\pi mc}\sqrt{J(J+1)}\left(1 + \frac{J(J+1) + S(S+1) - L(L+1)}{2J(J+1)}\right)$$

or

$$\boxed{\mu_J = \frac{eh}{4\pi mc}\, g\sqrt{J(J+1)},} \tag{30}$$

where

$$\boxed{g = 1 + \frac{J(J+1) + S(S+1) - L(L+1)}{2J(J+1)}.} \tag{31}$$

The quantity g is called the Landé *g factor*. It determines the splitting of the energy levels in the presence of a weak external magnetic field and shows that this splitting is determined by the values of L, S, and J. For levels in which the total spin S is zero, μ_J will be opposite in direction to $\boldsymbol{L}$, and the energy levels will split up in a magnetic field in a manner identical with that shown for the normal Zeeman effect.

Equation (30) is the defining equation for the Landé g factor. Remembering that

$$M_B = \frac{eh}{4\pi mc},$$

we can rewrite equation (30) as

$$\mu_J = M_B g J,$$

so that

$$g = \frac{\mu_J/M_B}{J}. \tag{32}$$

Now μ_J/M_B is the magnetic moment of the electronic system expressed in Bohr magnetons, and J is the total angular momentum of this system expressed in units of $h/2\pi$. *Thus the Landé g factor is the ratio of the magnetic moment of the system expressed in Bohr magnetons, to its angular momentum, expressed in units of* $h/2\pi$.

If the atom is placed in a magnetic field H which is relatively weak so that the coupling between $\boldsymbol{L}$ and $\boldsymbol{S}$ is not broken down, then their resultant J will precess about the direction of the magnetic field as an axis. The additional energy $\Delta\mathcal{E}$ due to the action of the magnetic field on this atomic magnet will be

$$\begin{aligned} \Delta\mathcal{E} &= \mu_J H \cos(J, H) \\ &= g \frac{eh}{4\pi mc} H\sqrt{J(J+1)} \cos(J, H). \end{aligned}$$

But $\sqrt{J(J+1)} \cos(J, H)$ is the projection of the vector J on the direction of the magnetic field, and is given by the magnetic quantum number m_J; so that

$$\Delta\mathcal{E} = \frac{eh}{4\pi mc} Hgm_J. \tag{33}$$

The quantity

$$\frac{eh}{4\pi mc} H$$

is called a *Lorentz unit;* it is a unit of energy used for expressing the splitting up of the energy levels in a magnetic field.

8-16. Anomalous Zeeman Effect

When the light from a sodium flame or arc, which has been placed in a magnetic field of about 30,000 gausses, is examined with the aid of a spectroscope of high resolving power, it is found that each of the lines of the principal series exhibits the following anomalous Zeeman pattern: the longer wavelength component, $3^2S_{1/2} - {}^2P_{1/2}$, splits into four lines, while the shorter wavelength component splits into six lines. The splitting of the

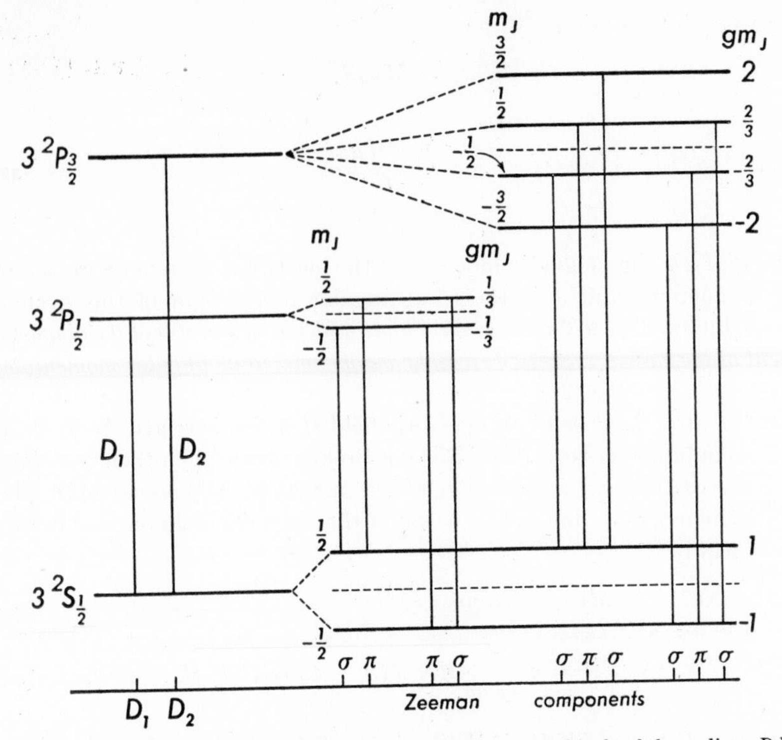

FIG. 8-16. Diagram showing the splitting of the energy levels of the sodium D lines in a weak magnetic field and the transitions giving rise to the anomalous Zeeman pattern according to the selection rule $\Delta m_j = 0, \pm 1$.

energy levels giving rise to these lines can be determined with the aid of equation (33). This will be done for the sodium D lines as typical of the lines of the principal series.

For the $3^2S_{1/2}$ energy level, $L = 0$, $S = \frac{1}{2}$, $J = \frac{1}{2}$; hence from equation (31)

$$g = 1 + \frac{\frac{1}{2}\cdot\frac{3}{2} + \frac{1}{2}\cdot\frac{3}{2}}{2\cdot\frac{1}{2}\cdot\frac{3}{2}} = 2.$$

Since m_J can have the values $\frac{1}{2}$ and $-\frac{1}{2}$, gm_J can have the values $+1$ and -1. Table 8-3 gives the values for the quantum numbers necessary for the determination of the splitting factor gm_J for each of the energy levels of the sodium D lines.

Figure 8-16 shows the Zeeman components which appear when the light from the source is viewed perpendicular to the direction of the magnetic field. The lines designated by σ are polarized with the electric vector

Table 8-3

State	L	S	J	g	m_J	gm_J
$3^2S_{1/2}$	0	$\frac{1}{2}$	$\frac{1}{2}$	2	$\frac{1}{2}, -\frac{1}{2}$	$1, -1$
$3^2P_{1/2}$	1	$\frac{1}{2}$	$\frac{1}{2}$	$\frac{2}{3}$	$\frac{1}{2}, -\frac{1}{2}$	$\frac{1}{3}, -\frac{1}{3}$
$3^2P_{3/2}$	1	$\frac{1}{2}$	$\frac{3}{2}$	$\frac{4}{3}$	$\frac{3}{2}, \frac{1}{2}, -\frac{1}{2}, -\frac{3}{2}$	$2, \frac{2}{3}, -\frac{2}{3}, -2$

perpendicular to the direction of the magnetic field while the lines designated by π are polarized parallel to the magnetic field. The polarization of these lines can be predicted from wave mechanical considerations which lead to the result that transitions for which $\Delta m_j = 0$ give rise to the π components, and the transitions for which $\Delta m_j = \pm 1$ give rise to the σ components. When the light is viewed parallel to the magnetic field, only the lines for which $\Delta m_j = \pm 1$ appear, and these are now circularly polarized. The direction of circular polarization for $\Delta m_j = +1$ is opposite to that for which $\Delta m_j = -1$. Thus the introduction of electron spin has led to complete agreement between the experimental results and the theory of the anomalous Zeeman effect.

8-17. The Stern-Gerlach Experiment and Electron Spin

A direct experimental demonstration of the existence of the magnetic moment of an electron, particularly that due to its spin, is given in an experiment first performed by Stern and Gerlach (1921), using neutral silver atoms. Similar experiments were performed later with other atoms such as hydrogen, lithium, sodium, potassium, copper, and gold. A glance at Table 8-2 will show that the normal state of each of these atoms is a $^2S_{1/2}$ state, for which $\boldsymbol{L} = 0$, $\boldsymbol{J} = \boldsymbol{S} = \frac{1}{2}$. That is, in the normal state of a silver atom, its entire magnetic moment is due to the spin of one electron. It has been shown that when such atoms are placed in a magnetic field of intensity H, they become oriented in such directions that $\boldsymbol{m}_J$, the projection of J in the direction of the magnetic field, can have the two values $+\frac{1}{2}$ and $-\frac{1}{2}$ only. The additional energy of the atom due to its position in the magnetic field is given by

$$\Delta \mathcal{E} = \frac{eh}{4\pi mc} Hgm_J. \tag{33}$$

If these small atomic magnets are placed in a uniform magnetic field, they will experience torques which will orient them with respect to the magnetic field. If the magnetic field is inhomogeneous, each atomic magnet will also experience a force which will accelerate it. The magnitude of this force on each magnet can be determined by differentiating equation (33)

…h respect to the space coordinate, say x, which yields

$$\boxed{F = \frac{eh}{4\pi mc}\frac{\partial H}{\partial x}\cdot g m_J,} \tag{34}$$

where $\partial H/\partial x$ determines the inhomogeneity of the magnetic field.

In the Stern-Gerlach experiment, a narrow beam of silver atoms coming from an oven O, after passing through the defining slits S_1 and S_2, was allowed to pass through an inhomogeneous magnetic field and recorded on plate P, as shown in Figure 8-17. The entire apparatus was in an evacuated chamber. The inhomogeneous magnetic field was produced by an

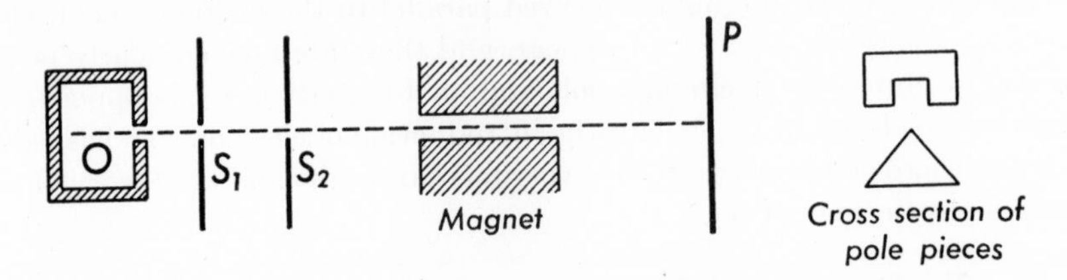

FIG. 8-17. Arrangement of apparatus in the Stern-Gerlach experiment.

electromagnet with specially designed pole pieces. One pole piece was in the form of a knife-edge, while the other pole piece had a channel cut in it parallel to the knife-edge. Each silver atom could assume only one of two possible directions in the magnetic field, given by $m_J = +\frac{1}{2}$ or $-\frac{1}{2}$. It has been shown that for the $^2S_{1/2}$ state, $g = 2$, and $gm_J = +1$ or -1, so that the force experienced by each atom due to the inhomogeneity of the field is

$$F = \pm\frac{eh}{4\pi mc}\cdot\frac{\partial H}{\partial x} = \pm M_B\frac{\partial H}{\partial x}, \tag{35}$$

where $$M_B = \frac{eh}{4\pi mc} = 0.927 \times 10^{-20} \text{ em units.}$$

In terms of the vector model, those atoms with electron spins directed parallel to the magnetic field will experience a force in one direction, while those with oppositely directed spins will experience a force in the opposite direction. According to this, the beam of atoms should split into two beams in its passage through the inhomogeneous magnetic field. This splitting of the beam into two parts of approximately equal intensity was actually observed in these experiments. Figure 8-18 shows the type of pattern observed in these experiments. From the amount of the separation of the two beams and the degree of inhomogeneity of the magnetic field, it was shown that the component of the magnetic moment of the atom in the direction of the field was equal to one Bohr magneton, M_B.

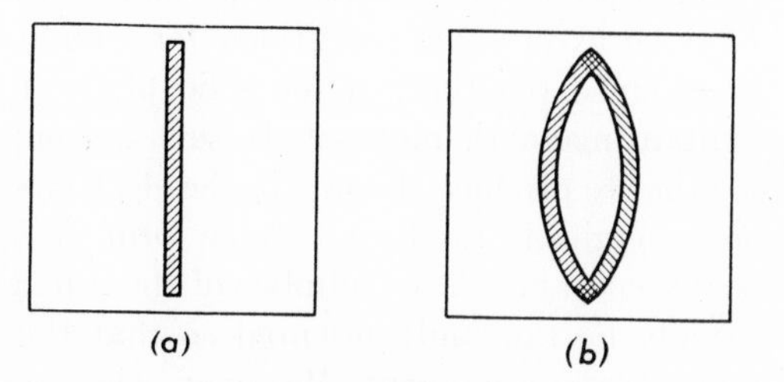

FIG. 8-18. Type of pattern on photographic plate made by a beam of silver atoms (a) without magnetic field on, (b) with magnetic field on.

The results of the Stern-Gerlach experiment, together with the explanation of the multiplicity of atomic energy levels and the anomalous Zeeman effect, strongly support the hypothesis of the existence of an electron spin.

8-18. Magnetic Properties of Atoms

The magnetic properties of an atom are due to the orbital motions of the electrons and to their spins. If the spins of the electrons are oriented so that the resultant spin is zero, the atom will have diamagnetic properties. This can be deduced by an application of Lenz's law; that is, if an external magnetic field is impressed upon a system containing such atoms, the emf induced in each electronic orbit will be such as to oppose the change inducing it. Hence the resultant magnetic field will be smaller than the impressed magnetic field. If the resultant spin of the atom is not zero, then the atom will behave as a small magnet with the magnetic dipole lining up parallel to the magnetic field. An assemblage of such atoms will behave as a paramagnetic substance. Of particular interest is an atom like iron, $Z = 26$. As shown in Table 8-2 the 26 electrons in the normal state have the configuration

$$1s^2 2s^2 2p^6 3s^2 3p^6 3d^6 4s^2.$$

All the subshells are filled with the maximum allowable number of electrons except the $3d$ subshell. For a completed subshell $\sum m_s = 0$. The maximum number of electrons that may be in a $3d$ subshell is 10, and for this number $\sum m_s = 0$; but with only 6 electrons in the $3d$ shell of iron, $\sum m_s$ may have any one of the values equivalent to 0, 2, or 4 Bohr magnetons to correspond to the possible spin orientations of the 4 missing electrons. The magnetic moment of the iron atom is known to be 4 Bohr magnetons; hence the 6 electrons in the $3d$ subshell must be aligned so that 5 of them have their ns oriented in one direction and 1 electron has its spin aligned opposite o them for a total magnetic moment of 4 Bohr magnetons. Assemblages of iron atoms in the vapor phase should thus be paramagnetic.

It is possible, under exceptional conditions, for a number of paramagnetic atoms to be grouped together, in the solid phase, to form a small *domain* with a resultant magnetic moment. In such a grouping, the atoms interact with each other to produce changes in the electronic configurations and thus alter their energies to produce a stable form. A crystal of such a substance will usually contain a large number of these magnetic domains. The latter will usually be randomly oriented so that the substance will exhibit no resultant magnetic moment. However, when a strong external magnetic field is applied to the substance, these domains will be lined up with their magnetic moments parallel to this field, and may retain some of this orientation when the external magnetizing field is removed. These substances then exhibit permanent magnetization or *ferromagnetism.* Among the ferromagnetic substances are iron, nickel, and cobalt, and some special alloys, such as the Heusler alloys which consist of copper, manganese and aluminum. Ferromagnetism is thus not an atomic property, but a property of a special arrangement of groups of atoms into magnetic domains.

8-19. Spectra of Two-Electron Atoms

Atoms of the alkaline earth elements, beryllium, magnesium, calcium, strontium, barium, and radium, have two electrons outside a closed configuration typical of the inert elements. The total angular momentum of any one of these atoms is merely the sum of the angular momenta of the two electrons outside the closed core. When the atom is in the normal state, both electrons have the same principal quantum number n and are in the completed subgroup for which $l = 0$. The application of Pauli's principle leads to the conclusion that the two electrons must have their spins in opposite directions, so that the total spin quantum number $\boldsymbol{S} = \boldsymbol{s}_1 + \boldsymbol{s}_2 = \frac{1}{2} - \frac{1}{2} = 0$. The total angular momentum $\boldsymbol{J} = \boldsymbol{L} + \boldsymbol{S} = 0$, so that the normal state is a singlet state and is designated by the symbol ${}^1S_0$.

The excited states of a two-electron system can arise from a variety of configurations of the two electrons consistent with the Pauli exclusion principle. The P states, for example, are due to those combinations of the angular momenta $\boldsymbol{l}_1$ and $\boldsymbol{l}_2$ whose vector sum $\boldsymbol{L} = \boldsymbol{l}_1 + \boldsymbol{l}_2$ is unity. For the D states $\boldsymbol{L} = \boldsymbol{l}_1 + \boldsymbol{l}_2 = 2$, and so on. The spin vector $\boldsymbol{S}$ can have only two values $\boldsymbol{S} = \frac{1}{2} + \frac{1}{2} = 1$ or $\boldsymbol{S} = \frac{1}{2} - \frac{1}{2} = 0$. If $\boldsymbol{S} = 0$, then $\boldsymbol{J} = \boldsymbol{L}$, and the state is a singlet state such as ${}^1P_1$ for $\boldsymbol{L} = 1$, ${}^1D_2$ for $\boldsymbol{L} = 2$, and so on. If $\boldsymbol{S} = 1$, then $\boldsymbol{J}$ can have the three values $L + 1$, L, $L - 1$, yielding a triplet state such as ${}^3P_2$, ${}^3P_1$, ${}^3P_0$, for $\boldsymbol{L} = 1$; ${}^3D_3$, ${}^3D_2$, ${}^3D_1$ for $\boldsymbol{L} = 2$, and so on. A two-electron system therefore has two distinct sets of energy levels, the

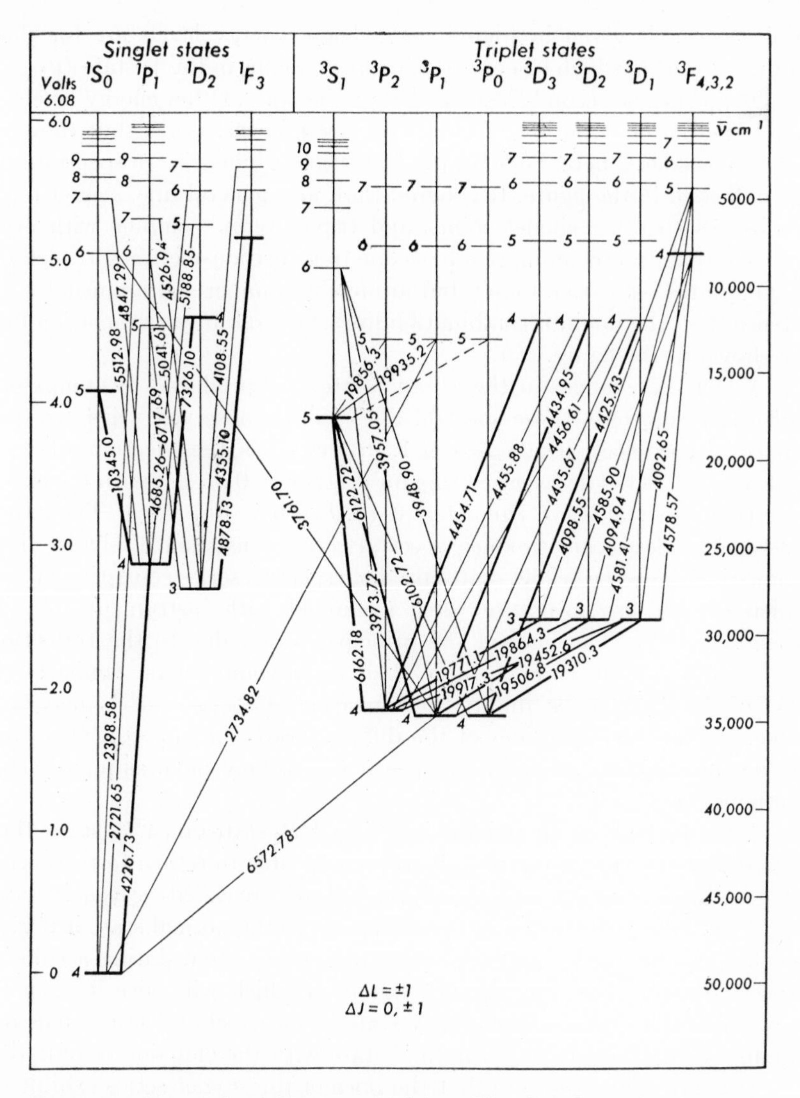

FIG. 8-19. Energy level diagram of calcium. Wavelengths are in angstroms.

singlet set arising from configurations in which the electron spins are in opposite directions, $S = 0$, and the triplet set arising from configurations in which the electron spins are in the same direction, $S = 1$. In this latter set must be included those states for which $L = 0$ and $S = 1$, even though J has only the single value unity. These states are designated as $^3S_1$ states, and are customarily called triplet states.

The energy level diagram of calcium showing some of the singlet and triplet states is given in Figure 8-19. These energy levels are for those configurations in which one electron always remains in the 4*s* state ($n_1 = 4$, $l_1 = 0$), while the second electron changes its state. Other energy levels, in which neither electron is in the 4*s* level, are known to exist, but they will not be considered here. Some of the transitions giving rise to spectral lines are indicated in the figure. It is found that, as a general rule, singlet terms combine with other singlet terms, and triplet terms combine with other triplet terms. Intercombination lines due to transitions between triplet and singlet states have been found, but are few in number and are usually less intense than the nonintercombination lines. Several intercombination lines are shown in the figure.

When the changes in the atomic states are produced by jumps of a single electron, only those spectral lines will be observed which are permitted by the selection rule $\Delta l = \pm 1$. In such cases, the selection rule for L is also $\Delta L = \pm 1$. The selection rule for J is $\Delta J = 0$ or ± 1, with the exception that the transition from $J = 0$ to $J = 0$ is forbidden. Transitions between singlet states produce spectral series consisting of singlet lines. Transitions between triplet states produce spectral series consisting of lines which exhibit fine structure when examined with instruments of high resolving power. The lines of the principal series, due to the transitions $5^3S_1 - n^3P_{2,1,0}$, never have more than three components. Similarly the lines of the sharp series, due to the transitions $4^3P_{2,1,0} - n^3S_1$, may have three components. The lines of the diffuse series, $4^3P_{2,1,0} - n^3D_{3,2,1}$ and of the fundamental series, $3^3D_{3,2,1} - n^3F_{4,3,2}$, may have as many as six components.

If a calcium atom should find itself in a 4^3P_2 state or a 4^3P_0 state, then, according to the selection rules, it will not be able to return to the normal state with the emission of radiation. Such states are called *metastable* states. The atom may go from the metastable state to the normal state if it gives up the appropriate amount of energy to another atom during a collision process. Or the atom may absorb radiation which will raise it from the metastable state to a higher energy state, from which, selection rules permitting, it may return to the normal state with the emission of radiation.

It is interesting to note that the lines of the singlet series exhibit the normal Zeeman effect, while the lines of the triplet series exhibit the anomalous Zeeman effect. This is in agreement with deductions from the Landé g formula. For the singlet series, $\boldsymbol{S} = 0$, $\boldsymbol{J} = \boldsymbol{L}$, and therefore $g = 1$, so that the splitting up of the energy levels will be in whole multiples of the Lorentz unit, and the permitted transitions will produce the normal Zeeman pattern.

In addition to the alkaline earth elements, there are other elements such as zinc, cadmium, and mercury, which possess singlet and triplet sets of atomic energy levels as determined from spectroscopic analysis. Examination of Table 8-2 shows that these atoms contain two electrons outside closed configurations. Helium, which possesses only two electrons, must also be included in the above group. An interesting point about helium is that no intercombination lines due to transitions between its triplet and singlet states have ever been found. Because of this fact, it was at one time supposed that there were two different kinds of helium, parhelium, possessing singlet states, and orthohelium, possessing triplet states. The difference between the two sets of states is, of course, due to the two possible orientations of the electron spin axes.

8-20. Nuclear Spin and Nuclear Particles

Many of the lines of the spectral series, when examined with spectroscopes of very high resolving power, are found to consist of several lines very close together. Such lines are said to exhibit *hyperfine* structure. Two distinct types of hyperfine structure have been observed. One type, in which the lines of a spectral series all have the same number of components, has been explained as due to the presence of two or more isotopes of the element. The discovery of the hydrogen isotope of mass number 2, discussed in §7-3, depended upon the finding of an additional component in the lines of the Balmer series displaced slightly from the Balmer lines coming from hydrogen atoms of mass number 1. The relative intensities of the components of a line are directly related to the relative abundance of the isotopes. Such isotopic hyperfine structure has been observed in the spectral lines of many elements.

The second type of hyperfine structure cannot be explained as due to the presence of isotopes because it has been found in the spectral lines of elements, such as bismuth, which are believed to consist of single isotopes only. In these cases, the number of components is different for different spectral lines, and their relative displacements are such that they cannot be explained on the basis of the existence of other isotopes. The explanation of this type of hyperfine structure of spectral lines, suggested by Pauli, is that the nucleus of the atom also spins about an axis, and possesses a nuclear angular momentum due to spin of amount

$$I \frac{h}{2\pi},$$

where I is the *nuclear spin quantum number*.

The total angular momentum of the atom will now be the vector sum of the nuclear angular momentum and the total electronic angular momentum, and is denoted by $F\ (h/2\pi)$ where

$$\boxed{F = I + J.} \tag{36}$$

F, the vector sum of I and J, is called the *hyperfine quantum number* and is restricted to integral or odd half-integral values. It is beyond the scope of this book to give an extended discussion of the analysis of hyperfine structure. Some of the results of this analysis, however, are of interest, since they have been used in predicting the types of particles that probably exist in the nucleus. For this reason, some of the values of the *nuclear* spin quantum number I are listed in Table 8-4.

An examination of Table 8-4 shows that the spin quantum number I is zero for isotopes of even atomic number and even mass number; that is,

Table 8-4

The Nuclear Spin Quantum Numbers of Some Elements

Atomic Number Z	Element	Isotopic Mass Number A	Nuclear Spin Quantum Number I
1	H	1	$\frac{1}{2}$
1	H	2	1
2	He	4	0
3	Li	6	1
3	Li	7	$\frac{3}{2}$
7	N	14	1
8	O	16	0
9	F	19	$\frac{1}{2}$
15	P	31	$\frac{1}{2}$
17	Cl	35	$\frac{3}{2}$
80	Hg	199	$\frac{1}{2}$
80	Hg	201	$\frac{3}{2}$
80	Hg	198, 200, 202, 204	0
82	Pb	207	$\frac{1}{2}$
82	Pb	204, 206, 208	0
83	Bi	209	$\frac{9}{2}$

the spectral lines from these isotopes exhibit no hyperfine structure. The isotopes whose spectral lines exhibit hyperfine structure can be classified into three groups: (1) for isotopes of even atomic number and odd mass number, I is an odd half-integer; (2) for isotopes of odd atomic number and odd mass number, I is also an odd half-integer, and (3) for isotopes of odd atomic number and even mass number, I is an integer.

The argument which follows is based on the assumption that the spin angular momentum of the nucleus is the vector sum of the spin angular momenta of the particles within the nucleus and that these spins are aligned with their axes either parallel or antiparallel. That is, we are carrying over into the nucleus the same type of hypothesis which was found to work for the electrons outside the nucleus. Before the discovery of the neutron, the nucleus was assumed to consist of A protons and $A-Z$ electrons; the resultant nuclear charge was therefore equivalent to Z protons. The total number of particles in the nucleus was thus $2A-Z$. Since $2A$ is always an even number, every element of odd atomic number would possess an odd number of particles, and its spin quantum number I should be an odd half-integer. This is not always found to be so experimentally. For example, nitrogen, ${}_7N^{14}$, has a spin quantum number $I = 1$. Similarly, the lithium isotope, ${}_3Li^6$, has a spin quantum number $I = 1$. Consider the odd isotopes of mercury of mass numbers 199 and 201. Since $Z = 80$, $2A-Z$ is an even number for each of these isotopes, but I is found to be an odd half-integer in each case. After the discovery of the neutron, Heisenberg suggested that the nucleus should consist of protons and neutrons only, and that each particle should have a spin angular momentum of $\frac{1}{2}\hbar$. On this basis the number of protons in the nucleus is equal to the atomic number Z, and the number N of neutrons in the nucleus is $A-Z$. The total number of particles in the nucleus is equal to the mass number A. The isotopes of any one element therefore differ only in the number of neutrons in the nucleus. The discrepancies in the values of the spin quantum numbers mentioned above now disappear. On Heisenberg's hypothesis, I should be an integer for isotopes of even atomic mass number, and should be an odd half-integer for isotopes of odd atomic mass number. These predictions are in agreement with experimental results.

8-21. Nuclear Magnetic Moments—Molecular Beam Method

We have shown that a nucleus has an angular momentum due to its spin. In addition, the nucleus also possesses a magnetic moment. Accurate data on the magnetic moments of atomic nuclei should provide additional information on the nature of nuclear forces and should also help in selecting an appropriate nuclear model. Very precise methods have been developed for the determination of nuclear magnetic moments. One of these, known as the *magnetic resonance method*, was developed by Rabi and his co-workers, and is a direct outgrowth of the Stern-Gerlach type of experiment. This experiment depends essentially upon resonance between the precession frequency of the nuclear magnet about a constant magnetic field direction and the frequency of an impressed high frequency magnetic field.

Just as the magnetic moment of an electron is expressed in terms of a Bohr magneton, so the nuclear magnetic moment is expressed in terms of a *nuclear magneton* M_n defined by the equation

$$M_n = \frac{eh}{4\pi Mc} \tag{37}$$

in which M is the mass of the proton. The nuclear magneton is thus only about 1/1840 of a Bohr magneton. If I is the nuclear spin quantum number, the angular momentum of the nucleus due to its spin is $Ih/2\pi$. Just as we introduced the Landé g factor to relate the magnetic moment of the electrons of an atom to their total angular momentum, so we can introduce a *nuclear g factor* to relate the magnetic moment μ of a nucleus to its spin angular momentum. *The nuclear g factor is defined as the ratio of the nuclear magnetic moment, expressed in units of nuclear magnetons, to the spin angular momentum, expressed in units of $h/2\pi$.* Thus

$$\boxed{g = \frac{\mu}{IM_n}} \cdot \tag{38}$$

Hence

$$\mu = gIM_n = gI\frac{eh}{4\pi Mc} \cdot \tag{39}$$

When a nucleus of magnetic moment μ is in a constant magnetic field of intensity H, it will precess about the direction of the magnetic field with

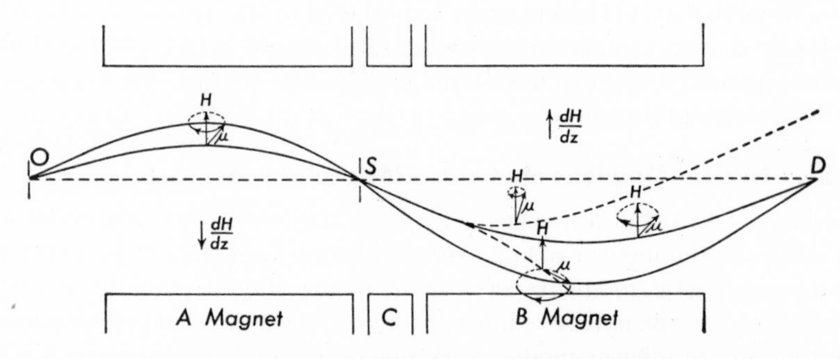

FIG. 8-20. Paths of molecules in the molecular beam resonance experiment. The two solid curves indicate the paths of two molecules which have different magnetic moments and velocities and whose moments are not changed during passage through the apparatus. This is indicated by the small gyroscopes drawn on one side of the paths, in which the projection of the magnetic moment along the field remains fixed. The two dotted curves in the region of the B magnet indicate the paths of two molecules, the projection of whose nuclear magnetic moments along the field has been changed in the region of the C magnet. This is indicated by means of the two gyroscopes drawn on the dotted curves, for one of which the projection of the magnetic moment along the field has been increased, and for the other of which the projection has been decreased.

a frequency ν given by Larmor's theorem

$$\nu = \frac{\mu H}{Ih} . \tag{40}$$

The magnetic moment μ of a nucleus can thus be found by determining the Larmor frequency ν which the nucleus of spin quantum number I acquires in a known constant magnetic field H. Instead of working with nuclei alone, Rabi and his co-workers used beams of molecules whose total electronic angular momentum is zero. Figure 8-20 shows the paths of typical molecules in the different magnetic fields used in the magnetic resonance experiment for measuring nuclear magnetic moments; Figure 8-21

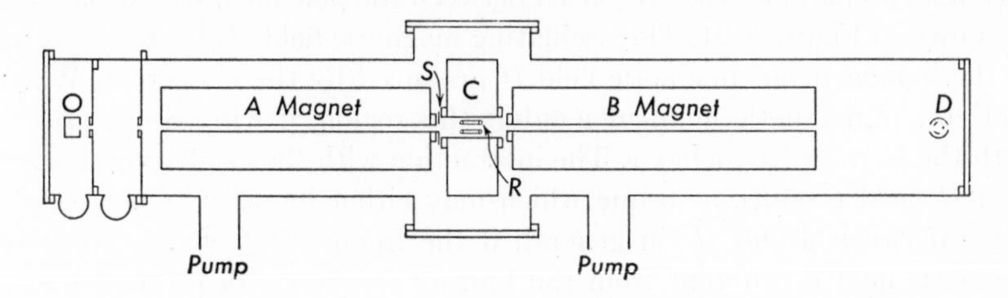

FIG. 8-21. Schematic diagram of the apparatus used in the molecular beam experiment.

is a schematic diagram of the apparatus. A narrow stream of molecules issues from the source at O. A very small fraction of these molecules will pass through the collimating slit S and reach the detector at D. In the absence of any inhomogeneous magnetic deflecting fields, the molecules traverse straight-line paths OSD and form the so-called *direct* beam.

The magnets A and B are specially designed to produce inhomogeneous magnetic fields. The magnetic fields are in the same direction, but their gradients, dH/dz, are in opposite directions as shown in Figure 8-20. A molecule with magnetic moment μ will be deflected in the direction of the gradient if μ_z, the projection of μ in the direction of the field, is positive, and will be deflected in the opposite direction if μ_z is negative. Molecules which left the source along the line OSD will be deflected to one side. Other molecules which leave O at some angle to the line OSD will follow paths indicated by the solid lines and reach the detector D. The force experienced by any such molecule in the inhomogeneous field due to the A magnet is

$$F = \mu_z \left(\frac{\partial H}{\partial z}\right)_A ; \tag{41}$$

a similar expression holds for the force due to the B magnet. The actual deflection produced by each magnetic field can be established from a knowledge of the velocity of the molecule, which is determined by the temperature of the source, and from the geometry of the apparatus. If no change occurs in μ_z as the molecule goes from the A field to the B field, the deflections in these fields will be in opposite directions. It is a simple matter to adjust the two magnetic field gradients to make these deflections equal in magnitude and thus bring the molecules to the detector, that is, to "refocus" the beam. When the two magnetic fields are properly adjusted, the number of molecules reaching the detector D in any given time interval is about the same whether the magnets are on or off.

Magnet C produces a homogeneous magnetic field of intensity H. In the same region there is a high frequency alternating magnetic field (not shown in Figure 8-20) produced by sending current in opposite directions through two parallel wires R placed between the pole faces of the magnet C, as shown in Figure 8-21. The oscillating magnetic field H_1 is at right angles to the homogeneous magnetic field H produced by the C magnet. When a molecule of magnetic moment μ enters this region, it will precess about H with the Larmor frequency ν. The interaction with the oscillating magnetic field H_1 will produce a torque which may either increase or decrease the angle between μ and H; in general, if the frequency f of the alternating magnetic field is different from the Larmor frequency of precession ν, the net effect produced will be small, since the torque produced by the alternating magnetic field will rapidly get out of phase with the precessional motion. But when $f = \nu$, the increase or decrease produced in the angle between μ and H will be cumulative and this change in angle will become quite large. The molecule will then follow one of the dotted paths when it gets into the region of the B magnet and will not enter the detector at D. In some of the experiments, the frequency of the alternating magnetic field is kept at a constant value, and the intensity of the magnetic field H produced by the C magnet is varied. Figure 8-22 is a typical curve which shows the beam intensity plotted as a function of the magnetic field strength H while the frequency of the alternating field is kept constant. It will be observed that resonance occurs for a definite value of H; the resonance value is the minimum value of the curve. The resonance curve of the Li^7 nucleus shown in Figure 8-22 was obtained with a beam of LiCl molecules. In other experiments with the Li^7 nucleus, molecular beams of LiF and Li_2 were used.

Solving equations (39) and (40) for g and substituting the resonance frequency f for the Larmor frequency ν, we get

$$g = \frac{4\pi Mc}{e}\frac{f}{H}. \qquad (42)$$

Since the values of the constants M, e, and c are accurately known, the substitution of the measured values of the resonance frequency f and the intensity of the homogeneous magnetic field H in equation (42) will yield the g factor for the particular nucleus under investigation. If its nuclear spin quantum number I is known, then

$$\mu = gI \tag{43}$$

will give the magnetic moment of the nucleus in nuclear magnetons, while substitution of the values of g and I in equation (39) will give the nuclear magnetic moment in em units. For example, in the case of the Li^7 nucleus, $I = 3/2$ and the measured value of g is 2.1688; hence its nuclear magnetic moment is 3.2532 nuclear magnetons.

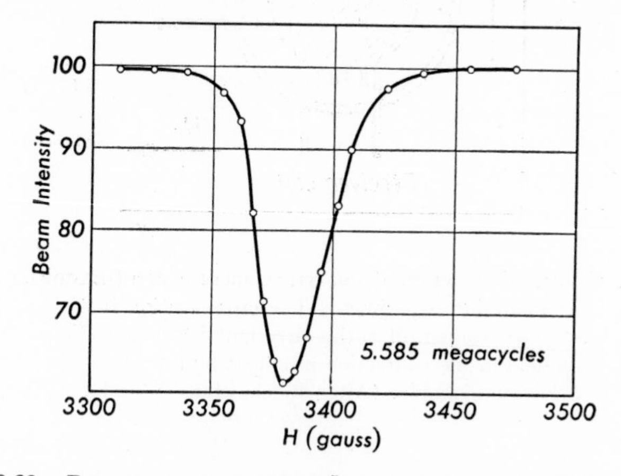

Fig. 8-22. Resonance curve of the Li^7 nucleus observed in LiCl.

Of very great importance in nuclear physics are the magnetic moments of the proton, deuteron, and neutron. Millman and Kusch (1941) made a precise measurement of the magnetic moment of the proton, while Kellogg, Rabi, Ramsey, and Zacharias (1939) made a precise determination of the ratio of the magnetic moments of the proton and deuteron. From these measurements the magnetic moment of the proton was found to be 2.7896 nuclear magnetons and that of the deuteron was found to be 0.8565 nuclear magneton. If we assume that a deuteron consists of a proton and a neutron and that the magnetic moment of the deuteron is the sum of the magnetic moments of the proton and the neutron, then the magnetic moment of the neutron is $\mu_n = -1.933$ nuclear magnetons. Alvarez and Bloch (1940) made an independent determination of magnetic moment of the neutron by sending a beam of slow neutrons through a modified type of molecular beam magnetic resonance apparatus. Using the value $I = 1/2$ for the spin of the neutron, they obtained $\mu_n = -1.935$ nuclear magnetons for the magnetic moment of free neutrons.

8-22. Nuclear Induction and Resonance Absorption

A significant modification of the magnetic resonance principle was proposed and developed by F. Bloch (1946). In the molecular beam experiments, the determination of the value of the nuclear moment consists in measuring the frequency of the alternating magnetic field at which the intensity of

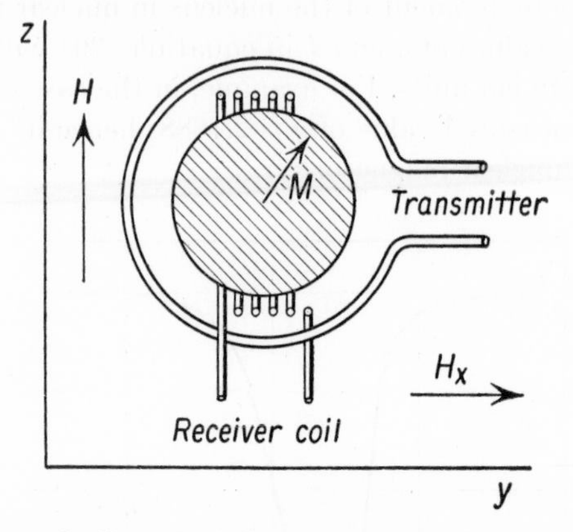

FIG. 8-23. Schematic diagram of the arrangement of the transmitter and receiver coils in the nuclear induction experiment. The cross section in the y-z plane of the spherical sample is shown shaded. M is the direction of the magnetic polarization, H is a constant magnetic field in the z direction produced by a magnet (not shown) with its poles above and below the sample. (After Bloch, Hansen, and Packard, *Phys. Rev.*, 70, 475, 1946.)

the molecular beam reached a minimum; this frequency is equal to the Larmor precession frequency of the nuclei in the constant magnetic field. The modification introduced by Bloch consists essentially in measuring the induced emf, or some effect due to this induced emf, produced by a change in the orientation of the nuclear magnetic moments in a sample of a substance. This sample is frequently in the form of a liquid or a solid.

The experimental arrangement used by Bloch and his co-workers is shown in outline in Figure 8-23. The sample under investigation, spherical in shape, is placed between the poles of an electromagnet which provides a constant magnetic field H in the z direction. A flat coil of several turns, called the transmitter coil, in the y-z plane, surrounds the spherical sample. Current of frequency f from a high frequency generator is supplied to this coil, producing an alternating magnetic field H_x in the x direction.

A second coil, called the receiver coil, surrounds the sample; this coil has its axis in the y direction. An emf will be induced in the receiver coil whenever the magnetic flux in the y direction is changed. The receiver coil is connected to an appropriate circuit to measure the emf induced in it.

The effect of the constant magnetic field H is to cause the nuclear magnets to precess about the z axis with the Larmor precessional frequency; each nuclear magnet will have a component of its magnetic moment in the direction of H. Since we are dealing with matter in bulk, the effect of this alignment is to produce a paramagnetic substance having a magnetic moment M per unit volume. Some time will be required to establish this magnetic moment after the application of the constant magnetic field; this time is called the *relaxation time* and may vary from a fraction of a second to thousands of seconds. The relaxation time depends upon the interactions between the nuclear magnetic moments and the electronic motions and configurations, and thus depends upon the temperature.

The magnetization of the sample will produce a magnetic flux in the system. Referring again to the figure, the receiving coil will record an emf only when the magnetic flux through it, in the y direction, is changed. A change in the magnetic flux will be produced by the action of the alternating magnetic field; the closer its frequency is to the Larmor precessional frequency of the nuclei in the constant magnetic field, the greater will be the change in flux produced.

In one of the earliest magnetic induction experiments, Bloch, Hansen, and Packard (1946), using water as the sample, observed a relaxation time of a few seconds. When a concentrated solution of $Fe(NO_3)_3$ in water was used, the relaxation time was found to be of the order of 10^{-4} to 10^{-5} sec. With this sample, they found that for a resonance frequency $f = \nu = 7.765 \times 10^6$ sec^{-1}, the value of the constant magnetic field $H = 1826$ gausses, yielding a nuclear g-value for the proton in agreement with the results obtained with the molecular beam experiments described previously. With improvement in the design of the apparatus, Bloch and his co-workers were able to make very accurate determinations of the ratios of the magnetic moment of the proton to that of the deuteron, the triton, and the neutron. Of great importance is the fact, demonstrated by Rogers and Staub (1949) using a rotating high frequency field, that the sign of the magnetic moment of the neutron is opposite to that of the proton.

The evaluation of the magnetic moment of any one type of particle depends upon an accurate knowledge of the value of the constant magnetic field at the resonance frequency. Since convenient material samples containing hydrogen, such as water, paraffin, oil, can be used in the nuclear induction experiments, Bloch pointed out that the procedure can be reversed to determine the value of the magnetic field in which nuclear resonance has been induced in such a sample. This method is now being widely used, for example, in measuring the magnetic fields in cyclotron magnets.

A method, parallel to the above, for measuring nuclear moments but using radiofrequency techniques, was developed by Purcell, Torrey, and Pound (1946). This is called the *magnetic resonance absorption method.* In their first experiment, they put a piece of paraffin, 850 cm^3, into a resonant cavity and placed the resonator in a strong magnetic field. Power was fed through a loop into the cavity at about 30×10^6 cycles/sec. The output of the resonator was balanced against a portion of the output of the generator. When properly balanced, the magnetic field was varied slowly; at one particular value of H, 7100 gausses, a sharp resonance absorption was observed. The frequency was 29.8×10^6 cycles/sec. The values of the proton magnetic moment calculated from these values of ν and H are in agreement with previously determined values within the limits of experimental error. They also suggested that this method could be used for accurate magnetic field determinations, and for the determination of the sign of the moment by using radiofrequency fields with rotating components.

The molecular beam magnetic resonance method, the nuclear induction methods, and the magnetic resonance absorption methods have been developed and refined to be methods of very great precision. It would take us too far afield to discuss the various refinements; we shall merely quote the results wherever needed.

The present values of the nuclear magnetic moments of the proton, neutron, and deuteron, in units of the nuclear magneton, are

$$\begin{aligned} \mu_{\mathrm{p}} &= 2.79255 \\ \mu_{\mathrm{n}} &= -1.91354 \\ \mu_{\mathrm{d}} &= 0.85737 \end{aligned} \tag{44}$$

It will be noted that the sum of the moments of the neutron and proton differs from the deuteron moment by 0.022 nuclear magnetons. There is no satisfactory explanation of this difference at present.

Problems

8-1. Using vector diagrams, determine the different values for the total orbital angular momentum of a two-electron system for which $l_1 = 3$ and $l_2 = 2$.

Ans. $L = 5, 4, 3, 2, 1$.

8-2. Using vector diagrams, determine the possible values of the total angular momentum of an f electron (**a**) according to the vector model, (**b**) according to wave mechanics. (**c**) Determine the angle between the vectors $\boldsymbol{s}$ and $\boldsymbol{l}$ in part (**b**).

Ans. (**a**) $j = \frac{7}{2}, \frac{5}{2}$.

(**b**) $j = \dfrac{\sqrt{63}}{2}, \dfrac{\sqrt{35}}{2}$.

(**c**) $60°$, $131° 49'$.

8-3. Using vector diagrams, determine the possible values of the total angular momentum of an electron system for which (**a**) $L = 2$, $S = 3$, (**b**) $L = 3$, $S = 2$.

8-4. Using vector diagrams, determine the possible values of the total angular momentum of an electron system for which (**a**) $L = 3$, $S = \frac{5}{2}$, (**b**) $L = 2$, $S = \frac{5}{2}$.

8-5. Determine the electron configuration of (**a**) barium in the normal state, and (**b**) mercury in the normal state.

8-6. Determine the angular velocity of the precessional motion of an electron orbit when a source of light is placed in a magnetic field of 30,000 gausses. Compare this precessional velocity of the orbit with the change in the angular velocity of the electron on the basis of the classical Lorentz theory.

Ans. 2.64×10^{11} sec^{-1}.

8-7. Determine the maximum change in the energy of a p electron due to the precessional motion of its orbit in a magnetic field of 30,000 gausses.

Ans. 2.76×10^{-16} erg.

8-8. Draw a diagram showing the relative separations of the sodium D lines and their Zeeman components produced by a magnetic field of 30,000 gausses. Use a wave number scale.

8-9. (**a**) Using the wavelengths given in the energy level diagram of calcium, determine the values of the two lowest resonance potentials. (**b**) If electrons of 2.8 ev energy are used to excite the calcium atoms, which spectral lines will be emitted by calcium?

8-10. Two resonance potentials have been observed with mercury vapor, 4.86 and 6.67 volts. The ionization potential of mercury is 10.43 volts. Compute (**a**) the wavelengths of the mercury resonance radiation, (**b**) the wave number of the lowest state of mercury. Check your results by reference to standard tables or energy level diagrams.

8-11. The wavelengths of the lines obtained on a spectrogram were measured and classified into three series as follows:

Principal Series	*Sharp Series*	*Diffuse Series*
6707.85A	8126.5A	6103.5A
3232.6	4971.9	4603.0
2741.3	4273.3	4132.3
2562.5	3985.8	3915.0
2475.3	3838.2	3794.7

From the above data the series limit, expressed in wave numbers, was determined as 43,486 cm^{-1} for the principal series, and 28,582 cm^{-1} for the sharp and diffuse series.

(**a**) Convert the wavelengths given above to wave numbers.
(**b**) Construct an energy level diagram using a wave number scale.
(**c**) Determine the ionization potential of this element and then place a voltage scale on the energy level diagram.
(**d**) Identify the element.

(e) Determine the first resonance potential of this element.
(f) Determine the principal quantum numbers for each energy level.

8-12. In the molecular beam magnetic resonance method, a resonance minimum is obtained for F^{19} nucleus with a beam of NaF at a frequency of 5.634×10^6 cycles per second in a homogeneous magnetic field of 1408 gausses. Calculate its nuclear magnetic moment in nuclear magnetons.

Ans. 2.622.

References

Bacher, R. F., and S. Goudsmit, *Atomic Energy States*. New York: McGraw-Hill Book Company, Inc., 1932.

Born, M., *Atomic Physics*. New York: G. E. Stechert & Company, 1951, Chap. VI.

Harrison, G. R., R. C. Lord, J. R. Loofbourow, *Practical Spectroscopy*. New York: Prentice-Hall, Inc., 1948.

Herzberg, G., *Atomic Spectra and Atomic Structure*. New York: Dover Publications, 1944, Chaps. I, II.

Hume-Rothery, W., *Atomic Theory for Students of Metallurgy*. London: The Institute of Metals, 1948, Parts II, III, and VI.

Moore, Charlotte E., *Atomic Energy Levels*. Washington, D. C.: National Bureau of Standards, Circular 467, Vol. I, 1949; Vol. II, 1952.

Owen, F. E., and E. Teller, *The Structure of Matter*. New York: John Wiley & Sons, Inc., 1949, Chaps. III, VII, VIII, IX, and XI.

Richtmyer, F. K., and E. H. Kennard, *Introduction to Modern Physics*. New York: McGraw-Hill Book Company, Inc., 1947, Chap. VIII.

Sawyer, R. A., *Experimental Spectroscopy*. New York: Prentice-Hall, Inc., 1951.

White, H. E., *Introduction to Atomic Spectra*. New York: McGraw-Hill Book Company, Inc., 1934.

Wood, R. W., *Physical Optics*. New York: The Macmillan Company, 1934, Chaps. V, XVII, XXI.

X-Ray Spectra

9-1. Characteristic X-Ray Spectra

Moseley (1913) made a systematic investigation of the characteristic x-ray spectra of the elements. The elements investigated were used as targets in x-ray tubes and the radiation from each target was analyzed with the aid of a single crystal spectrometer. A potassium ferrocyanide crystal was mounted on the spectrometer table and the spectrum was recorded on a photographic plate. The spectrometer and the photographic plate were placed in an evacuated chamber to avoid absorption of the long wavelength x-rays in the air. The spectral lines observed were grouped into two series, a short wavelength group known as the K series, and a comparatively long wavelength group known as the L series. The wide separation of these two series of lines is illustrated in Figure 9-1 for the case of silver in which the K series wavelengths extend from 0.486A to 0.563A, while the L series lines are in the wavelength range 3.3A to 4.7A. Other investigators have found two other series of lines of still longer wavelengths in the heavier elements, $Z > 66$, classified as M series and N series.

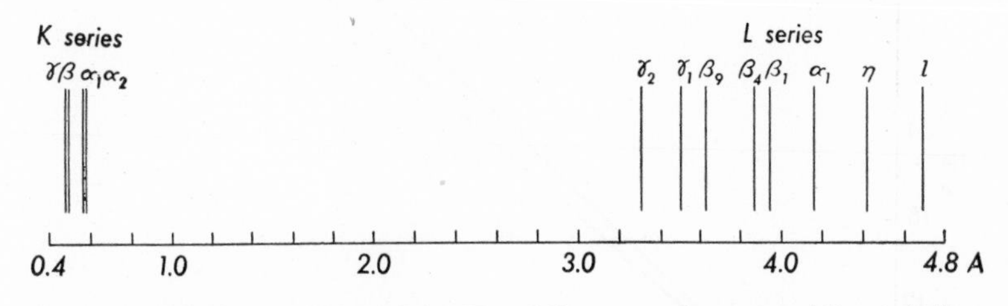

FIG. 9-1. Relative positions of the K and L x-ray series spectral lines of silver.

Moseley found that the character of a given series was practically the same for all the elements studied, and that the frequency of a particular line of a series varied in a regular manner from element to element in the periodic table. By plotting the square root of the frequency of one of the lines, say the K_α line (the most intense line of the K series), against the atomic number of the element emitting this line, Moseley obtained a straight line. Figure 9-2 shows such a graph, now known as a Moseley diagram. The K_α line is actually a doublet; in Moseley's work this doublet was not resolved but appeared as a single line. The equation of any one of the lines on a Moseley diagram, to a good approximation, is given by

$$\boxed{\nu = C(Z - a)^2} \tag{1}$$

where C and a are constants. For the K_α line, C was found to be equal to $\frac{3}{4}Rc$, where R is the Rydberg constant, c is the speed of light, and a was

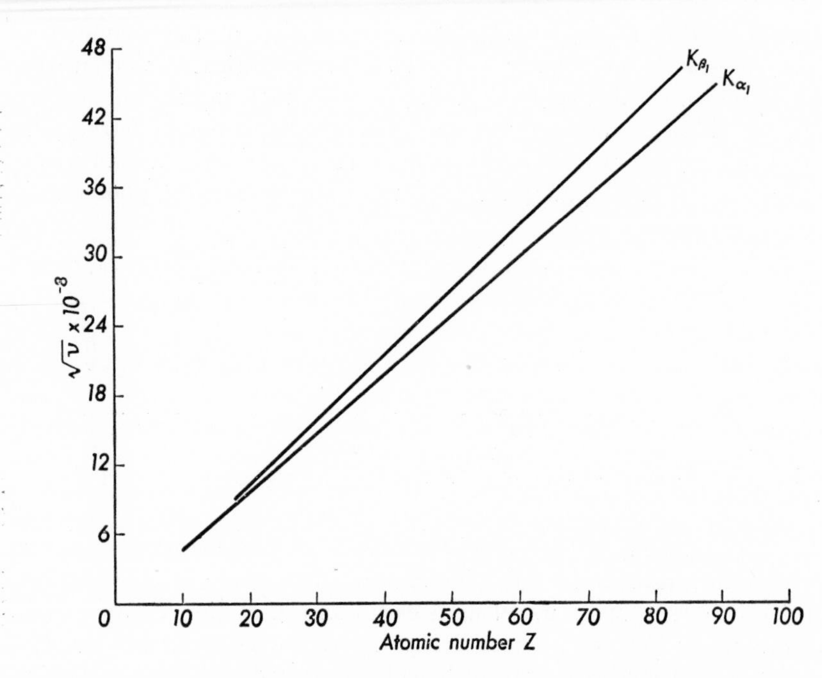

FIG. 9-2. Moseley diagram in which the square root of the frequency is plotted against the atomic number of the emitting element for two lines of the K series.

found to be practically 1. The equation for the frequency of the K_α line of any element can therefore be written as

$$\nu_{K_\alpha} = \tfrac{3}{4}Rc(Z - 1)^2. \tag{2}$$

It must be remembered that Moseley did this work almost a half century ago. Some of the elements now known were then unknown. The atomic number of an element merely represented its position in the arrangement of the elements according to their atomic weights. In order to obtain a straight line for the curve, $\sqrt{\nu}$ against Z, Moseley had to rearrange the orders of nickel and cobalt, assigning the lower atomic number to the element of higher atomic weight. Furthermore a gap had to be left at $Z = 43$, showing the existence of an element, technetium, then unknown.

Moseley's work followed closely upon the introduction of Rutherford's nuclear theory of the atom and Bohr's theory of hydrogen. The relationship between Bohr's theory and Moseley's work can best be shown by rewriting equation (2) for the frequency of the K_α line to read

$$\nu_{K_\alpha} = cR(Z - 1)^2 \left(\frac{1}{1^2} - \frac{1}{2^2}\right). \tag{3}$$

The interpretation of this equation on the Bohr theory is that the K_α line is emitted when an electron goes from the orbit of principal quantum number $n = 2$ to the orbit of principal quantum number $n = 1$. The appearance of the factor $(Z - 1)$ rather than Z in equation (3) can be explained by assuming that the electron which goes from orbit $n = 2$ to $n = 1$ is "screened" from the total nuclear charge Z by the negative charge of a single electron. This explanation can best be understood by considering the manner in which x-rays are produced. The element in the target consists of neutral atoms in which the first shell, $n = 1$, contains two electrons, and, according to Pauli's principle, no more electrons can get into this K shell. The only time an electron can go from the L shell, $n = 2$, to the K shell is when one of the electrons is missing from the K shell. The obvious inference is that, during the operation of the x-ray tube, a cathode ray knocks out an electron from the K shell of an atom. Since most of the other shells have their full quota of electrons, this K electron will have to go either to one of the unoccupied outer levels or completely outside the atom, depending upon the amount of energy transferred to the atom by the incident cathode ray. As a result of this process, the K shell will now have only one electron in it. If an electron from the L shell should go into the K shell, it will do so with the emission of a quantum of radiation whose frequency is that of the K_α line. The electron which goes from the L shell to the K shell moves in an electric field which is essentially that of the positive nuclear charge and the negative charge of the single electron still remaining in the K shell. This electric field is therefore equivalent to that of a positive charge of magnitude $(Z - 1)e$. The effect of the outer electrons on this electric field can be shown to be very small.

9-2. X-Ray Energy Level Diagram

A simplified energy level diagram can be used to show the changes in atomic configuration which give rise to the K and L series of x-ray spectral lines. In this diagram, Figure 9-3, the zero energy level is taken as that of the normal state of the neutral atom. This differs from the optical case in which the zero level of energy is that of the ionized atom. Let us assume that the cathode ray which is incident on an atom has sufficient energy to remove one electron from the K shell to the outside of the atom. If $\mathcal{E}_K$ represents the work done in removing this K electron, then the energy of the system can be represented at a level $\mathcal{E}_K$ above the zero level. This atom is now ionized with one electron missing from the K shell.

Let us consider the same neutral atom once more and suppose that the impinging cathode ray has not sufficient energy to remove an electron from the K shell, but does have sufficient energy to remove one from the

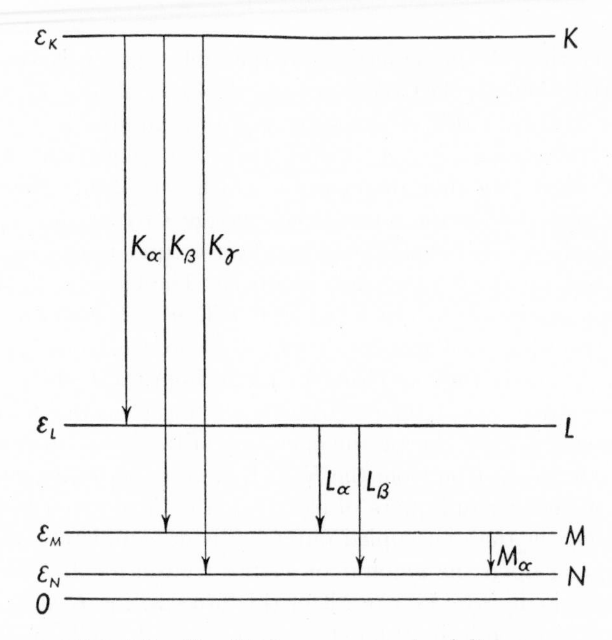

FIG. 9-3. Simplified x-ray energy level diagram.

L shell to the outside. Then, if the atom is ionized by the removal of one electron from the L shell, the energy of the system will be $\mathcal{E}_L$, and can be represented by a line at the proper height above the zero level. Similarly $\mathcal{E}_M$ represents the work done in ionizing a neutral atom by removing an electron from the M shell, and $\mathcal{E}_n$ represents the work done in removing an electron from the N shell of a neutral atom.

Suppose that the atom is now in the energy state $\mathcal{E}_K$, that is, one electron is missing from the K shell. If an electron goes from the L shell to the K shell, the atom will then be in the energy state represented by $\mathcal{E}_L$; that is, one electron will now be missing from the L shell. The frequency of the spectral line radiated when an electron goes from the L to the K shell, or when the energy state of the atom is changed from $\mathcal{E}_K$ to $\mathcal{E}_L$, is given by Bohr's frequency condition:

$$\nu_{K_\alpha} = \frac{\mathcal{E}_K - \mathcal{E}_L}{h}. \tag{4}$$

There is also a definite probability that an electron might go from the M shell directly to the K shell, leaving the atom in the energy state $\mathcal{E}_M$. The line emitted in this transition is the K_β line; its frequency is given by

$$\nu_{K_\beta} = \frac{\mathcal{E}_K - \mathcal{E}_M}{h}. \tag{5}$$

Or an electron may go from the N shell directly to the K shell with the emission of the K_γ spectral line of frequency

$$\nu_{K_\gamma} = \frac{\mathcal{E}_K - \mathcal{E}_N}{h}. \tag{6}$$

Similar analyses can be used for the transitions producing the L and M series of spectral lines. For example, if the atom is in the energy state $\mathcal{E}_L$, an electron may go from the M shell to the L shell with the emission of the L_α line of frequency

$$\nu_{L_\alpha} = \frac{\mathcal{E}_L - \mathcal{E}_M}{h}. \tag{7}$$

When the voltage across the x-ray tube is sufficiently high, a very large number of atoms in the target of the tube will be raised to the energy state $\mathcal{E}_K$, others to the energy state $\mathcal{E}_L$, and so on, by the action of the cathode rays incident upon the target. The K series of spectral lines will be emitted by those atoms in which the electrons go directly from the L, M, or N shells to the K shell; the L series of spectral lines will be emitted by those atoms in which the electrons go directly from the M or N shells to the L shell. The intensity of a spectral line will be proportional to the number of atoms in which the appropriate transitions take place. The K_α line, for example, is the most intense line of the K series, while the K_γ line is the faintest one. In most of the atoms in the energy state $\mathcal{E}_K$, therefore, electrons go from the L shells to the K shells. Stated in a different manner, the probability that an electron will go from the L shell to the K shell is much greater than the probability that an electron will go from the M shell directly to the K shell. The probability that an electron will go from the N shell to the K shell is very small.

With the precision and resolving power available in modern x-ray spectroscopy, many of the lines have been resolved into two or more components. The K_α line, for example, has been resolved into two components

$K_{\alpha 1}$ and $K_{\alpha 2}$ for all elements of atomic number greater than 15. The K_β line has been resolved into two components for most of the elements of atomic number greater than 36. The K_γ line has not yet been resolved. The fine structure observed in x-ray spectral lines must obviously be due to the multiplicity of some of the energy levels. One might determine this multiplicity from an analysis of the emission spectra. It will be more instructive, however, to show how this multiplicity of the energy levels can be determined by more direct experiments in which electrons from the inner shells of atoms are removed from them by the action of x-rays from an external source. This is an extension of the photoelectric effect to the region of x-ray wavelengths. There are two general experimental methods for investigating this phenomenon. One is to study the absorption spectra of the x-rays; the other is to determine the energies of the electrons ejected from the atoms.

9-3. X-Ray Absorption Spectra

A method for studying the x-ray absorption spectrum of an element is illustrated in Figure 9-4. The continuous spectrum from some suitable target T is used in this experiment. A narrow beam of x-rays coming through the slits S_1 and S_2 is incident upon the absorbing material A containing

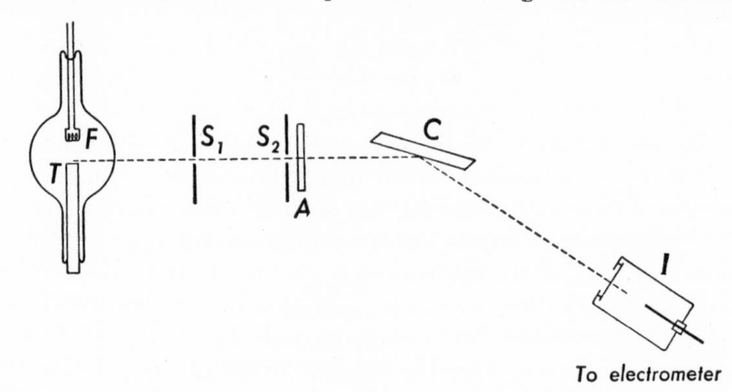

FIG. 9-4. Diagram showing the arrangement of apparatus for measuring the absorption of x-rays.

the element under investigation. The transmitted beam is then analyzed by the crystal C of the x-ray spectrometer, and the intensity of each wavelength λ is measured by the ionization it produces in the ionization chamber I. A photographic plate may be used in place of the ionization chamber; the intensity will then be determined by the blackening on the photographic plate.

Each particular setting of the crystal corresponds to a definite wavelength given by Bragg's law $n\lambda = 2d \sin \theta$. The usual procedure is to measure the intensity, I_0, of a given wavelength with the absorbing material removed from the path of the x-rays, then to insert the absorbing material in the path of the x-rays and measure the new intensity I for the same wavelength. This procedure is repeated over a wide range of wavelengths. For each particular wavelength,

$$\boxed{I = I_0 \epsilon^{-\mu x},} \qquad (8) \quad \text{(Chap. 5, Eq. [18])}$$

where μ is the absorption coefficient for the wavelength used, and x is the thickness of the absorbing material.

The results of a typical experiment, using a thin foil of silver as the absorbing material, are shown in Figure 9-5 where the mass absorption coefficient μ/ρ (see §5-13) is plotted against the wavelength λ. It is found that the mass absorption coefficient increases with the wavelength, approximately as λ^3, until a particular wavelength λ_K, at the position K, is reached, at which wavelength μ/ρ drops suddenly to a lower value. In the wavelength region between K and L_{I}, the mass absorption coefficient again increases as λ^3; at L_{I} it drops in value. There are three such breaks in the curve close together marked L_{I}, L_{II}, and L_{III}. The wavelength at which the first break occurs is called the wavelength of the K absorption limit. The other breaks occur at the L_{I}, L_{II}, and L_{III} absorption limits.

In the case of silver, the wavelength of the K absorption limit is $\lambda_K = 0.4845$A. This is slightly less than the shortest wavelength which occurs in the K series lines, the K_γ line, for which $\lambda = 0.4860$A (see Table 9-1). In the production of the lines of the K series, it was found that an amount of energy, $\mathcal{E}_K$, had first to be supplied to the atom to remove an electron from the K shell, after which an electron from some outer shell, in going into the K shell, would emit a quantum of radiation. The energy of this quantum is, of course, always less than $\mathcal{E}_K$, as shown by equations (4), (5), and (6). When the element forms the target of an x-ray tube, this energy, $\mathcal{E}_K$, comes from the kinetic energy of the incident cathode rays or electrons. When the element, however, is used as an absorber of x-rays, this energy must come from the incident x-rays. If the energy of an incident quantum or photon, $h\nu$, is greater than $\mathcal{E}_K$, the photon will be able to knock an electron out of the K shell, thus raising the atom to the energy state $\mathcal{E}_K$. The smallest value of the energy of a photon which will be able to remove an electron from the K shell is

$$h\nu_K = \mathcal{E}_K = \frac{hc}{\lambda_K} \qquad (9)$$

where λ_K and ν_K represent the wavelength and frequency, respectively, of the K absorption limit. If the energy of the incident photon, $h\nu$, is less

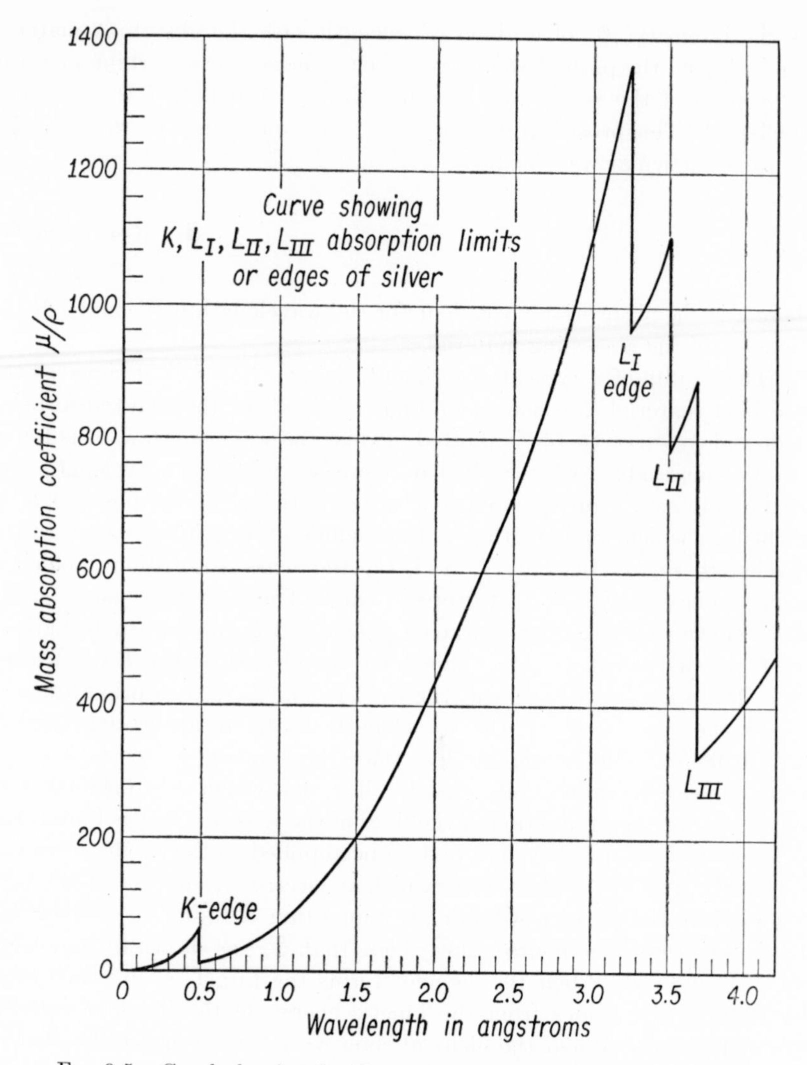

FIG. 9-5. Graph showing the K and L x-ray absorption limits of silver.

than $\mathcal{E}_K$, then the photon will not be able to remove an electron from the K shell, but it may have enough energy to be able to remove an electron from one of the higher levels, L, M, or N.

The fact that there are three absorption limits L_{I}, L_{II}, and L_{III} very close together, and in the range of wavelengths of the L series, indicates that the L shell probably consists of three energy levels. The wavelength of the L_{I} absorption limit is smaller than that of any line of the L series. The energy of each one of the states L_{I}, L_{II}, and L_{III} can be obtained from

Table 9-1

Wavelengths of the K Series Lines and the K Absorption Limit for Some Elements
(*Wavelengths in* A.)

Element	K_{α_2}	K_{α_1}	K_{β_2}	K_{β_1}	K_{γ}	K Abs Limit
29 Cu	1.5443	1.5405	—	1.3922	1.3810	1.3802
42 Mo	0.7135	0.7092	0.6328	0.6323	0.6209	0.6197
46 Pd	0.5898	0.5855	0.5211	0.5105	0.5102	0.5090
47 Ag	0.5638	0.5594	0.4977	0.4970	0.4870	0.4855
74 W	0.2138	0.2090	0.1852	0.1844	0.1795	0.1786
78 Pt	0.1904	0.1856	—	0.1640	0.1592	0.1580
79 Au	0.1852	0.1804	—	0.1593	0.1546	0.1535
82 Pb	0.1703	0.1655	—	0.1464	0.1416	0.1408
92 U	0.1313	0.1267	—	0.1121	0.1086	0.1068

the graph with the aid of equations of the type of equation (9); thus, for example,

$$\mathcal{E}_{L_{\rm I}} = \frac{hc}{\lambda_{L_{\rm I}}} \cdot \tag{10}$$

It is difficult to obtain the wavelengths of the M absorption limits by this method because of the absorption of these long wavelength x-rays by the element under investigation. It will be recalled that the absorption coefficient varies as the cube of the wavelength. In the case of silver, the wavelength of the M limit is about 10 times that of the L limit, so that the absorption would be approximately 1000 times as great. However, the wavelengths of the M absorption limits have been determined in this manner for some of the heavier elements. In each case, five absorption limits were found in the M region, indicating that the M shell consists of five energy levels close together.

9-4. X-Ray Critical Voltages

The correctness of the above interpretation of the absorption limits can be demonstrated in a fairly direct manner by using the element under investigation as the target in an x-ray tube and controlling carefully the voltage across the tube. The maximum kinetic energy which the electrons incident upon the target possess is Ve where V is the voltage across the tube. The energy required to remove an electron from the K shell of an atom can be expressed as

$$\mathcal{E}_K = h\nu_K = \frac{hc}{\lambda_K} = V_K e. \tag{11}$$

The critical voltage, V_K, is the minimum voltage which, when applied between the anode and the cathode of the x-ray tube, will give the impinging electron enough energy to remove electrons from the K shells. If the voltage across the tube is less than V_K, the atoms in the target cannot be raised to the energy state $\mathcal{E}_K$; hence the lines of the K series will not appear in the spectrum. When the voltage across the tube is increased until the value V_K is reached, then all the lines of the K series appear simultaneously. This indicates that many of the atoms were raised to the energy state $\mathcal{E}_K$, making possible transitions to lower energy states with the radiation of quanta corresponding to the lines of the K series.

The critical voltage for the production of the K lines of silver, for example, can be determined from equation (11) by substituting for λ_K its value 0.4845A, and the accepted values for e, h, and c, yielding $V_K = 25.6$ kilovolts. When the voltage across a silver target x-ray tube is, say, 20 kilovolts, the spectrum is found to consist of the L series lines superimposed on the continuous radiation. When the voltage across the tube is increased, the intensities of these two spectra are increased, but no new lines appear until the voltage across the tube reaches the value 25.6 kilovolts, when all the lines of the K series appear simultaneously. Further increase in voltage produces an increase in the intensities of the characteristic spectra relative to the continuous spectrum.

9-5. Magnetic Spectrum Analysis

The x-ray energy levels of an atom can be determined in an independent way by utilizing the photoelectric effect with x-rays of known wavelength. If an x-ray quantum of energy $h\nu$ ejects an electron from an inner shell of the atom, thereby raising the atom to a higher energy state, then the kinetic energy of the ejected electron will be given by

$$\tfrac{1}{2}mv^2 = h\nu - \mathcal{E}_{K,L}\ldots \tag{12}$$

where $\mathcal{E}_{K,L}\ldots$ represents the appropriate final energy state of the atom. By measuring the energy of the ejected electron, it is possible to determine the particular energy level from which it was ejected.

H. R. Robinson developed the magnetic spectrograph for determining the velocities of the ejected electrons. A diagram of the apparatus is shown in Figure 9-6. The element to be investigated, usually in the form of a very thin foil, is placed upon a holder at C. A narrow beam of monochromatic x-rays, usually the intense $K\alpha$ line from a known target material, enters through the thin window W in the evacuated box B and strikes the element on C. The entire apparatus is in a uniform magnetic field of intensity H perpendicular to the plane of the figure. The electrons which are ejected from the element at C move in circular paths under the influence of the magnetic field. Only those electrons which pass through the slit S will be able to strike the photographic plate P. Because of the geometry

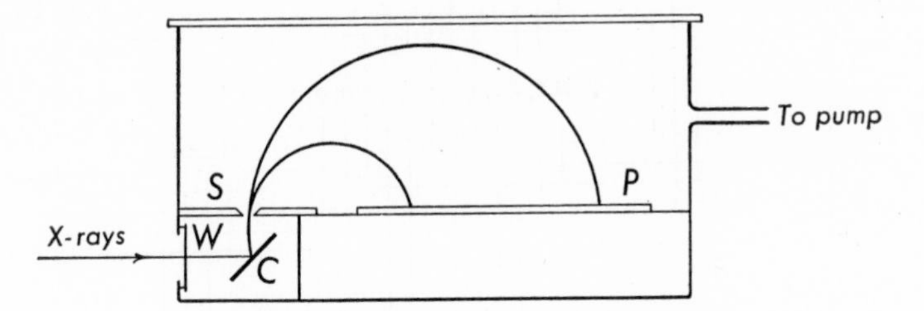

FIG. 9-6. Robinson's magnetic spectrograph.

of the apparatus, all electrons with the same velocity will be focused at the same distance from the source C. The radius of the electronic path is half the distance from C to the point on the photographic plate which has been blackened by the electrons.

The velocities of the electrons ejected from C can be found with the aid of the well-known equation

$$Hev = \frac{mv^2}{r}$$

or

$$v = Hr \cdot \frac{e}{m}, \tag{13}$$

where r is the radius of the path of an electron. In any one experiment, the electron ejected from the innermost shell will have the smallest velocity and its path will have the smallest radius r. Electrons ejected from the outer shells of the atom, such as the M and N shells, will have greater energy and be focused farther out on the photographic plate. From the positions of the lines on the photographic plate, the energies of the ejected electrons can be computed. By substituting the value of the electronic energy in equation (12), the energy required to remove the electron from its particular shell can be determined.

The values of the energy levels of a large number of elements were determined in this way by Robinson. His measurements are in agreement with results obtained from x-ray absorption spectra. In addition, he determined the energy values of the M levels of many elements as well as some of the N levels.

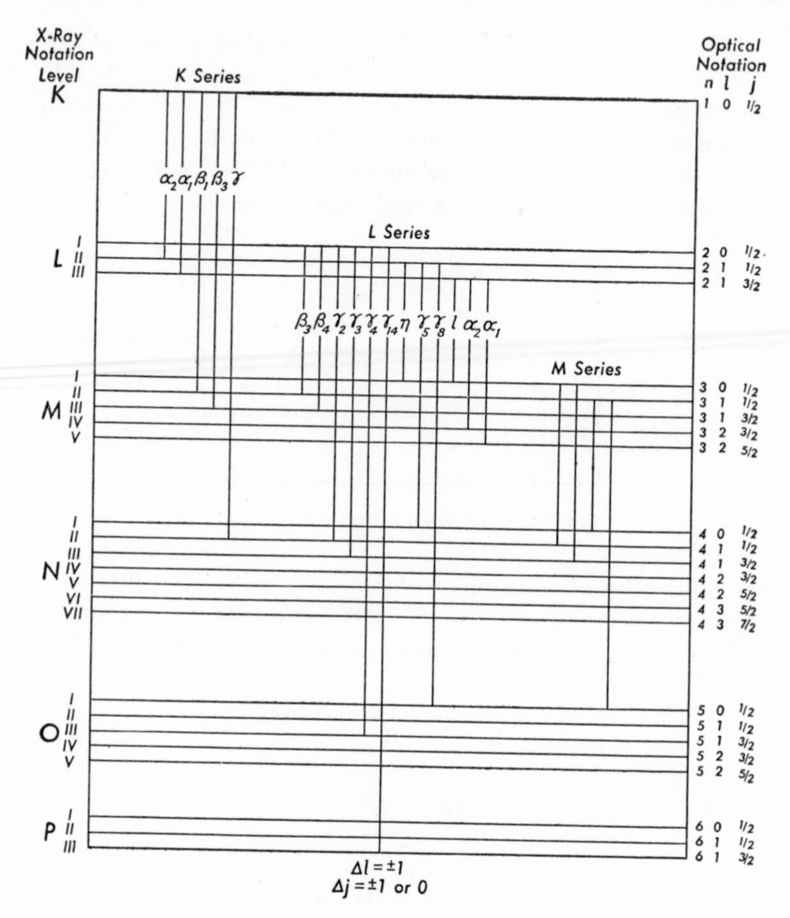

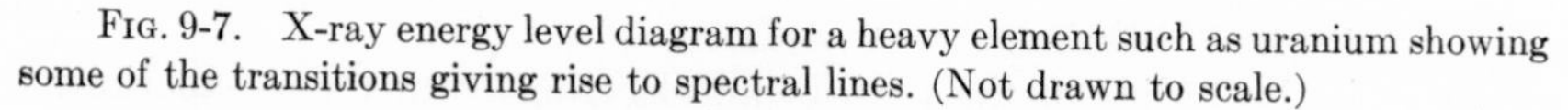

FIG. 9-7. X-ray energy level diagram for a heavy element such as uranium showing some of the transitions giving rise to spectral lines. (Not drawn to scale.)

9-6. X-Ray Terms and Selection Rules

The x-ray term structure or energy level diagram can be built up from analyses of the emission and absorption spectra of the elements, and from the determination of the energy levels by the magnetic spectrum analysis of the energies of electrons ejected from these levels. The complete energy level diagram of uranium, $Z = 92$, is shown in Figure 9-7, with the x-ray notation for these levels and some of the transitions giving rise to the x-ray spectral lines. It must be remembered that each x-ray energy level represents a state of an atom which has one electron missing from a closed shell. Pauli pointed out that in a configuration in which an electron is missing from a completed subgroup, the spectral term is the same as if that one electron alone occupied the subgroup. Normally there are two 1*s* electrons in the K shell; if one electron is removed, the energy state of the atom will be that of a $1s$ electron, namely, $^2S_{1/2}$, just as in the case of an alkali atom. The L shell consists of two subgroups, one for which $l = 0$ and the other $l = 1$. There are normally two electrons in the subgroup $n = 2, l = 0$; if one $2s$ electron is removed, the energy state of the atom will be that of a single electron for which $n = 2, l = 0$, namely, a $2s\ ^2S_{1/2}$ configuration. This is the energy level L_{I}. There are normally six $2p$ electrons in the completed subgroup $n = 2, l = 1$. If one $2p$ electron is removed, the energy state of the atom will be a P state; this state will be a doublet state corresponding to the two possible values of j, that is, $j = \frac{1}{2}$, or $j = \frac{3}{2}$. The two energy states L_{II} and L_{III} therefore correspond to the doublet terms $^2P_{1/2}$ and $^2P_{3/2}$ respectively, again similar to the terms of the alkali atoms. This procedure can be carried out for each of the subgroups. For example, the removal of an electron from a subgroup for which $l = 2$ gives rise to the $^2D_{3/2}$ and $^2D_{5/2}$ terms. The optical notations and the (n, l, j) values for each energy level are shown in the figure. One difference between x-ray energy levels and alkali terms should be noted: the higher x-ray energy states are designated by the smaller quantum numbers.

The selection rules for the permitted transitions are the same as those for the alkali atoms, namely,

$$\Delta L = \pm 1.$$

$$\Delta J = 0 \text{ or } \pm 1.$$

While no restrictions are placed on changes in the principal quantum number n, transitions for which $\Delta n = 0$ are very rare, and the lines produced by such transitions are of very small intensity. The above selection rules account for the transitions giving rise to the more intense lines of the x-ray spectral series. Some fainter lines, forbidden by the above selection rules, have also been observed, as well as some lines which cannot be accounted for by any transitions between states represented in the energy level diagram.

9-7. Radiationless Transitions—Auger Effect

When an electron is ejected from the K level of an atom by an x-ray photon, there is a probability that an electron from the L level of the same atom will go to the K level with the consequent emission of a K_α x-ray photon. Transitions of this type give rise to the fluorescent spectra of the atom. The electron ejected from the K level is a photoelectron. Auger (1925), in a cloud chamber investigation of the photoelectrons ejected from atoms of argon, observed many instances in which the K photoelectron track had associated with it a smaller electron track. The smaller track represented an electron with much less energy than the K photoelectron. Furthermore, the two tracks had a common origin. Auger interpreted this effect as due to a radiationless transition; that is, instead of a K_α x-ray photon being emitted when an L electron went into the K level, the energy was used to eject a second electron from the L level, leaving it doubly ionized. This process might be imagined as one in which a K_α photon is formed when an electron goes from the L to the K level, and that this photon then ejects an electron from the already ionized L level, leaving it doubly ionized. This would correspond to an *internal conversion* in which the K_α photon ejects a photoelectron from the ionized L level of the same atom. Since no radiation gets outside the atom, this is actually a radiationless transition. This effect is called the *Auger effect* and the electron emitted in this radiationless transition is called an *Auger electron.*

We can apply the photoelectric equation to the Auger effect. Before the emission of the Auger electron the atom was in the K state; after the ejection of the Auger electron the atom has two electrons missing from the L level; we shall designate this as the LL state. The kinetic energy of the Auger electron will be the difference between the energy of the K state, $\mathcal{E}_K$, and the energy of the LL state, $\mathcal{E}_{LL}$, that is,

$$\tfrac{1}{2}mv^2 = \mathcal{E}_K - \mathcal{E}_{LL}. \tag{14}$$

There are other possibilities besides the K-LL transition; for example, after an L electron has gone to the K level, an Auger electron might be ejected from the M level, so that the final state of the atom is one in which L and M levels are each singly ionized. This state can be designated as an LM state and the radiationless transition would be designated as a K-LM transition. Other possible Auger transitions can readily be inferred.

Although the Auger effect was first discovered in connection with the x-ray photoelectric effect, any other method of ionizing an atom by the removal of an electron from an inner shell may lead to an Auger transition. Such effects have been observed in some optical spectra, and, of greater interest, in readjustments of the electronic levels following nuclear disintegrations, particularly K-electron capture, and internal conversion following gamma-ray emission (see §10-11).

9-8. Production of Characteristic X-Ray Spectra

Although characteristic x-ray spectra are most commonly produced by bombarding elements with electrons, other methods are also used. Any method that causes the removal of an electron from one of the inner levels will result in the production of characteristic x-ray spectra. When photons of sufficient energy bombard a substance, as, for example, in the photoelectric effect with x-rays, the subsequent readjustment of the electrons in the atoms results in the emission of the characteristic x-ray spectra. Such spectra are frequently termed *x-ray fluorescent spectra.* The x-ray fluorescent spectra are usually of low intensity, but frequently are the best way of analyzing the nature of the element in an unknown sample.

Characteristic x-ray spectra can also be produced by bombarding a target with positive ions, such as high energy protons and alpha particles.

Characteristic x-ray spectra whose origins can be traced to readjustments in the electronic configurations of atoms following nuclear disintegrations have also been observed. In one type of nuclear disintegration known as *electron capture*, in which the nucleus of an atom captures one of the electrons from the same atom, the strongest evidence for this process is the emission of the characteristic x-ray spectrum. The origin of this

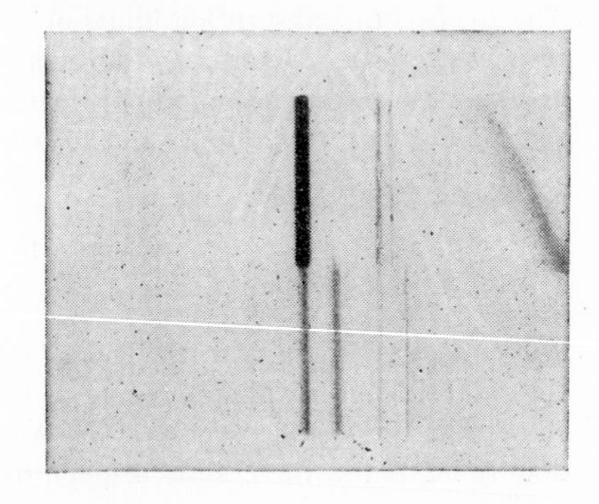

FIG. 9-8. Photograph obtained with curved crystal x-ray spectrometer. Upper half shows the K_α, K_β, and K_γ lines of Ag emitted as a result of the decay of Cd^{107} by electron capture. Lower half shows K_α lines of Ag and Cd used for calibration; these are followed by the K_β lines. (Photograph by J. E. Edwards, M. L. Pool, and F. C. Blake.)

spectrum is traced by comparing it with the known x-ray spectra of neighboring elements. If the atomic number of the original element is Z, the x-ray spectrum observed is always found to be the characteristic spectrum of the element of atomic number $Z - 1$. For example, it was inferred that one of the radioactive isotopes of cadmium, $Z = 48$, $A = 107$, disintegrates by electron capture to form silver, $Z = 47$, $A = 107$. To check this inference, Edwards, Pool, and Blake (1945) examined the x-rays emitted by a small sample of this isotope of cadmium, using a curved crystal x-ray spectrograph with a mica crystal. A copy of the photograph obtained by them is shown in Figure 9-8. The upper half shows the K_α, K_β and K_γ lines of silver emitted by the radioactive source; the lower half is a calibration photograph showing the K_α lines of Cd and Ag. This photograph shows that the x-rays are emitted by the silver formed in the radioactive decay (electron capture) of cadmium.

Problems

9-1. After studying the x-ray spectrum of platinum, determine the minimum voltage that must be used across the x-ray tube to produce the K series lines.

Ans. 79 kv.

9-2. Using the data in Table 9-1, calculate the energies, in electron volts, of the

L_{II} and L_{III} energy levels for the elements listed in the table. Plot the square roots of these energies against atomic number and discuss any regularities observed in these curves. How do these curves compare with the Moseley diagram?

9-3. In an experiment with the magnetic spectrograph, the $K_{\alpha 1}$ line from a silver target x-ray tube is incident upon a thin copper foil inside the spectrograph. If the intensity of the magnetic field is 100 gausses, calculate the radius of the smallest electron path that will be observed. What is the origin of these electrons?

Ans. 3.88 cm.

9-4. The K_α x-ray photons of molybdenum are incident upon a thin foil of tungsten in a magnetic spectrograph in which the field intensity is 150 gausses. The L_I, L_{II}, L_{III} absorption limits of tungsten are 1.021A, 1.071A, and 1.211A, respectively. (**a**) Determine the energies of the electrons ejected from these levels. (**b**) Determine the radii of their paths in the magnetic field. (**c**) Calculate the separation of the lines of this magnetic spectrum.

9-5. The L_I absorption limit of bismuth is 0.756A. Determine the minimum energy of a beam of x-ray photons which can produce the L and M fluorescent spectral series of bismuth.

9-6. (**a**) Assuming that the energy required to remove a second electron from the L level is approximately equal to that required to remove the first electron, show that the kinetic energy of an Auger electron from an atom which is left doubly ionized in the L state is given by

$$\tfrac{1}{2}mv^2 = \mathcal{E}_K - 2\mathcal{E}_L.$$

(**b**) Calculate the kinetic energy of such an Auger electron emitted by a copper atom if the L_I absorption limit of copper is 13A.

9-7. An Auger electron is ejected from a tungsten atom, leaving the latter ionized in the L and M states. Calculate the kinetic energy of this electron if the L_I absorption limit of tungsten is 1.02A and the M_I absorption limit is 4.37A.

References

Compton, A. H., and S. K. Allison, *X-Rays in Theory and Experiment.* New York: D. Van Nostrand Company, Inc., 1935, Chaps. I, VII, VIII.

Richtmyer, F. K., and E. H. Kennard, *Introduction to Modern Physics.* New York: McGraw-Hill Book Company, Inc., 1947, Chap. X.

Siegbahn, M., *The Spectroscopy of X-Rays.* New York: Oxford University Press, 1925, Chaps. IV–VI, VIII.

NUCLEAR PHYSICS

Natural Radioactivity

10-1. Résumé of Some Known Properties of Nuclei

Many of the important properties of atomic nuclei, as well as the experimental evidence for these properties, were discussed in previous chapters. It was shown that the total number of nucleons in a nucleus is equal to the mass number A of the particular isotope of the element. A nucleon thus has a mass number 1, and may be either a proton or a neutron. It was further shown that the number of protons in the nucleus is equal to the atomic number, Z, of the element, and that the number N of neutrons in the nucleus is $A-Z$.

From the results of the experiments on the scattering of alpha particles, it was concluded that the nucleus occupies only a very small fraction of the volume of an atom and that nuclear radii do not exceed 10^{-12} cm. It was further shown that the nucleus possesses angular momentum due to spin and also possesses a magnetic moment.

In this and the following chapters we shall discuss many nuclear processes and transformations which not only are interesting in themselves but also provide additional information concerning the nucleus. Among these processes and transformations are (1) the natural radioactivity of some of the heavier elements, (2) the disintegration of nuclei by bombardment with particles and radiation, (3) artificial radioactivity induced by the bombardment of nuclei with particles and radiation, and (4) nuclear fission.

10-2. Natural Radioactive Transformations

An element which is naturally radioactive usually is found to emit either alpha particles or beta particles. Sometimes gamma rays accompany the emission of these particles. When the nucleus of an atom emits an alpha particle, the atom is transformed into a new atom, since its atomic mass is decreased by four units and its atomic number is decreased by two units. For example, radium, with $A = 226$ and $Z = 88$, is known to emit alpha particles; hence the product of this transformation, known as radon, or radium emanation, will have $A = 222$ and $Z = 86$. That we are dealing with nuclear transformations is confirmed by the fact that radium, which is a solid, is in the same chemical group as barium, while radium emanation is one of the inert gases. In this particular case it is easy to separate the product from its parent substance. When a beta particle is emitted by a nucleus of atomic number Z, the atomic number of the new atom formed becomes $Z + 1$, but the mass remains practically unaltered since the mass of a beta particle is negligible in comparison with that of a nucleus. Thus, in beta disintegration, the mass number remains the same, and parent and product atoms form a pair of *isobars*.

The rate at which a particular radioactive material disintegrates is a constant independent of all physical and chemical conditions. Given a large number of atoms of any one radioactive element, the average number, dN, that will disintegrate in a small time interval, dt, is found to be proportional to the number of atoms, N, present at the time t; that is,

$$-dN = \lambda N dt, \tag{1}$$

where λ is a constant for the particular radioactive element. Integrating this equation, we get

$$\boxed{N = N_0 \epsilon^{-\lambda t},} \tag{2}$$

where N_0 represents the number of atoms present at the time $t = 0$. Equation (2) shows that the number of atoms of a given radioactive substance decreases exponentially with time provided that no new atoms are introduced. Half of the material will have disintegrated at the end of a certain time interval T, which can be determined by setting $N = N_0/2$ and $t = T$ in equation (2), yielding

$$\lambda T = \log_\epsilon 2,$$

so that

$$\boxed{T = \frac{0.693}{\lambda}.} \tag{3}$$

T is called the *half-life* of the element. It can be seen that at the end of a time interval equal to $2T$, one quarter of the original material will still be in existence. The number of atoms still in existence at any time t is shown in Figure 10-1. It is impossible to tell just when one particular atom will disintegrate because radioactive disintegrations follow the laws of chance or probability. At the end of a certain time t, N of the original atoms will still be in existence. In the next interval of time dt, dN of these atoms will have disintegrated. The *average lifetime*, T_a, of a single atom may be computed by multiplying dN, the number of atoms disintegrating, by the time, t, during which they existed, summing these products over all the

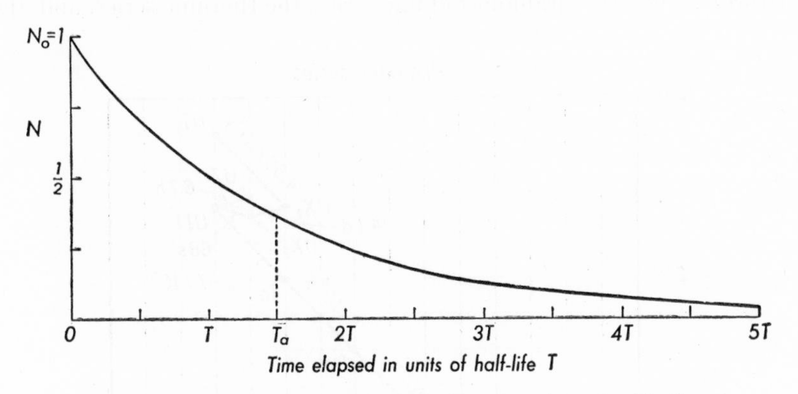

FIG. 10-1. Exponential decay of a radioactive element with time.

atoms, and then dividing by the total number of atoms at the start, N_0. Thus

$$T_a = \frac{\int_0^{N_0} t dN}{N_0}.$$

Now, from equation (2),

$$dN = -N_0 \lambda \epsilon^{-\lambda t} \, dt;$$

substitution of this value for dN in the above equation yields

$$T_a = -\int_\infty^0 t\lambda\epsilon^{-\lambda t} \, dt = +\int_0^\infty t\lambda\epsilon^{-\lambda t} \, dt,$$

which yields

$$\boxed{T_a = \frac{1}{\lambda}.} \tag{4}$$

The reciprocal of the disintegration constant λ is thus the average lifetime of a radioactive atom. If the half-life is known from experimental data, then the average lifetime, $1/\lambda$, can be computed from equation (3).

The half-lives, and hence the average lifetimes, vary considerably among the naturally radioactive elements. Radium, for example, has a half-life of 1620 years, while that of radon is 3.82 days. Thorium C′ has the shortest half-life, 3×10^{-7} second, while thorium has one of the longest, 1.39×10^{10} years.

10-3. Radioactive Series

Practically all of the naturally radioactive elements lie in the range of atomic numbers from $Z = 81$ to $Z = 92$. These elements have been grouped into three series, the uranium-radium series, the thorium series, and the

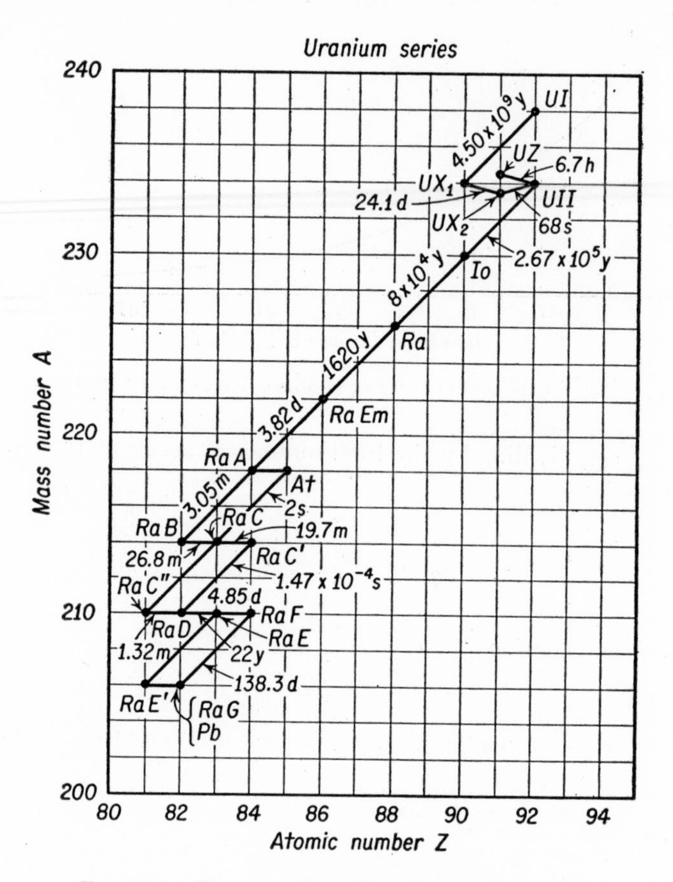

FIG. 10-2. The naturally radioactive uranium series.

actinium series. Any one of the radioactive elements can be traced back through a series of transformations to the parent element of the series. The uranium series, shown in Figure 10-2, starts with uranium I ($A = 238$, $Z = 92$), and goes through a series of transformations which involve the emission of alpha and beta particles forming such substances as radium, radium emanation, radium A . . . down to radium G ($A = 206$, $Z = 82$), which is isotopic with lead and is not radioactive. In the figure, the mass number A is plotted against the atomic number Z. An emission of an alpha particle is indicated by a displacement down by four units and to the left by two units; an emission of a beta particle by a displacement to the right of one unit.

An interesting *branching* takes place at radium C. Of all the RaC atoms disintegrating, 99.96 per cent do so with the emission of a beta particle forming RaC′, which then disintegrates with the emission of an

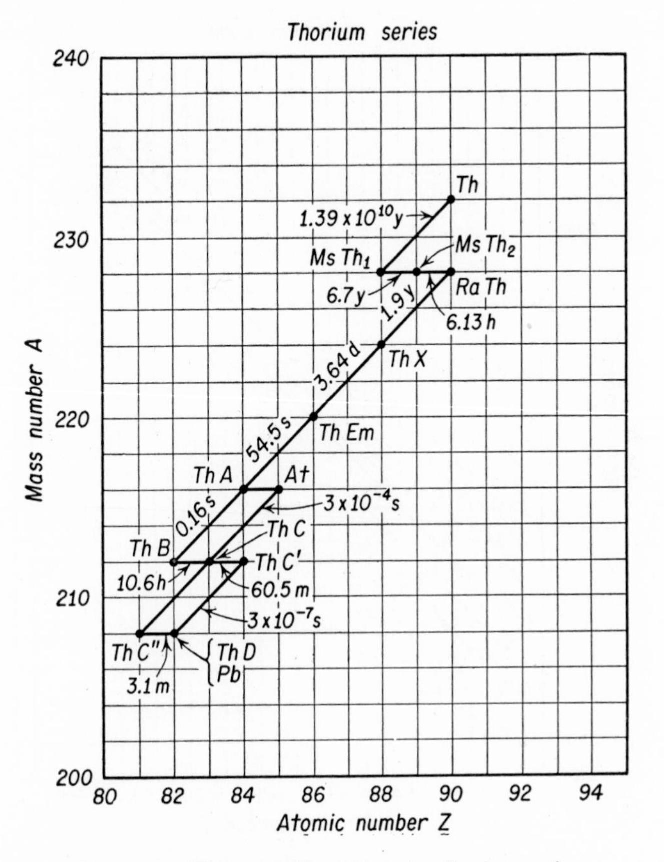

Fig. 10-3. The naturally radioactive thorium series.

alpha particle forming RaD. In the second branch, about 0.04 per cent of the RaC atoms disintegrate with the emission of an alpha particle forming RaC″, and when the latter disintegrates, it does so with the emission of a beta particle forming RaD. Branching also occurs at radium A, $Z = 84$, $A = 218$. In 99.96 per cent of the cases, radium A emits an alpha particle forming radium B; in 0.04 per cent of the cases, radium A emits a beta (β^-) particle forming the element astatine (symbol At), $Z = 85$, $A = 218$. Astatine has a short half-life of about 2 seconds, emitting an alpha particle to form radium C.

Another interesting type of transformation occurs when UX_1 ($Z = 90$, $A = 234$) emits a beta (β^-) particle to form UX_2 ($Z = 91$, $A = 234$). It was found that UX_2 disintegrates by emitting beta particles with two different half-lives, and since it was common to assume a half-life to be associated with a definite element, two names were given to the nuclei

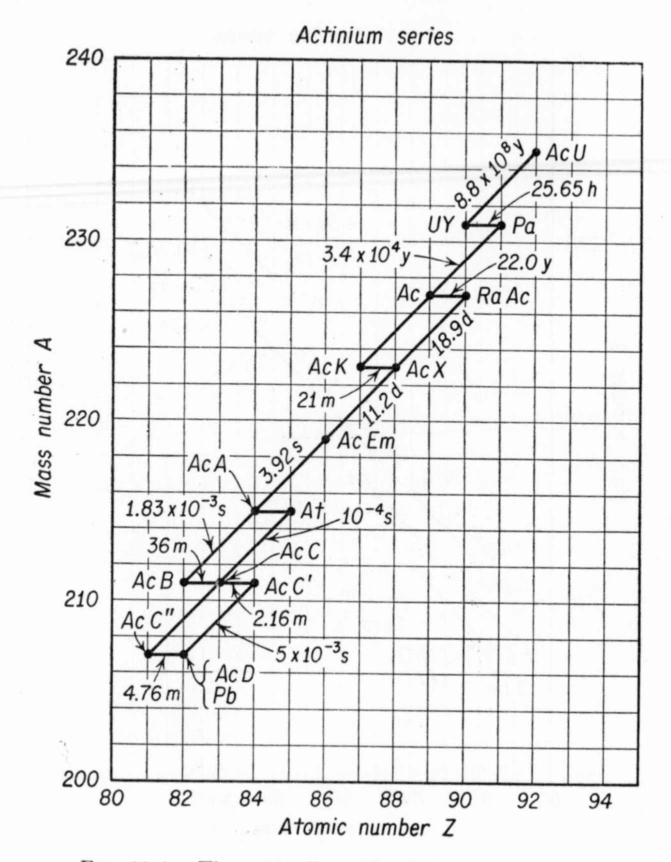

FIG. 10-4. The naturally radioactive actinium series.

formed by the disintegration of UX_1: the 68-second half-life was assigned to UX_2, and the 6.7-hour half-life was assigned to UZ. In 1921 Hahn showed that UX_2 and UZ form a pair of *nuclear isomers*, that is, they are *different energy states* of the same nucleus; later Feather and Bretscher showed that the members of this pair of nuclear isomers are *genetically related*, that is, one type of nucleus is formed from the other. In this particular case, the nucleus of UX_2 has 0.394 Mev more energy than the nucleus of UZ. UX_2 may disintegrate directly to UII, $Z = 92$, $A = 234$, by the emission of a beta particle, or UX_2 may first emit a gamma ray of

0.394 Mev going to a lower isomeric state, called UZ, which then disintegrates with a half-life of 6.7 hours by emitting a beta particle forming UII.

The subject of nuclear isomers will be considered in greater detail in §12-9.

The thorium series, as shown in Figure 10-3, starts with thorium (A = 232, Z = 90), goes through a series of transformations in many respects similar to the uranium series, and ends with thorium D (A = 208, Z = 82), which is also isotopic with lead. The actinium series, as shown in Figure 10-4, was at one time believed to be an independent series, but its origin has been traced to an isotope of uranium, known as actino-uranium. This is the famous isotope of uranium of mass number 235 (see §13-2). The end product of the actinium series is actinium D (A = 207, Z = 82), which is another isotope of lead.

10-4. The Neptunium Series

Each of the three naturally occurring radioactive series discussed above starts with a long-lived isotope. Physicists have often speculated about the possibility of the occurrence of other radioactive series, the isotopes of which may have disappeared or may be in such extremely small concentrations as to be undetectable by common methods. One type of speculation revolved around the fact that the mass numbers of the substance of the three known series could be represented by a set of numbers: $4n$ (for the thorium series), $4n + 2$ (for the uranium series), and $4n + 3$ (for the actinium series), where n is an integer. It was felt that there might have been a $4n + 1$ series, and that perhaps traces of it still exist.

With the discovery of *transuranic elements*, that is, elements of atomic number greater than 92, and with the ability to produce many different isotopes of both old and new elements, it was possible to trace a fourth radioactive series, a $4n + 1$ series. This series is called the *neptunium series*, after the longest-lived isotope, neptunium, Z = 93, A = 237, of this series. This series is represented in Figure 10-5. It will be noted that the origin of this series can be traced back to americium and plutonium. The series ends, not in a stable isotope of lead, but in the stable isotope of bismuth, Z = 83, A = 209. Recently very small amounts of neptunium and plutonium have been separated from pitchblende, a uranium-bearing ore. We shall discuss some of the methods for producing the isotopes of this series in Chapters 13 and 15.

10-5. Radioactive Isotopes of the Lighter Elements

Among the elements of atomic numbers less than 81 only seven are known to have naturally occurring radioactive isotopes. These are listed in Table 10-1, together with the nature of the particle emitted by each radioisotope and its half-life. It will be observed that six of these are beta-particle

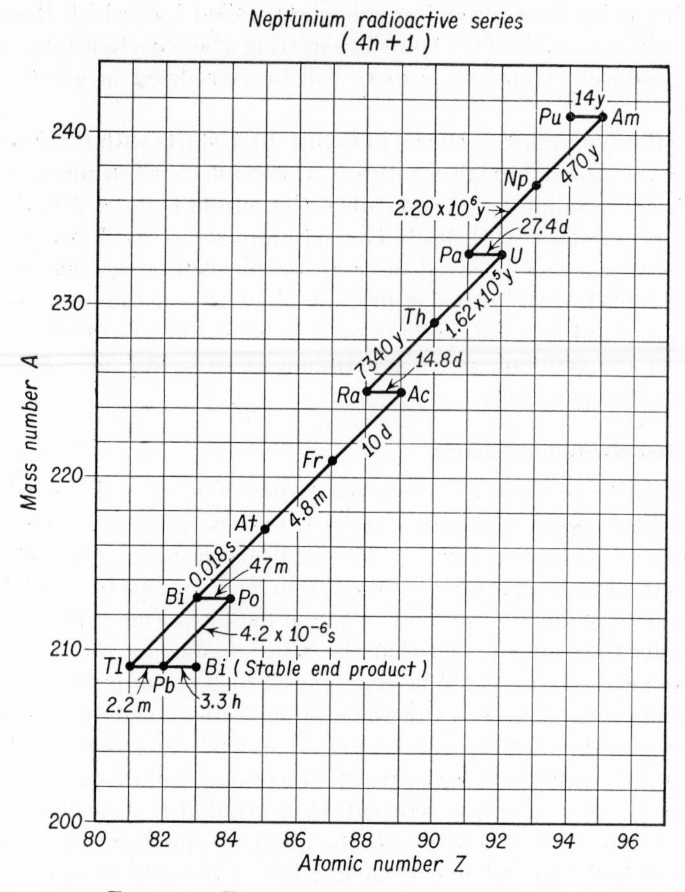

FIG. 10-5. The neptunium radioactive series.

Table 10-1

Atomic No.	Element	Mass No.	Type of Radio-activity	Half-Life in Years
1	Hydrogen	3	beta	12.5
6	Carbon	14	beta	5580
19	Potassium	40	beta; electron capture	18.3×10^{8}
37	Rubidium	87	beta	6×10^{10}
62	Samarium	152	alpha	1×10^{12}
71	Lutetium	176	beta; electron capture	2.4×10^{10}
75	Rhenium	187	beta	4×10^{12}

emitters and one, samarium, is an alpha-particle emitter. The half-lives of all but the first two are extremely long. The fact that the half-lives of H^3 and C^{14} are comparatively short implies that they are being produced continually. It has been definitely established that these isotopes are produced by the bombardment of N^{14} in the atmosphere by cosmic-ray neutrons (see §11-13).

In contrast to the small number of naturally occurring radioactive isotopes found in nature, it is now possible to produce, by a variety of methods, radioactive isotopes for all of the elements.

10-6. Alpha-Particle Disintegration Energy

We have already shown that alpha particles emitted by radioactive substances have velocities of the order of 10^9 cm/sec and kinetic energies of about 5 to 10 Mev. In discussing a nuclear transformation, several conservation laws must be taken into consideration, such as the conservation of energy, the conservation of momentum, and the conservation of charge. An alpha-particle disintegration can be represented by means of a *nuclear reaction equation* of the type

$$_{Z}\mathrm{El}^{A} \rightarrow {}_{Z-2}\mathrm{El}^{A-4} + {}_{2}\mathrm{He}^{4} + Q_{\alpha}, \tag{5}$$

where El stands for the chemical symbol representing the particular element under discussion, and $_2He^4$ represents the alpha particle emitted. This equation shows that charge is conserved; the element of nuclear charge Ze is transformed into a new element of nuclear charge $(Z - 2)e$ with the emission of an alpha particle of charge $2e$. The quantity Q_α is called the *disintegration energy* and represents the total energy released in this process. This energy consists of the kinetic energy of the alpha particle and the kinetic energy of the product nucleus, and comes from the difference in mass between the parent nucleus and the product nuclei. The disintegration energy Q_α can be readily evaluated in terms of the kinetic energy $\mathcal{E}_\alpha$ of the alpha particle with the aid of the principles of conservation of energy and momentum.

Suppose that the mass of the parent atom is M_1; let us assume it to be at rest. When it emits an alpha particle of mass M and velocity v, the residual atom of mass M_2 will recoil with a velocity v_2 such that

$$M_2 v_2 = Mv.$$

Now

$$Q_\alpha = \tfrac{1}{2}M_2 v_2^2 + \tfrac{1}{2}Mv^2.$$

Eliminating v_2 from these two equations, we obtain

$$Q_\alpha = \frac{1}{2}\frac{M}{M_2}Mv^2 + \tfrac{1}{2}Mv^2,$$

and calling the kinetic energy of the alpha particle $\mathcal{E}_\alpha = \frac{1}{2}Mv^2$, we can write

$$Q_\alpha = \mathcal{E}_\alpha\left(\frac{M}{M_2} + 1\right). \tag{6}$$

To a very close approximation we can replace the ratio of the masses by the ratio of the mass numbers; thus

$$\frac{M}{M_2} = \frac{4}{A - 4}$$

where A is the mass number of the parent atom. Hence the disintegration energy can be written as

$$\boxed{Q_\alpha = \frac{A}{A - 4}\,\mathcal{E}_\alpha.} \tag{7}$$

10-7. Range of Alpha Particles

There are several methods for investigating the alpha particles which are emitted by radioactive nuclei. Their velocities may be measured by the magnetic spectrograph method described in §3-5. Another method fre-

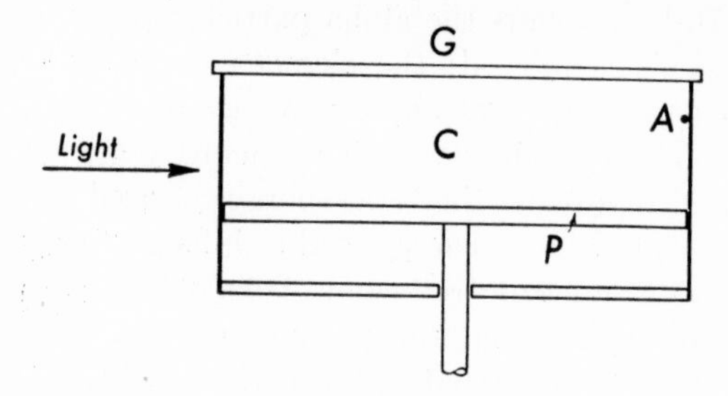

FIG. 10-6. Schematic diagram of a Wilson cloud chamber.

quently used for investigating the alpha particles is the determination of the range of the particle in a gas such as hydrogen, nitrogen, or air, using a Wilson cloud chamber. This apparatus consists essentially of a cylinder C containing a gas saturated with water vapor, and a piston P which may be lowered very rapidly to produce a sudden expansion of the gas in chamber C, as shown in Figure 10-6. As a result of this expansion, the gas is cooled and becomes supersaturated with water vapor. If there are any ions present in the gas, the water vapor will condense on these ions, forming small droplets. These droplets may be viewed or photographed through the glass plate G covering the top of the cylinder; illumination is usually supplied through a window in the wall of the chamber. If a source of alpha particles is placed inside the chamber at A, then, in their passage through the gas in the chamber, the alpha particles will ionize the gas molecules along their paths. During each expansion of the gas, water droplets form on the ions, showing the path of each individual alpha particle. Typical alpha-ray tracks are shown in Figure 10-7. These tracks are in general

FIG. 10-7. Tracks of alpha particles from thorium (C + C′) in a Wilson cloud chamber showing two distinct ranges. (From Rutherford, Chadwick, and Ellis, *Radiations from Radioactive Substances*. By permission of The Macmillan Company, publishers.)

straight lines almost up to the end of the range. Occasionally a track is bent sharply or else it branches off into two tracks. These are usually ascribed to collisions with nuclei; they will be discussed in detail later (§11-1).

Another method for determining the range of alpha particles in a gas is to measure the ionization produced in a gas at different distances from the source of the alpha particles. A typical arrangement for this type of measurement is shown in Figure 10-8. The source of alpha particles, A, is placed in a recess in a block of lead, providing a fairly well-collimated beam of alpha rays. The ionization chamber consists of a wire grid G and a plate P connected to an electrometer for measuring the ionization produced in the narrow region between P and G. The distance between the alpha-particle source and the ionization chamber is usually varied by moving the source. Typical curves showing the ionization produced at different distances from the source are shown in Figure 10-9. It will be noticed that for the greater part of the range, the ionization current in the first part of the range is practically constant, then increases and reaches its maximum value just before the end of the range. The peak near the end of the range is due to an increase in the efficiency of ionization by slow alpha particles.

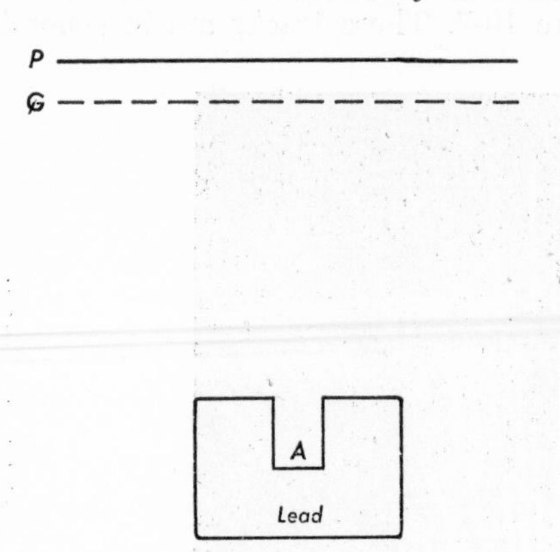

FIG. 10-8. Schematic diagram of apparatus for measuring the range of alpha particles.

It has been found that, in most cases, the alpha particles from a given element have a very definite range. This range R is usually expressed in centimeters of air at 15°C and at a pressure of 76 cm of mercury. The

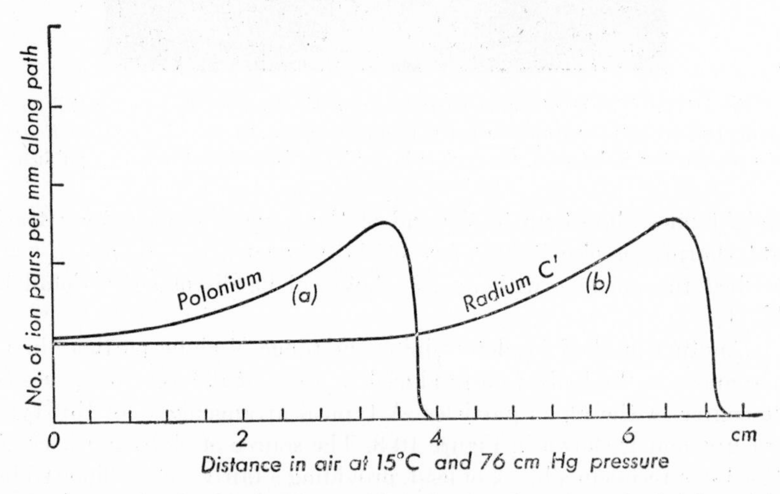

FIG. 10-9. Graphs showing the specific ionization along the path of alpha particles from (a) polonium, (b) radium C′.

ranges of the alpha particles from some of the elements are given in Table 10-2 together with their energies as determined by Halloway and Livingston. The alpha particles from some of the elements, such as thorium C′, fall into several groups of ranges corresponding to their velocity spectrum.

Table 10-2

Range and Energy of Alpha Particles

Element	Mean Range in cm in Air at 15°C	Energy in Mev
Polonium	3.842	5.298
Radon	4.051	5.486
Radium A	4.657	5.998
Thoron	5.004	6.2818
Thorium A	5.638	6.774
Radium C′	6.907	7.680
Radium C′	7.792	8.277
Radium C′	9.04	9.066
Radium C′	11.51	10.505
Thorium C′	8.570	8.776
Thorium C′	9.724	9.488
Thorium C′	11.580	10.538

The relationship between the range of an alpha particle and its velocity cannot be expressed by any one simple formula, but those of medium range are found to follow Geiger's empirical formula

$$R = av^3, \tag{8}$$

where a is a constant numerically equal to 9.6×10^{-28} when R is expressed in cm and v in cm per sec.

An important relationship exists between the range of an alpha particle and the average lifetime of the emitter, known as the *Geiger-Nuttall law,* which is usually written in the form

$$\boxed{\log R = A \log \lambda + B,} \tag{9}$$

where A is a constant which has practically the same value for each of the three radioactive series and B is a constant which has a different value for each series. This relationship is plotted for each series in Figure 10-10; the range R is expressed in cm and the disintegration constant λ is expressed in sec^{-1}. This equation has been used to estimate the half-lives of some of the products of disintegration which could not be easily determined by direct measurements.

10-8. Beta-Ray Spectra

The most commonly used method for determining the energies of the beta particles emitted by radioactive elements is the measurement of the radii of curvature of their paths in a magnetic field of known intensity H. Various experimental arrangements have been used in making these

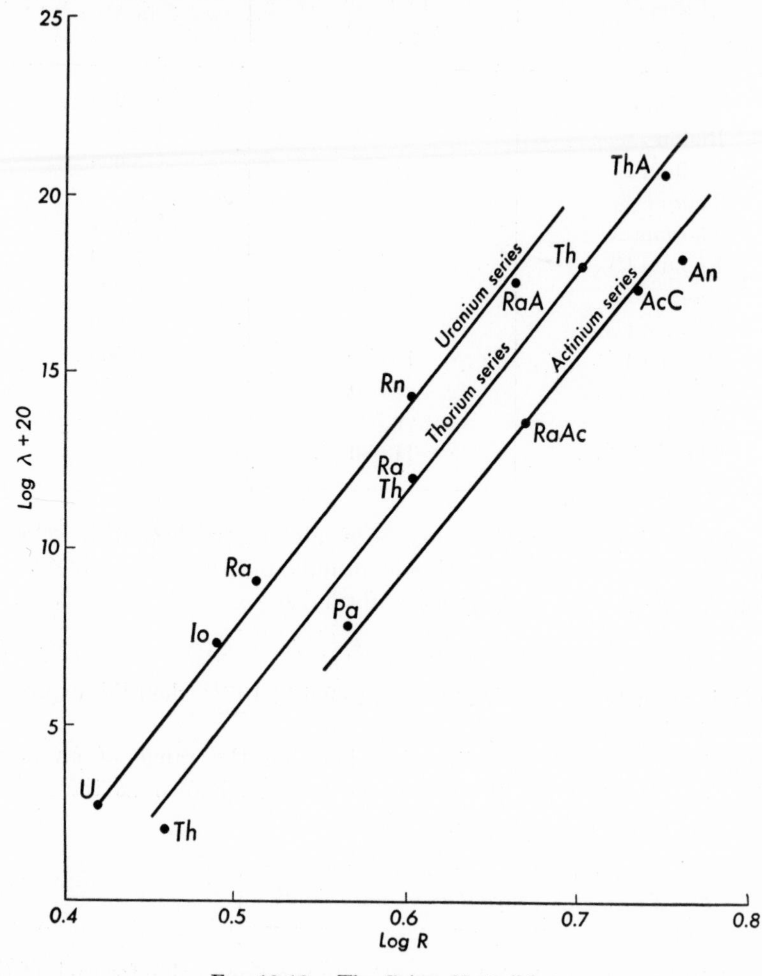

Fig. 10-10. The Geiger-Nuttall law.

measurements. One arrangement is practically identical with that used by Robinson, as shown in Figure 9-6, for the determination of the velocities of the electrons ejected by x-rays from an element placed at C. In the magnetic spectrum analysis of beta rays, C is replaced either by a fine wire on which the radioactive substance has been placed, or else by a small thin-walled glass tube containing the radioactive substance. The beta rays are recorded on a photographic plate and their velocity distribution determined.

Another method for detecting the beta rays is shown in Figure 10-11, in which the photographic plate is replaced by a Geiger counter *G* and the beta rays from the source at *C* are bent around by the magnetic field and focused upon the aperture *O*. In this type of experiment the number of beta particles entering the aperture *O* is counted at a given value of the

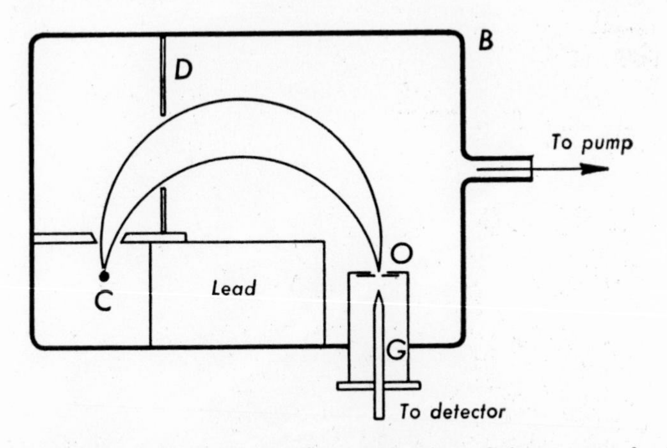

FIG. 10-11. Robinson's magnetic spectrograph using a Geiger counter for detecting beta particles.

magnetic field of intensity *H*. The intensity of the magnetic field is then changed to a new value and the number of beta particles entering the aperture *O* is again determined. In this manner the velocity distribution of the beta particles is determined. The radius of curvature of the path of a beta particle in a magnetic field can also be determined by photographing the track of the beta particle in a Wilson cloud chamber, as shown in Figure 10-12.

The results of these measurements show that there are apparently two distinct types of beta-ray spectra, one a sharp line spectrum, and the other a continuous spectrum. It has definitely been shown, however, that the sharp line spectra are due to electrons which have been ejected from the *K*, *L*, *M*, and *N* shells of the atom by the action of gamma rays from the nucleus of the same atom or neighboring atoms; this is similar to the photoelectric effect with x-rays and presents a very convenient means for determining the energies of the gamma rays (§10-12). The continuous beta-ray spectrum is that produced by the electrons which have been ejected from the nuclei of radioactive atoms. The curve in Figure 10-13 shows the continuous beta-ray spectrum of radium E. The number of particles having a given energy is plotted as ordinate, and the energy of these particles, expressed in million electron volts, as abscissa. It will be noted that the curve has a definite upper limit for the energy of the disintegration electrons and also passes through a maximum toward the

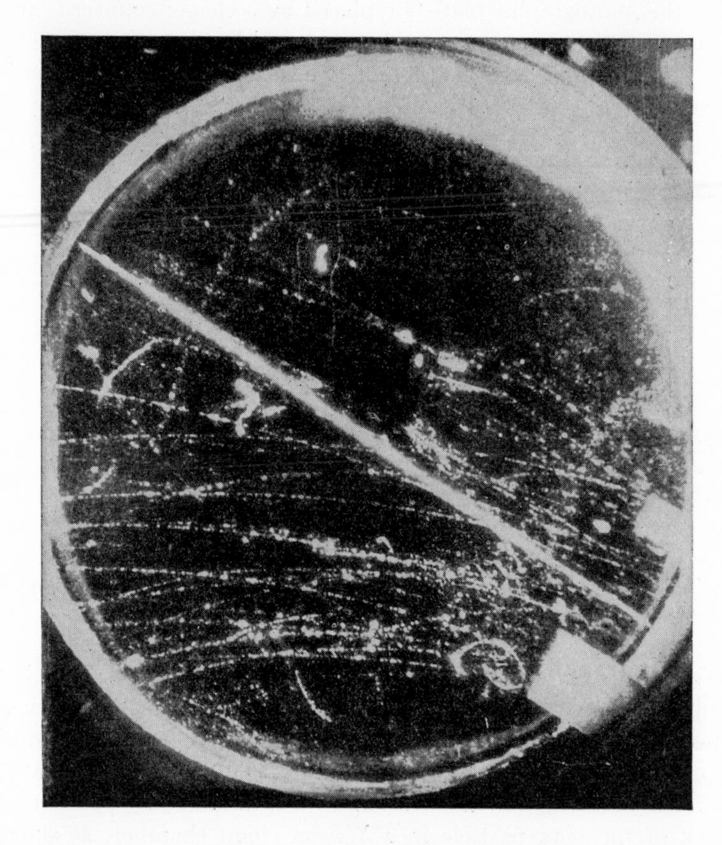

Fig. 10-12. Cloud-chamber photograph of beta-ray tracks in a magnetic field of 1000 gausses. The beta rays come from the disintegration of B^{12}; their energies range from about 6 to 12 Mev. The heavy track across the diameter of the chamber is that of a proton of about 9 Mev energy. (Photograph taken by H. R. Crane.)

low energy part of the spectrum. It will be shown that the end-point energy represents the energy which is released in this radioactive disintegration. Table 10-3 gives some of the end-point energies of the continuous spectra of some of the beta-ray emitters.

The beta-ray spectrum of an element differs remarkably from most of the other spectra characteristic of the same element in that these characteristic spectra, optical, x-ray, alpha ray, and gamma ray, are line spectra, while the beta-ray spectrum is a continuous one. It was found possible to interpret the optical and x-ray line spectra in terms of the changes in atomic energy states due to changes in the extranuclear electronic configurations. It seems reasonable to try to extend this interpretation to the line spectra of the particles emitted by radioactive nuclei.

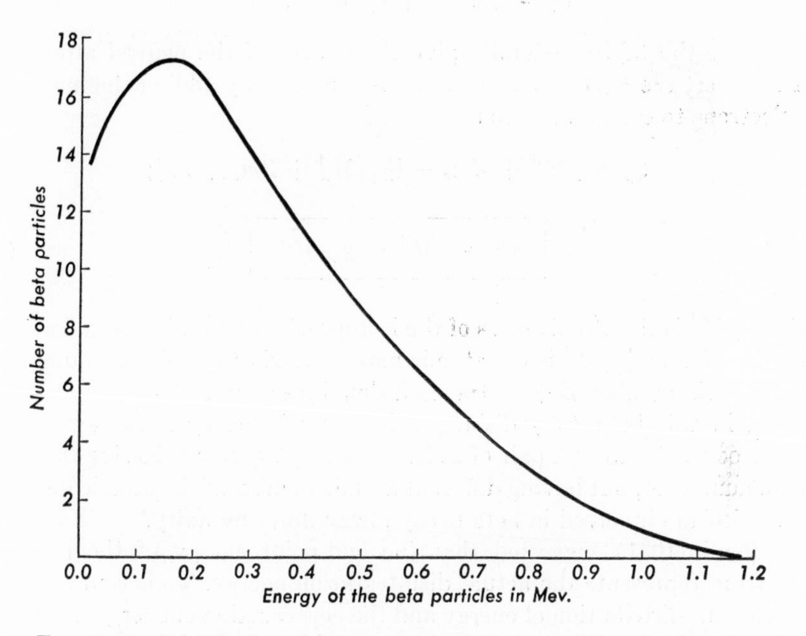

FIG. 10-13. Distribution of energy among the beta particles of radium E.

Table 10-3

End-Point Energies of Some Beta-Ray Spectra

Z	Element	A	Radioactive Isotope	End-Point Energy in Mev	Half-Life
82	Pb	214	RaB	0.72	26.8 m
83	Bi	210	RaE	1.17	4.85 d
87	Fr	223	AcK	1.20	21 m
89	Ac	228	Ms Th_2	1.55	6.13 h
90	Th	231	UY	0.21	25.65 h

10-9. Beta-Particle Disintegration

The energy available for a beta (β^-) disintegration is provided by the difference in mass between the initial nucleus of mass number A and atomic number Z, and the sum of the masses of the final particles, that is, the nucleus of atomic number $Z + 1$, and mass number A, and the beta particle. The disintegration energy is thus

$$Q_\beta = {}_ZM_n^A - [{}_{(Z+1)}M_n^A + m_e].$$

Since the tables generally give the masses of the neutral atoms, we can convert the nuclear masses to atomic masses by adding the masses of Z electrons to each term, thus

$$Q_\beta = {}_ZM_n^A + Zm_e - [{}_{Z+1}M_n^A + Zm_e + m_e];$$

hence

$$\boxed{Q_\beta = {}_ZM^A - {}_{Z+1}M^A} \qquad (10)$$

where ${}_ZM^A$ is the atomic mass of the isotope of mass number A and atomic number Z, and ${}_{Z+1}M^A$ is the atomic mass of the isotope of mass number A and atomic number $Z + 1$. Hence a definite amount of energy Q_β is released in this beta (β^-) disintegration. It will be noted that the beta decay occurs between a pair of *isobars*; that is, two atoms having the same mass number A, but having different atomic numbers. The atomic numbers of the isobars involved in beta decay alway differ by unity.

Pauli (1931) suggested that the end-point energy of the beta-ray spectrum represents the actual disintegration energy. To account for the continuous distribution of energy and the conservation of energy in nuclear processes, Pauli suggested that two particles are emitted by the nucleus in a beta-ray disintegration, and that the total energy of these two particles is a constant which is equal to the end-point energy observed in the beta-ray spectrum. One of the particles is the electron itself and the other particle is assumed to be a neutral particle of negligible rest mass; this particle is called a *neutrino*. There is another reason for the introduction of the neutrino into beta-particle disintegrations: the principle of the conservation of angular momentum must also be satisfied in nuclear processes. In a beta-decay process the mass number of the product nucleus is the same as that of the parent nucleus; hence the change in nuclear angular momentum, if any, must be integral. Since the emitted beta particle is known to have a spin angular momentum of $\frac{1}{2}\hbar$, another particle, the neutrino, having a spin angular momentum of $\frac{1}{2}\hbar$, must be emitted simultaneously. The neutrino is not observed directly in the beta-decay process because it carries no charge and has a very small probability of interacting with other particles. Only recently (1953) has there been any direct experiment on the interaction of free neutrinos with matter (§12-8).

The remaining problem is to determine the origin of the electron and neutrino. The present view, stated in an elementary way, is that the neutron breaks up into a proton which remains in the nucleus, and an electron and a neutrino which are ejected from the nucleus. This is analogous to the emission of a light quantum when an atom goes from one energy state to another. There are no photons in the atom, but when an atom goes from a state characterized by one set of quantum numbers to another state, a photon is emitted. One may imagine the neutron to represent one quantum state of a nucleon and the proton to represent another quantum state of the same nuclear particle. When this particle goes from the neutron quantum state to the proton quantum state, it does so with the emission of a pair of particles, an electron and a neutrino. This process can be represented by the equation

$$n \rightarrow p + \beta^- + \nu, \tag{11}$$

where n represents the neutron, p the proton, and ν the neutrino.

The beta-ray disintegration energy Q_β, given by equation (10), is equal to the end-point energy of the beta-ray spectrum only when the transition is from the *ground state*, or state of lowest energy, of the parent nucleus, to the ground state of the product nucleus. The rest mass of the neutrino is assumed to be negligible.

10-10. Gamma-Ray Spectra

In many cases, gamma rays are found to accompany the emission of alpha particles and beta particles. It has been shown that the gamma rays are of the same nature as x-rays, that the wavelengths of some of the low energy gamma rays have been measured by means of a single crystal spectrometer; and that the wavelengths of some of the higher energy gamma rays have been measured with the curved crystal focusing spectrometer (§5-9). Two other well-known effects have been used successfully in studying the gamma rays; one is the photoelectric effect; the other is the Compton effect.

The gamma rays have been found to consist of sharp lines of definite wave lengths. Just as characteristic x-rays were shown to be emitted as the result of changes in atomic energy states, so the emission of gamma rays can be ascribed to changes in nuclear energy states. A plausible hypothesis is that the transformation of an atom with the emission of either an alpha or a beta particle may leave the product nucleus in an excited state, and that the gamma rays are emitted when the product nucleus goes to lower excited states or to the normal state. There is considerable experimental evidence which shows that gamma rays come from the product nucleus; most of this evidence is derived from analyses of the sharp line beta-ray spectra.

10-11. Gamma Rays from Beta-Particle Emitters

It was noted previously that the sharp line beta-ray spectra were produced by a type of photoelectric effect in which some of the gamma rays from the nucleus ejected electrons from the K, L, M, or N shells of the atom. The fact that these electrons are ejected from their shells with very definite energies indicates that the gamma rays themselves must have sharply defined energies, and thus should show sharp line gamma-ray spectra. Those gamma-ray spectra which have been studied with the crystal spectrometer have been found to consist of several lines of definite wavelength, in agreement with the above conclusions.

Whenever a gamma-ray photon of frequency ν and energy $h\nu$ ejects an electron from one of the atomic shells, say the K shell, it must supply an amount of energy $\mathcal{E}_K$ to remove this electron, thus leaving the extranuclear part of the atom in an excited state. The kinetic energy of the electron will be given by

$$\tfrac{1}{2}mv^2 = h\nu - \mathcal{E}_K. \tag{12}$$

If the velocity of the electron is very large, then, of course, the relativity expression for the kinetic energy must be used. Similar equations will hold for electrons ejected from the L, M, and N shells. By measuring the energies of the ejected electrons with the magnetic spectrograph, and using the values of the atomic energy levels from x-ray data, it is possible to compute the energy and hence the frequency of the gamma rays emitted by a nucleus. This will be illustrated for the case of the gamma rays emitted during the beta-ray transformation of radium D ($Z = 82$) to radium E ($Z = 83$).

The magnetic spectrum analysis of the beta-ray spectrum of RaD shows five sharp lines superposed on the continuous spectrum. The measured values of the energies of these lines are listed in Table 10-4. The gamma-ray spectrum emitted as a result of the transformation RaD to RaE, as determined by the crystal method, is exceedingly simple; it consists of a single line of wavelength $\lambda = 0.261$A. This corresponds to an energy $h\nu = 0.472 \times 10^5$ ev for the gamma-ray photon. On the assumption that the gamma rays come from the product nucleus, RaE, the electrons ejected by these gamma rays must come from the electronic shells of this type of atom. Since RaE is an isotope of bismuth, $Z = 83$, the excited energy states of the atom can easily be determined from tables of x-ray absorption limits. It is then possible to locate the probable origin of the electrons giving rise to the sharp line beta-ray spectrum. The origin of these electrons is shown in Table 10-4, as well as the energy of each shell as obtained from x-ray data for the element bismuth. The sum of the kinetic energy of the ejected electron and the energy required to remove the electron from the atom should equal the energy of the gamma ray.

Table 10-4

Determination of Gamma-Ray Energy from Sharp Line Beta-Ray Spectrum for Transformation RaD $\xrightarrow{\beta}$ RaE
(*Energies in electron volts.*)

Line No.	Kinetic Energy of Ejected Electron	Origin of Ejected Electron	Energy of Excited State of Atom	Energy of Electron + Energy of Excited State	Energy of Gamma-Ray Photon from Crystal Measurement	Wave-length of Gamma Ray in A
1	0.309×10^5	L_{I}	0.163×10^5	0.472×10^5	0.472×10^5	0.261
2	0.315	L_{II}	0.157	0.472		
3	0.338	L_{III}	0.134	0.472		
4	0.433	M_{I}	0.040	0.473		
5	0.461	N_{I}	0.010	0.471		

The results are in very good agreement with the spectroscopic measurement of the energy of the gamma-ray line.

It will be noticed that no electrons are ejected from the K shell of RaE by the gamma rays. From x-ray data, it is known that the K absorption limit of RaE ($Z = 83$) is $\lambda = 0.137$A, corresponding to an energy of 0.90×10^5 electron volts. This is much greater than the energy of the gamma-ray photon; hence it will not be able to eject any electron from the K shell of radium E.

Internal conversion is the name of the process whereby a gamma-ray photon emitted by a nucleus gives up all of its energy in ejecting an electron from one of the extranuclear shells of the same atom; this process is sometimes represented by the symbol IC. The *internal conversion* of the gamma-ray energy into kinetic energy of electrons, by means of the photoelectric effect, leaves the atoms in excited states. In returning to the normal state, these atoms should emit characteristic x-rays corresponding to the changes in the atomic energy states. These x-rays have been observed and measured in many cases, and afford additional checks on the assignment of the origins of the ejected electrons.

As has previously been mentioned, the total disintegration energy in a beta decay is the energy difference between the ground state of the parent nucleus and the ground state of the product nucleus. In the beta decay of RaD to RaE discussed above, the product nucleus is left in an excited state approximately 47 kev above the ground state. The beta-ray spectrum of RaD has recently been measured by Insch, Balfour, and Curran (1952) and found to consist of very low energy beta particles with an end-point energy of about 18 kev. They also measured the IC electrons and found that their energies extended to about 46.7 kev. Thus the disintegration energy of the beta decay, RaD to RaE, is about 65 kev. Figure 10-14 is a nuclear energy level diagram illustrating this process:

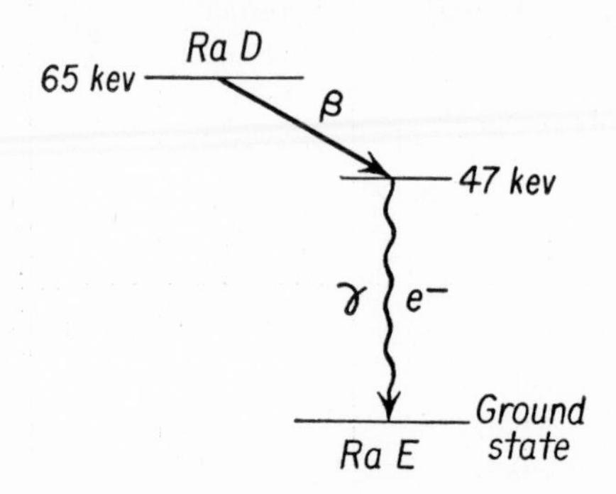

FIG. 10-14. Decay of RaD by beta emission to an excited state of RaE; the latter then goes to the ground state by gamma-ray emission.

RaD decays by beta emission to an excited state of RaE; the latter disintegrates by a gamma-ray transition of 47 kev to the ground state. A fraction of these gamma rays is internally converted into photoelectrons, giving rise to the sharp line beta-ray spectrum.

Similar analyses have been made of the sharp line beta-ray spectra of most of the other beta-ray emitters, leading to determinations of the energies and wavelengths of the gamma-ray spectra of these elements. Wherever possible, these wavelengths have been checked by independent measurements with the crystal spectrometer.

10-12. Gamma Rays Accompanying Alpha-Particle Emission

Some radioactive nuclei which emit alpha particles also emit gamma rays of definite frequencies. Careful measurements of the gamma-ray energies and the alpha-particle energies have led to the conclusion that the gamma rays are emitted by the product nucleus which has been left in an excited state after the emission of an alpha particle. As a simple example, consider the alpha-particle transformation of radium into radon. The gamma-ray spectrum accompanying this transformation has been found to consist of a single line of wavelength $\lambda = 0.0652$A, and of energy 1.89×10^5 ev. Now, the alpha particles emitted during this disintegration have been found to have energies of 47.95×10^5 ev and 46.11×10^5 ev, respectively. The difference between these two energies is 1.84×10^5 ev, practically the same as the energy of the gamma-ray photon. This fact can be explained by assuming that when a normal radium nucleus emits an alpha particle with an energy of 47.95×10^5 ev, the product nucleus, radon, is in its normal state, but when a radium nucleus emits an alpha particle with an energy of 46.11×10^5 ev, the product nucleus is left in an excited state and then returns to the normal state by the emission of a gamma-ray photon, as shown in Figure 10-15. The energy of this gamma-ray photon

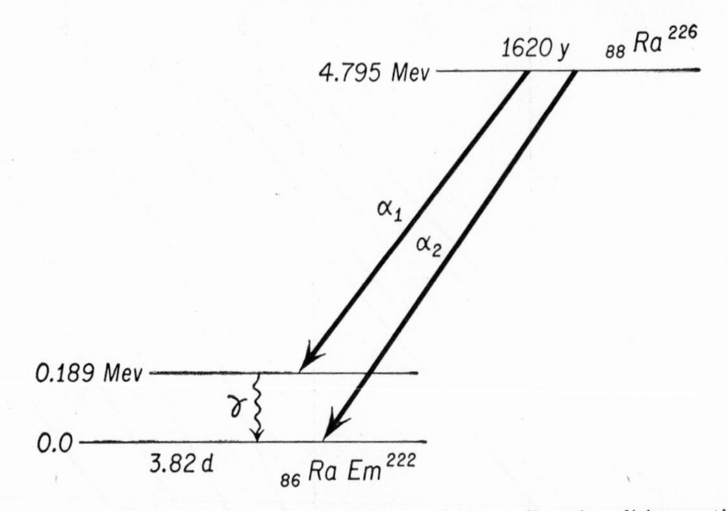

FIG. 10-15. Nuclear energy level diagram of the radioactive disintegration of radium.

should therefore be equal to the difference in energies observed in the alpha-particle spectrum of radium.

Similar correlations between alpha-particle energies and the energies of the gamma-ray photons have been established in several other cases. These correlations have naturally led to attempts to construct nuclear energy level diagrams similar to those made for the extranuclear portion of the atom. In most cases the data necessary for constructing such diagrams are as yet insufficient. Nuclear energy level diagrams can be constructed for those processes which have been well authenticated by experiment.

As we have seen in the two simple cases shown in Figures 10-14 and 10-15, nuclear energy level diagrams are useful not only for tabulating nuclear events but also for assigning the order in which the radiation is emitted and for determining the proper nucleus which is the source of this radiation. As other modes of disintegration are discovered and studied, these diagrams become valuable for correlating data from a wide variety of experiments and also for predicting the existence or probable occurrence of certain types of nuclear transformations. We shall discuss many of these topics in the following chapters.

10-13. Disintegration of ThC

We have seen that in each radioactive series there are some isotopes in which branching occurs; that is, a certain fraction of the nuclei emits alpha particles and another fraction emits beta particles. The branching in the

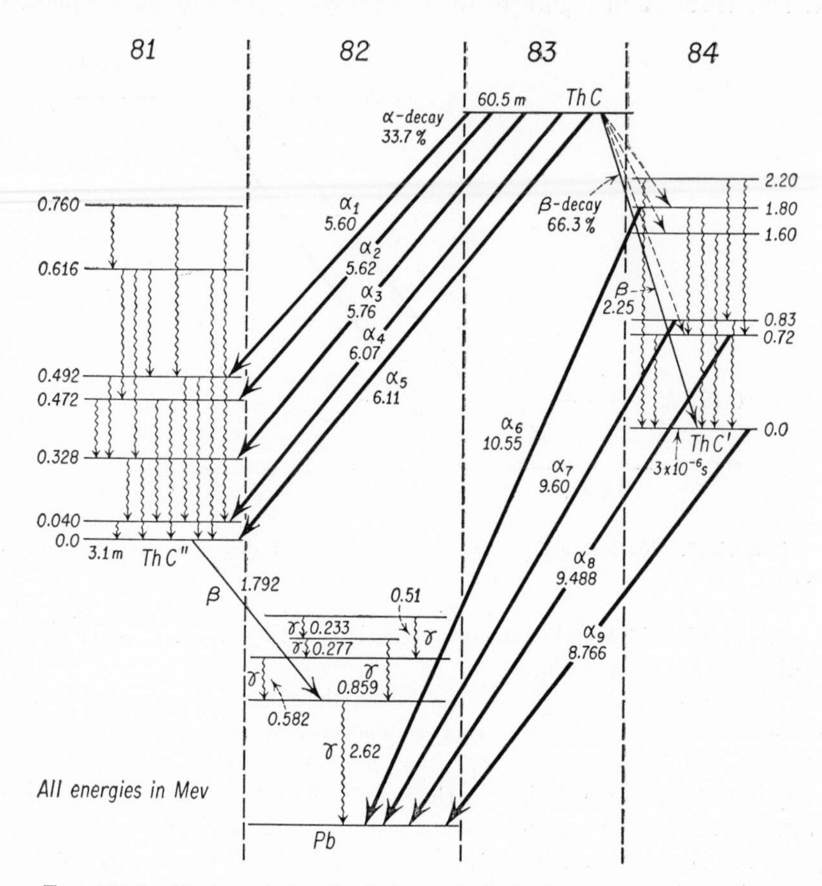

FIG. 10-16. Nuclear energy level diagram of the disintegration of ThC. (After *Nuclear Data,* National Bureau of Standards, Circular 499.)

disintegration of ThC in which alpha decay occurs in 33.7 per cent of the disintegrations, and beta decay in 66.3 per cent of the disintegrations, has been studied very thoroughly and has led to the nuclear energy level scheme shown in Figure 10-16. The wavy lines between energy levels of any one isotope represent the gamma rays emitted during the indicated transition between two levels. Of the seven levels in the ThC″, five are definitely accounted for in terms of the alpha-particle spectrum of the parent element, ThC. The lowest level in ThC″ is taken as its *ground state* and the energies of the excited states are given in Mev with the ground state taken as zero.

The beta disintegration of ThC leads to ThC′; its lowest state is taken as the ground state with the energies of the other levels assigned with respect to it. To account for several of these levels, it is possible that the beta-ray spectrum is actually complex; this is indicated by the dashed arrows. ThC′ emits alpha particles of four different energies in decaying to a stable form of lead. The fine structure of this alpha-particle spectrum may be readily accounted for, as shown in the figure, by assuming that they start from different levels of the ThC′ nuclei but all end in the same Pb^{208} nuclear level.

The *long-range alpha particles* of ThC′ are those which have their origins in the excited states of ThC′; they are relatively few in number, of the order of 10^{-4} of the number of alpha particles emitted from the ground state of ThC′ to the ground state of lead.

ThC″ decays by beta emission to an excited state of Pb^{208}, and the latter then emits gamma rays in going to the ground state. To account for the different excited levels of Pb^{208}, it is necessary to assume that the beta-ray spectrum of ThC″ is complex, although only the end-point energy spectrum of 1.792 Mev has been definitely established. Following this beta decay, the nucleus of Pb^{208} goes from its excited state to the ground state by the emission of a gamma-ray photon of 2.62 Mev. The latter radiation, in spite of the fact that it comes from the Pb nucleus, is often called a ThC″ gamma ray because it accompanies the emission of beta rays from a sample containing ThC″.

10-14. Continuous Bremsstrahlung from Beta Emitters

In addition to any characteristic sharp line, gamma-ray spectra that may be emitted following beta-ray emission, it is possible for a beta-emitting substance to emit electromagnetic radiation which will have a continuous distribution in energy, or frequency. This radiation, a type of *bremsstrahlung*, may have two different origins. One type may be due to the radiation emitted when a beta particle, in its passage through a substance, is accelerated whenever it passes close to any of the nuclei of the substance. This is analogous to the production of the continuous x-rays in an x-ray tube. This type of continuous radiation from a beta emitter is called *outer* or *external bremsstrahlung.* It may be produced in the passage of the beta rays through the beta-emitting substance itself, or it may be produced by allowing the beta rays to pass through another substance, such as aluminum, lead, or the like. Theory predicts that the intensity of the outer bremsstrahlung should be proportional to the square of the charge and inversely proportional to the square of the mass of the beta particle. This type of radiation was first discovered by J. A. Gray (1911), who bombarded various substances with beta rays from RaE and measured the intensity of the electromagnetic radiation thus produced.

The second type of bremsstrahlung has its origin in the readjustment of the charges in the nucleus as a result of the emission of a beta particle. This type is called *inner* or *internal bremsstrahlung*. C. S. Wu (1941) measured the intensity of the inner bremsstrahlung emitted by a radioactive isotope of phosphorus, P^{32}. This isotope of phosphorus emits beta rays having an end-point energy of 1.72 Mev but does not emit any characteristic gamma rays. The intensity of the radiation was measured by means of an ionization chamber, and the results found to be in agreement with theoretical predictions of Knipp and Uhlenbeck, and F. Bloch. Wu also compared the relative intensities of the inner bremsstrahlung with the outer bremsstrahlung by completely stopping the beta rays in an aluminum absorber. The intensity of the inner bremsstrahlung was found to be about a quarter of that of the outer bremsstrahlung.

Problems

[NOTE: A *curie* is a unit of radioactivity equal to 3.7×10^{10} disintegrations per second.]

10-1. (**a**) Determine the constants A and B of the Geiger-Nuttall law. (**b**) How do these constants depend upon the particular radioactive series? (**c**) Using the data from Figure 10-4, calculate the range of the alpha particles from AcU.

Ans. (**c**) 3.13 cm.

10-2. From the data in Table 10-2 plot a curve of energy against range of the alpha particles.

10-3. From the data in Table 10-2 plot a curve of the range of the alpha particles against the cube of their velocities and compare this curve with Geiger's law.

10-4. Radium disintegrates with a comparatively long half-life, $T = 1620$ yr, into radon, which in turn disintegrates with a comparatively short half-life, $T = 3.8$ da. In such cases the rate at which radium disintegrates can be considered practically constant, and if the radium is kept in a closed container, the amount of the product radon builds up to a steady value; that is, just as much radon is formed during a short time interval as the amount which disintegrates during the same time interval. The product is then said to be in *secular equilibrium* with the parent substance.

(**a**) Show that the rate at which radon accumulates in the presence of radium is given by

$$\frac{dN}{dt} = \lambda_1 N_1 - \lambda_2 N$$

where N is the amount of radon present at any instant, N_1 is the original amount of radium, and λ_2 and λ_1 are their respective disintegration constants.

(**b**) If the amount of radium is assumed to remain constant, show that the amount of radon present after a time t is given by

$$N = \frac{\lambda_1}{\lambda_2} N_1(1 - \epsilon^{-\lambda_2 t}).$$

(**c**) Show that after a sufficient lapse of time for secular equilibrium to be established, the amount of radon present is

$$N_2 = \frac{\lambda_1}{\lambda_2} N_1.$$

10-5. (**a**) From problem 10-4, plot a curve with N/N_2 as ordinates and the time (in units of T) as abscissae.

(**b**) Suppose that after a long time t, the amount of radon N_2 is pumped off; if we start measuring the amount of radon present from this instant, then $N = N_2\epsilon^{-\lambda_2 t}$. Plot this equation with N/N_2 as ordinates on the same axes as part (**a**).

(**c**) Sum the ordinates of the two curves and discuss the results.

10-6. (**a**) From the data of Table 10-1, compute the value of the disintegration constant λ in sec^{-1} for K^{40}. (**b**) Using the above value of λ, determine the number of beta particles per second emitted by one gram of K^{40}. (**c**) Using the value of the normal abundance of K^{40} in a sample of potassium, compute the number of beta particles per second emitted by one gram of potassium.

Ans. (**a**) 1.2×10^{-17} sec^{-1}.
(**b**) 1.8×10^5.
(**c**) 21.6.

10-7. Using the value of the half-life of U^{238} from Figure 10-2, (**a**) compute the disintegration constant in sec^{-1}, and (**b**) calculate the number of alpha particles per second emitted by one gram of uranium.

10-8. Using the value of the half-life of radium emanation (radon) from Figure 10-2, (**a**) compute its disintegration constant in sec^{-1}; (**b**) calculate the number of alpha particles per second emitted by 1 cm^3 of radon at 1 atmosphere pressure and 0°C.

10-9. Using the value of the abundance of rubidium 87, calculate the number of beta particles per second emitted by 100 gm of rubidium.

10-10. Assuming that 90 per cent of the disintegrations of potassium 40 result in beta emission, and using the known abundance of this isotope, calculate the number of beta particles per minute emitted by a crystal of potassium chloride whose mass is 200 gm.

10-11. Calculate the number of alpha particles per second emitted by 3 milligrams of radium. Express this activity in millicuries.

10-12. Calculate the number of alpha particles per second emitted by 2 cm^3 of radon at normal temperature and pressure. Express this activity in millicuries.

10-13. Determine the amount of polonium necessary to provide a source of alpha particles of 5 millicuries.

10-14. Using the data of Table 10-2, compute the disintegration energy of the alpha-particle decay of polonium.

10-15. (**a**) Compute the disintegration energy in the alpha-particle decay of radium, $Z = 88$, $A = 226$, from the data on the atomic masses. (**b**) From this, calculate the kinetic energy of the alpha particle and compare it with the measured value of 4.795 Mev.

Ans. (**a**) 4.88 Mev.
(**b**) 4.795 Mev.

10-16. The K conversion electron from Cs^{137} produces a sharp line in its beta-ray spectrum whose momentum, measured with a magnetic spectrometer, yields a value of $Hr = 3381$ gauss cm. The binding energy of this K electron is 37.44 kev. (**a**) Determine the kinetic energy of the conversion electron. (**b**) Determine the energy of the converted gamma-ray photon.

Ans. (**a**) 624.33 kev.
(**b**) 661.77 kev.

10-17. The gamma-ray photon from Cs^{137}, when incident upon a piece of uranium, ejects photoelectrons from its K shell. The momentum, measured with a magnetic beta-ray spectrometer, yields a value of $Hr = 3083$ gauss cm. The binding energy of a K electron in uranium is 115.59 kev. Determine (**a**) the kinetic energy of the photoelectrons, and (**b**) the energy of the gamma-ray photons.

Ans. (**a**) 545.35 kev.
(**b**) 661.94 kev.

References

Cork, N. M., *Radioactivity and Nuclear Physics*. New York: D. Van Nostrand Company, Inc., 1950.

Feather, N., *Nuclear Physics*. London: Cambridge University Press, 1936, Chaps. I, IV, V.

Rasetti, F., *Elements of Nuclear Physics*. New York: Prentice-Hall, Inc., 1936, Chaps. I–IV.

Rutherford, E., J. Chadwick, and C. B. Ellis, *Radiations from Radioactive Substances*. London: Cambridge University Press, 1930, Chaps. I, X–XII.

chapter **11**

Disintegration of Nuclei

11-1. Discovery of Artificial Disintegration

The artificial transmutation of one element into another, the dream of alchemists for centuries, was first definitely accomplished by Rutherford in 1919 in a very simple type of experiment. A diagram of the apparatus used by Rutherford is shown in Figure 11-1. The chamber C was filled with a gas such as nitrogen, and alpha particles from a radioactive source at A were absorbed in the gas. A sheet of silver foil F, itself thick enough

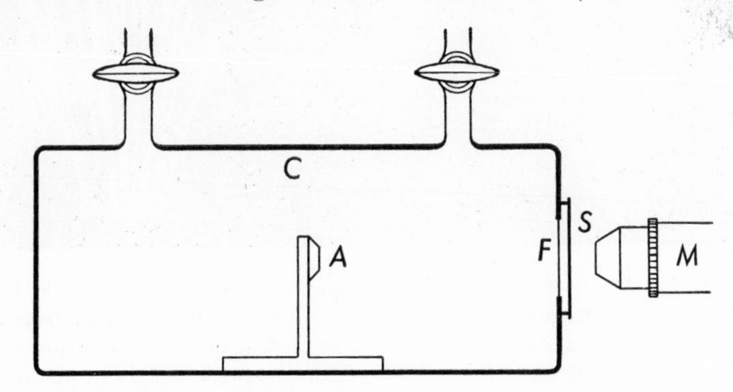

Fig. 11-1. Diagram of the apparatus used by Rutherford in the first successful experiment on artificial disintegration of nuclei.

to absorb the alpha particles, was placed over an opening in the side of the chamber. A zinc sulfide screen S was placed outside this opening and a microscope M was used for observing any scintillations occurring on the screen S. Scintillations were observed when the chamber was filled with nitrogen, but when the nitrogen was replaced by oxygen or carbon dioxide, no scintillations were observed on the screen S. Rutherford concluded that the scintillations were produced by high energy particles which were ejected from nitrogen nuclei as a result of the bombardment of these nuclei by the alpha particles. Magnetic deflection experiments indicated that these particles were hydrogen nuclei, or protons. Later experiments by Rutherford and Chadwick showed that these ejected protons had ranges up to 40 cm in air. Other light elements in the range from boron to potassium were also disintegrated by bombardment with alpha particles. Since then alpha particles, used as projectiles, have been successful in causing the disintegration of many elements.

The disintegration of nuclei has also been studied with the aid of the Wilson cloud chamber. One of the first of these investigations was that of Blackett, who photographed the tracks of alpha particles in a Wilson cloud chamber containing about 90 per cent nitrogen and 10 per cent

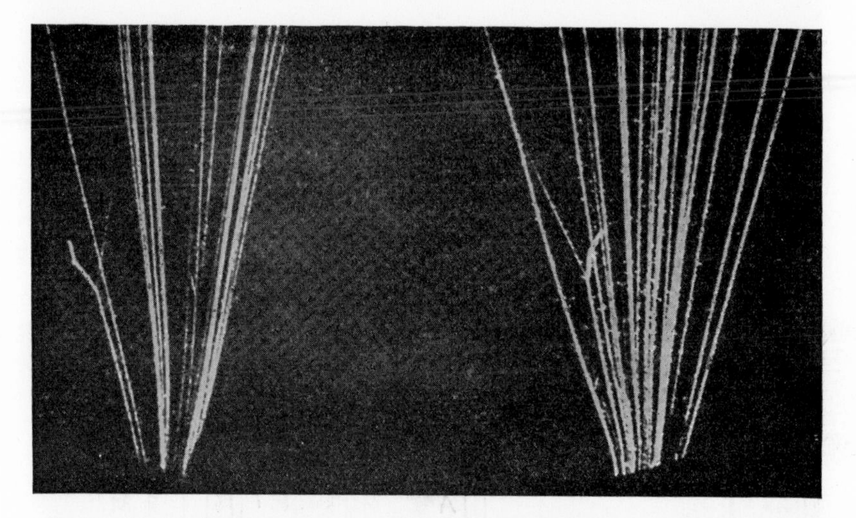

FIG. 11-2. A pair of stereoscopic photographs of alpha-particle tracks in a cloud chamber containing nitrogen. One of the alpha particles is captured by a nitrogen nucleus resulting in the disintegration of the compound nucleus into a proton (thin track) and an oxygen ion (thick track). (From Rutherford, Chadwick, and Ellis, ***Radiations from Radioactive Substances***. By permission of The Macmillan Company, publishers.)

oxygen. The majority of the tracks photographed were straight tracks typical of alpha-particle tracks. Many of the tracks were observed to be forked tracks, indicating that an elastic collision had taken place between an alpha particle and a nitrogen nucleus. It is an easy matter to distinguish between the track made by an alpha particle and that made by a nitrogen nucleus. The heavier particle produces more ion pairs per centimeter of path and thus forms a thicker track. Of about 500,000 tracks photographed, 8 tracks were of an unusual type. Each of these was a forked track containing two branches, as shown in Figure 11-2, one a very thick track, the other a very thin track. The thick track is ascribed to a slow-moving oxygen ion, the thin track to a fast-moving proton.

In order to be able to measure accurately the lengths of the tracks and the angles which the forked components make with the original direction of the alpha particle, it is necessary to photograph them from two different positions so as to be able to determine the plane in which the tracks are formed. A common method is to use two cameras at right angles to one another, thus obtaining a pair of stereoscopic photographs from which the correct space relationships of the several tracks can be determined. Measurements on the type of tracks illustrated in Figure 11-2 showed that the momentum of the system was conserved but that the sum of the kinetic energies of the particles after impact was less than the kinetic energy of the alpha particle before impact. On the basis of a theory of the nucleus advanced by Bohr (1936), the disintegration of nitrogen by bombardment with alpha particles may be thought of as consisting of two separate parts. The first is the capture of the alpha particle by the nitrogen nucleus resulting in the formation of a new *compound nucleus*; the second is the breaking up of the compound nucleus into two particles one of which is a proton. These two processes can be represented by means of a *nuclear reaction* equation analogous to one representing a chemical reaction. The nuclear reaction equation for this process is

$$ {}_2\mathrm{He}^4 + {}_7\mathrm{N}^{14} \rightarrow ({}_9\mathrm{F}^{18}) \rightarrow {}_8\mathrm{O}^{17} + {}_1\mathrm{H}^1. \tag{1}$$

The alpha particle, since it is a helium nucleus, is represented by the symbol ${}_2\mathrm{He}^4$. In order to satisfy the principle of the conservation of charge, the atomic number of the compound nucleus must be the sum of the atomic numbers of the helium and nitrogen nuclei. The compound nucleus formed in this case is fluorine, $Z = 9$. The symbol representing the compound nucleus will always be enclosed in parentheses. Since this unstable fluorine disintegrates with the emission of a proton, the remaining part, or product nucleus, must be oxygen, $Z = 8$.

The guiding principle in determining which isotope of an element is formed during a nuclear reaction is that the mass number of the compound nucleus must equal the sum of the mass numbers of the initial particles, and also the sum of the mass numbers of the final particles. This is not the same as the principle of the conservation of mass, since the mass numbers differ slightly from the actual values of the atomic masses. The principle of conservation of mass is no longer a separate and independent principle, but is part of the more general principle of the conservation of energy, since, as has previously been noted, a mass m is equivalent to an amount of energy mc^2, where c is the speed of light. Equation (1) can be rewritten to satisfy the general principle of the conservation of energy as

$$ {}_2\mathrm{He}^4 + {}_7\mathrm{N}^{14} \rightarrow ({}_9\mathrm{F}^{18}) \rightarrow {}_8\mathrm{O}^{17} + {}_1\mathrm{H}^1 + Q \tag{2}$$

where Q represents the energy evolved or absorbed during the nuclear reaction. If Q is positive, energy has been evolved, and if Q is negative, energy has been absorbed. Q is called the *nuclear reaction energy* or the *disintegration energy*, and is equal to the difference in the masses of the initial and final particles. If the sum of the masses of the final particles exceeds that of the initial particles, Q must be negative; the energy absorbed in such a nuclear reaction must have been obtained from the kinetic energies of the particles. If $\mathcal{E}_1$ is the kinetic energy of the alpha particle just before capture, $\mathcal{E}_2$ the kinetic energy of the proton, and $\mathcal{E}_3$ the kinetic energy of the product nucleus, then

$$\boxed{Q = \mathcal{E}_2 + \mathcal{E}_3 - \mathcal{E}_1.} \tag{3}$$

In those cases in which Q is positive, the sum of the kinetic energies of the final particles will be greater than the kinetic energy of the incident alpha particle. In practically all cases the kinetic energy of the nucleus which captures the alpha particle is comparatively small and may be neglected in this type of calculation.

In the above reaction, equation (2), the best value of Q obtained from measurements of the kinetic energies of the particles, is

$$Q = -1.26 \text{ Mev}.$$

The value of Q can be compared with the difference in the masses of the initial and final particles, using the values of the atomic masses given in Appendix IV.

Initial Particles		*Final Particles*	
He^4 =	4.00388	H^1 =	1.00815
N^{14} =	14.00755	O^{17} =	17.00453
	18.01143		18.01268

The masses of the final particles exceed those of the initial particles by the amount

$$\Delta m = 0.00125 \text{ amu}.$$

Remembering that 1 amu = 931.2 Mev, the calculated value of Q becomes

$$Q = -0.00125 \times 931.2 \text{ Mev} = -1.16 \text{ Mev}.$$

These two results agree very well within the limits of error of the experiment.

The results of this calculation show that the masses determined by means of the mass spectrograph check very well with those calculated from nuclear reaction data. If, in any one nuclear reaction, three of the four masses are known, a measurement of the reaction energy is sufficient to yield the mass of the fourth atom.

11-2. The α-p Reaction

The disintegration of the nitrogen nucleus by alpha particles is historically the first of a series of nuclear reactions in which an alpha particle is captured by a nucleus forming a compound nucleus which immediately disintegrates into a new nucleus by the ejection of a proton. Such reactions are known as the *α-p* type of reaction, in which the first letter, *α*, designates the nature of the bombarding particle, and the second letter, *p*, designates the nature of the ejected particle. The *α-p* type of reaction has been observed with most of the lighter elements up to selenium. This type of artificial disintegration may be represented by the nuclear reaction equation

$$_{Z}X^{A} + {}_{2}He^{4} \rightarrow ({}_{Z+2}Cp^{A+4}) \rightarrow {}_{Z+1}Y^{A+3} + {}_{1}H^{1} + Q, \qquad (4)$$

where Cp represents the compound nucleus formed as a result of the capture of an alpha particle by the atom X of mass number A and atomic number Z; the ejection of a proton from this compound nucleus results in the formation of a new atom Y of mass number $A + 3$ and atomic number $Z + 1$. In the majority of these cases, the reaction energy, or the disintegration energy Q, has been found to be negative. A few of these *α-p* reactions are listed below.

$$\begin{aligned}
&{}_{5}B^{10} + {}_{2}He^{4} \rightarrow ({}_{7}N^{14}) \rightarrow {}_{6}C^{13} + {}_{1}H^{1} && Q = +4.4 \text{ Mev}\\
&{}_{9}F^{19} + {}_{2}He^{4} \rightarrow ({}_{11}Na^{23}) \rightarrow {}_{10}Ne^{22} + {}_{1}H^{1} && Q = +1.58 \text{ Mev}\\
&{}_{13}Al^{27} + {}_{2}He^{4} \rightarrow ({}_{15}P^{31}) \rightarrow {}_{14}Si^{30} + {}_{1}H^{1} && Q = +2.26 \text{ Mev}\\
&{}_{14}Si^{28} + {}_{2}He^{4} \rightarrow ({}_{16}S^{32}) \rightarrow {}_{15}P^{31} + {}_{1}H^{1} && Q = -2.23 \text{ Mev} \qquad (5)\\
&{}_{16}S^{32} + {}_{2}He^{4} \rightarrow ({}_{18}A^{36}) \rightarrow {}_{17}Cl^{35} + {}_{1}H^{1} && Q = -2.10 \text{ Mev}\\
&{}_{19}K^{39} + {}_{2}He^{4} \rightarrow ({}_{21}Sc^{43}) \rightarrow {}_{20}Ca^{42} + {}_{1}H^{1} && Q = -0.89 \text{ Mev}\\
&{}_{21}Sc^{45} + {}_{2}He^{4} \rightarrow ({}_{23}V^{49}) \rightarrow {}_{22}Ti^{48} + {}_{1}H^{1} && Q = -0.3 \text{ Mev}
\end{aligned}$$

A simpler notation is frequently used to represent nuclear reactions. In this notation, the symbols for the bombarding particle and the particle released in the reaction are placed in parentheses, in the order stated; the parentheses are written between the symbol for the target nucleus and that for the product nucleus. Thus the above reactions (5) would be written as $B^{10}(\alpha,p)C^{13}$, $F^{19}(\alpha,p)Ne^{22}$, $Al^{27}(\alpha,p)Si^{30}$, and so forth. It is generally not necessary to write the atomic number with the chemical symbol, since one is uniquely determined by the other.

The compound nuclei formed in the first five nuclear reactions listed in (5) have mass numbers identical with those of stable isotopes of the respective elements. However, these compound nuclei are not in their *ground state*; each compound nucleus is in an *excited state*. The mass of the compound nucleus is greater than the mass of the stable form. This can be verified readily by a calculation similar to that made for reaction (2).

In most of these artificial disintegration experiments it is desirable to have the bombarded element in the form of a solid, so that when a stream of alpha particles is directed against this solid target, a larger fraction of them will be absorbed in a very small volume. The effectiveness of the alpha particles in producing this type of disintegration is dependent upon the energies of the alpha particles and upon the nuclear charge. A measure of this effectiveness, sometimes called the *yield*, is the ratio of the number of protons produced to the number of alpha particles completely stopped in the target. The yield for the α-p type of reaction ranges in val-

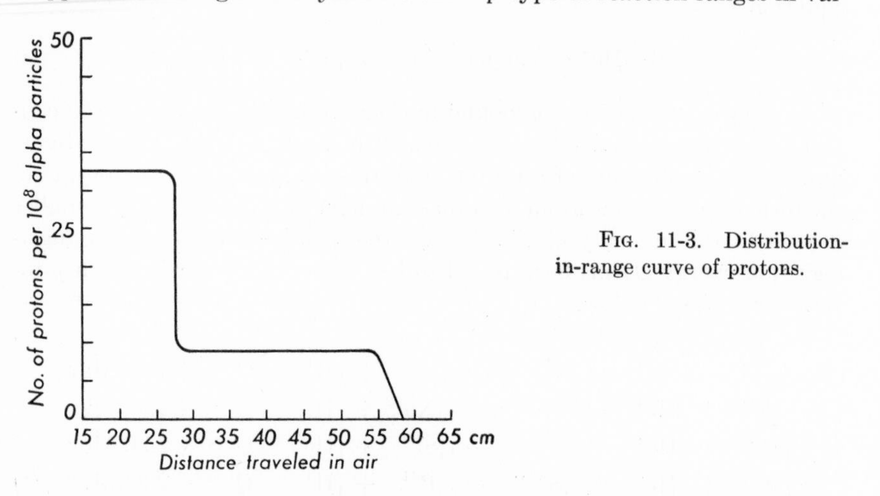

FIG. 11-3. Distribution-in-range curve of protons.

ues from 10^{-7} to 10^{-5} for alpha particles of 3 to 8 Mev incident upon elements of small atomic number.

One of the α-p reactions which has been studied very carefully is that in which aluminum formed the target for the alpha particles. The energies of the protons emitted in this reaction have been studied for different values of the energy of the incident alpha particles. One method of presenting these results is shown in the curve in Figure 11-3. This curve is known as a distribution-in-range curve. It is obtained by plotting the number of protons penetrating a certain thickness of air, or its equivalent, as ordinate against the corresponding value of the absorber thickness. It will be noticed that the protons produced in this particular experiment form two homogeneous groups, one of about 28 cm range, and the second of about 58 cm range. Other homogeneous groups of protons have been observed, using alpha particles of different energies. Of the protons observed in this reaction those with the longest range had a range of about 66 cm.

The fact that protons are ejected with definite ranges, or definite energies, indicates that the product nucleus, in this case silicon, possesses several energy levels. The product nucleus is left in the ground state by the ejection of the proton of longest range, and it is left in one of its excited states by the ejection of a proton of smaller range. One might then expect gamma rays to be emitted during this reaction by those nuclei which go from the excited states to the normal or ground state, and the energies of these gamma rays should be equal to the differences in the energies of the various proton groups. Gamma rays have actually been observed in the above reaction and in several of the other α-p reactions.

The value of the reaction energy, Q, listed with each of the α-p type of reaction, is the largest reaction energy, and corresponds to the emission of protons of maximum range. In each case, therefore, the product nucleus is left in its normal state. Reactions in which Q has been measured accurately have been used for the determination of the masses of the product nuclei. The values of the atomic masses obtained in this way can be used as independent checks on the measurements made with the mass spectrograph. In some cases where such data are not available, the nuclear reaction equations form the only reliable methods for determining the masses of the isotopes formed in the reaction.

11-3. Discovery of the Neutron

The capture of an alpha particle by a nucleus does not always result in the emission of a proton by the compound nucleus formed as a result of this capture. In one particular reaction studied, that resulting from the bombardment of beryllium by alpha particles, a very penetrating type of radiation was found to be emitted by the newly formed compound nucleus. It was at first assumed that this radiation was of the nature of gamma rays, resulting from the nuclear reaction

$$ {}_4\mathrm{Be}^9 + {}_2\mathrm{He}^4 \rightarrow ({}_6\mathrm{C}^{13}) \rightarrow {}_6\mathrm{C}^{13} + h\nu $$

where $h\nu$ is the energy of the gamma-ray photon. The measurements of Bothe and Becker (1930) of the absorption of these rays in lead showed that each photon should possess an energy of about 7 Mev. The Curie-Joliots (1932) showed that these rays had the very interesting property of being able to knock out protons from paraffin and other substances containing hydrogen. The protons knocked out of paraffin by these rays had a range in air of about 40 cm, or an energy of about 5 Mev. Assuming that these protons were produced as the result of elastic collisions with the gamma-ray photons, calculations showed that each photon must have possessed an amount of energy of about 55 Mev. These results were entirely inconsistent with the results from the experiments on the absorption of these rays in lead. Furthermore, the amount of energy available for gamma radiation, when computed for the above reaction from the known masses of the particles, is much less than 55 Mev. If an alpha particle of 5 Mev energy is captured by a beryllium nucleus, the energy available for the emission of a gamma ray from the carbon nucleus can be obtained as follows:

$$_4\text{Be}^9 + {_2\text{He}^4} + \mathcal{E}_1 \rightarrow (_6\text{C}^{13}) \rightarrow {_6\text{C}^{13}} + h\nu$$

$$9.01503 + 4.00388 + .00536 = 13.00751 + h\nu$$

or

$$h\nu = 0.01676 \text{ amu} = 15.6 \text{ Mev};$$

that is, the maximum amount of energy available for the gamma-ray photon is 15.6 Mev. Chadwick (1932) performed a series of experiments on the recoil of nuclei which were struck by the rays coming from beryllium bombarded by alpha particles, and showed that if these rays were assumed to be gamma rays, then the results of the experiments led to values for the energies of these rays which depended upon the nature of the recoil nucleus. For example, the protons ejected from paraffin had energies of 5.7 Mev which led to a value of 55 Mev for the energy of the gamma ray; nitrogen recoil nuclei had energies of about 1.2 Mev, indicating that the photon which struck this nucleus must have had an energy of about 90 Mev. In general, if the recoil atoms are to be attributed to collisions with photons, then the amount of energy that has to be assigned to the photon will increase with the increase in mass of the recoil atom. This is contrary to the principles of conservation of energy and momentum during collisions. However, Chadwick showed that all these difficulties disappear completely if we adopt the hypothesis that the radiation coming from the beryllium bombarded with alpha particles does not consist of photons, but consists of particles of mass very nearly equal to that of the proton but having no charge. These particles are called *neutrons* and are formed as a result of the reaction

$$_4\text{Be}^9 + {_2\text{He}^4} \rightarrow (_6\text{C}^{13}) \rightarrow {_6\text{C}^{12}} + {_0n^1} \tag{6}$$

where $_0n^1$ is the symbol representing the neutron, showing that it has zero charge and mass number unity.

One arrangement used by Chadwick for demonstrating the existence and properties of neutrons is shown in Figure 11-4. The source of alpha particles is a disk D on which polonium has been deposited. This disk and the beryllium target are placed in an evacuated chamber C. The neutrons coming from the beryllium pass through the thin wall of this chamber and enter the ionization chamber I through the thin window w. This ionization chamber is connected to an amplifier and then to a recording device such as an oscillograph, a loud-speaker, or an electrical counter.

Since the neutrons possess no electric charge, they produce no ionization directly in their passage through the chamber. But some neutrons which strike the walls of the ionization chamber cause the ejection of nuclei which then produce ions in the chamber, and are thus recorded on the film of the oscillograph or on the electrical counter; if a loud-speaker is used, a "click" is heard for every nucleus which produces intense ionization. The results of these experiments show that when the neutrons from beryllium go directly into the ionization chamber, a few counts per minute are recorded. If thin sheets of lead are placed in front of the ionization chamber, the number of counts produced is not reduced appreciably. If, however, a thin slab of paraffin is placed in front of the window w, then

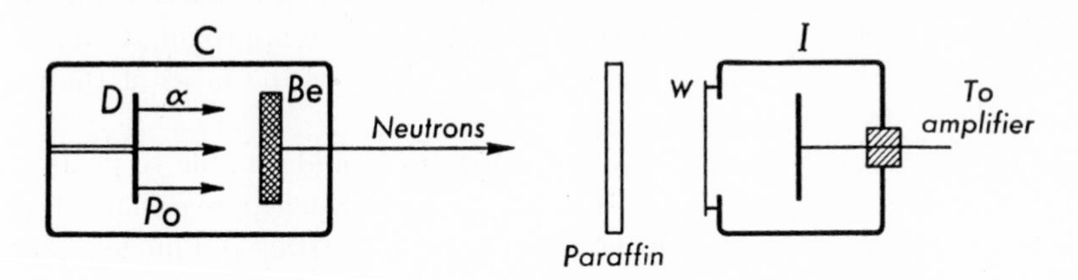

FIG. 11-4. Arrangement of apparatus for the detection of neutrons.

the number of counts per minute increases markedly. This increase is due to the fact that the neutrons, in collisions with the nuclei of the hydrogen atoms contained in paraffin, give up a considerable fraction of their energy to those nuclei or protons, and those protons which enter the ionization chamber are then recorded. If the paraffin is removed and the neutrons are allowed to enter the chamber directly, the number of counts falls immediately to its former low value. This is just the opposite of what would happen if radiation of the nature of gamma rays were used; that is, the introduction of any absorbing material in the path of the gamma radiation produces a decrease in the intensity of the transmitted radiation. The radiation from beryllium therefore cannot be of the nature of gamma rays.

When neutrons pass through matter, they lose energy as a result of collisions with other nuclei and so give rise to the recoil atoms. If the mass of the neutron is approximately unity, then in collision with hydrogen nuclei the ejected protons will have velocities of all values up to a maximum which is the same as the velocity of the neutrons. The mass M of the neutron can be calculated, to a first approximation, from the measured values of the maximum velocities of the hydrogen and nitrogen recoil atoms. It can be shown, on the basis of mechanics, that the maximum velocity of the recoil nucleus is given by

$$v = \frac{2M}{M + M_r} V, \tag{7}$$

where V is the velocity of the incident neutron, v the velocity of the recoil atom, and M_r the mass of the recoil atom. If two experiments are performed, one in which the maximum velocity of the recoil protons is measured, and the other in which the maximum velocity of the recoil nitrogen atoms is determined, then

$$\frac{v_{\mathrm{H}}}{v_{\mathrm{N}}} = \frac{M + M_{\mathrm{N}}}{M + M_{\mathrm{H}}}. \tag{8}$$

In Chadwick's experiment the measured value of the maximum velocity of the recoil proton, v_{H}, was 3.3×10^9 cm/sec, and of the recoil nitrogen atoms, $v_{\mathrm{N}} = 4.7 \times 10^8$ cm/sec. The assumption that the mass of nitrogen is 14 times that of hydrogen yields $M = 1.15$ as the approximate mass of the neutron. More accurate measurements yield for the mass of the neutron, $M = 1.008987$ (§11-12).

Because of their lack of charge, neutrons should be able to penetrate atomic nuclei very easily, and a study of these nuclear reactions should yield valuable information concerning nuclear properties and nuclear structure (§11-13).

11-4. The α-n Reaction

The bombardment of beryllium by alpha particles with the subsequent emission of neutrons is one of many nuclear reactions of the type designated as an α-n type and is given by the formula

$$_{\mathrm{Z}}\mathrm{X}^{\mathrm{A}} + {}_2\mathrm{He}^4 \rightarrow ({}_{\mathrm{Z+2}}\mathrm{Y}^{\mathrm{A+4}}) \rightarrow {}_{\mathrm{Z+2}}\mathrm{Y}^{\mathrm{A+3}} + {}_0n^1 + Q. \tag{9}$$

A few of these reactions are listed below.

$$\begin{array}{llll} {}_3\mathrm{Li}^7 + {}_2\mathrm{He}^4 \rightarrow ({}_5\mathrm{B}^{11}) & \rightarrow {}_5\mathrm{B}^{10} & + {}_0n^1 \\ {}_4\mathrm{Be}^9 + {}_2\mathrm{He}^4 \rightarrow ({}_6\mathrm{C}^{13}) & \rightarrow {}_6\mathrm{C}^{12} & + {}_0n^1 \\ {}_5\mathrm{B}^{11} + {}_2\mathrm{He}^4 \rightarrow ({}_7\mathrm{N}^{15}) & \rightarrow {}_7\mathrm{N}^{14} & + {}_0n^1 \\ {}_7\mathrm{N}^{14} + {}_2\mathrm{He}^4 \rightarrow ({}_9\mathrm{F}^{18}) & \rightarrow {}_9\mathrm{F}^{17} & + {}_0n^1 \\ {}_9\mathrm{F}^{19} + {}_2\mathrm{He}^4 \rightarrow ({}_{11}\mathrm{Na}^{23}) & \rightarrow {}_{11}\mathrm{Na}^{22} & + {}_0n^1 \\ {}_{13}\mathrm{Al}^{27} + {}_2\mathrm{He}^4 \rightarrow ({}_{15}\mathrm{P}^{31}) & \rightarrow {}_{15}\mathrm{P}^{30} & + {}_0n^1 \end{array} \tag{10}$$

In many α-n reactions the product nuclei are left in excited states as is evidenced by the fact that gamma rays have been observed in some of these reactions. For example, in the beryllium reaction, gamma rays have been observed consisting of three definite lines with energies of 2.7, 4.47, and 6.7 Mev.

The energies of the neutrons emitted in the α-n type of reaction can be investigated in several different ways. One method is to measure the ranges of the protons which are ejected from paraffin by the action of the neutrons. Another method is to irradiate the gas in a cloud chamber with the neutrons and to measure the ranges of the nuclei which are set in motion as a result of collisions with the neutrons. A third method is to allow the neutrons to fall on a photographic emulsion, parallel to, or at a small angle to the plane of, the photographic plate. Although the neutrons do not leave tracks in the emulsion, the protons ejected by them from the light elements in the emulsion do leave developable grains. After the plates have been developed, the ranges of the protons in the emulsion can be measured with a microscope; these ranges can then be converted to

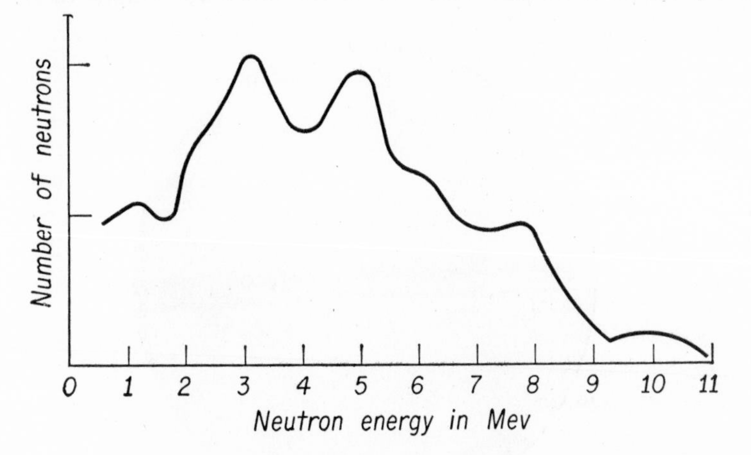

Fig. 11-5. Energy distribution of neutrons from the α-n reaction with Be, using alpha particles from polonium. (After Whitmore and Baker, *Phys. Rev.*, 78, 799, 1950.)

energies by proper calibration of such plates with protons of known energies. From such experiments it has been found that the neutrons from an α-n reaction possess very high energies; in many cases the energies of the neutrons have been found to consist of several sharp energy groups.

Whitmore and Baker have recently (1950) measured the energy distribution of the neutrons from the α-n reaction of beryllium, using polonium as the source of alpha particles. They used the photographic emulsion technique, making a total of nearly 7000 observations on three separate plates. Figure 11-5 shows the energy distribution curve they obtained. It will be observed that there are intense maxima at 3.2, 4.8, and 7.7 Mev, and an upper limit to the energy of the neutrons at 11 Mev. There are indications of smaller maxima at 1.2, 5.8, and 9.7 Mev.

11-5. Discovery of the Positron

Shortly after the discovery of the neutron, another new particle, the *positron*, was discovered by C. D. Anderson (1932) in his experiments on the particles produced by the action of the very penetrating rays known as *cosmic rays*, which come to the earth from all directions in space. Anderson was taking Wilson cloud-chamber photographs of the tracks of the particles in a strong magnetic field. A few tracks were found to be curved, showing that they were formed by charged particles passing through the gas in the cloud chamber. From the appearance of these tracks, they were judged to be due to particles of electronic mass and electronic charge, but from the direction of the curvature of these tracks it was evident that the particles producing them must have been positively charged. Anderson called these particles *positrons*. One of the first photographs to establish

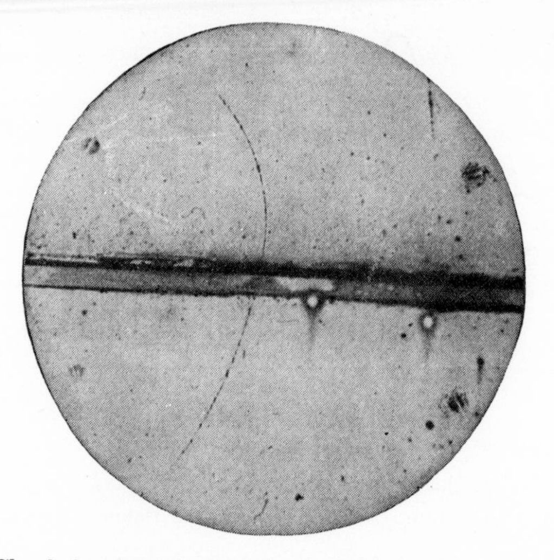

FIG. 11-6. Cloud-chamber photograph of the path of a positron in a magnetic field. The positron originated at the bottom of the chamber and passed through a sheet of lead 6 mm thick. The magnetic field is directed into the paper. (Photograph by Carl D. Anderson.)

definitely the existence of a positron is shown in Figure 11-6. The particle originated at the bottom of the chamber, passed through a lead plate 6 mm thick, and then continued with a smaller amount of energy. From the curvatures of these two parts of the track in the magnetic field of known strength, in this case directed into the plane of the figure, and from the amount of ionization along the paths, it was concluded that the positron had an energy of 63 Mev before entering the lead and emerged from it with 23 Mev energy. Figure 11-7 shows a pair of stereoscopic pictures of the tracks of a group of charged particles produced at the top of the cloud chamber by the action of cosmic rays. Three of the tracks are produced by electrons and three by positrons.

About a year after the discovery of the positron by Anderson, sources of positrons became plentiful and easily obtainable as a result of the dis-

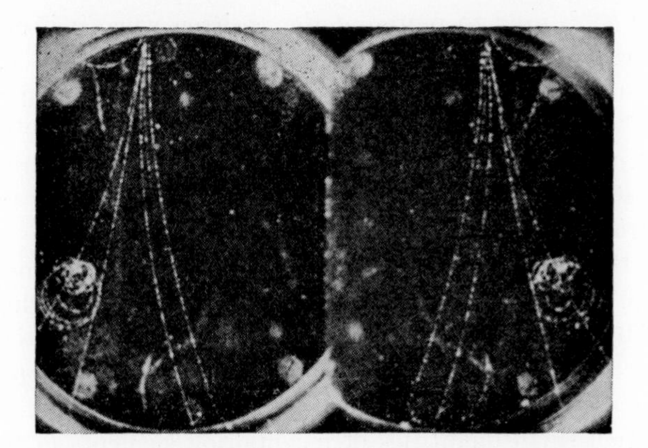

FIG. 11-7. A pair of stereoscopic photographs of the tracks of a group of charged particles produced in a cloud chamber by the action of cosmic rays. The picture on the left is the direct image; the one on the right is a reflected image. The magnetic field of 7900 gausses is directed into the paper. In the picture on the left the three tracks on the left are electron tracks, and the three on the right are positron tracks. The energies of these particles, from left to right, are 3.5, 55, 190, 78, 70, and 90 Mev. (Photograph by Carl D. Anderson.)

covery by the Curie-Joliots of the phenomenon of artificial or induced radioactivity.

11-6. Discovery of Artificial or Induced Radioactivity

One of the most important discoveries in nuclear physics came from experiments on the bombardment of light nuclei by alpha particles. In the course of such experiments using boron and aluminum as targets, M. and Mme Curie-Joliot (1934) observed that the bombarded substances continued to emit radiations even after the source of alpha particles had been removed. Ionization measurements and magnetic deflection experiments showed that the radiations consisted of positrons. Further, the intensity of the radiation was found to decrease exponentially with time, just as in the case of the naturally radioactive elements. The half-life, T, of the positron disintegration was measured in each case. The explanation of this phenomenon given by the Curie-Joliots was that the product nucleus formed in the α-n reaction in each case was an unstable isotope, which then disintegrated with the emission of a positron. The nuclear reactions for these elements are

$$_5B^{10} + {}_2He^4 \rightarrow ({}_7N^{14}) \rightarrow {}_7N^{13} + {}_0n^1$$

then

$$_7N^{13} \rightarrow {}_6C^{13} + \beta^+, \quad T = 10.1 \text{ min.} \tag{11}$$

$$_{13}Al^{27} + {}_2He^4 \rightarrow ({}_{15}P^{31}) \rightarrow {}_{15}P^{30} + {}_0n^1$$

then

$$_{15}P^{30} \rightarrow {}_{14}Si^{30} + \beta^+, \quad T = 2.5 \text{ min.} \tag{12}$$

The symbol β^+ is used to represent the positron when it is emitted by a nucleus. Occasionally the symbol $_{+1}e^0$ is used to represent the positron since its charge is equal to that of a proton and its mass number is zero. A glance at the table of known stable isotopes (Appendix V) reveals that the product nuclei formed in the α-n reactions listed above are not among the known stable isotopes, but that the nuclei formed after the emission of the positron are known stable isotopes.

One of the best methods for the identification of an element is chemical analysis. Because of the minute amount of material which is made radioactive by alpha-particle bombardment, it is necessary to use a somewhat indirect chemical test to identify the radioactive isotope. The general method used is to dissolve the irradiated substance and then to add to this solution small quantities of neighboring elements in the ordinary inactive form. The various elements are then separated by chemical methods, generally the precipitation of an insoluble salt, and sometimes the formation of a gaseous compound. These materials are put in different tubes and each one is tested for radioactivity. The chemical identification of the radioelement is then easily made. The Curie-Joliots made chemical tests on each of the materials investigated and in each case they were able to identify the radioactive isotope. For example, in the boron reaction, they made a target of boron nitride, BN, irradiated it with alpha particles for several minutes, and then heated it with caustic soda. One of the products of this chemical reaction was gaseous ammonia, NH_3. The fact that this ammonia was the only one of the chemical substances which was radioactive indicated that the nitrogen, $_7N^{13}$, was the radioelement produced in this experiment. Its half-life was found to be the same as that produced in other boron targets, while no radioactivity was observed when ordinary nitrogen was used as a target.

Many nuclei formed in α-n reactions are unstable and disintegrate with the emission of positrons. A few of these are given below, together with the measured half-lives.

$$
\begin{aligned}
{}_{9}F^{17} &\rightarrow {}_{8}O^{17} + \beta^+, & T &= 1.2 \text{ min.}\\
{}_{11}Na^{22} &\rightarrow {}_{10}Ne^{22} + \beta^+, & T &= 2.6 \text{ yr.}\\
{}_{13}Al^{26} &\rightarrow {}_{12}Mg^{26} + \beta^+, & T &= 7 \text{ sec.}\\
{}_{14}Si^{27} &\rightarrow {}_{13}Al^{27} + \beta^+, & T &= 4.9 \text{ sec.}\\
{}_{15}P^{30} &\rightarrow {}_{14}Si^{30} + \beta^+, & T &= 2.5 \text{ min.}\\
{}_{17}Cl^{34} &\rightarrow {}_{16}S^{34} + \beta^+, & T &= 33 \text{ min.}
\end{aligned}
\tag{13}
$$

11-7. Induced Beta Decay

After the discovery of induced radioactivity by the Curie-Joliots, physicists throughout the world began a program of producing radioactive isotopes by bombarding nuclei of the different elements with a variety of projectiles obtained both from natural radioactive sources and from particle accelerators. As we shall see, there are now radioactive isotopes for all the elements. Most of these are beta-ray emitters, alpha-particle emission being confined almost exclusively to the heavier elements.

Although the beta-particle emitters produced in the α-n reactions described above are positron emitters, induced beta decay can also take place by negative beta-particle emission. A few α-p reactions lead to the formation of radioactive isotopes which decay by negative beta-particle emission. One of these, for example, is the following:

$$_5B^{11} + {_2He^4} \rightarrow (_7N^{15}) \rightarrow {_6C^{14}} + {_1H^1}, \quad Q = 0.75 \text{ Mev}.$$

followed by $\quad {_6C^{14}} \rightarrow {_7N^{14}} + \beta^-; \quad T = 5580 \text{ yr}. \qquad (14)$

The beta-ray spectra, both positive and negative, of the artificially produced beta emitters are similar to those of natural beta emitters, that is, each spectrum shows a continuous distribution of energy up to the maximum end-point energy. We have already shown that the negative beta-ray emission can be explained by assuming a neutron to disintegrate into a proton, an electron, and a neutrino, thus:

$$n \rightarrow p + \beta^- + \nu. \qquad (15)$$

To account for the emission of positrons, it is assumed that the other type of nucleon, the proton, disintegrates into a neutron, a positron, and a neutrino, thus:

$$p \text{ (in nucleus)} \rightarrow n \text{ (in nucleus)} + \beta^+ + \nu. \qquad (16)$$

However, since the mass of the proton is less than that of the neutron, the process given by equation (16) can occur only if sufficient energy is supplied to the proton by the other particles of the atomic system. The disintegration of the proton can thus occur only for a proton which is in the nucleus.

We have shown (§10-9) that the disintegration energy in negative beta decay is equal to the difference in masses between the initial atom and the product atom. However, this is not the case for positron emission. The energy available for a β^+-disintegration is the difference in mass between the initial nucleus $_ZM_n^A$ and the sum of the masses of the final particles, that is, the nucleus $_{Z-1}M_n^A$ and the positron, m_e, thus

$$\mathcal{E} = {_ZM_n^A} - [_{Z-1}M_n^A + m_e]. \qquad (17)$$

To convert to atomic masses, let us add Z electronic masses to each term, obtaining

$$\mathcal{E} = {_ZM_n^A} + Zm_e - [_{Z-1}M_n^A + (Z-1)m_e + 2m_e]$$

from which

$$\boxed{\mathcal{E} = {}_{Z}M^{A} - {}_{Z-1}M^{A} - 2m_e,} \tag{18}$$

where ${}_{Z}M^{A}$ is the atomic mass of the parent atom and ${}_{Z-1}M^{A}$ is the atomic mass of the product atom. The disintegration energy of a positron disintegration is thus less than the difference in atomic masses of the parent and product atoms by the energy equivalent of two electronic masses, that is, by $2m_ec^2$, where c is the speed of light.

In both positive and negative beta decay, the parent and daughter (product) nuclei form a pair of isobars. In the case of β^--decay, the disintegration energy is equal to the maximum kinetic energy of the beta-ray spectrum, but in the case of β^+-decay, the disintegration energy is the sum of the kinetic energy of the beta-ray spectrum plus twice the rest mass energy of the electron. In other words, in β^+-decay, the difference in energy between the parent *atom* and the daughter *atom* must be at least $2m_ec^2$, that is, approximately 1 Mev. Another way of describing this is to say that when the nucleus emits a positron, an electron must also be released from the external part of the atom in order that the product atom be electrically neutral.

11-8. Projectiles for Nuclear Experiments

As soon as the success of the experiments on the disintegration of nuclei by alpha-particle bombardment was recognized, physicists began designing and building devices for imparting high energies to particles such as electrons, protons, deuterons (nuclei of deuterium), and helium nuclei, as well as for producing high energy x-rays. Among these devices are the *Van de Graff electrostatic generators*, the *betatrons*, the *cyclotrons*, and the *linear accelerators*. The physical principles at the basis of their operation will be discussed in Chapter 16. In addition, *nuclear reactors*, utilizing the phenomenon of *nuclear fission* (see Chapter 13), provided intense sources of neutrons, gamma rays, neutrinos, and charged particles.

In this chapter we shall discuss nuclear reactions involving the large variety of projectiles now available and only occasionally shall we refer to the type of source used in their production. It may simply be noted that the energies of these projectiles can range all the way from a small fraction of an electron volt to well over two billion electron volts.

11-9. Simple Alpha-Particle Capture; Radiative Capture

Both the α-p and α-n reactions described previously involve the emission of a nuclear particle by the compound nucleus. However, it is possible for the compound nucleus formed by the capture of an alpha particle to go to a more stable configuration without emitting a particle but emitting a gamma-ray photon instead. This phenomenon of the simple capture, or radiative capture, of alpha particles was first observed by Bennet, Roys, and Toppel (1950). They used comparatively low energy alpha particles produced by accelerating helium ions by means of an electrostatic generator. The energies of the alpha particles could be accurately controlled

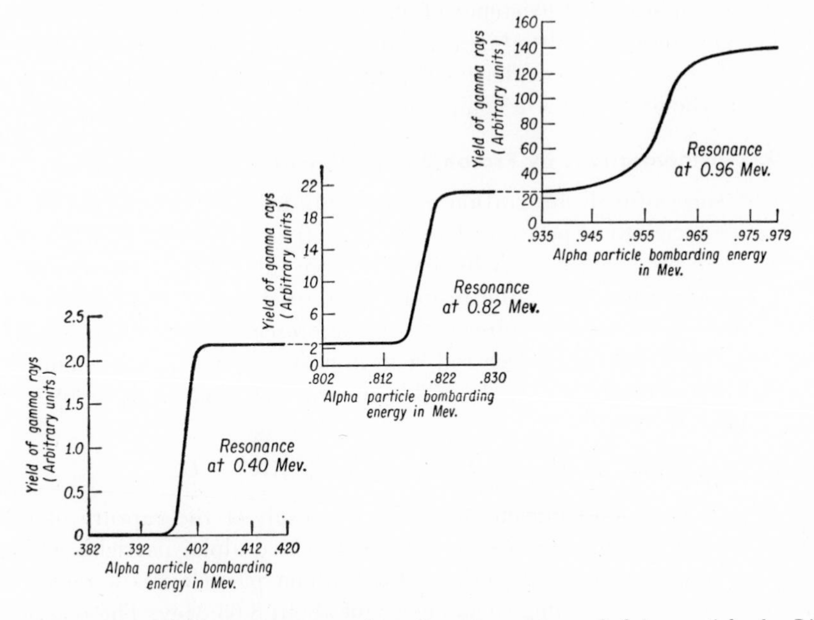

FIG. 11-8. Yield of gamma rays in radioactive capture of alpha particles by Li^7. (After Bennett, Roys, and Toppel, *Phys. Rev.*, 82, 20, 1951.)

and measured. Various light elements, such as lithium, beryllium, and boron, were used as targets for these projectiles. The radiative capture process can be called an α-γ process.

For the case of lithium, $Z = 3$, $A = 7$, the reaction is

$$_3Li^7 + {}_2He^4 \rightarrow ({}_5B^{11}) \rightarrow {}_5B^{11} + h\nu, \tag{19}$$

where $h\nu$ represents the gamma-ray photon emitted by the compound nucleus $_5B^{11}$ in going to a more stable configuration. Figure 11-8 shows the yield of gamma-ray photons as a function of the bombarding energy of the alpha particles. It will be noted that there is a sharp increase in yield at about 0.4 Mev, after which the intensity levels off until the energy of the alpha particle reaches about 0.82 Mev, at which point there is another sharp increase in the yield of gamma-ray photons. Another sudden increase in yield was observed at about 0.96 Mev, but this was not quite as sharp as the earlier two increases in yield.

The sharp increases in the yield of gamma rays at alpha-particle energies of 0.4, 0.82, and 0.96 Mev are interpreted as *resonance capture* of the alpha particle, that is, the probability of capture is comparatively large at these energies. That the yield curve presents a steep slope at these energies rather than sharp maxima is due to the fact that a thick target was used rather than a thin one. These resonances are ascribed to the compound nucleus and indicate the existence of energy levels in this nucleus.

The gamma rays emitted in a radiative capture process are sometimes called *capture γ-rays*. The radiative capture process is one type of evidence confirming the existence of a compound nucleus.

11-10. Disintegrations by Proton Bombardment

The first successful disintegration experiments utilizing protons as bombarding particles were performed by Cockcroft and Walton (1932). The protons were produced in a hydrogen discharge tube operated at voltages up to 500,000 volts. When the protons were used to bombard a lithium target, alpha particles were observed on a fluorescent screen. This experiment was later repeated by Dee and Walton, using a Wilson cloud chamber for detecting the alpha particles. This nuclear reaction is given by the equation

$$ {}_3Li^7 + {}_1H^1 \rightarrow ({}_4Be^8) \rightarrow {}_2He^4 + {}_2He^4 + Q; \tag{20} $$

that is, the compound nucleus formed as a result of the capture of the proton by the lithium nucleus breaks up into two alpha particles which travel in almost opposite directions. Each alpha particle has a range of 8.31 cm in air corresponding to an energy of about 8.63 Mev. The reaction energy Q is found to be 17.28 Mev, and checks very well with the value obtained from the difference in the masses of the initial and final particles.

There are many other interesting disintegrations produced by bombardment with protons. The nuclear reaction which occurs with the lithium target containing only the isotope of mass number 6 is given by the equation

$$ {}_3Li^6 + {}_1H^1 \rightarrow ({}_4Be^7) \rightarrow {}_2He^4 + {}_2He^3 + Q, \tag{21} $$

in which two helium atoms, one of mass number 4, and the other of mass number 3, are produced with ranges of 0.8 cm and 1.2 cm respectively. The measured value of Q is 3.94 Mev. A few of the other reactions observed are given below.

$$ \begin{aligned} {}_5B^{11} + {}_1H^1 &\rightarrow ({}_6C^{12}) \rightarrow {}_4Be^8 + {}_2He^4 \\ {}_{11}Na^{23} + {}_1H^1 &\rightarrow ({}_{12}Mg^{24}) \rightarrow {}_{10}Ne^{20} + {}_2He^4 \\ {}_{17}Cl^{35} + {}_1H^1 &\rightarrow ({}_{18}A^{36}) \rightarrow {}_{16}S^{32} + {}_2He^4 \end{aligned} \tag{22} $$

The disintegrations listed above can be classified as *p-α* reactions, since one of the final products is an alpha particle.

The $B^{11}(p,\alpha)Be^8$ reaction has been studied very extensively and it has been found that in the majority of cases the beryllium nucleus is left in an excited state and then disintegrates with the emission of two alpha particles.

Not all reactions in which the proton is the bombarding particle are of the p-α type. In the case of beryllium two different reactions have been observed, one in which an alpha particle is emitted and another in which

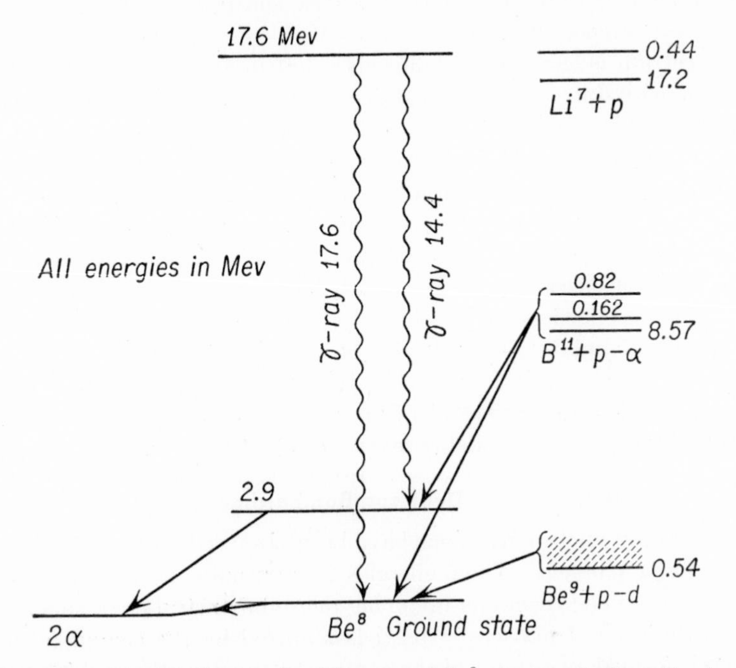

FIG. 11-9. Simplified energy level diagram of Be^8, showing its formation by three methods using protons as projectiles together with the modes of decay of three of the levels of Be^8. (After Hornyak, Lauritsen, Morrison, and Fowler, *Revs. Modern Phys.*, 22, 310, 1950.)

a deuteron is emitted. The latter is called a *p-d* reaction, where *d* represents the deuteron. These reactions are given by the equations

$$\begin{aligned} {}_4Be^9 + {}_1H^1 &\rightarrow ({}_5B^{10}) \rightarrow {}_3Li^6 + {}_2He^4 \\ {}_4Be^9 + {}_1H^1 &\rightarrow ({}_5B^{10}) \rightarrow {}_4Be^8 + {}_1H^2. \end{aligned} \quad (23)$$

Gamma rays have also been observed as the result of the bombardment of an element by protons. In some of these cases the gamma-ray photons possess such high energies that the only possible explanation seems to be that the proton is simply captured by the nucleus, and that the compound nucleus thus formed is in an excited state. This nucleus then returns to its normal state with the emission of a gamma-ray photon of definite energy. This process is designated as a p-γ reaction and is a simple proton capture process; the emitted gamma rays are capture gammas. One such example is the reaction

$$_3\text{Li}^7 + {_1\text{H}^1} \rightarrow (_4\text{Be}^8) \rightarrow {_4\text{Be}^8} + h\nu. \tag{24}$$

The capture gamma-ray spectrum has been investigated by Walker and McDaniel, who found a very intense sharp line of 17.6 Mev energy and a less intense broad line of 14.4 Mev energy. The interpretation of this spectrum is that the Be^8 nucleus is left in an excited state in the p-γ reaction with Li^7; it then can decay to the ground state by emitting a gamma-ray photon of 17.6 Mev, or it may emit a photon of 14.4 Mev and then disintegrate into two alpha particles. The latter process has been studied by Burcham and Freeman. They measured the alpha-particle energies and found them centered about an energy of 1.38 Mev when the bombarding protons had an energy of 440 kev. These results lead to a value of the excited state of Be^8 as 2.9 Mev above the ground state.

The three processes in which Be^8 is formed, namely, $\text{B}^{11}(p,\alpha)\text{Be}^8$, $\text{Be}^9(p,d)\text{Be}^8$, and $\text{Li}^7(p,\gamma)\text{Be}^8$, can be represented in a simplified energy level diagram shown in Figure 11-9. It will be noted that Be^8, even in the ground state, is unstable and disintegrates into two alpha particles. Its half-life is very short, probably less than 2×10^{-14} sec.

11-11. Disintegration by Deuteron Bombardment

A great many nuclear reactions have been observed with deuterons as the bombarding particles. Their energies have usually been of the order of several Mev. The reactions involving deuterons may be classified according to the type of particle or particles emitted by the compound nucleus which is formed as a result of the capture of the deuteron. Alpha particles, protons, and neutrons have been produced in these processes. In some cases the product nucleus, formed as a result of the emission of one of these particles, is radioactive and disintegrates with the emission of a positron or an electron. Gamma rays have been observed in some of the reactions which involve the emission of a particle. In a few cases the compound nucleus has been observed to break up into three particles. Only a few typical examples of each of these reactions resulting from the capture of a deuteron will be considered in this section.

One of the simplest and most important of these reactions is the one in which the deuterons are used to bombard a target containing deuterons. Deuteron targets have been made by freezing heavy water (deuterium oxide) onto a surface kept cold by means of liquid air. Other deuterium targets have been made out of compounds such as ammonium sulfate, in which the ordinary hydrogen was replaced by deuterium. Two different nuclear reactions have been observed as a result of the bombardment of deuterium by deuterons:

$$_1H^2 + {_1H^2} \rightarrow ({_2He^4}) \rightarrow {_1H^3} + {_1H^1} + Q, \quad (25)$$

and

$$_1H^2 + {_1H^2} \rightarrow ({_2He^4}) \rightarrow {_2He^3} + {_0n^1} + Q. \quad (26)$$

The first of these reactions has been studied with the aid of a Wilson cloud chamber, which enabled the particles to be identified as isotopes of hydrogen of mass numbers 1 and 3. The ranges of these particles in air have been found to be 14.7 cm and 1.6 cm, respectively, yielding a value for $Q = 4.03$ Mev. With the value of Q, and the known masses of H^1 and H^2, the mass of H^3, sometimes called *tritium,* can be determined very accurately. This is at present the most accurate method for determining the mass of H^3, and the value given in Appendix IV has been calculated in this way.

The dependence of the cross section for the production of tritium, H^3, in the $H^2(d,p)H^3$ reaction, on the energy of the incident deuteron has recently been determined by Cook and Smith (1953) by bombarding a thin target of deuterium absorbed in zirconium films with deuterons of comparatively low energy, 50 to 100 kev. The results showed a linear dependence of total cross section on deuteron energy.

Hydrogen of mass number $A = 3$ is unstable. O'Neal and Goldhaber showed that it disintegrates with the emission of a beta particle as follows:

$$_1H^3 \rightarrow {_2He^3} + \beta^-, \qquad T = 12.5 \text{ yr.} \quad (27)$$

The beta rays emitted by this radioactive isotope of hydrogen have a maximum kinetic energy of only 18 kev.

The energy of the neutrons formed in the bombardment of deuterium by deuterons has been investigated by observing the recoil tracks of the atoms of the gas in a cloud chamber. It was observed that the neutrons were practically homogeneous in energy. Recent measurements show that the energy of the neutrons emitted at right angles to the direction of motion of the deuterons is 2.38 Mev plus one quarter of the deuteron energy. This reaction forms a very convenient source of neutrons of known energy. Furthermore, neutrons have been observed for comparatively low values of incident deuteron energies, that is, of the order of 6 kev. The neutron yield increases rapidly with the deuteron energy. The value of the reaction energy has been found to be $Q = 3.18$ Mev, and with this value of Q the mass of He^3 can be determined.

Some of the nuclear reactions produced by the capture of a deuteron by lithium which have been observed are as follows:

$$
\begin{aligned}
&{}_3\mathrm{Li}^6 + {}_1\mathrm{H}^2 \rightarrow ({}_4\mathrm{Be}^8) \rightarrow {}_2\mathrm{He}^4 + {}_2\mathrm{He}^4, \qquad Q = 22.23 \text{ Mev.}\\
&{}_3\mathrm{Li}^6 + {}_1\mathrm{H}^2 \rightarrow ({}_4\mathrm{Be}^8) \rightarrow {}_3\mathrm{Li}^7 + {}_1\mathrm{H}^1\\
&{}_3\mathrm{Li}^7 + {}_1\mathrm{H}^2 \rightarrow ({}_4\mathrm{Be}^9) \rightarrow {}_2\mathrm{He}^4 + {}_2\mathrm{He}^4 + {}_0n^1\\
&{}_3\mathrm{Li}^7 + {}_1\mathrm{H}^2 \rightarrow ({}_4\mathrm{Be}^9) \rightarrow {}_3\mathrm{Li}^8 + {}_1\mathrm{H}^1,
\end{aligned}
\tag{28}
$$

followed by $\quad {}_3\mathrm{Li}^8 \rightarrow {}_4\mathrm{Be}^8 + \beta^-, \qquad T = 0.88$ sec.

The lithium isotope of mass number 8 is radioactive and disintegrates with the emission of a beta particle. The beta rays liberated in the disintegration of Li^8 have a continuous energy distribution up to a maximum;

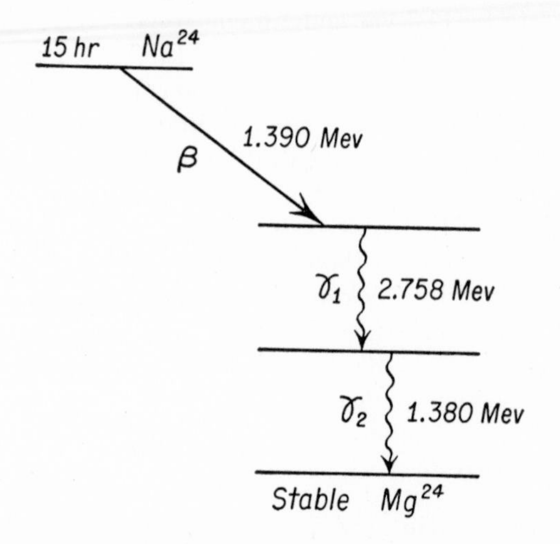

FIG. 11-10. Energy level diagram of the beta decay of Na^{24} to an excited state of Mg^{24}. The latter decays to the stable ground state of Mg^{24} by emitting two gamma-ray photons in cascade.

the end point is about 12 Mev. The Be^8 nucleus formed in this reaction is unstable and breaks up into two alpha particles.

In the case of carbon bombarded by deuterons, two reactions have been observed:

$$
\begin{aligned}
&{}_6\mathrm{C}^{12} + {}_1\mathrm{H}^2 \rightarrow ({}_7\mathrm{N}^{14}) \rightarrow {}_6\mathrm{C}^{13} + {}_1\mathrm{H}^1\\
&{}_6\mathrm{C}^{12} + {}_1\mathrm{H}^2 \rightarrow ({}_7\mathrm{N}^{14}) \rightarrow {}_7\mathrm{N}^{13} + {}_0n^1,
\end{aligned}
\tag{29}
$$

followed by $\quad {}_7\mathrm{N}^{13} \rightarrow {}_6\mathrm{C}^{13} + \beta^+.$

The half-life of the radionitrogen formed in this reaction is identical with that observed in the reaction produced by the capture of an alpha particle by boron. The positron spectrum shows a continuous range of energies. The maximum value of the positron energy in this case is 1.24 Mev.

Reactions with deuterons as projectiles have led to *d-p*, *d-n*, and *d-α* processes with elements throughout the periodic table. Of some interest is the disintegration of sodium by deuteron bombardment. The following two reactions have been observed:

$$
\begin{aligned}
&{}_{11}\mathrm{Na}^{23} + {}_{1}\mathrm{H}^{2} \rightarrow ({}_{12}\mathrm{Mg}^{25}) \rightarrow {}_{12}\mathrm{Mg}^{24} + {}_{0}n^{1} \\
&{}_{11}\mathrm{Na}^{23} + {}_{1}\mathrm{H}^{2} \rightarrow ({}_{12}\mathrm{Mg}^{25}) \rightarrow {}_{11}\mathrm{Na}^{24} + {}_{1}\mathrm{H}^{1},
\end{aligned}
\tag{30}
$$

followed by

$$
{}_{11}\mathrm{Na}^{24} \rightarrow {}_{12}\mathrm{Mg}^{24} + \beta^{-}, \qquad T = 15.0 \text{ hrs.}
$$

The magnesium formed in the *d-n* reaction is left in a stable state. The magnesium formed in the decay of the radioactive sodium is left in an excited state and decays to the ground state by emitting two gamma-ray photons in cascade as shown in Figure 11-10.

Radioactive sodium has been used as a "tracer" in many physiological experiments.

The gamma-ray spectrum emitted by the disintegration of Na^{24} has been investigated by R. Hofstadter and J. A. McIntyre (1950) with a scintillation counter utilizing a thallium activated sodium iodide crystal, NaI (Tl). A narrow beam of gamma rays from a sample of Na^{24} (about 1 millicurie) traveled through the middle of the crystal. In Figure 11-11, the number of counts per minute of the scintillations produced by the gamma rays is plotted against the pulse height in volts. The origin of each line on the graph is indicated thereon. When gamma rays traverse matter they eject electrons from it either by a Compton process or by a photoelectric process. The electrons thus ejected give up some of their energy to produce visible light, or scintillations, within the crystal. The lines on the graph marked "Compton" are produced by scintillations which have their origin in the Compton electrons; the lines marked "Photoelectric" have their origin in the scintillations produced by the action of the photoelectrons. In addition, if the energy of the gamma-ray photons exceeds $2m_ec^2$, where m_e is the rest mass of the electron, the gamma-ray photon may, in the presence of a strong electric field, disintegrate into an electron and a positron (see §14-3). The sum of the kinetic energies of this pair is $h\nu - 2m_ec^2$ where $h\nu$ is the energy of the gamma-ray photon. The line marked "Pairs due to 2.76 Mev" is due to scintillations produced by the electron-positron pairs formed by the disintegration of 2.76 Mev photons.

The energy to be assigned to each of the lines obtained with the scintillation spectrometer is determined by calibrating it with gamma-ray photons of known energy. In this case Hofstadter and McIntyre used the 1.17 Mev and 1.33 Mev gamma-ray photons of Co^{60} for calibration purposes; these are shown in the insert on the graph. The lines obtained with the scintillation spectrometer are ascribed to two gamma-ray photons from Na^{24}, one of 1.38 Mev, and the other of 2.76 Mev.

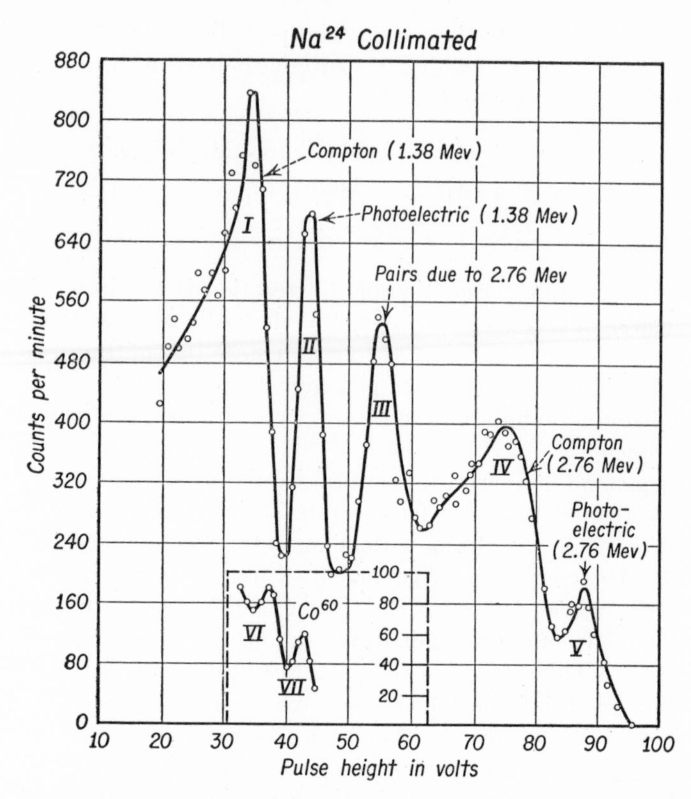

FIG. 11-11. Graph of the gamma-ray spectrum of Na^{24} taken with a NaI scintillation spectrometer. The peaks are due to the two gamma-ray photons of 1.38 Mev and 2.76 Mev. The Co^{60} curve was used for calibrating the spectrometer. (Courtesy of R. Hofstadter and J. A. McIntyre.)

11-12. Disintegration of Nuclei by Photons

Atomic nuclei have been disintegrated by high energy photons. In most cases this process of *photodisintegration* results in the emission of neutrons by the nuclei which have been raised to excited states by the absorption of these photons. In the early experiments, high energy gamma-ray photons were used, but with the development of the betatron, x-ray photons of sufficiently high energy have become available for these experiments. Of very great interest is the disintegration of the deuteron, the lightest of the complex nuclei, by the action of the gamma rays. This nuclear reaction is

$$ {}_1H^2 + h\nu \rightarrow ({}_1H^2) \rightarrow {}_1H^1 + {}_0n^1. \tag{31} $$

According to our present view of the structure of the nucleus, the deuteron consists of a proton and a neutron held together by some force of attraction. A measurement of the minimum amount of energy necessary to disrupt the deuteron would also give the binding energy of the proton and neutron in the nucleus. Chadwick and Goldhaber, who discovered the above reaction, used gamma rays from ThC″, and measured the energy of the protons liberated by the amount of ionization they produced. The energy of the gamma-ray photon is known to be 2.62 Mev. If the energies of the neutron and proton released in this reaction are subtracted from this, the result should be the binding energy of these particles. Since the neutron and proton have nearly equal masses, when the deuteron disintegrates, the two particles will have approximately equal energies. Hence the energies of the two particles can be obtained by merely doubling the measured value of the proton energy. They obtained a value of 0.45 Mev for the total kinetic energy of the final particles yielding a binding energy of 2.17 Mev. More recent experiments yield a value of 2.226 Mev for the deuteron binding energy.

Since the masses of the proton and deuteron are known very accurately from measurements with the mass spectrograph, the photodisintegration of the deuteron affords the most accurate means of determining the mass of the neutron. The value so determined is 1.008987.

To produce the photodisintegration of the heavier nuclei, the energy of the incident photon must exceed the binding energy of the particle to be ejected. In many cases in which photodisintegration results in the emission of a neutron, the product nucleus is radioactive; the reaction can then be studied by observing this radioactivity and determining its half-life. The particular isotope involved in this photodisintegration can then more readily be identified. Baldwin and Koch (1945) performed such experiments using the high energy x-ray photons emitted from the betatron. By varying the energy of the x-ray photons used in irradiating the samples of material, they were able to determine the minimum amount of energy, that is, the *threshold* for the photodisintegration of several different nuclei in the range of atomic numbers $Z = 6$ to $Z = 47$. In each case the effect produced by the photodisintegration was measured by the intensity of the beta rays emitted by the irradiated sample. Figure 11-12 shows a typical curve obtained by irradiating flat plates of iron, 10 cm $\times$ 8 cm $\times$ 1 cm, with x-rays for ten minutes, and then placing the iron plate near a counter sensitive to beta rays. From the curve, the threshold of iron, $A = 53$, is found to be 14.2 Mev.

The γ-n reaction has since been studied very extensively, and threshold values have been determined for a very large number of nuclei. Sher, Halpern, and Mann determined the thresholds of many γ-n reactions by detecting the emitted neutrons with a boron trifluoride-filled proportional counter. Just as the γ-n reaction with deuterium gave the binding energy of the neutron to the proton, so the threshold value of the γ-n reaction with any isotope of mass number A will give the binding energy of the neutron in the nucleus of the isotope of mass number $A - 1$. We shall consider the threshold values again in our discussion of the structure of the nucleus (§12-4).

In addition to the γ-n reactions other reactions have been observed in the photodisintegration of nuclei. Among these are the γ-p reaction in

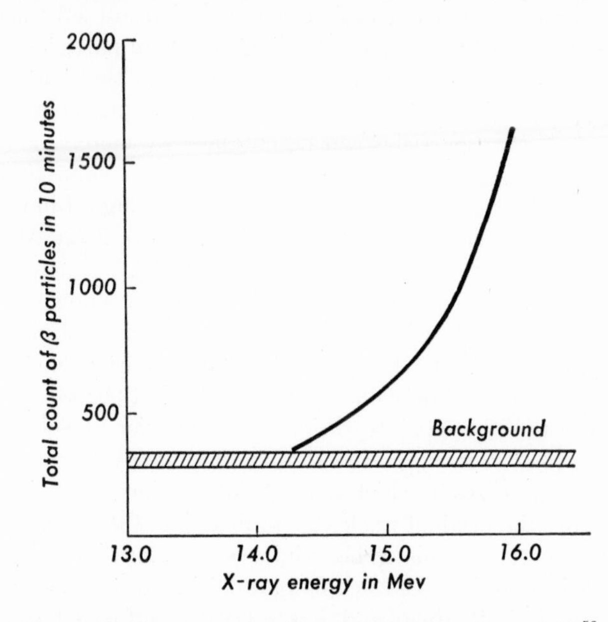

Fig. 11-12. Excitation curve for the photodisintegration of Fe^{53} showing the threshold at 14.2 Mev.

which a proton is emitted, the γ-d reaction in which a deuteron is emitted, and the γ-t reaction, in which *triton*, the nucleus of ${}_1H^3$, and the γ-α reaction in which an alpha particle is emitted. The following are typical of the above nuclear photodisintegrations:

$$\begin{aligned} &Be^9(\gamma,p)Li^8 \\ &B^{10}(\gamma,d)Be^8 \\ &B^{11}(\gamma,t)Be^8 \\ &C^{12}(\gamma,\alpha)Be^8. \end{aligned} \tag{32}$$

The above reactions may be considered as the reverse of the capture gamma processes mentioned previously. The last three photodisintegrations show that different nuclear reactions can be used to produce a given nucleus, in this case Be^8.

11-13. Disintegration by Neutron Bombardment

Neutrons, because they possess no electric charge, have proved to be very effective in penetrating the positively charged nuclei, thereby producing nuclear transformations. Not only are high energy neutrons capable of penetrating the nucleus, but comparatively *slow* neutrons have also been found to be extremely effective. A great deal of work has been done with slow neutrons, and the information so obtained is the basis of the nuclear model proposed by Bohr. The simplest method of obtaining slow neutrons is to allow the fast neutrons from some source, such as the alpha-particle–beryllium reaction, to pass through some hydrogen-containing substance such as paraffin or water. A neutron gives up a large fraction of its energy in a collision with a hydrogen nucleus, and after many collisions it will come to thermal equilibrium with the material; that is, its average energy will be equal to the energy of thermal agitation, which is equivalent to $\frac{1}{40}$ electron volt at room temperature. In one type of reaction, n-α, the capture of a slow neutron results in the emission of an alpha particle. Two such cases which have been studied extensively are

$$\begin{aligned} {}_3\mathrm{Li}^6 + {}_0n^1 &\rightarrow ({}_3\mathrm{Li}^7) \rightarrow {}_1\mathrm{H}^3 + {}_2\mathrm{He}^4 \\ {}_5\mathrm{B}^{10} + {}_0n^1 &\rightarrow ({}_5\mathrm{B}^{11}) \rightarrow {}_3\mathrm{Li}^7 + {}_2\mathrm{He}^4. \end{aligned} \tag{33}$$

The n-α reaction with boron is widely used as a sensitive detector of neutrons, particularly in ionization chamber work. In some cases, the ionization chamber is lined with a boron compound; more frequently, the ionization chamber is filled with a boron gas such as BF_3, boron trifluoride. The ionization in the chamber is produced by the alpha particle released in the n-α reaction with boron.

Neutron-induced nuclear disintegrations can also be studied with a cloud chamber. A. B. Lillie (1952) investigated the disintegration of oxygen and nitrogen by 14 Mev neutrons obtained from the $\mathrm{H}^3(d,n)\mathrm{He}^4$ reaction. The deuterons had an energy of 200 kev, and a monoenergetic beam of neutrons was obtained at an angle of 90° to the deuteron beam. The neutrons entered a cloud chamber filled with oxygen or nitrogen at a pressure of one atmosphere and containing water vapor. Figure 11-13 is a stereoscopic photograph showing the disintegrations produced with oxygen in the chamber. The forked tracks are produced by the products of the reaction $\mathrm{O}^{16}(n,\alpha)\mathrm{C}^{13}$. The neutron paths are not visible, since neutrons are non-ionizing particles. The alpha-particle track is the longer one, and the track of the product nucleus C^{13} is the shorter one. Figure 11-14 is an interesting photograph showing several different processes taking place when nitrogen is used in the cloud chamber. There is a typical forked track produced by the $\mathrm{N}^{14}(n,\alpha)\mathrm{B}^{11}$ reaction. In addition there are two examples of the disintegration of the compound nucleus (N^{15}) into three

FIG. 11-13. Stereoscopic photographs of disintegrations produced by bombarding oxygen in a cloud chamber with high energy neutrons. Neutrons enter from the top of the picture. The forked tracks are produced by alpha particles (longer track), and C^{13} ions (shorter track). (Photograph by Lillie, *Phys. Rev.*, 87, 716, 1952.)

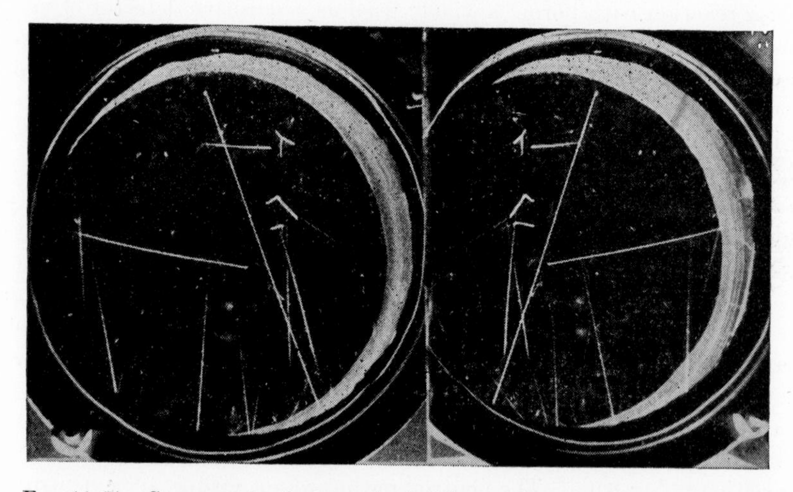

FIG. 11-14. Stereoscopic photograph of disintegrations produced by bombarding nitrogen in a cloud chamber with high energy neutrons. The neutrons enter from the top of the picture. In addition to a forked track, there are two cases of a three-particle disintegration. There is also a disintegration in which a hydrogen nucleus, either p, d, or t, is emitted; this is the long track which crosses the chamber and leaves. (Photograph by Lillie, *Phys. Rev.*, 87, 716, 1952.)

particles, two of which are alpha particles. This reaction equation is

$$_{7}N^{14} + {}_{0}n^{1} \rightarrow ({}_{7}N^{15}) \rightarrow {}_{3}Li^{7} + {}_{2}He^{4} + {}_{2}He^{4}. \quad (34)$$

When fast neutrons are captured by heavier nuclei resulting in the emission of an alpha particle, the product nucleus is usually radioactive. Some typical reactions are

$$_{11}Na^{23} + {}_{0}n^{1} \rightarrow ({}_{11}Na^{24}) \rightarrow {}_{9}F^{20} + {}_{2}He^{4},$$

followed by

$$_{9}F^{20} \rightarrow {}_{10}Ne^{20} + \beta^{-}, \quad T = 12 \text{ sec.}$$

$$_{13}Al^{27} + {}_{0}n^{1} \rightarrow ({}_{13}Al^{28}) \rightarrow {}_{11}Na^{24} + {}_{2}He^{4}, \quad (35)$$

followed by

$$_{11}Na^{24} \rightarrow {}_{12}Mg^{24} + \beta^{-}, \quad T = 15.0 \text{ hr.}$$

The capture of a neutron may sometimes result in the emission of a proton by the compound nucleus. This *n-p* process has been observed with slow neutrons in the case of nitrogen in the reaction

$$_{7}N^{14} + {}_{0}n^{1} \rightarrow ({}_{7}N^{15}) \rightarrow {}_{6}C^{14} + {}_{1}H^{1}, \quad (36)$$

followed by

$$_{6}C^{14} \rightarrow {}_{7}N^{14} + \beta^{-}, \quad T = 5580 \text{ yr.}$$

The other *n-p* reactions performed with fast neutrons, have usually resulted in the production of nuclei which are radioactive, emitting β^{-}-particles. Some typical reactions are

$$_{16}S^{32} + {}_{0}n^{1} \rightarrow ({}_{16}S^{33}) \rightarrow {}_{15}P^{32} + {}_{1}H^{1},$$

followed by

$$_{15}P^{32} \rightarrow {}_{16}S^{32} + \beta^{-}, \quad T = 14.59 \text{ da.}$$

$$_{29}Cu^{65} + {}_{0}n^{1} \rightarrow ({}_{29}Cu^{66}) \rightarrow {}_{28}Ni^{65} + {}_{1}H^{1}, \quad (37)$$

followed by

$$_{28}Ni^{65} \rightarrow {}_{29}Cu^{65} + \beta^{-}, \quad T = 2.56 \text{ hr.}$$

The above *n-p* type of reaction has several interesting consequences. It will be noticed that the bombarded nucleus and the final stable nucleus are identical, while the incident neutron has been transformed, apparently, into a proton and an electron. If the mass of the intermediate radioactive nucleus, for example, P^{32}, is equal to the mass of the initial nucleus, S^{32}, then the energy available for the radioactive disintegration must come from the mass difference between a neutron and a hydrogen atom plus the initial energy of the neutrons. If slow neutrons are used as bombarding particles, the energy available is equivalent to 0.000842 amu or 0.784 Mev. Now the end-point energy of the beta-ray spectrum is equal to the disintegration energy, and if this end-point energy is less than 0.784 Mev, then slow neutrons will be effective in producing the above reaction. But if the end-point energy exceeds 0.784 Mev, the additional energy must come from the kinetic energy of the incident neutrons; hence only fast neutrons can then be effective in producing this reaction. For example, the end-point energy of the beta-ray spectrum from P^{32} is 1.70 Mev; hence only fast neutrons bombarding S^{32} will be effective in producing this reaction. This reaction can then also be used to differentiate between slow and fast neutrons.

Another interesting conclusion is that if the mass of the nucleus formed in an n-p reaction exceeds the mass of the bombarded nucleus by more than 0.000842 amu, then only fast neutrons will be effective in producing this reaction.

Sometimes the capture of a neutron is not accompanied by the emission of a particle, but by the emission of a gamma-ray photon. In this case the compound nucleus is evidently raised to one of its excited states as the result of this capture, and then returns to its normal state with the emission of a gamma-ray photon. Such gamma rays have been observed coming from the paraffin used to slow down neutrons. The ultimate capture of some of the slow neutrons by the hydrogen nuclei in the paraffin yields the reaction

$${}_1\mathrm{H}^1 + {}_0n^1 \rightarrow ({}_1\mathrm{H}^2) \rightarrow {}_1\mathrm{H}^2 + h\nu. \tag{38}$$

This process is just the reverse of the photodisintegration of the deuteron discussed in the previous section.

A measurement of the energy of the gamma-ray photon emitted in an n-γ reaction with a nucleus of mass number A will yield the binding energy of the neutron in the nucleus of mass number $A + 1$. The results so obtained can be used as a check on the binding energies obtained in the γ-n reactions. Of great importance for nuclear theory is the binding energy of the neutron and proton. Bell and Elliott (1950) recently performed an experiment for the determination of this binding energy, using the thermal neutrons from the Chalk River nuclear reactor. The neutrons were allowed to strike a block of paraffin, and the energy of the capture gamma rays was measured by means of the photoelectric effect they produced in a thin sheet of uranium. The energies of the photoelectrons thus produced were measured in a magnetic-lens beta-ray spectrometer, using a Geiger counter to detect the electrons. The spectrometer was calibrated by using the ThC$''$ γ-ray line of 2.615 Mev and measuring the photoelectrons produced by it. The K photoelectrons gave a very sharp peak, making precise measurements possible. The value of the K ionization energy of uranium was taken as 116 kev. Using the above data Bell and Elliott obtained a value of 2.230 Mev for the binding energy of a neutron and a proton in a deuteron.

The n-γ reaction has been observed with a great many elements, particularly the heavier ones. In most cases, the isotopes formed by the capture of a neutron have been found to be radioactive. A few typical cases are

$$
\begin{aligned}
&{}_{29}\mathrm{Cu}^{65} + {}_{0}n^{1} \rightarrow ({}_{29}\mathrm{Cu}^{66}) \rightarrow {}_{29}\mathrm{Cu}^{66} + h\nu, \\
\text{followed by} \quad &{}_{29}\mathrm{Cu}^{66} \rightarrow {}_{30}\mathrm{Zn}^{66} + \beta^{-}, \quad T = 4.34 \text{ min.} \\
&{}_{79}\mathrm{Au}^{197} + {}_{0}n^{1} \rightarrow ({}_{79}\mathrm{Au}^{198}) \rightarrow {}_{79}\mathrm{Au}^{198} + h\nu, \\
\text{followed by} \quad &{}_{79}\mathrm{Au}^{198} \rightarrow {}_{80}\mathrm{Hg}^{198} + \beta^{-}, \quad T = 2.7 \text{ days.}
\end{aligned}
\tag{39}
$$

There are many cases in which the capture of a fast neutron has resulted in the emission of two neutrons by the compound nucleus. In most cases the product nucleus is unstable. A few such cases follow:

$$
\begin{aligned}
&{}_{19}\mathrm{K}^{39} + {}_{0}n^{1} \rightarrow ({}_{19}\mathrm{K}^{40}) \rightarrow {}_{19}\mathrm{K}^{38} + {}_{0}n^{1} + {}_{0}n^{1}, \\
\text{followed by} \quad &{}_{19}\mathrm{K}^{38} \rightarrow {}_{18}\mathrm{A}^{38} + \beta^{+}, \quad T = 7.5 \text{ min.} \\
&{}_{51}\mathrm{Sb}^{121} + {}_{0}n^{1} \rightarrow ({}_{51}\mathrm{Sb}^{122}) \rightarrow {}_{51}\mathrm{Sb}^{120} + {}_{0}n^{1} + {}_{0}n^{1}, \\
\text{followed by} \quad &{}_{51}\mathrm{Sb}^{120} \rightarrow {}_{50}\mathrm{Sn}^{120} + \beta^{+}, \quad T = 16.6 \text{ min.}
\end{aligned}
\tag{40}
$$

The ability to produce a radioactive isotope of almost any element has made a new tool available to the chemist, biologist, and physiologist for the detailed study of various processes. By introducing the radioactive isotope along with the nonradioactive isotopes of an element, the progress of this element can be traced in the process under investigation by means of the beta rays emitted by the radioactive isotope. In many cases a choice of several different half-lives is available to suit the needs of the particular experiment. A great deal of work has already been done with the radioactive isotopes of carbon, sodium, iron, phosphorus, and iodine used as *tracers* in various processes.

11-14. Radioactive Disintegration of the Neutron

Shortly after the discovery of the neutron by Chadwick, the first accurate determination of its mass by Chadwick and Goldhaber showed that its mass was greater than that of a proton. This led them to suggest that a neutron should be unstable and should decay radioactively into a proton, an electron, and a neutrino. The Fermi theory of beta decay indicated that its half-life should be of the order of 30 minutes. Early experiments to find this radioactivity were unsuccessful primarily because of the unavailability of a sufficiently intense source of neutrons. With the development of nuclear reactors, intense sources of neutrons became available.

A. H. Snell and his co-workers (1948), using the neutrons from the Oak Ridge pile, were able to detect protons coming out laterally from a beam of thermal neutrons. They were later able to show the presence of electrons which were emitted simultaneously with the protons and estimated the half-life as between 10 and 30 minutes. J. M. Robson (1951), using the much more intense source of neutrons available from the Chalk River pile, made a more accurate determination of the half-life of the radioactive disintegration of the neutron and determined its beta-ray spectrum.

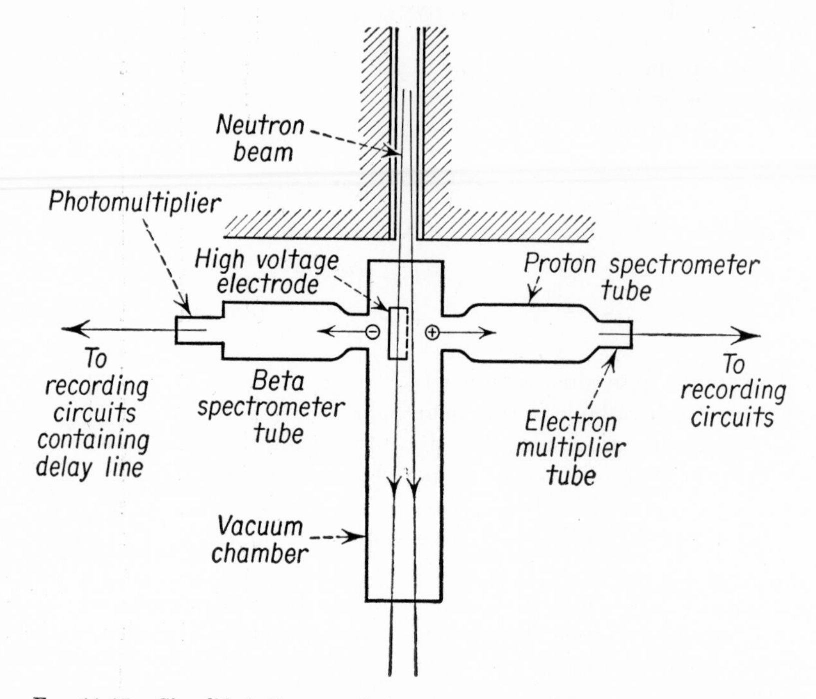

FIG. 11-15. Simplified diagram of the apparatus used by J. M. Robson to show the radioactive decay of the neutron.

The apparatus used by Robson is sketched in Figure 11-15. A collimated beam of thermal neutrons from the reactor enters a vacuum chamber. The neutron beam was about 1.2 inches in diameter and had an intensity of about 1.5×10^{10} thermal neutrons per second. Some of the neutrons decayed in their flight through the vacuum chamber. The protons released in this decay were deflected out of the neutron beam by means of an electrostatic field into a magnetic-lens spectrometer and detected with an electron multiplier tube. The beta rays emitted during this disintegration were deflected to the left into a beta-ray magnetic-lens spectrometer and were detected with a scintillation counter using anthracene crystals as the phosphor. The two detectors, one for protons and one for beta rays, were connected to a coincidence circuit which would register only when pulses from the two detectors arrived there simultaneously. However, owing to its greater mass, the proton would move more slowly through its spectrometer system and would be delayed with respect to the electrons; calculations gave this delay as about 0.9 microsecond. A delay line was built into the beta-ray detecting system which would delay the beta-ray pulses by 0.9 microsecond. Figure 11-16 shows the graph of the coincidence rate between the beta particles and protons plotted against the energy of the beta particles; the values of the latter were determined with the beta-ray spectrometer. The distribution in momentum of the beta rays is shown in Figure 11-17. The end-point energy of this spectrum is found to be 785 kev;

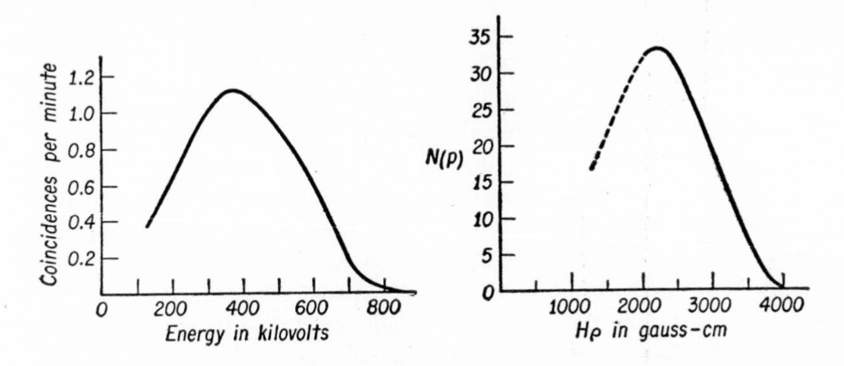

Fig. 11-16. Graph showing the coincidence rate between beta particles and protons resulting from the neutron decay, plotted against beta-particle energy. (After Robson, *Phys. Rev.*, 83, 352, 1951.)

Fig. 11-17. Momentum spectrum of the beta particles emitted in neutron decay. Below $H\rho = 2000$ gauss cm the curve is unreliable because of instrumental effects. (After Robson, *Phys. Rev.*, 83, 352, 1951.)

the results of the coincidence curve are in agreement with this end-point energy. This value of the end-point energy is in excellent agreement with the mass difference of 784 kev between a neutron and a proton.

The value of the half-life of the neutron was calculated from a determination of the density of the neutron beam and the number of neutrons decaying per unit time per unit volume. The neutron density was determined by inserting manganese foils in the beam and measuring their activities against the activities of standard manganese foils of identical thickness which had previously been calibrated. The value so obtained was 1.16×10^4 neutrons per cm^3 at the center of the beam. The number of neutrons decaying per unit time per unit volume was estimated from the number of protons per unit time striking the first electrode of the electron multiplier and the volume of the beam where the protons originate. The value so determined was 630 neutrons per minute per cm^3 of the neutron beam. The half-life T obtained from these values is

$$T = \frac{1.16 \times 10^4}{630} \times 0.693 = 12.8 \text{ min.}$$

The probable error in this value given by Robson is 18 per cent.

11-15. Electron Capture by Nuclei

In nuclear reactions, the extranuclear electrons may usually be ignored, except in a few special cases. For example, we saw that the sharp line beta-ray spectrum was due to the internal conversion of the gamma-ray photons and provided a method for measuring the energy of these photons. In the case of β^+-decay we found (§11-7) that, in addition to the positron emitted by the nucleus, an electron must be emitted from the external part of the atom in order that the product atom be neutral, thus involving the release of a minimum amount of energy equal to $2m_ec^2$ or about 1 Mev. There is, however, an alternative method to β^+-decay in which a given parent atom forms the same product atom, and that is by the *capture* of one of the external electrons by the nucleus. This process of decay is known as *electron capture*. Usually a K electron will be the one that is captured by the nucleus, although one of the others may be captured instead; hence this process is sometimes designated simply as *K capture.*

The capture of the K electron by the nucleus will leave the product atom in an excited state with one electron missing from the K shell; it will then return to the normal state by the emission of x-rays characteristic of the product atom. This type of nuclear reaction is often detected by means of the x-rays emitted during this process.

Probably the most clear-cut example of K-electron capture is the radioactive disintegration of vanadium, ${}_{23}V^{49}$, into titanium, ${}_{22}Ti^{49}$, with the capture of a K electron by the vanadium nucleus to form a titanium atom in the K state. This reaction was investigated carefully by Walke, Williams, and Evans, who found that vanadium decays only by K-electron capture with a half-life $T = 600$ days. The radioactive vanadium was formed by bombarding titanium with deuterons, the following reactions taking place:

$$\begin{aligned} &{}_{22}Ti^{48} + {}_1H^2 \rightarrow ({}_{23}V^{50}) \rightarrow {}_{23}V^{49} + {}_0n^1 \\ \text{then} \quad &{}_{23}V^{49} + {}_{-1}e^0 \rightarrow {}_{22}Ti^{49}, \quad T = 600 \text{ da.} \end{aligned} \tag{41}$$

The active product was separated chemically from the titanium and found to be vanadium, but no radiations of any kind other than Ti $K\alpha$ radiation were found to be emitted by the vanadium precipitate. The only conclusion, therefore, is that the excited vanadium nucleus captured one of its K electrons to form titanium with one electron missing from its K shell with the subsequent emission of x-rays characteristic of titanium. Furthermore, the intensity of these x-rays diminishes exponentially with the time, so that at the end of 600 days, the intensity has dropped to half its original value.

The fact that no radiation other than x-rays is emitted in the radioactive disintegration of vanadium by K-electron capture to titanium indicates that the product titanium nucleus is in the ground state or state of lowest energy. Since the capture of an electron by the nucleus results in the change of a proton into a neutron, this must be accompanied by the emission of a neutrino in order to conserve the angular momentum of the nucleus.

In many cases of radioactive disintegration by K-electron capture, gamma rays are emitted; in other cases the disintegration can take place either by positron emission or by K-electron capture, so that both processes are observed in the same radioactive sample. For example, the isotope of beryllium of mass number $A = 7$, which disintegrates by K-electron capture, also emits gamma rays of 0.480 Mev. The reaction is

$$\begin{aligned} {}_4\mathrm{Be}^7 + {}_{-1}e^0 &\rightarrow ({}_3\mathrm{Li}^7) \\ ({}_3\mathrm{Li}^7) &\rightarrow {}_3\mathrm{Li}^7 + h\nu, \quad T = 54.5 \text{ da.} \end{aligned} \tag{42}$$

This radioactive beryllium isotope can be produced by any of the following reactions:

$$\begin{aligned} {}_3\mathrm{Li}^7 + {}_1\mathrm{H}^1 &\rightarrow ({}_4\mathrm{Be}^8) \rightarrow {}_4\mathrm{Be}^7 + {}_0n^1 \\ {}_3\mathrm{Li}^6 + {}_1\mathrm{H}^2 &\rightarrow ({}_4\mathrm{Be}^8) \rightarrow {}_4\mathrm{Be}^7 + {}_0n^1 \\ {}_5\mathrm{B}^{10} + {}_1\mathrm{H}^1 &\rightarrow ({}_6\mathrm{C}^{11}) \rightarrow {}_4\mathrm{Be}^7 + {}_2\mathrm{He}^4. \end{aligned} \tag{43}$$

The nuclear energy level diagram illustrating the decay of Be^7 by K-electron capture is shown in Figure 11-18. In 89 per cent of the cases, the decay is to the ground state of Li^7, but in 11 per cent of the cases the decay is to an excited state from which the Li^7 nucleus goes to the ground state by emitting a gamma-ray photon of 0.480 Mev energy. The energy released in the K-capture process in which the Li^7 nucleus is formed in the ground state is 0.864 Mev. This value has been determined from the disintegration energy or Q value of the Li^7 (p,n) Be^7 reaction which is 1.646 Mev, and the energy equivalent of the neutron-proton mass difference of 0.784 Mev. The energy equivalent of the Be^7-Li^7 mass difference is thus 0.862 Mev; since this is less than the minimum energy required for positron decay, the Be^7 nucleus can decay only by K-electron capture. Its half-life is 54.5 days.

One of the many examples in which both positron emission and K capture has been observed is found in the disintegration of Cd^{107}. This isotope of cadmium can be formed by any one of the following reactions:

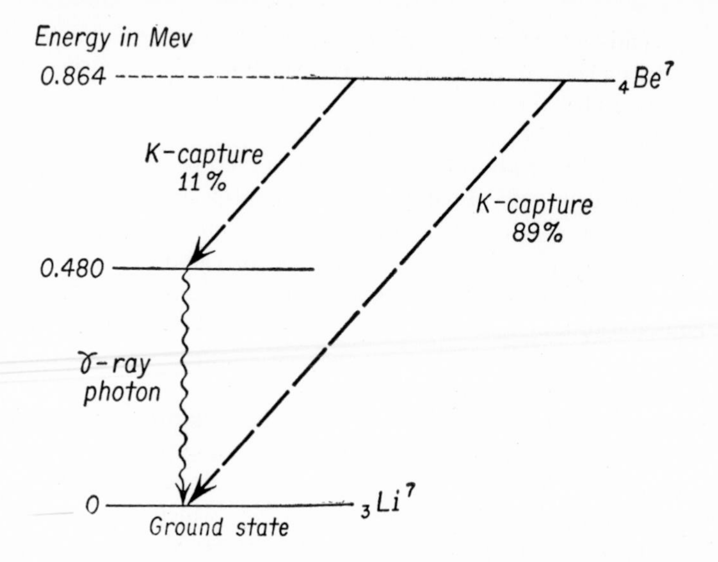

FIG. 11-18. Nuclear energy level diagram showing decay of Be^7 by K-electron capture.

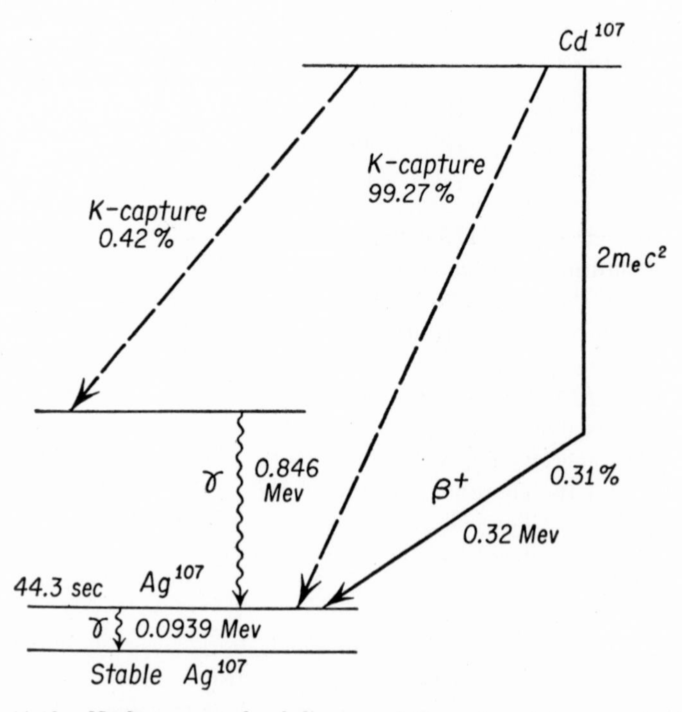

FIG. 11-19. Nuclear energy level diagram of the modes of decay of Cd^{107} to an isomeric state of Ag^{107}. (After *Nuclear Data*, National Bureau of Standards, Circular 499.)

$Cd^{106}(n,\gamma)$ Cd^{107}, $Ag^{107}(d,2n)$ Cd^{107}, and $Ag^{107}(p,n)$ Cd^{107}. The disintegration is given by either of the following equations

$$_{48}Cd^{107} \rightarrow {}_{47}Ag^{107} + \beta^+$$

or

$$_{48}Cd^{107} + {}_{-1}e^0 \rightarrow {}_{47}Ag^{107}, \quad T = 6.7 \text{ hr.} \tag{44}$$

As shown in Figure 11-19, the greatest probability is for a transition by K capture to an excited state of Ag^{107}, the latter then decaying to the ground state by the emission of a gamma-ray photon of 0.0939 Mev. A process with much smaller probability is K capture leading to a higher excited state of silver followed by the emission of a gamma-ray photon of 0.846 Mev leading to the lower excited state of silver mentioned above. The smallest probability is the emission of a positron by Cd^{107} leading to the lower excited state of Ag^{107}. The maximum kinetic energy of the positron is 0.32 Mev; hence the disintegration energy is $2m_ec^2 + 0.32$ Mev or about 1.33 Mev.

Another interesting feature of this particular decay is that the silver nucleus formed can exist in the lower excited state for a measurable time before going to the stable ground state with the emission of a gamma-ray photon of 0.0939 Mev of energy. Ag^{107} in this excited state behaves as a radioactive nucleus decaying to the ground state with a half-life of 44.3 seconds. A nucleus which can exist in an excited state for a measurable length of time is called an *isomer*, and this particular excited state is often referred to as an *isomeric state*. We shall discuss nuclear isomers in greater detail in §12-9.

Problems

11-1. A particle of mass M moving initially with velocity V makes an elastic collision with a particle of mass m initially at rest. Using the principles of the conservation of energy and momentum, show that if the particle of mass m is given a velocity v in the same direction as V, then

$$v = \frac{2M}{M + m} V.$$

11-2. A particle of mass M_1, kinetic energy E_1, velocity V_1, and momentum P_1 is captured by a nucleus (M_0, E_0, V_0, P_0) at rest. A light particle (M_2, E_2, V_2, P_2) is ejected and the heavy particle (M_3, E_3, V_3, P_3) recoils. Using the principles of conservation of energy and momentum, show that when the light particle is emitted at an angle of 90° with the path of the incident particle, the energy of the light particle is

$$E_2 = \frac{M_3}{M_2 + M_3}\left(Q - \frac{M_1 - M_3}{M_3} E_1\right)$$

where Q is the energy equivalent of the difference in mass between the initial particles and the final particles.

11-3. A beam of 0.40 Mev deuterons is directed against a deuterium target. Calculate the energy of the neutrons emitted at 90° with respect to the incident beam; use the atomic mass data of Appendix IV.

11-4. Using the equation derived in problem 11-2, calculate the energy of the neutrons emitted at an angle of 90° to the deuteron beam in an $H^3(d, n)He^4$ reaction. The kinetic energy of the deuterons is 200 kev.

Ans. 14.1 Mev.

11-5. When ${}_5B^{11}$ is bombarded with 200 kev protons, alpha particles of 4.41 cm range in air are emitted at right angles to the path of the incident beam. Using the result of problem 11-2, determine the mass of the residual ${}_4Be^8$ nucleus.

Ans. 8.00794.

11-6. In the reaction

$$ {}_7N^{14} + {}_0n^1 \rightarrow ({}_7N^{15}) \rightarrow {}_6C^{14} + {}_1H^1 + Q $$

Q is 0.55 Mev. Assuming all the other atomic masses known, calculate the mass of ${}_6C^{14}$.

11-7. When lithium is bombarded with protons, the following reaction occurs:

$$ {}_3Li^6 + {}_1H^1 \rightarrow ({}_4Be^7) \rightarrow {}_2He^4 + {}_2He^3 + Q. $$

The measured value of the reaction energy $Q = 3.945$ Mev. Calculate the mass of He^3 from this reaction.

11-8. (**a**) Using the principles of conservation of energy and momentum, show that the reduction in energy $\Delta\mathcal{E}$ of a neutron in a central elastic collision with a nucleus of mass number A is given by

$$ \Delta\mathcal{E} = \mathcal{E}\left[1 - \left(\frac{A-1}{A+1}\right)^2\right] $$

where $\mathcal{E}$ is the original energy of the neutron.

Calculate the fractional energy loss of a neutron colliding with (**b**) a proton, (**c**) a deuteron, and (**d**) a carbon nucleus, $A = 12$.

11-9. Calculate the Q value for the formation of P^{31} in the ground state in the reaction $Si^{30}(d,n)P^{31}$ from the following cycle of nuclear reactions:

1. $Si^{30} + d \rightarrow Si^{31} + p + 4.367$ Mev
2. $Si^{31} \rightarrow P^{31} + \beta^- + 1.51$ Mev
3. $n \rightarrow p + \beta^- + 0.782$ Mev.

Ans. 5.095 Mev.

11-10. Calculate the Q value for the formation of P^{30} in the ground state in the reaction $Si^{29}(d,n)P^{30}$ from the following cycle of nuclear reactions:

1. $P^{31} + \gamma \rightarrow P^{30} + n - 12.37$ Mev
2. $P^{31} + p \rightarrow Si^{28} + He^4 + 1.909$ Mev
3. $Si^{28} + d \rightarrow Si^{29} + p + 6.246$ Mev
4. $2d \rightarrow He^4 + 23.834$ Mev.

Ans. 3.31 Mev.

11-11. The following data were taken with a sample of nitogen in a ${}_7N^{14}(\gamma,n)$ reaction:

Time after Irradiation in Minutes	1	2	3	4	5	8	10	12	14	16	18	20	24
Counts/ Minute	520	485	450	410	390	310	290	240	210	190	160	140	100

(**a**) Plot the logarithm of the number of counts per minute against the time in minutes. (**b**) Determine the half-life of this activity.

11-12. When chlorine, $A = 37$, is bombarded with neutrons, gamma rays are emitted and the resultant nucleus is radioactive, emitting beta particles. A target containing chlorine was bombarded with neutrons for a short time, after which counts were taken of the number of beta particles emitted in successive ten-minute intervals. These counts, after correction for background readings, were as follows: 344, 267, 235, 189, 160, 145, 112, 97, 81, 65, 55, 50, 39, 37, 27, 25, 20, 14, 14, 11, 9.

(**a**) Write the equation for each reaction. (**b**) Plot a curve of the logarithm of the activity (number of counts per ten minutes), against the time in minutes. (**c**) From the slope of the above curve determine the half-life of the beta-ray emitter.

Ans. (c) 39 min.

11-13. The Q value of the $Ne^{22}(d,p)Ne^{23}$ reaction is 2.96 Mev. Calculate the atomic mass of Ne^{23}.

11-14. The Q value of the $F^{19}(n,p)O^{19}$ reaction is -3.9 Mev. (**a**) Determine the threshold value of the neutron energy for this reaction. (**b**) Determine the atomic mass of O^{19}.

11-15. The Q value of the $Na^{23}(n,\alpha)F^{20}$ reaction is -5.4 Mev. (**a**) Determine the threshold value of the neutrons for this reaction. (**b**) Determine the atomic mass of F^{20}.

11-16. The Q value of the $O^{18}(p,\alpha)N^{15}$ reaction is 3.97 Mev, while that for the $N^{15}(p,\alpha)C^{12}$ reaction is 4.96 Mev. Calculate the atomic mass of N^{15} from each of these reactions.

11-17. The Q value of the $Li^6(d,n)Be^7$ reaction has been found to be 3.40 Mev. Determine the atomic mass of Be^7.

11-18 The Q value of the reaction $H^2(d,p)H^3$ is 4.03 Mev. Calculate the atomic mass of H^3.

11-19. The threshold value for the reaction of $O^{16}(\gamma,n)O^{15}$ is 15.6 Mev. Calculate the atomic mass of O^{15}.

11-20. The threshold value for the reaction $O^{18}(\gamma,p)N^{17}$ is 16.35 Mev. (**a**) Calculate the atomic mass of N^{17}, assuming the others known. Compare this value with that given in Appendix IV, and account for the difference in terms of the disintegration process. (**b**) O^{17} promptly emits a neutron forming O^{16} in the ground state. Write the reaction equation. Using the atomic mass determined above, calculate the kinetic energy of the neutron.

11-21. The Q value of the reaction $Li^7(p,n)Be^7$ is -1.645 Mev. Using the known atomic masses of Be^7 and Li^7, calculate the mass difference $(n - H^1)$. Express this mass difference in kev.

11-22. Using the measured Q values of the four reactions given below, and the accepted value of the atomic mass of H^2, calculate the atomic mass of He^4.

1. $Be^9(d,\alpha)Li^7$, $\quad Q_1 = 7.151$ Mev
2. $Be^9(p,d)Be^8$, $\quad Q_2 = 0.558$ Mev
3. $Be^8(\alpha)He^4$, $\quad Q_3 = 0.089$ Mev
4. $Li^7(p,\alpha)He^4$, $\quad Q_4 = 17.338$ Mev.

Compare this value with the value of the mass of He^4 given in Appendix IV.

11-23. In bombarding copper with deuterons, J. M. Cork (1941) observed characteristic x-rays coming from the target at an angle of 90° to the beam. To determine whether the radiation came from the copper or from zinc formed in the process of K-electron capture, he put thin strips of copper, nickel, and iron adjacent to one another over a photographic plate and exposed it to the radiation. He found that the iron foil almost completely absorbed the radiation, while the copper and nickel foils reduced the intensity only slightly. Using the following data, (**a**) determine the source of the radiation. (**b**) What would have been the source of the radiation if nickel and iron foils had shown strong absorption, while the copper foil showed weak absorption?

Data:

CuK_α line = 1.541A
ZnK_α line = 1.438A

K-absorption edge of:
Fe = 1.739A
Ni = 1.484A
Cu = 1.377A

References

Bethe, H. A., and M. S. Livingston, "Nuclear Dynamics, Experimental," *Revs. Modern Phys.*, 9, 245, 1937.

Bleuler, E., and G. J. Goldsmith, *Experimental Nucleonics.* New York: Rinehart & Company, Inc., 1952.

Feather, N., *Nuclear Physics.* London: Cambridge University Press, 1936, Chaps. VII–XI.

Hollander, J. M., I. Perlman, and G. T. Seaborg, Table of Isotopes, *Revs. Modern Phys.*, 25, 469, 1953.

Nuclear Data. Compiled by K. Way, L. Fano, R. Scott, and K. Thew. Washington, D. C.: National Bureau of Standards, Circular 499, 1950, 1951.

Pollard, E., and W. L. Davidson, Jr., *Applied Nuclear Physics.* New York: John Wiley & Sons, Inc., 1951.

Rasetti, F., *Elements of Nuclear Physics.* New York: Prentice-Hall, Inc., 1936, Chap. VI.

Rutherford, E., J. Chadwick, and C. B. Ellis, *Radiations from Radioactive Substances.* London: Cambridge University Press, 1930, Chaps. X–XII.

chapter **12**

Nuclear Processes

12-1. Stability of Nuclei

There are about 1000 different isotopes now known, but only about 25 per cent of these are stable. It can thus be inferred that stable configurations of nucleons are the exception rather than the rule. Figure 12-1 is a graph of the neutron number N plotted against the proton number Z of the stable isotopes. The region of stability on this neutron-proton diagram is rather narrow. For low mass numbers $N/Z = 1$, and this ratio increases to a value of about 1.6 for large mass numbers. Lines of constant A can be drawn at angles of 135° with the Z axis; such lines pass through isobars. In general, lines of constant A pass through one or two stable isobars. There are only four cases of such lines passing through three stable isobars, at $A = 96$, 124, 130, and 136. These are shown on the graph.

Another interesting point is that more than half of the stable nuclei contain even numbers of protons and even numbers of neutrons; they are referred to as even-even nuclei About 20 per cent have even Z, and odd N (even-odd nuclei) and an almost equal number have odd Z and even N, but only four stable nuclei have odd Z and odd N. The odd-odd nuclei are $_1H^2$, $_3Li^6$, $_5B^{10}$, and $_7N^{14}$.

Points to the right of the stability region of Figure 12-1 represent unstable nuclei which have an excess of protons or a deficiency of neutrons; their most probable mode of decay will be by positron emission or electron capture. Points to the left of the stability region represent unstable nuclei with an excess of neutrons or a deficiency of protons; their most probable mode of decay will be by negative beta-particle emission. However, heavy particle emission is a competing process. As we have seen, compound nuclei formed in an excited state may disintegrate by emitting protons, neutrons, or alpha particles in going toward more stable forms. Among the fission products (§13-4), neutron emission competes with beta decay to form stable nuclei.

Stability is, in a sense, a relative property depending upon our ability to measure long lifetimes, that is, very weak activities. With improvements in experimental techniques, some of the isotopes now considered stable may be found to be radioactive with long lifetimes.

For a given assemblage of nucleons forming a nucleus of mass number A, there is one configuration for which the energy is a minimum. This

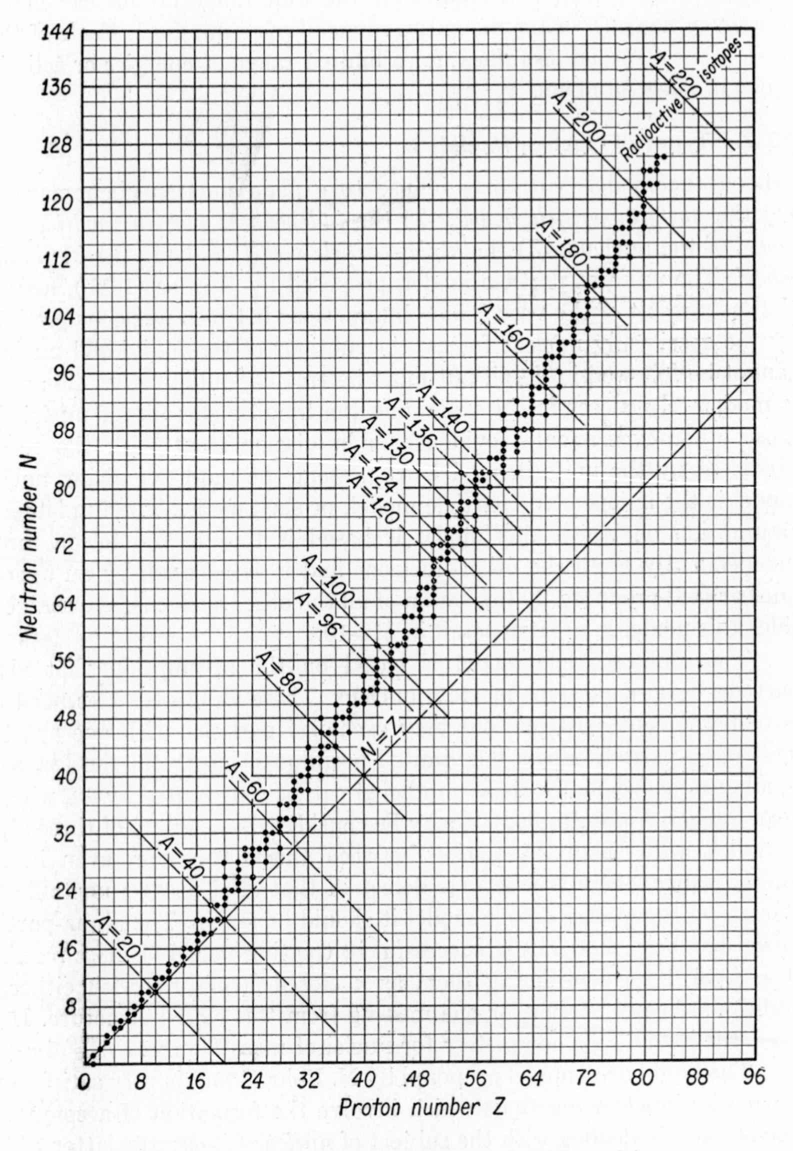

FIG. 12-1. Neutron-proton diagram of stable nuclei.

configuration is called the *ground state* of the nucleus; every other configuration is called an *excited state*. The difference in energy between an excited state of a nucleus and its ground state is called the *excitation energy* of that state. Several different nuclear models have been proposed to account for the behavior of nuclei, but at present there is no single nuclear model which is adequate for the wide range of nuclear energies of a given nucleus, or for the entire range of mass numbers. Each of these models has a special usefulness for a limited range of energies or a limited range of mass numbers.

12-2. Types of Nuclear Models

Among the models currently in use to explain nuclear phenomena are (1) the *uniform particle model*, (2) the *independent particle model* or *shell model* of the nucleus, (3) the *alpha-particle model*, and (4) the *liquid drop model*. The uniform particle model, proposed by Wigner (1937), assumes that as a result of the very strong interactions between nucleons produced by the specifically nuclear forces, the motions of the individual nucleons cannot be followed in detail but must be treated statistically. This model is moderately successful in explaining the binding energies of nuclei, but most other experimental evidence is in disagreement with the results predicted by the uniform model. At present the most promising nuclear model is the independent particle model, or shell model. The fundamental assumption on which this model is based is that each nucleon moves independently of all the other nucleons and is acted upon by an average nuclear field produced by the action of all the other nucleons. We shall consider this model in greater detail in §12-10.

The alpha-particle model is based on the assumption that alpha particles form subgroups inside a nucleus. These alpha particles need not have permanent existence but may exchange particles with one another. The alpha-particle model has limited usefulness, mostly in the low mass number range where the mass number A can be represented by $4n$, where n is an integer. For example, C^{12} may be considered as a group of three alpha particles, with small interaction between them. However, even in this limited range, there is a serious defect in that ${}_4Be^8$ is very unstable, although on the alpha-particle model it should be stable. The alpha-particle model has been moderately successful in treating nuclei of mass numbers $A = 4n + 1$ by considering them as n closed structures with either an additional heavy particle or one missing from this closed structure. However, the model fails completely for nuclei of mass numbers $A = 4n + 2$.

The liquid drop model proposed by N. Bohr (1937) is very satisfactory in treating nuclear reactions which involve the formation of a compound nucleus and in dealing with the subject of *nuclear fission*; the latter will be discussed more fully in Chapter 13. The fundamental assumption at the basis of the liquid drop model is that a nucleus may be considered as analogous in its behavior to that of a drop of liquid with a definite surface tension and with the nucleons behaving in a manner similar to that of molecules in a liquid. The disintegration of nuclei by the emission of particles is analogous to the evaporation of molecules from the surface of a liquid. The density of a liquid is independent of the size of the drop; this is essentially the same for nuclear matter. The analogy between a nucleus and a drop of liquid thus has many useful features and will be used where convenient.

12-3. The Compound Nucleus

Most of the nuclear processes discussed in the previous chapter in which a nucleus was bombarded by particles or photons to form a compound nucleus involved particle or photon energies of less than about 40 Mev. The existence of a compound nucleus was amply demonstrated in the n-γ and p-γ types of reactions; the product nucleus of one of these reactions is simply a lower energy state of the compound nucleus. We shall consider reactions as low energy reactions if the energies of the bombarding particles are less than 40 Mev. The compound nucleus is always formed in an excited state. It may go to a state of lower energy by the emission of a gamma-ray photon or it may be unstable and disintegrate by particle emission, the latter process being the more probable one.

A given compound nucleus may be formed in several different ways by using different projectiles directed against suitable targets. The compound nucleus exists for a time which is long in comparison with the time of transit of a nucleon across the nuclear diameter. The energy of a nucleon is of the order of a few Mev, so that its velocity is of the order of 10^9 cm/sec; the nuclear diameter is of the order of 10^{-12} cm, so that the time of transit of a nucleon across a diameter is of the order of 10^{-21} sec.

In Bohr's theory of the compound nucleus, the assumption is made that a projectile which is captured by a nucleus gives up its energy to a few nucleons, and, as a result of the interaction of these nucleons with all the others, the energy is quickly distributed among all the nucleons of the compound nucleus. Hence, when a compound nucleus disintegrates, its mode of disintegration is independent of the mode of formation, and depends only upon the particular state of the nucleus thus formed. The disintegration of a compound nucleus by particle emission implies that energy exchanges take place among the nucleons until a particle or a group of particles acquires sufficient energy to leave the nucleus. This energy must be in excess of the binding energy of the emitted particle or particles in the compound nucleus.

12-4. The Potential Barrier

When a compound nucleus is formed by bombarding a target with fast neutrons, the capture cross section, σ_c, of the target nuclei is

$$\sigma_c = \pi R^2 \tag{1}$$

where R is the nuclear radius, given by

$$R = r_0 A^{1/3} \tag{2}$$

with the radius parameter $r_0 = 1.2 \times 10^{-13}$ cm. This means that there is practically no interaction between the neutron and the nucleus until the neutron gets within a distance R from its center. One can conclude from this that the forces acting on the neutron are *specifically nuclear forces* which have a very *short range of action,* probably of the order of nuclear dimensions. For slow neutrons, the capture cross section varies inversely with the velocity v of the neutron; thus

$$\sigma_c = k/v \tag{3}$$

where the constant k depends upon the nature of the target nucleus. This dependence upon velocity may be explained by the fact that the distance between the neutron and the target nucleus is determined by the De Broglie wavelength, $\lambda = h/mv$; hence the interaction between them may take place at larger distances.

The problem is somewhat different when a charged particle such as a proton or an alpha particle is used as a projectile because of the Coulomb force between the projectile and the nucleus. This is a long-range force since it varies as r^{-2} where r is the distance between them. Since the potential in a Coulomb field varies as $1/r$, the potential energy U of a system consisting of a nucleus of charge Ze and a proton of charge e is Ze^2/r. This will be the potential energy of the system at distances $r > R$, as shown in Figure 12-2. At distances $r < R$, the specifically nuclear forces come into play and the potential energy of the system drops sharply. Without adequate knowledge of the nature of these nuclear forces, it is impossible to draw a graph to represent accurately the potential energy for distances less than R from the center of the nucleus. For simplicity, a constant value U_0 has been assumed for the potential energy of this sytem. The two regions have been joined at $r = R$ by a smooth curve.

A positively charged particle approaching a nucleus would encounter a *barrier* due to the Coulomb force of repulsion between them; this is sometimes called a *Coulomb barrier*. The maximum height H of this curve is called the *barrier height;* the magnitude of the barrier height for a Coulomb potential barrier is Ze^2/R. For a nucleus of low atcmic number such as magnesium, ${}_{12}\mathrm{Mg}^{27}$, for example, the barrier height H for protons as projectiles is approximately 4 Mev, while for a heavy nucleus such as ${}_{92}\mathrm{U}^{238}$ it is about 15 Mev. On the basis of classical physics, a proton should have a kinetic energy in excess of the Coulomb barrier in order to be able to penetrate the nucleus. Protons with kinetic energies less than the barrier energy H are stopped and repelled before they get within the range of the specifically nuclear forces. We know from experiment, however, that some of the protons do penetrate the potential barrier. A qualitative explanation of this barrier penetration can be given on the basis of wave mechanics. Referring to Figure 12-2, suppose that a proton of kinetic energy $\mathcal{E}_1 < H$ is fired at a nucleus. There is a definite probability that this proton will penetrate the potential barrier. This probability is calculated by replacing the particle by its De Broglie wave and setting up the Schroedinger equa-

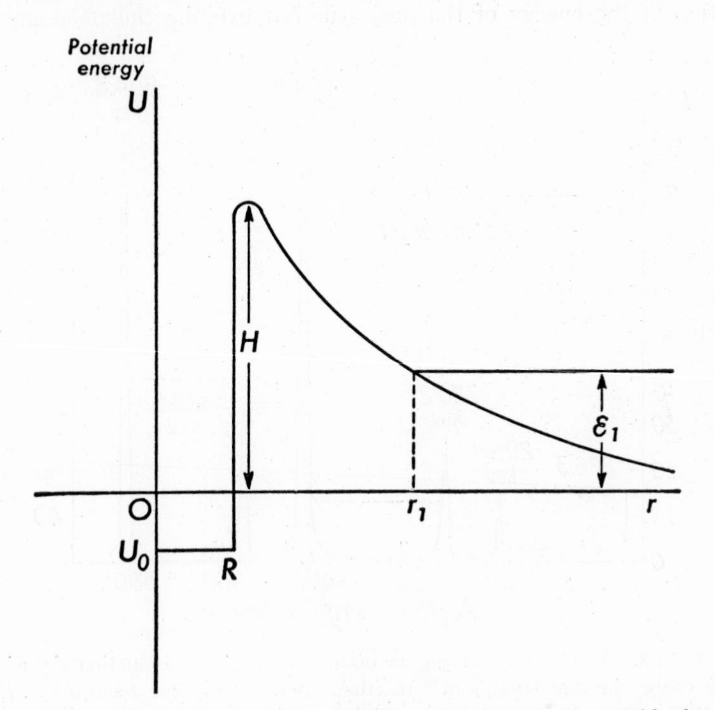

FIG. 12-2. Assumed form of the potential energy curve in the neighborhood of a nucleus. R is the radius of the nucleus.

tion for this problem with suitable boundary conditions. The solution of this equation shows that when the wave approaches the potential wall, it is partly reflected and partly transmitted, just as in any problem of wave motion. The *probability of penetration*, also called the *transparency* of the barrier, is defined as the ratio of the intensity of the transmitted wave to the intensity of the incident wave. The penetration probability is thus obtained from the ratio of the square of the amplitude of the transmitted wave to the square of the amplitude of the incident wave. The solution of the Schroedinger equation shows that the probability of penetration of the potential barrier is small for proton energies which are small fractions of the barrier height, and increases to unity as the energy of the particle approaches that of the height of the Coulomb barrier.

The probability of penetration of a potential barrier by a positively charged projectile can be determined experimentally by measuring the yield of a given reaction in which protons are the incident particles. Experiments already discussed, in which alpha particles (§§11-2, -4, -9), protons (§11-10), and deuterons (§11-11) were the bombarding particles, show that the transparency of the Coulomb barrier is not always a smooth function of the energy of the projectile but exhibits the phenomenon of

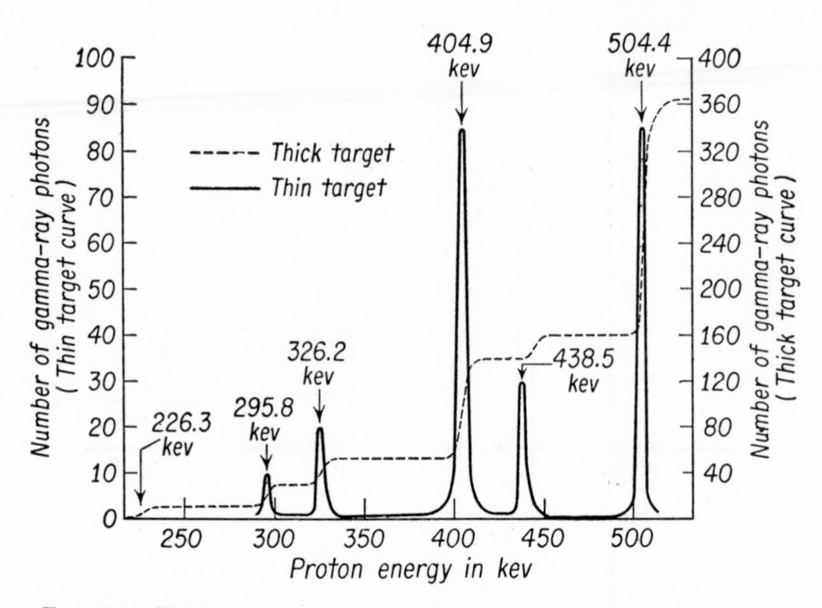

FIG. 12-3. Yield curve showing the resonance energies as a function of the incident proton energy in the $Al^{27}(p,\mu)Si^{28}$ reaction. (After Hunt and Jones, *Phys. Rev.*, 89, 1287, 1953.)

resonance. A resonance energy is shown by a sharp increase in the yield, as shown in Figure 11-8, and hence in the probability of penetration, for a given value of the energy of the projectile. A resonance energy is evidence of the existence of a sharp energy level in the compound nucleus. Since the state of a compound nucleus is independent of the manner in which the compound nucleus is formed, a particular energy level may be formed by one of several different reactions. For example, when Hunt and Jones (1953), investigated the ${}_{13}Al^{27}(p,\gamma){}_{14}Si^{28}$ reaction, they found five resonances for proton energies less than 0.5 Mev, as shown in Figure 12-3, whereas the barrier height is about 4 Mev. Here the yield was obtained by counting the gamma-ray photons emitted by the compound nucleus ${}_{14}Si^{28}$. It will also be noted that the resonances appear as sharp maxima when the target is very thin, while they appear as sudden increases in the yield when the target is thick.

12-5. Alpha-Particle Decay

The radioactive disintegration of a nucleus by alpha-particle emission was first successfully explained in terms of the penetration of a potential barrier by Gamow, Condon, and Gurney (1928). Alpha particles emitted from any given type of nucleus of atomic number Z come out with the same kinetic energy $\mathcal{E}_\alpha$; its value is much smaller than the potential barrier of such a nucleus. For example, the height of the potential barrier of U^{238} is about 30 Mev, while the kinetic energy of the emitted alpha particles is only 4.2 Mev. Let us assume that there is an energy level inside the nuclear

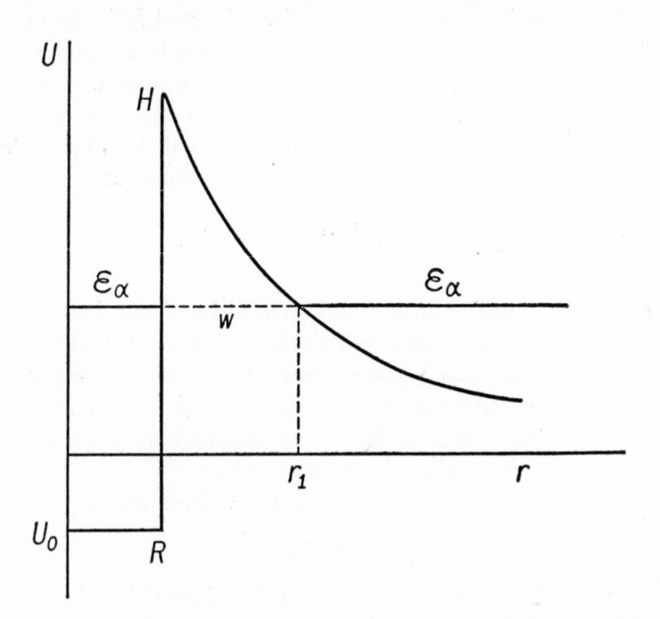

Fig. 12-4. Potential energy U of a nucleus and an alpha particle as a function of the distance r from the center of the nucleus. The width of the potential barrier is w.

radius R in the nucleus of atomic number Z and mass number A. Let us further assume that an alpha particle exists in the nucleus or is formed from two protons and two neutrons, and possesses this energy $\mathcal{E}_\alpha$. On the basis of wave mechanics, there is a definite probability that this alpha particle will penetrate the potential wall of width w and find itself at point r_1 just outside the nucleus (see Figure 12-4). At this point its energy $\mathcal{E}_\alpha$ is the potential energy of an alpha particle, of charge $2e$, in the Coulomb field of a nucleus of charge $(Z - 2)e$, and hence is

$$\mathcal{E}_\alpha = 2(Z - 2)e^2/r_1. \tag{4}$$

The alpha particle is then repelled from the nucleus and, at large distances from it, the energy of the alpha particle is entirely kinetic.

The problem of alpha-particle decay is to determine the lifetime τ of the alpha particle in the nucleus; this is the reciprocal of the probability per unit time, λ, for the escape of the alpha particle from the nucleus. The latter will depend upon the transparency of the potential wall. The solution of the Schroedinger equation for this problem shows that the transparency is proportional to the term

$$\epsilon^{-\frac{2}{\hbar}\int_R^{r_1}\sqrt{2M(U-\mathcal{E}_\alpha)}dr} \tag{5}$$

where U is the potential energy as a function of r, and M is the mass of the alpha particle. Inside the nucleus the particle oscillates and strikes the potential wall periodically. If we assume that it moves with an average speed $\bar{v}$, then the frequency with which it strikes the wall is $\bar{v}/2R$. The product of this frequency and the transparency will be practically equal to the probability per unit time of escape of the alpha particle, thus

$$\lambda = \frac{\bar{v}}{2R}\,\epsilon^{-\frac{2}{\hbar}\int_R^{r_1}[2M(U-\mathcal{E}_\alpha)]^{\frac{1}{2}}dr}. \tag{6}$$

The exponent, which is usually designated by G, can be evaluated for the given potential barrier. The calculations of λ give qualitative agreement with experiment. The equation has been used to compute nuclear radii by substituting the measured values of λ and $\mathcal{E}_\alpha$. This is one of the methods for obtaining R and the results so obtained are in good agreement with those values of R obtained by other methods.

It is also worth noting that equation (6) written as

$$\lambda = \text{const}\ \epsilon^{-G} \tag{7}$$

is one form of the Geiger-Nuttall law (§10-7), since G is a function of the energy and hence of the range of the alpha particle. A fair approximation for G yields

$$G = \frac{8\pi^2e^2}{h}\frac{Z}{v} \tag{8}$$

where v is the velocity of the alpha particle outside the nucleus. The constant factor has a different value for each of the radioactive series.

12-6. Beta-Particle Decay

In the two previous chapters we considered in some detail the types of radioactive beta-particle disintegration both in naturally occurring isotopes and in artificially produced isotopes. It was found that beta decay is a common type of disintegration throughout the entire range of mass numbers. Beta decay involves two isobaric nuclides of mass number A and produces a change in nuclear charge from Ze to $(Z + 1)e$ if an electron is emitted, and a change to $(Z - 1)e$ if a positron is emitted or an electron is captured. We have discussed the energy changes accompanying these disintegrations and the spectral distributions of the β^-- and β^+-particles. We have also given sufficient evidence that electrons do not exist as free particles in the nucleus and hence must be created at the instant of nuclear disintegration. For β^--emission it was suggested that a neutron decays into a proton, an electron, and a neutrino; thus

$$n \rightarrow p + e^- + \nu. \tag{9}$$

Since the mass of the neutron exceeds that of the proton and electron, this type of disintegration is energetically possible for free neutrons. This has actually been observed; the end-point energy was found to be 785 kev, practically identical with the mass difference ${}_0n^1 - {}_1\mathrm{H}^1$ of 782 kev. The half-life of the free neutron in space was found to be about 12.8 minutes.

A positron was assumed to be produced by the disintegration in the nucleus of a proton into a neutron which stays in the nucleus, and a positron and a neutrino which are emitted; thus

$$p \text{ (in nucleus)} \rightarrow n \text{ (in nucleus)} + e^+ + \nu. \tag{10}$$

However, since the mass of the proton is less than that of the neutron and positron, the proton remains a stable particle in free space. The difference in energy, in this case 782 kev $+ 2m_ec^2 = 1.802$ Mev, must be supplied by the system in which β^+- emission occurs.

Electron capture can be written as

$$p + e^- \rightarrow n + \nu. \tag{11}$$

Here also the sum of the masses of the proton and electron is less than that of the neutron by 782 kev, and hence this reaction cannot occur with free protons and electrons but can only occur in an atomic system where the deficiency in energy may be supplied by the other particles.

A satisfactory theory of beta disintegration should be able to predict the spectral distribution of the beta particles which is found experimentally, and should relate beta distintegration to the energy states of the isobars involved in the process. Such a theory has been developed by E. Fermi (1934); as experimental procedures have become more refined, their results have been found to be in better agreement with the predictions of the Fermi theory. For example, the Fermi theory gives the distribution in energy and in momentum of the beta particles which is in agreement with those found experimentally. For allowed transitions the spectral distribution is of the form given by

$$N(p)dp = Cp^2(\mathcal{E}_{\mathrm{m}} - \mathcal{E})^2F(Z,p)dp \tag{12}$$

where $N(p)$ is the number of beta particles emitted with momenta lying between p and $p + dp$, C is a constant for the nuclei involved in the beta decay, $\mathcal{E}_m$ is the maximum energy of the emitted beta particles and is the end-point energy of the spectrum, $\mathcal{E}$ is the kinetic energy of the beta particle, $F(Z,p)$ is a Coulomb correction factor which takes into account the Coulomb interaction between the nuclear particles and the beta particle, and Z is the atomic number of the product nucleus.

A more convenient way of plotting the experimental results and checking with the theory was suggested by Kurie (1936). Writing the equation in the form

$$\sqrt{\frac{N(p)}{p^2F(Z,p)}} = k(\mathcal{E}_m - \mathcal{E}), \tag{13}$$

we see that if $\sqrt{\frac{N(p)}{p^2F(Z,p)}}$ is plotted against the energy, a straight line should be obtained with an energy intercept at $\mathcal{E}_m$. Figure 12-5(a) is a Kurie plot of the negative beta-particle spectrum of Cu^{64}, and Figure 12-5(b) is a Kurie plot of the positron spectrum of Cu^{64} obtained by Owen and Cook (1949) using very thin uniform sources prepared by evaporating the activated copper onto a thin aluminum foil. In making a Kurie plot it is common to express the energy in unit of m_ec^2. These spectra give straight lines down to very low energies in agreement with the Fermi theory of beta decay.

12-7. Comparative Half-Lives for Beta Decay

The number of beta particles $N(p)$ emitted per unit time per unit momentum interval is proportional to the probability per unit time, λ_β, the beta disintegration constant. It is to be expected that the probability of disintegration should depend upon the energy available for the transition, and upon the characteristics of the initial nuclear state and the final nuclear state. A nuclear state is characterized by its energy, by its angular momentum I in units of $\hbar$, and by the arrangement of the nuclear particles. This arrangement is described by the term *parity* and is designated as either *even* or *odd*. This term arises from the nature of the wave function used to describe the state of the system. The wave function may be either an even function of the coordinates of the particles or an odd function. An even function is one in which a change in sign of the coordinates leaves the function unchanged. Just as in optical and x-ray spectra, the transitions between nuclear states giving rise to beta-ray spectra are governed by selection rules, some transitions being more favored than others. One set of selection rules applies to the case in which the beta particle and the neutrino are emitted with opposite spins so that the resultant change in angular

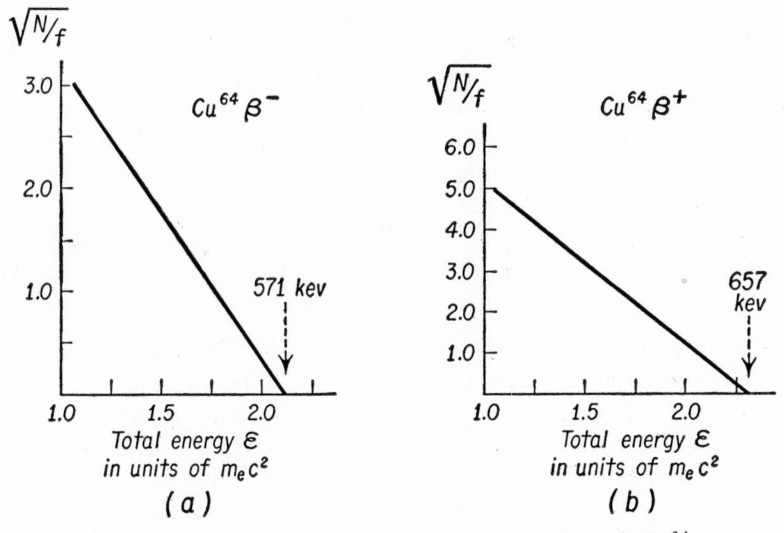

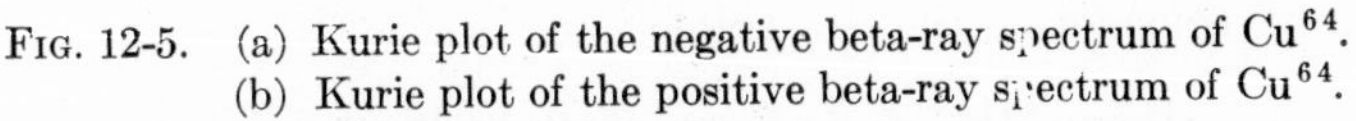

FIG. 12-5. (a) Kurie plot of the negative beta-ray spectrum of Cu^{64}.
(b) Kurie plot of the positive beta-ray spectrum of Cu^{64}.

The value of the end-point energy is indicated by the arrow in each plot. (After Owen and Cook, *Phys. Rev.*, 76, 1727, 1949.)

momentum of the nucleus is zero. The Fermi selection rules for allowed transitions is thus

$$\Delta I = 0, \text{ no change of parity.} \tag{14}$$

If the beta particle and the neutrino are emitted with their spins parallel, the selection rules, known as the Gamow-Teller selection rules, are

$$\Delta I = \pm 1, \text{ or } 0, \text{ no change of parity;}$$

$$\text{the transitions} \qquad I_i = 0 \text{ to } I_f = 0 \text{ are not allowed.} \tag{15}$$

Other changes of state than those given by the above selection rules do occur but are classed as *forbidden transitions,* there being different degrees of forbiddenness, such as first forbidden (with $\Delta I = \pm 1, 0$, change of parity), second forbidden, and higher orders of forbiddenness. It is beyond the scope of this book to consider beta-ray spectroscopy in greater detail. However, there is another interesting approach to this subject in terms of the *comparative half-lives* of the beta-particle disintegrations.

The probability per second, λ_β, for beta disintegration can be computed from equation (12) by integrating over all values of the electron momentum from 0 to p_m where p_m is the maximum momentum, obtaining

$$\lambda_\beta = Cf \tag{16}$$

where
$$f = \int_0^{p_m} p^2(\mathcal{E}_m - \mathcal{E})^2 F(Z,p)dp; \tag{17}$$

values of the function f are available in tables. Substituting for λ_β its value

$$\lambda_\beta = \frac{\ln 2}{T} = Cf,$$

we get
$$\boxed{fT = \text{constant.}} \tag{18}$$

The product fT is called the *comparative half-life*. The numbers obtained for the comparative half-lives vary over such a wide range, from about 10^3 to 10^{18}, that it is more common to use value of log fT in discussing comparative half-lives. Log fT values of about 3-5 correspond to allowed transitions, with higher values for the unfavored or forbidden transitions.

An idea of the usefulness of the concept of comparative half-lives can be obtained by considering the two transitions

$$_1H^3 \rightarrow {}_2He^3 + \beta^- + \nu, \quad T = 12.46 \text{ yr} \tag{19}$$

and
$$n \rightarrow p + \beta^- + \nu, \quad T = 12.8 \text{ min.} \tag{20}$$

Langer and Moffat (1952) made an accurate determination of the end-point energy of the beta-ray spectrum of tritium and found it to be 17.95 kev. Using the previously determined half-life and tables of values of the function f, they obtained the value

$$fT = 1014 \text{ sec}$$

from which
$$\log fT = 3.006.$$

Langer and Moffat suggested that if we assume that the comparative half-life of the beta decay of the neutron is the same as that for tritium, then, using the end-point energy of the beta-ray spectrum of the neutron as 782 kev, the half-life of the neutron should be 10.4 min. This is in agreement, within the limits of experimental error, with the results of Robson's experiment which yields a half-life of 12.8 ± 2.5 min.

12-8. Evidence for the Neutrino

The existence of the neutrino has been postulated to account for beta decay, and also for several types of meson decay (see Chapter 14). The properties assigned to the neutrino make it very difficult to detect it by a direct experiment, and, until recently, all of the experiments were of an indirect type. The neutrino as postulated is a particle which has no charge, has a spin angular momentum of $\frac{1}{2}\hbar$, may have zero rest mass, or a rest mass small in comparison with that of the electron, and has energy and momentum.

One of the earliest attempts to show experimentally that the neutrino hypothesis was correct was a cloud-chamber experiment by Crane and Halpern (1938) on the negative beta disintegration of Cl^{38}. From the principle of conservation of linear momentum, it is obvious that if only an electron is emitted, then the product nucleus should recoil with a momentum equal and opposite to that of the electron. If a neutrino is emitted simultaneously with the electron, then some of the momentum will be carried away by it. The distribution of momentum between the two light particles is such that when the energy of the electron is large, its momentum is also large and that of the neutrino is negligible. When the energy of the electron is small, its momentum is also small and that of the neutrino should become significant experimentally; that is, the recoil momentum of the product nucleus should be greater than that of the electron. In the cloud-chamber experiment mentioned above, Crane and Halpern measured the recoil momenta of product nuclei, some of which were associated with high energy electrons and others with low energy electrons. They found that for high energy beta-particle emission, the momentum of the product nucleus was equal to that of the electron, but for low energy beta-particle emission, the momentum of the nucleus was greater than that of the electron. The accuracy of the experiment was not very great, one of the difficulties being due to the fact that the velocity of the heavy nucleus was small, and instead of measuring the length of a track, the number of droplets produced was counted. The assumption was made that the energy required to produce an ion pair was the same for a heavy nucleus as for an alpha particle.

Additional experiments on the recoil of nuclei produced in beta disintegrations have been performed with improved techniques; these have confirmed the above results. Some of the experiments involved electron capture; for example, Rodeback and Allen (1952) investigated the disintegration of A^{37} by electron capture with the reaction

$$_{18}A^{37} + _{-1}e^0 \rightarrow _{17}Cl^{37} + \nu + Q. \tag{21}$$

The energy Q released in this reaction is simply equal to the difference in mass $A^{37} - Cl^{37}$ which is 816 kev, assuming that the neutrino rest mass is negligible. It has been found that about 93 per cent of electrons captured come from the K shell of argon; the subsequent readjustment of the outer electrons in the product nucleus Cl^{37} results in the emission of Auger electrons in 90 per cent of the transitions, with x-rays being emitted in the other 3 per cent.

The experiment consisted in measuring the velocity of the recoiling nucleus, using the apparatus sketched in Figure 12-6. The chamber was kept at a low pressure of 10^{-5} mm Hg, the effective volume of the argon being the small shaded region in the figure. The Auger electrons traveled to grid 1 into the electron detector, and the recoil Cl^{37} ions traveled in a field-free region to grid 2 and then into the recoil detector. Electron multipliers were used as detectors. The time of flight of the Cl^{37} ions was measured by a 20-channel delayed coincidence circuit. The results are shown in the

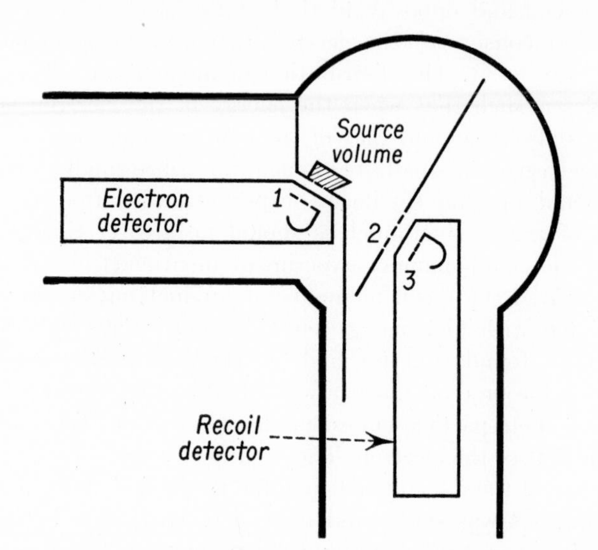

FIG. 12-6. Schematic diagram of the apparatus for measuring the time-of-flight of recoil nuclei Cl^{37} formed in the electron capture process of A^{37}. Shaded region indicates the effective source volume. (After Rodeback and Allen, *Phys. Rev.*, 86, 447, 1952.)

solid curve of the graph of Figure 12-7, with the dashed curve giving the distribution expected from monoenergetic recoil ions. This was calculated on the basis of the conservation of linear momentum between the neutrino and the recoil nucleus, with the reaction energy Q carried away by both of them. The agreement with experiment is thus good.

The first direct experiment to detect the neutrino by its interaction with matter, specifically by its interaction with protons, has recently been performed by F. Reines and C. L. Cowan, Jr. (1953). They utilized the very great supply of neutrinos being continuously emitted in the beta decay of the fission fragments which are produced during the operation of a large nuclear reactor (§13-2). The reaction expected between a neutrino ν and a proton p is the formation of a neutron n and the emission of a positron, the reaction equation being

$$\nu + p \rightarrow n + \beta^{+}. \tag{22}$$

To detect this reaction, the neutrinos are allowed to enter a large liquid scintillation counter; the organic liquid of this counter contains hydrogen sufficient to produce a proton density of the order of 5×10^{22} proton/cm^3. The estimated cross section of the above reaction is of the order of 6×10^{-20} barn, and with the large volume (10 ft^3) of liquid used, the number of these events should be about 10 to 30 per hour.

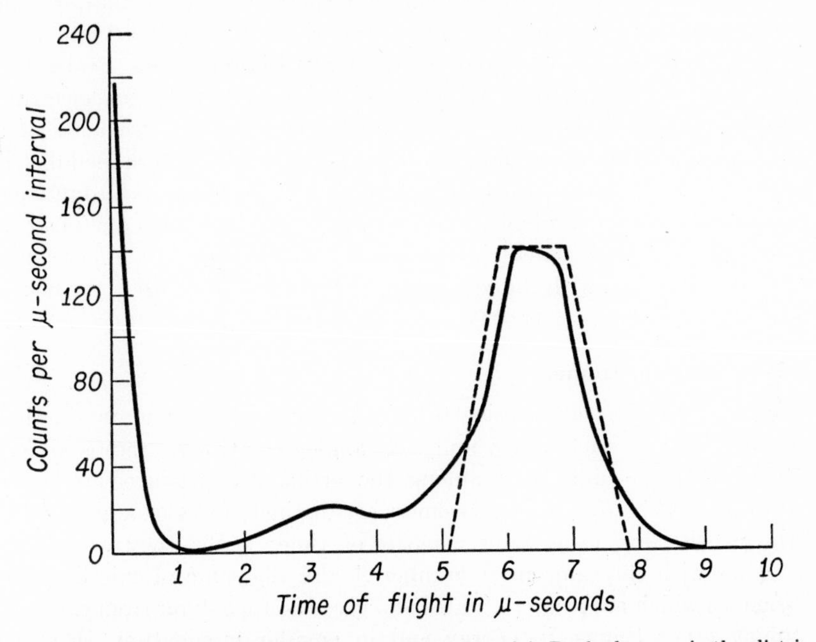

FIG. 12-7. Time-of-flight distribution of recoil nuclei. Dashed curve is the distribution expected from monoenergetic recoils from the source volume. (After Rodeback and Allen, *Phys. Rev.*, 86, 449, 1952.)

In order to be certain that the above reaction was taking place, effects due to both the neutron and the positron had to be detected. The positrons, in their passage through the liquid, give rise to annihilation radiation, and this, in turn, produces the scintillations which are detected by a suitable number of photomultiplier tubes placed around the tank containing the scintillation liquid. To detect the neutrons, some cadmium was added to the liquid; the neutrons were captured by the cadmium in an n-γ reaction. The scintillations produced by these capture gamma rays occurred about 5 microseconds after those of the annihilation radiation and were also detected by photomultiplier tubes. The annihilation radiation and the capture gamma rays could also be distinguished by the slightly different characteristics of the pulses produced by them in the detectors. The two pulses were fed into a delayed coincidence circuit and yielded 0.41 ± 0.20 delayed counts per minute, in good agreement with the expected value.

An upper limit on the rest mass m_ν of the neutrino may be obtained from a determination of the shape of the beta-ray spectrum on a Kurie plot near the end-point energy for a beta emitter for which the end-point energy is small. In such a case, the effect of the neutrino rest mass will be very noticeable. For zero neutrino rest mass, the Kurie plot will be a straight line; for a finite rest mass, the Kurie plot will deviate from a straight line near the end-point energy toward lower values. Probably the best atom to work with is H^3; the end point of its beta-ray spectrum is 18 kev. Langer and Moffat (1952) made accurate measurements of this beta-ray spectrum and compared the experimentally determined distribution on a Kurie plot with distributions that would have been obtained if the neutrino rest mass had values of 0, 250, 500, and 1000 ev. Their data are consistent with a neutrino rest mass of zero, with an upper limit of 250 ev. Compared with the rest mass of an electron, 0.51 Mev, the neutrino rest mass does not exceed 0.05 per cent of the rest mass of an electron.

12-9. Nuclear Isomers

We have already had occasion to refer to the existence and production of nuclear isomers, such as UZ and UX_2 among the natural radioactive substances (§10-3) and Ag^{107} among the artificially produced radioactive substances (§11-15). Nuclear isomers are distinct states of a given isotope which exist for measurable lengths of time; hence they are different *nuclides* with the same mass number A and the same atomic number Z. Nuclides which are isomeric states of a given isotope differ from each other, among other things, in energy and in angular momentum. If I is the angular momentum, in units of $\hbar$, of the ground state of a nucleus, and I_m is the angular momentum, also in units of $\hbar$, of an isomeric state, then, in general,

$$|I_m - I| > 1 \tag{23}$$

and represents a transition which has a degree of forbiddenness with respect to beta decay. There is thus an analogy between an isomeric state of a nucleus and a metastable state of an atom. The excited isomeric state is often termed a *metastable state*, and the letter m is sometimes written following the mass number to designate it. Thus the metastable state of bromine, $A = 80$, would be designated as Br^{80m}.

Bromine is of historical interest since it was the first case in which nuclear isomers were produced artificially, and their existence made certain by chemical separation of the nuclear isomers. When a sample containing bromine was bombarded by slow neutrons, radioactive elements were formed which disintegrated with the emission of negative beta particles with three different half-lives, 18 min, 4.4 hr, and 36 hr. Chemical tests showed that the radioactive elements were isotopes of bromine. But there are only two stable isotopes of bromine of mass numbers 79 and 81, and only the following two reactions can take place:

$$
\begin{aligned}
& {}_{35}\mathrm{Br}^{79} + {}_0n^1 \rightarrow ({}_{35}\mathrm{Br}^{80}) \rightarrow {}_{35}\mathrm{Br}^{80} + h\nu, \\
\text{followed by} \quad & {}_{35}\mathrm{Br}^{80} \rightarrow {}_{36}\mathrm{Kr}^{80} + \beta^-; \\
\text{and} \quad & {}_{35}\mathrm{Br}^{81} + {}_0n^1 \rightarrow ({}_{35}\mathrm{Br}^{82}) \rightarrow {}_{35}\mathrm{Br}^{82} + h\nu, \\
\text{followed by} \quad & {}_{35}\mathrm{Br}^{82} \rightarrow {}_{36}\mathrm{Kr}^{82} + \beta^-.
\end{aligned}
\tag{24}
$$

Now when bromine was bombarded with gamma-ray photons, the following reactions were observed:

$$
\begin{aligned}
& {}_{35}\mathrm{Br}^{79} + h\nu \rightarrow ({}_{35}\mathrm{Br}^{79}) \rightarrow {}_{35}\mathrm{Br}^{78} + {}_0n^1, \\
\text{followed by} \quad & {}_{35}\mathrm{Br}^{78} \rightarrow {}_{34}\mathrm{Se}^{78} + \beta^+; \\
\text{and} \quad & {}_{35}\mathrm{Br}^{81} + h\nu \rightarrow ({}_{35}\mathrm{Br}^{81}) \rightarrow {}_{35}\mathrm{Br}^{80} + {}_0n^1, \\
\text{followed by} \quad & {}_{35}\mathrm{Br}^{80} \rightarrow {}_{36}\mathrm{Kr}^{80} + \beta^-.
\end{aligned}
\tag{25}
$$

Again three periods were observed, 6.3 min, 18 min, and 4.4 hr. Two of these periods are common to both sets of reactions and must therefore be

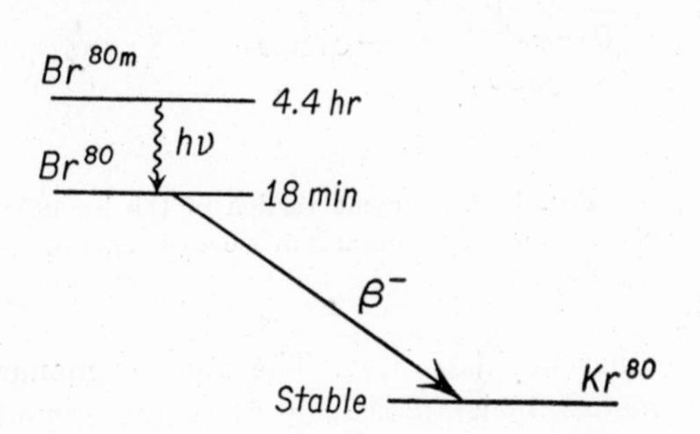

FIG. 12-8. Original version of isomeric states and transitions of Br^{80}.

assigned to the isotope which is common to both sets of reactions, namely, bromine of mass number 80.

The existence of two beta-decay periods of 4.4 hr and 18 min can be explained by assuming that there are two isomeric states of bromine 80; Br^{80m}, the metastable state, and Br^{80}, the ground state, with beta-ray emission taking place only from the ground state with a half-life of 18 min, as shown in Figure 12-8. Transitions from the metastable state to the ground state take place by gamma-ray emission with a half-life of 4.4 hrs. When Br^{80} is formed, the 18 min activity decreases fairly rapidly; after a sufficient time has elapsed, Br^{80} is formed by the decay of Br^{80m} with a half-life of 4.4 hr; that is, there is radioactive equilibrium between these two states, and the beta decay has the same period as the transition from the metastable state to the ground state.

Since the early work on bromine, further investigations with improved techniques have shown additional modes of disintegration of Br^{80}, and advances in quantum radiation theory have led to the assignment of angular momentum quantum numbers as shown in Figure 12-9. The metastable state of Br^{80m} has a half-life of 4.4 hr and decays by emitting two gamma-ray photons in cascade, one of energy 0.049 Mev, and the

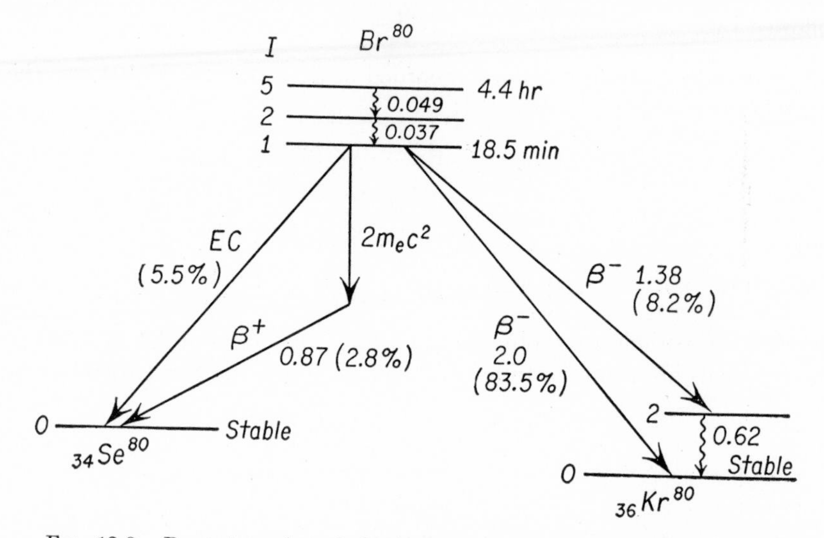

FIG. 12-9. Present version of the isomeric states and transitions of Br^{80}. The energy of each transition is in Mev. (After Scharff-Goldhaber and McKeown, *Phys. Rev.* 92, 356, 1953.)

other of 0.037 Mev. The angular momentum quantum number of the metastable state is $I_m = 5$; for the ground state it is $I = 1$. The intermediate state is assigned the value $I' = 2$. The ground state of Br^{80} has a half-life of 18.5 min, and its most probable mode of decay is by negative beta-particle emission either to the stable state of Kr^{80} or, to a smaller extent, to an excited state of $_{36}Kr^{80}$. However, it has been found that Br^{80} may also decay from the ground state by positive beta-particle emission or by electron capture, in each case going to the ground state of $_{34}Se^{80}$.

Two nuclear isomers, one of which has been formed by the gamma-ray decay of the other, are said to be *genetically related*. The Br^{80} isomers are genetically related and so are the radioactive isomers UZ and UX_2, with the ground state (UX_2) having a half-life of 1.17 min and the metastable state (UZ) having a half-life of 6.7 hr. Most nuclear isomers are genetically related. An example of nongenetically related nuclear isomers is that of

${}_{49}\mathrm{In}^{116}$, shown in Figure 12-10. No gamma-ray transitions have been observed between the two isomeric states; each state decays by β^--emission to ${}_{50}\mathrm{Sn}^{116}$, the upper isomeric state having a complex beta-ray spectrum which has been analyzed into three spectra with different end-point energies.

With the increase in the resolving time of detectors and detecting circuits has come an increase in the ability to measure nuclear states of short lifetimes. Lifetimes of the order of 10^{-9} sec are now measurable; hence the number of known nuclear isomers is increasing rapidly.

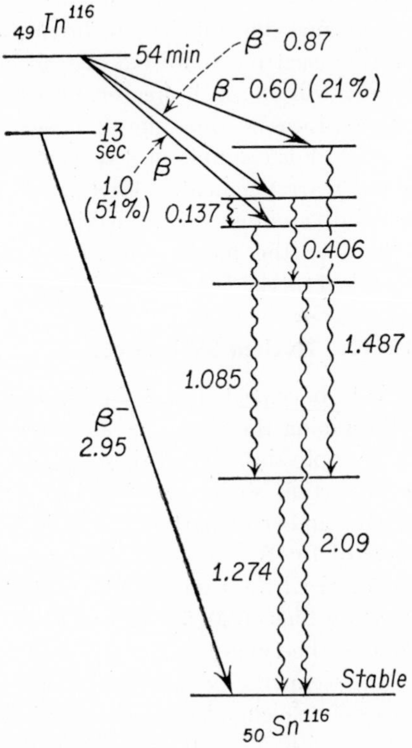

FIG. 12-10. Transitions from non-genetically related isomeric states of In^{116} to Sn^{116}. (After Goldhaber and Hill, *Revs. Modern Phys.*, 24, 208, 1952.)

The assignment of angular momentum quantum numbers to excited states of nuclei is a difficult problem. There is as yet no direct method for measuring the angular momenta of such states comparable to the methods available for the ground states. Among the latter are hyperfine structure of atomic spectra and nuclear magnetic resonance (§§8-21, 22). Present methods for assigning angular momentum quantum numbers to excited states of nuclei depend upon an analysis of the radiation emitted and a comparison with predictions from quantum electrodynamics. A check of the assignment is often made with predictions from nuclear models. At present the strong spin-orbit coupling model seems to give very good agreement with the assignment of values of I from experiments on isomeric transitions.

The chemical separation of nuclear isomers is often possible owing to the processes which follow the emission of gamma-ray photons. The general idea is to break a chemical bond which holds the isomeric nucleus in a compound. If the gamma-ray photon is emitted with high energy and hence with comparatively large momentum, the nuclear recoil momentum and energy may be sufficient to break the chemical bond. If an internal conversion electron is emitted instead of a photon, the recoil momentum and energy will be much greater, owing to the finite rest mass of the electron. Other processes than simple nuclear recoil may accompany internal conversion. For example, if a K electron is ejected from the atom, the subsequent rearrangement of electrons may include the fall of the valence electron into an inner shell, breaking the chemical bond and forming a free ion. Whatever the mechanism of breaking the chemical bond, appropriate chemical methods can then be used to separate the nuclear isomers.

12-10. Nuclear Shell Structure

It is to be expected that the ideas and concepts that proved so effective in determining the electronic structure of atoms should be carried over into nuclear physics. One of these ideas is that of *shell structure* or *level structure* with certain shells *closed* owing to the stability of the system with the given number of particles. The idea of closed nuclear shells was first put forward by W. Elsasser (1934); more recently, Maria G. Mayer (1948) summarized the experimental facts to show that nuclei containing 20, 50, or 82 protons or 20, 50, 82, or 126 neutrons form very stable configurations. Among the types of evidence used by Mayer was the isotopic abundance of the elements, particularly those with $Z > 33$. For example, those isotopes of an element with an isotopic abundance greater than 60 per cent are ${}_{38}Sr^{88}$, with $N = 50$, ${}_{56}Ba^{138}$, and ${}_{58}Ce^{140}$ with $N = 82$. These isotopes have even mass numbers; they are sometimes referred to as *even isotopes.* Another type of evidence is the number of stable isotopes of a given element. For example, tin, $Z = 50$, has the largest number of stable isotopes, ten, of any element. Lead, $Z = 82$, has four stable isotopes; lead is also the end product of the naturally occurring radioactive series. There are seven stable *isotones,* that is, nuclides with the same number of neutrons, for $N = 82$; these are Xe^{136}, Ba^{139}, Ce^{140}, Pr^{141}, Nd^{142}, and Sm^{144}. On the other hand, there is only one stable isotope with $N = 81$, and only one stable isotope with $N = 83$. Also, there are six isotones with $N = 50$, but only one each for $N = 49$ and $N = 51$.

Evidence for the existence of a closed shell for 126 neutrons comes from several facts. Two of these are (1) the heaviest isotope of lead, $A = 208$, has $N = 126$; (2) when alpha-decay energies are plotted against the neutron number of the product nucleus, there is a sharp dip in energy when N drops below 126; this indicates a larger binding energy for the 126th neutron.

Other evidence for the existence of closed shells at $N = 50$, 82, and 126 may be obtained from the fact that the so-called *delayed neutron emitters* among the fission products of uranium 235 are $_{36}Kr^{87}$, with $N = 51$, and $_{54}Xe^{137}$, with $N = 83$; the binding energy of the last neutron in each case is so small that a neutron can be readily evaporated from each one forming Kr^{86}, $N = 50$, and Xe^{136}, $N = 82$, respectively. Also, the absorption cross section for neutrons as a function of neutron number is very small for nuclei with neutron numbers $N = 50$, 82, and 126.

The nuclear shell model is limited in its application to the ground states and low-lying excited states of nuclei. The present experimental evidence is that there are closed nuclear shells at neutron and proton numbers 2, 8, 20, 28, 50, and 82, and neutron number 126. The problem is to determine the order in which these shells are filled as nucleons are added to make heavier nuclei. This is similar to the problem encountered in the assignment of electrons to the different electronic level configurations of the atom. Quantum mechanical calculations have been made to determine this order using the idea of a strong coupling between the orbital angular momentum of a nucleon and its spin angular momentum, particularly by Mayer (1949) and by Haxel, Jensen, and Suess (1949). In one calculation, a single nucleon is assumed to move in a field due to the other nucleons whose potential has the shape of a square well. The results obtained from the square-well potential are not in complete agreement with experimental results obtained from analyses of beta-ray spectra, from measurements of magnetic moments, and from experiments on isomeric transitions. The results from such experiments have been used to modify the theoretical results. In addition, since each nucleon has a spin of $\frac{1}{2}\hbar$, the *Pauli exclusion principle* must be applied; this principle, as applied to the nucleus, states that *no two identical particles can be in the same quantum state.* A nuclear quantum state is usually specified by its total quantum number and by its parity.

A single nucleon is assumed to move in an orbit with an angular momentum l, in units of $\hbar$, in a nuclear field due to all the other nucleons. Each nucleon also has an angular momentum due to spin of $\frac{1}{2}\hbar$. The spectroscopic notation developed for electron configurations is taken over to describe nucleon configurations. Thus, the values for the orbital angular momentum l have letters associated with them as indicated:

l value:	0	1	2	3	4	5	6
notation:	*s*	*p*	*d*	*f*	*g*	*h*	*i*

The assumption of strong spin-orbit coupling means that in determining the total angular momentum of the nucleus, the total angular moment j of each nucleon is first determined; then these j values are added, subject to the usual quantum conditions. This type of coupling is referred to as the j-j coupling, in contrast to the Russell-Saunders or L-S coupling. The total angular momentum j for a single nucleon is

$$j = l + \tfrac{1}{2}, \qquad \text{or} \qquad l - \tfrac{1}{2}, \tag{26}$$

except in the case of $l = 0$. The value of j is always an odd-half integer. The j value is frequently written as a subscript in the lower right corner of the letter representing the l value. It can be seen that there are two possible energy levels for the same l value except for $l = 0$. In agreement with previous practice (§8-20), the total angular momentum quantum number of the nucleus is designated by the letter I. It was previously called the spin angular momentum quantum number of the nucleus; the term *spin* has been enlarged to include the angular momentum due to the nucleonic orbital motion as well.

Let us examine a few nuclei to see how the shell model is used. The nucleus of deuterium has $N = 1$, $Z = 1$; hence the ground state is an s state in which each nucleon has a j value of $\frac{1}{2}$. Experiment shows that $I = 1$; hence the spin of the neutron is parallel to that of the proton. There are two nuclei with $A = 3$; they are ${}_1H^3$ and ${}_2He^3$. In each case the value of $I = \frac{1}{2}$. For ${}_1H^3$, $N = 2$, $Z = 1$, so that the $s_{1/2}$ shell has its full complement of 2 neutrons with spins in opposite directions, and the proton is in an $s_{1/2}$ shell with $j = \frac{1}{2}$. On the other hand, $N = 1$, $Z = 2$, for ${}_2He^3$, so that the 2 protons complete the $s_{1/2}$ proton shell with their spins in opposite directions, and the neutron is in its $s_{1/2}$ shell with $j = \frac{1}{2}$. Two such nuclei, having the same number of nucleons A but in which the protons and neutrons are interchanged, are called *mirror nuclei.* For $A = 4$, there is only one known nucleus, the stable alpha-particle configuration of ${}_2He^4$. Here $N = 2$ and $Z = 2$ and the $1s_{1/2}$ shell is filled for both neutrons and protons. The spins of the protons are opposed, as are those of the neutrons. Experimentally, $I = 0$, in agreement with the above results. Also the binding energy of the alpha particle is very large, approximately 28 Mev.

There is no nucleus known with $A = 5$ which exists for a measurable length of time. There are two nuclei with $A = 6$; the stable nucleus ${}_3Li^6$, and the radioactive nucleus ${}_2He^6$. Since the first shell is closed with 2 protons and 2 neutrons, the two additional nucleons must go in a shell of higher energy. The spin-orbit coupling model predicts that the next shell is not a $2s_{1/2}$ shell but a $2p_{3/2}$ shell. The latter may contain up to four nucleons of one kind. Thus for ${}_3Li^6$, with $N = 3$ and $Z = 3$, the extra neutron and proton go into the $2p_{3/2}$ shells. Since $I = 1$, the spins of these nucleons must be parallel. There is at present no measured value of I for the ground

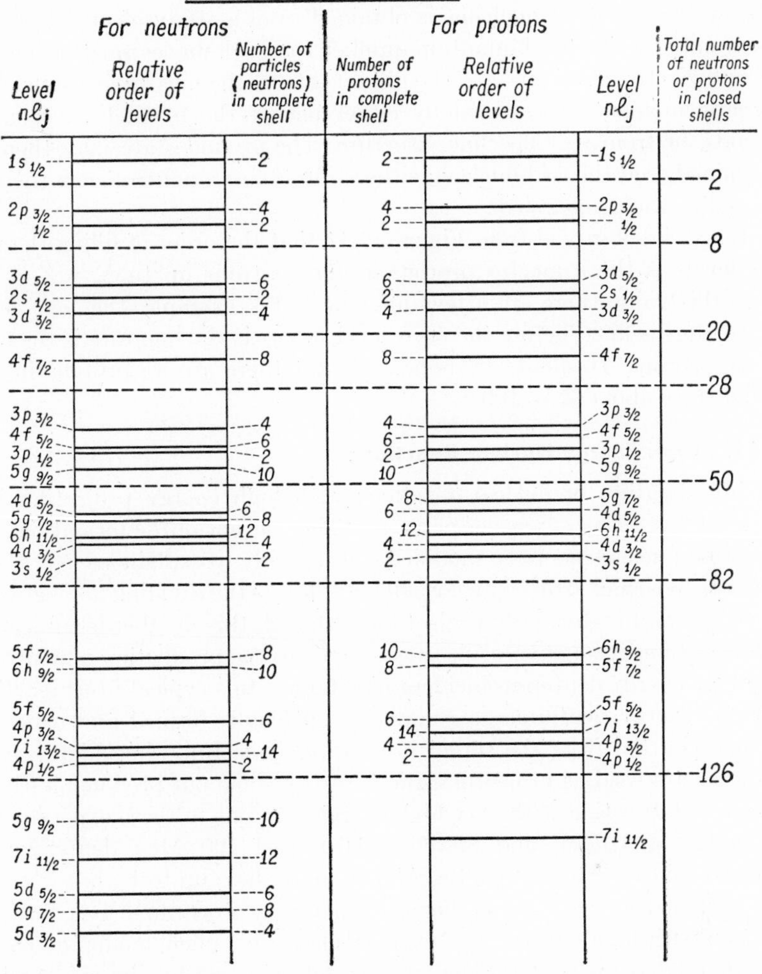

Fig. 12-11. Order of level assignments in nuclei on the basis of the shell model of the nucleus. (After Klinkenberg, *Revs. Modern Phys.*, 24, 65, 1952.)

state of $_2He^6$, but the shell model predicts that the two extra neutrons go into the $2p_{3/2}$ shell, and their spins must be opposed, so that I should be zero.

The assignment of nucleons can be continued on this shell model, checking with experimental results where available. Figure 12-11 shows the order in which the different levels appear and the maximum possible number of protons or neutrons in a given level. For example, the magic number 8 fits $_8O^{16}$, with $N = Z = 8$. This is a very stable nucleus; the measured value of $I = 0$. A great deal of information for determining the order in which shells are occupied by nucleons is obtained from a study of nuclei of odd mass numbers. The total quantum number I of such nuclei must be an odd half-integer. Its value can often be obtained from the measured value of its magnetic moment determined by either one of the magnetic resonance methods, or from its hyperfine structure. The ground state may then be determined, and the odd nucleon, either a proton or a neutron, can then be assigned to the proper shell.

It will be observed from Figure 12-11 that the order of filling the nuclear levels is the same for protons as for neutrons up to $N = Z = 50$. Above this value there are a few differences. For example, the $4d_{5/2}$ level for neutrons is filled before the $5g_{7/2}$ level, whereas the opposite is the case for the protons. It should be remarked that there are no protons in the ground state above $Z = 100$.

12-11. High Energy Nuclear Reactions

The investigation of nuclear reactions with high energy projectiles has produced several new types of processes. The concept of the formation of a compound nucleus has to be modified considerably to explain some of these processes. We shall arbitrarily consider 50 Mev as the dividing line between low energy and high energy projectiles, although this number is subject to wide variations. One of these processes involves the production of neutrons using high energy deuterons incident on a target. In a typical $(d\text{-}n)$ reaction with low energy deuterons, a compound nucleus is formed and neutrons are then emitted from the target in all directions. But when high energy deuterons are used as projectiles, the neutrons come out predominantly in the forward direction with very high energies. In one of these experiments, Hemholtz, McMillan, and Sewell (1947) used 190 Mev deuterons to bombard thin targets such as Be, Al, Cu, and others up to U; in each case they obtained a very narrow beam of neutrons proceeding in a forward direction with high energy. The explanation of this phenomenon given by R. Serber (1947) is that the deuteron is not captured by the nucleus but passes close by it, practically at grazing incidence; the proton is *stripped* off and the neutron continues with about the same velocity as the deuteron. Because of the high velocity of the deuteron, the duration of the interaction between it and the nucleus is very small, so that very little change is produced in the motion of the neutron in this *stripping* process. The final velocity of the neutron will be the vector sum of the velocity of the center of mass of the deuteron plus the velocity of the neutron relative to the center of mass. For a high energy deuteron the latter is comparatively small so that the final velocity of the neutron will have a very large component in the forward direction; its energy will be approximately half that of the deuteron.

A phenomenon allied to that of stripping, observed at lower energies, but resulting in a *d-p* process, occurs when a high energy deuteron passes close to the nucleus, say at a distance between R and $3R$, where R is the nuclear radius. The Coulomb force between the target nucleus and the proton in the deuteron may be sufficient to break the bond between the proton and the neutron, the proton being repelled and the neutron being captured by the nucleus. This process, which is a special type of stripping, is sometimes called the *Oppenheimer-Phillips process.*

The inverse of stripping is a process in which a projectile, such as a proton, a neutron, or a deuteron, picks up another particle as it passes close to the nucleus. Among these processes, called *pickup*, are *p-d*, *n-d*, and *d-t* reactions. These reactions differ from similar reactions in which a compound nucleus is formed by the fact that the particle formed in pickup has a large forward momentum, whereas particles emitted by compound nuclei show practically isotropic distributions of momenta in the center of mass system. Examples of reactions in which pickup occurs are

$$Be^9(d,t)Be^8 \quad \text{and} \quad C^{13}(d,t)C^{12}.$$

Another important process, observed when high energy particles bombard a target, involves the emission of several nuclear fragments such as protons, neutrons, and alpha particles. This process is known as *spallation.* When observed in a cloud chamber, or in a photographic research nuclear emulsion, the result of spallation is the production of a *star;* several examples of stars are given in Chapter 14. When a target of medium atomic weight is bombarded by high energy particles, the spallation products usually cover a large range of mass numbers and atomic numbers. For example, in one experiment Lindner and Perlman (1950) bombarded thin strips of antimony metal with high energy deuterons and alpha particles; the isotopes formed in the target were separated by chemical means and identified by measurements of the half-lives and absorption characteristics of their radiations with Geiger counters. Targets bombarded with 190 Mev deuterons yielded a large number of nuclides with atomic numbers ranging from $Z = 52$ down to $Z = 39$, and mass numbers ranging from $A = 124$ down to $A = 87$. Similar results were obtained with 380 Mev alpha particles as projectiles. Many of the isotopes formed were found to be neutron deficient and decayed by electron capture.

The production of such a large number of different nuclides by bombarding a target with one kind of particle of high energy must involve several different types of nuclear reactions with the formation of a compound nucleus being only one type. Serber (1947) examined the various possibilities and indicated that among them are the transfer of only a part of the projectile energy to a nucleus in a single collision; the projectile with reduced energy makes collisions with another nucleus, transferring a different amount of energy; some of the particles emitted in these collisions act as projectiles in bombarding other nuclei. Low energy particles may be captured by other nuclei resulting in the formation of a compound nucleus with ensuing reactions which are already known.

Spallation may also be produced with high energy neutrons as projectiles. Marquez (1952) bombarded a copper target with neutrons having a range of energies from 300 to 440 Mev with a peak at 370 Mev. Chemical separation of the nuclides produced, and subsequent analyses of these nuclides showed, a series of products extending from ${}_{22}Ti^{45}$ to ${}_{29}Cu^{64}$.

The method of indicating a spallation reaction by a concise notation depends upon the knowledge that is available concerning the reactants and the products. For example, if ${}_{26}Fe^{52}$, which is one of the spallation products, is produced by the bombardment of ${}_{29}Cu^{63}$ by a neutron, we may write the reaction as

$$ {}_{29}\mathrm{Cu}^{63} + {}_{0}n^{1} \rightarrow {}_{26}\mathrm{Fe}^{52} + \text{nuclear fragments}. \qquad (27)$$

In this reaction, it is apparent that the charge ${}_{26}Fe^{52}$ is 3 units less, and its mass number is 12 units less, than those of the reactants. This may be represented schematically by writing the reaction as

$$ {}_{29}\mathrm{Cu}^{63}(n,3z12a){}_{26}\mathrm{Fe}^{52}. \qquad (28)$$

This group of fragments may consist of one alpha particle, one proton, and seven neutrons, in which case the reaction may be written as

$$ {}_{29}\mathrm{Cu}^{63}(n,\alpha p7n){}_{26}\mathrm{Fe}^{52}. \qquad (29)$$

In addition to the above processes two other types of processes of great importance in nuclear physics will be discussed in the succeeding chapters. One of these is the production of new types of particles, called *mesons*, by bombarding substances with high energy protons and neutrons (see Chapter 14). The other process is *nuclear fission*. As we shall see (Chapter 13), although fission can occur spontaneously in special cases or be produced by low energy neutrons, in general, high energy projectiles are required to produce this process.

Problems

12-1. (**a**) Calculate the difference between the binding energy of a nucleus of C^{12} and the sum of the binding energies of three alpha particles. (**b**) Assuming that these alpha particles form a triangular structure with three "alpha-particle bonds" between them, calculate the binding energy provided by each alpha-particle bond.

Ans. (**a**) 7.33 Mev.
(**b**) 2.45 Mev.

12-2. What target isotope must be used to form the compound nucleus ($_{11}Na^{24}$) when the projectile is (**a**) a neutron, (**b**) a proton, and (**c**) an alpha particle?

12-3. Determine the De Broglie wavelength of (**a**) a thermal neutron whose energy is 0.025 ev; (**b**) a neutron whose energy is 200 kev.

12-4. Calculate the Coulomb barrier of $_{47}Ag^{108}$ (**a**) for protons and (**b**) for alpha particles.

12-5. (**a**) Calculate the distance of closest approach r_1 of an alpha particle having a kinetic energy of 4.2 Mev to a nucleus of charge $Ze = 90e$. (**b**) Using the value of R as the radius of the nucleus of uranium, calculate the width w of the potential barrier through which the alpha particle must pass in the disintegration of U^{238}.

12-6. Show that if the neutrino rest mass is m_ν, then the energy $\mathcal{E}_R$ of a recoil nucleus in an EC process is given by

$$\mathcal{E}_R = (\mathcal{E}_\nu^2 - m_\nu^2 c^4)/2Mc^2$$

where M is the mass of the recoil nucleus and $\mathcal{E}_\nu$ is the total energy available for the process.

12-7. Neglecting the neutrino rest mass, calculate the energy of the recoil nucleus for the *EC* reaction with (**a**) Be^7, and (**b**) A^{37}. (**c**) Calculate the velocity of the ion in each case.

12-8. C^{14} disintegrates by β^-- emission with an end-point energy of 0.155 Mev. Neglecting the neutrino rest mass, (**a**) calculate the recoil energy of the product nucleus. (**b**) A beta particle with an energy of 0.055 Mev is emitted in a direction at 135° to the direction of motion of the recoil nucleus. Determine the momenta of the three particles involved in this disintegration.

12-9. The end-point energy of the negative beta-ray spectrum of He^6 is 3.50 Mev. (**a**) Determine the recoil energy of the product nucleus. (**b**) A beta particle is ejected with a kinetic energy of 1.5 Mev at an angle of 90° to the direction of motion of the recoil nucleus. Determine the momenta of the three particles involved in this disintegration.

12-10. (**a**) Write the reaction equation for electron capture by Be^7. (**b**) Determine the Q value of this reaction. (**c**) Determine the recoil energy of the product nucleus.

Ans. (**b**) 0.875 Mev.
(**c**) 57.3 ev.

12-11. (**a**) Write the equation for the β^--decay of P^{32}. (**b**) Calculate the Q value for this decay. (**c**) When the angle between the recoil nucleus and the beta particle is 130°, the recoil momentum of the nucleus yields a value of

$Hr = 5750$ gauss cm, and that of the beta particle a value of 2150 gauss cm. Using a vector diagram, determine the momentum of the neutrino.

Ans. (b) 1.70 Mev.
(c) 4700 gauss cm.

12-12. A gamma-ray photon of energy $h\nu$ is emitted from the nucleus of an atom of mass M. (**a**) Derive an expression for the kinetic energy of the recoiling nucleus. (**b**) Ba^{137} emits a gamma-ray photon of 0.66 Mev during an isomeric transition. Calculate the recoil kinetic energy of the atom in ev.

Ans. 1.7 ev.

12-13. (**a**) Derive an expression for the recoil kinetic energy of an atom which emits a conversion electron of momentum p. (**b**) The momentum of the conversion electron in its path of radius R in a uniform magnetic field of strength H is HeR. Show that the recoil kinetic energy is given by

$$\mathcal{E}_k = \frac{e^2}{2} \frac{(HR)^2}{M}$$

where all quantities are in cgs em units. (**c**) The measured value of the momentum of the conversion electrons from Cs^{137} is given as 3380 gausses cm. Determine the recoil energy in ev.

Ans. 4 ev.

References

Bethe, H., *Elementary Nuclear Theory*. New York: John Wiley & Sons, Inc., 1947.

Blatt, J. M., and V. F. Weisskopf, *Theoretical Nuclear Physics*. New York: John Wiley & Sons, Inc., 1952.

Feingold, A. M., Table of *ft* Values in Beta Decay. *Revs. Modern Phys.*, 23, 11, 1951.

Fermi, E., *Nuclear Physics*. Notes compiled by J. Orear, A. H. Rosenfeld, and R. A. Schluter from a course given by E. Fermi. Chicago: The University of Chicago Press, 1950.

Goldhaber, M., and R. D. Hill, "Nuclear Isomerism and Shell Structure," *Revs. Modern Phys.*, 24, 179, 1952.

Segrè, E., and A. C. Helmholtz, "Nuclear Isomerism," *Revs. Modern Phys.*, 21, 271, 1949.

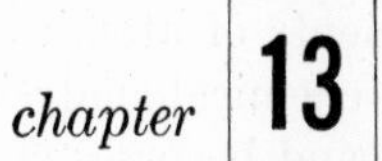

Nuclear Fission

13-1. Discovery of Nuclear Fission

By 1934 a reasonable amount of data had been accumulated on the disintegration of nuclei which were bombarded by neutrons to lead Fermi and his co-workers to try to produce elements of atomic number greater than 92 by bombarding uranium with neutrons. In their early experiments they found four beta-ray activities with different half-lives as a result of bombarding uranium with neutrons. Now uranium is a naturally radioactive substance which disintegrates with a long half-life by the emission of alpha particles; hence these beta-ray activities indicated that some new process was taking place. This new process was interpreted as the formation of one or more *transuranic* elements, that is, elements of atomic number greater than 92. Some chemical tests were therefore tried to verify this hypothesis. Element 93, for example, is a chemical homologue of manganese; that is, it occurs in the same column of the periodic table. In one chemical experiment, a manganese salt was added to a solution of a uranium salt which had been bombarded with neutrons and then precipitated out as manganese dioxide. Two of the beta-ray activities came down with the precipitate. Other chemical tests were tried which ruled out the possibility that these beta-ray activities could be due to any of the elements in the range of atomic numbers 86 to 92 inclusive. It was therefore concluded that element 93 had been produced. A chemist, Noddack, criticized this conclusion on the basis that many elements are precipitated with MnO_2 and suggested the possibility that the bombarded nuclei were split into nuclei of elements of lower atomic number. This suggestion was apparently ignored, and other workers, particularly I. Curie and her co-workers, and Hahn, Strassmann, and Meitner, entered this field in search of the transuranic elements. Uranium, thorium, and protactinium were bombarded with neutrons and many different beta-ray activities discovered. These were carefully checked by both physical and chemical methods to determine the nature of the emitters, and until early in 1939 they were generally ascribed to radioactive substances of atomic number greater than 92. Several new radioactive series were suggested to account for these activities; each one started with uranium and by a series of beta-particle disintegrations led to elements of atomic numbers as high as 96 and 97. It must be pointed out that chemical analysis in this region of the periodic table is extremely difficult and becomes even more difficult because of the very small samples of newly formed radioactive material available.

In 1939 Hahn and Strassmann found, after a series of very careful chemical experiments, that one of the radioactive elements formed by the bombardment of uranium with neutrons was an isotope of the element barium, $Z = 56$. Another of the radioactive elements thus formed was the rare-earth element lanthanum, $Z = 57$. It is obvious that the lanthanum is formed by the beta decay of the barium. Hahn and Strassmann therefore suggested that the beta-ray activities previously ascribed to transuranic elements are probably produced by radioactive isotopes of elements of lower atomic number. The process that is started by bombarding uranium with neutrons is one in which the new uranium nucleus becomes unstable and splits up into two nuclei of medium atomic masses; if one nucleus formed is barium, $Z = 56$, the other nucleus must be krypton, $Z = 36$. This type of disintegration process in which a heavy nucleus splits up into two nuclei of nearly comparable masses is called *nuclear fission.*

As soon as the discovery of nuclear fission was announced early in 1939, physicists in laboratories throughout the world where neutron sources were available immediately repeated and confirmed these experiments. Within the next two years the results were extended to include the nuclear fission of thorium and protactinium, the measurement of the energies of the bombarding neutrons necessary to produce fission in the particular isotope of the heavy element, the amount of energy released in nuclear fission, and analyses of the products of nuclear fission together with their genetic relationships.

13-2. Fission of Uranium

In the process of nuclear fission a very much greater amount of energy is released than that ever previously encountered in any nuclear or atomic process. In addition to the release of energy, the fission of uranium was accompanied by the emission of several neutrons. It was immediately apparent that these neutrons could be utilized, under proper conditions, to produce fission of other uranium nuclei and thus a *chain reaction* could be initiated which could result in the release of tremendous amounts of energy. The first successful *nuclear reactor* utilizing the fission of uranium nuclei in a self-sustaining chain reaction was constructed at Chicago and operated successfully on December 2, 1942. This reactor, sometimes known as a *uranium graphite pile* because of the manner in which it was constructed, was built under the direction of E. Fermi by groups headed by W. H. Zinn and H. L. Anderson. Since then many other nuclear reactors of various designs have been built throughout the world.

An idea of the amount of energy released in nuclear fission can be obtained by considering one example of the fission of uranium, $Z = 92$, $A = 235$, assuming that the fission products are barium, $Z = 56$, $A = 141$, and krypton, $Z = 36$, $A = 92$, with the prompt release of 3 neutrons. We can write the equation for this reaction as

$$ {}_0n^1 + {}_{92}U^{235} \rightarrow ({}_{92}U^{236}) \rightarrow {}_{56}Ba^{141} + {}_{36}Kr^{92} + 3{}_0n^1 + Q \quad (1) $$

where Q represents the energy released in this reaction. This energy is provided by the difference in mass between the initial products and the final products. A simple way of calculating this difference in mass is with the aid of the packing fraction curve, as shown in Figure 2-23. The following are approximate packing fractions obtained from this curve:

Packing fractions × 10^4	Mass defect × 10^4
${}_0n^1 = 90$	90
${}_{92}U^{235} = 5$	1175
${}_{36}Kr^{92} = -8$	−736
${}_{56}Ba^{141} = -3$	−423
$3{}_0n^1$ —	270
Δm	2154

Since the number of nucleons before and after the fission process is the same, the difference between the mass defects of the nuclides on the two sides of the equation is equal to their difference in mass. In this particular case, the decrease in mass is 0.2154 amu. Since 931 Mev = 1 amu, this decrease in mass corresponds to a release of energy of about 200 Mev. This value is more than 20 times as great as that released in the average alpha-particle disintegration (5 to 10 Mev), and millions of times greater than that released in the process of combustion.

The fission of a nucleus results in the production of two massive particles having equal and opposite momenta. Figure 13-1 is a cloud-chamber photograph of the fission of uranium showing the tracks of two massive fragments traveling practically in opposite directions. The kinetic energies of these fission particles are in the inverse ratio of their masses. These fission products are unstable, each having an excess number of neutrons. Each particle may emit one or two neutrons shortly after fission but in a time too short to be measured, probably in less than 10^{-15} second.

Such neutrons are called *prompt neutrons;* they have been included in equation (1). Other neutrons may be emitted later; such neutrons are called *delayed neutrons* (see §13-7).

Uranium fission can be produced by both slow and fast neutrons. On the basis of Bohr's theory of nuclear processes, nuclear fission takes place in two steps: (1) the formation of the compound nucleus in which the energy is temporarily stored among the different degrees of freedom of the nuclear particles in a manner similar to that of thermal agitation of

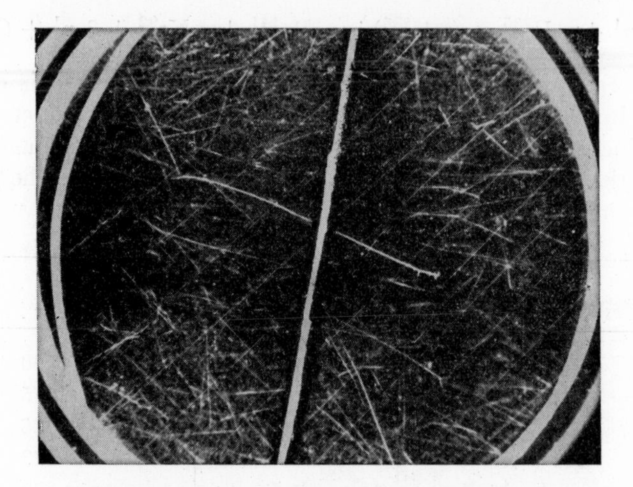

FIG. 13-1. Cloud-chamber photograph of the tracks produced by two fission particles; these particles are the products of the fission of uranium which has captured a neutron. The uranium is on the foil shown in the center of the chamber. (From a photograph by J. K. Bøggild, K. J. Brøstrom, and T. Lauritsen.)

a liquid, and (2) the transformation of a sufficient portion of this energy into potential energy of deformation of the compound nucleus which will lead to its fission. The possibility of the occurrence of fission by bombarding a nucleus with neutrons depends, therefore, on the difference between the critical energy $\mathcal{E}_c$ of such an unstable deformation of the nucleus and the energy used to excite the nucleus; the latter is determined by the binding energy, W_n, of the added neutron. Bohr and Wheeler have made estimates of these values for some of the heavy elements; these are listed in Table 13-1.

From Table 13-1 it can be seen that the uranium isotope of mass number $A = 235$ should be responsible for the fission produced by slow neutrons. This was confirmed experimentally by Nier, Booth, Dunning, and Grosse. They first separated small quantities of the uranium isotopes, $A = 235$ and $A = 238$, by means of the mass spectrometer, and then bombarded each of these isotopes with slow neutrons. They observed practically no fission with uranium, $A = 238$, but did get a fairly large

Table 13-1

Bombarded Nucleus	Compound Nucleus	Critical Energy $\mathcal{E}_c$ in Mev	Binding Energy W_n in Mev	$\mathcal{E}_c - W_n$ in Mev
92 U 234	92 U 235	5.0	5.4	−0.4
92 U 235	92 U 236	5.3	6.4	−1.1
92 U 238	92 U 239	5.9	5.2	0.7
91 Pa 231	91 Pa 232	5.5	5.4	0.1
90 Th 232	90 Th 233	6.9	5.2	1.7
90 Io 230	90 Io 231	6.5	5.3	1.2

number of fissions with $A = 235$. Furthermore, the rate of fission per microgram of uranium 235 observed in this experiment was in good agreement with the number obtained under the same experimental conditions from unseparated samples of uranium containing the normal percentage of uranium 235.

13-3. Energies of the Fission Fragments

The measurement of the kinetic energy of the fission fragments and the distribution in energy among these fragments has been carried on over a period of years, some by calorimetric methods, but mostly by ionization

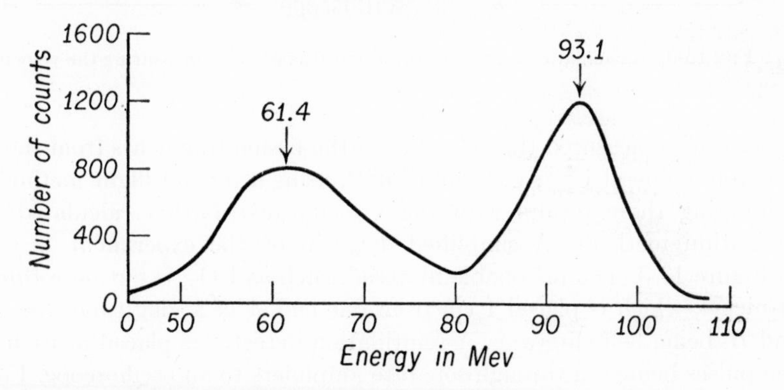

Fig. 13-2. Energy spectrum of the fission fragments produced in the slow neutron fission of uranium 235. (After Fowler and Rosen, *Phys. Rev.*, 72, 928, 1947.)

methods. Fowler and Rosen (1947) using a specially designed ionization chamber, determined the distribution in energy of the fragments from the fission of U^{235} by both slow and fast neutrons. Figure 13-2 shows the distribution in energy among the fission fragments of the slow neutron fission of U^{235}. There are two definite peaks to the curve, one at 61.4 Mev and the other at 93.1 Mev. They obtained a similar curve for the distribution in energy of the fragments from the fission of U^{235} by fast neutrons with a range of energy from 1 kev to about 1 Mev, with the peaks shifted slightly to higher energies. The kinetic energy of a fission fragment was calculated from the ionization current on the assumption that the energy required to produce an ion pair in the gas of the chamber is the same for a fission product as for an alpha particle.

The assumption that the energy required to produce an ion pair in a gas is the same for a highly charged fission fragment as for an alpha particle is open to question. This problem was investigated by Leachman

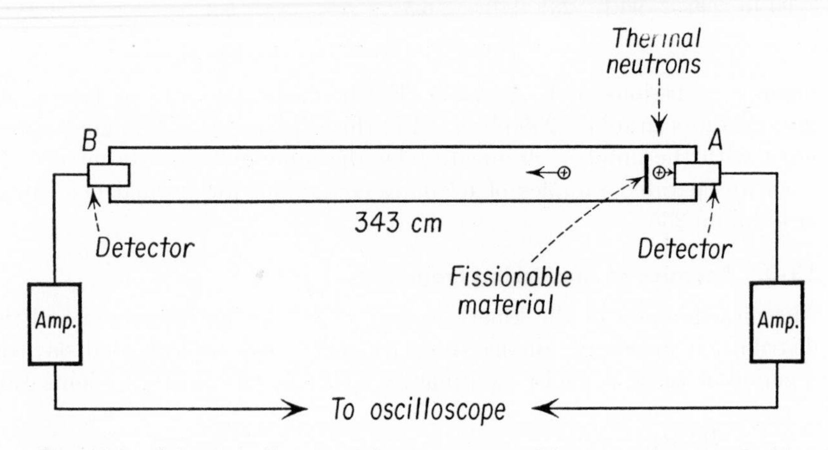

FIG. 13-3. Schematic diagram of the apparatus used for measuring the velocities of fission fragments.

(1952), who measured the velocities of the fission fragments from the slow neutron fission of U^{233}, U^{235}, and Pu^{239}, using a time-of-flight method and comparing these results with the velocity distribution calculated from ionization methods. A simplified diagram of the experiment is shown in Figure 13-3. The fissionable material, such as UO_3, is put on a thin foil of nickel, which is placed 1 cm from one end A of a long tube; the other end B, being 343 cm away. A scintillation detector is placed at each end, the pulses being fed through separate amplifiers to an oscilloscope. Fission is induced by slow neutrons from a nuclear reactor. When fission occurs, one fragment travels 1 cm and produces a pulse, the other fragment travels 343 cm and produces a pulse; the time interval between these pulses is then determined from the oscillograph record. The results for the distribution in velocity of the fission fragments for U^{235} are shown in the full curve of Figure 13-4; the dashed curve is that computed from ionization measurements. The curves have the same general features; the peaks of the curve obtained by the time-of-flight method are both shifted to higher velocities relative to the curve obtained from ionization methods. From these data, the shift in the peak for the light fragment is 5.7 Mev and that for the heavy fragment is 6.5 Mev.

Using the previously measured kinetic energies of the fission fragments, 61.4 Mev and 93.1 Mev, and adding the above values of 5.7 Mev and

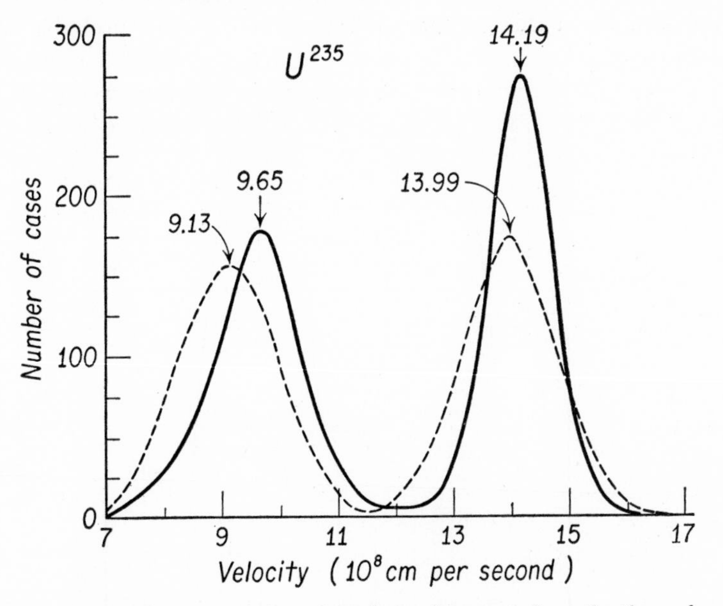

FIG. 13-4. Distribution in velocity of the fission fragments from the thermal neutron fission of uranium 235. (After Leachman, *Phys. Rev.*, 87, 444, 1952.)

6.5 Mev, we obtain for the total kinetic energies of the fission fragments 166.7 Mev.

Similar results were obtained for the velocity distributions of the fragments from the thermal neutron fission of U^{233} and Pu^{239}.

13-4. Some Products of Nuclear Fission

Many different atomic nuclei have been produced by the fission of uranium and thorium as a result of bombarding them with neutrons. Most of these fission products have been identified by chemical tests; others, by means of the x-rays emitted by the excited atoms produced during fission. In many cases the particular isotopes produced have been identified by comparing their half-life periods with those produced by other types of nuclear reactions. The fact that so many different fission products have been produced indicates that the excited uranium or thorium nucleus can split up in many different ways. All of the presently known fission products are elements in the middle of the periodic table with atomic numbers ranging from $Z = 30$ to $Z = 63$.

The relative distribution of the different nuclides among the fission products depends upon the energy of excitation available for the fission process. Figure 13-5 is a graph showing the fission yield (in percentages) plotted against the mass number of the fission fragment for the fission of uranium 235. From this graph, it is seen that the most probable values

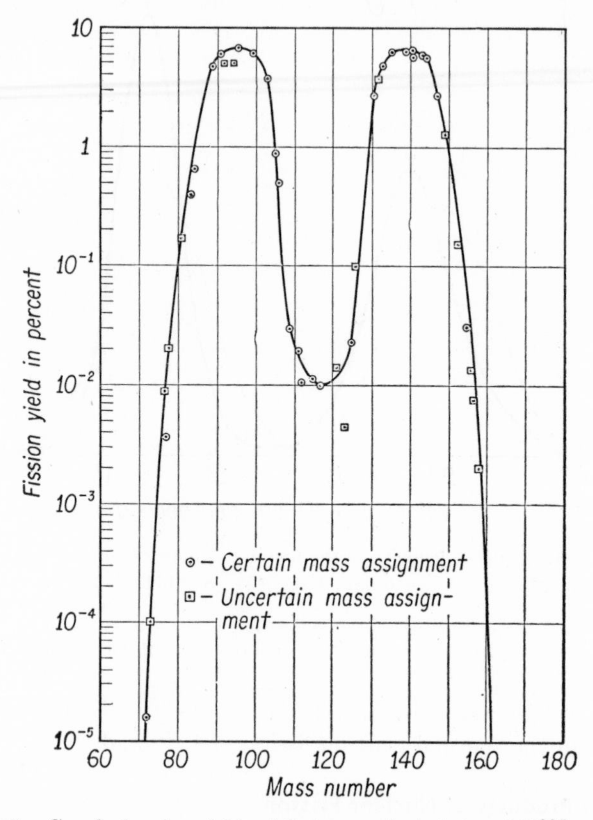

FIG. 13-5. Graph showing yields of fission product chains of U^{235} as a function of mass number. (After "Plutonium Project Report on Nuclei Formed in Fission," *Revs. Modern Phys.*, 18, 539, 1946.)

for the mass numbers of the two fission fragments are about 95 and 139 when two prompt neutrons are emitted simultaneously. It will be observed that the yield passes through a minimum at mass number 117, corresponding to fragments of equal mass. The yield curve drops rapidly at mass numbers 72 and 162.

The ratio of the number of neutrons to the number of protons, that is N/Z, for uranium is about 1.6. For stable elements in the range of atomic numbers 30 to 63, the range of maximum values of N/Z is 1.3 to 1.5; hence the fission fragments will have an excess of neutrons. The fission products will therefore be unstable; they will thus go to a more stable form either by beta disintegration or by the emission of one or more excess neutrons. Neutrons emitted a measurable time after the fission process are called *delayed neutrons;* they play an important role in the control of nuclear reactors. The beta-decay chain leading to a stable nuclide has been followed for a great many fission products. For example, the heaviest stable isotope of barium has a mass number 138; hence barium 141, one of the fission products of uranium, is unstable because it has an excess of 3 neutrons. The beta-decay chain of barium 141 has been found to be

$$_{56}Ba^{141} \xrightarrow[18\text{ min}]{} {}_{57}La^{141} \xrightarrow[3.7\text{ hr}]{} {}_{58}Ce^{141} \xrightarrow[28\text{ da}]{} {}_{59}Pr^{141}. \qquad (2)$$

The end product of this chain is a stable isotope of praseodymium. Similarly, krypton 92 is unstable and starts a beta-decay chain which ends in a stable isotope of zirconium:

$$_{36}Kr^{92} \xrightarrow[2.4\text{ sec}]{} {}_{37}Rb^{92} \longrightarrow {}_{38}Sr^{92} \xrightarrow[2.7\text{ hr}]{} {}_{39}Y^{92} \xrightarrow[3.5\text{ hr}]{} {}_{40}Zr^{92}. \qquad (3)$$

The assignment of the mass number to the particular isotope produced in the fission process is aided by the production of the same beta activity by other methods. For example, the 3.5-hr activity of ytterbium 92 can be produced in an *n-p* reaction with zirconium. Similarly, the 28-day activity of cerium can be produced by an *α-n* reaction with barium as well as by several other reactions.

13-5. Neutrons Released in the Fission of Uranium

One of the first problems to be solved is the determination of the number of neutrons released for each fission process produced. Szilard and Zinn (1939) performed an experiment to determine the number of fast neutrons emitted in the fission of uranium by slow neutrons. The arrangement of the apparatus used by them is shown in Figure 13-6. The neutrons were emitted as a result of the photodisintegration of beryllium by the action of the gamma rays from radium. A helium-filled ionization chamber F connected to a linear amplifier was used as a detector of fast neutrons. The neutrons from the beryllium B were slowed down by the paraffin C, and then bombarded the uranium oxide contained in the cylindrical box E. When desired, the uranium oxide could be shielded from the slow neutrons by interposing a sheet of cadmium H. A cadmium sheet G was also used to shield the ionization chamber from slow neutrons.

When the uranium oxide was exposed to the action of slow neutrons by the removal of the shield H, Szilard and Zinn observed 50 pulses per minute in the helium ionization chamber. When the cadmium shield was in place, only 5 pulses per minute were obtained. The difference of 45 pulses per minute must therefore be due to fast neutrons emitted from the uranium under the action of the thermal neutrons.

In order to estimate the number of fast neutrons emitted per fission under the action of slow or thermal neutrons, the helium ionization chamber was replaced by another chamber which was lined with a layer of uranium

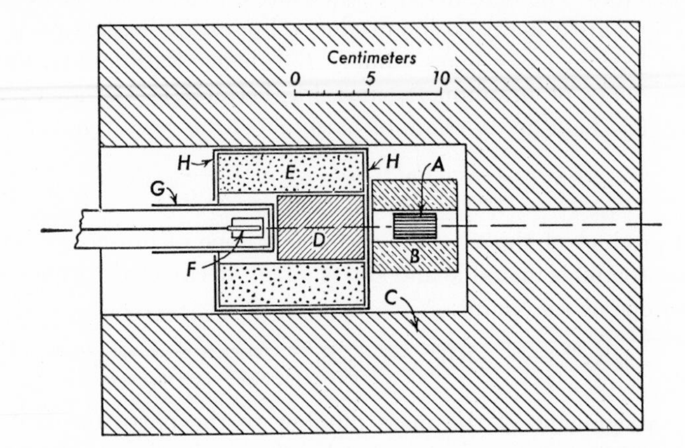

FIG. 13-6. Arrangement of the apparatus for the observation of the emission of fast neutrons from uranium bombarded by slow neutrons. *A*, radium; *B*, beryllium block; *C*, paraffin; *D*, lead block; *E*, box filled with uranium oxide; *F*, ionization chamber; *G*, cap of cadmium sheet; *H*, shield of cadmium sheet.

oxide of known area. The fast neutrons which entered this ionization chamber produced fission of some of the uranium, and the number of fissions per minute was counted. Making some reasonable assumptions concerning the range of fission particles in uranium oxide, they then were able to estimate the number of fissions per minute produced in the large amount of uranium oxide in the cylinder *E*. Combining this result with the count of the number of fast neutrons which were recorded by the helium ionization chamber, Szilard and Zinn estimated that two fast neutrons were emitted per fission of uranium by slow neutrons.

In a further refinement of this experiment the uranium oxide was replaced by a cell containing about 430 grams of uranium metal, and a high-pressure spherical ionization chamber containing hydrogen at 10 atmospheres pressure and argon at 8 atmospheres pressure was used to determine the number of neutrons emitted per fission. The ionization chamber was connected to an oscillograph and the pulses due to the recoil protons produced by collisions with the high energy fission neutrons were recorded photographically. Since the probability or cross section for scattering of protons by neutrons is a function of the neutron energy, the distribution of energy among the fission neutrons was also determined. The result of this experiment led to a value of 2.3 neutrons per fission.

At about the same time (1939) von Halban, Joliot, and Kowarski made a determination of the number of neutrons per fission of uranium and obtained a value of 3.5 ± 0.7. After the start of World War II, physicists in the United States decided to withhold further information on the results of experiments on nuclear fission because of its obvious importance in producing a nuclear chain reaction. After 1945 some information on this subject began to be released. In 1950, information was released giving the average number of neutrons emitted per fission of uranium 235 by thermal neutrons as 2.5 ± 0.1.

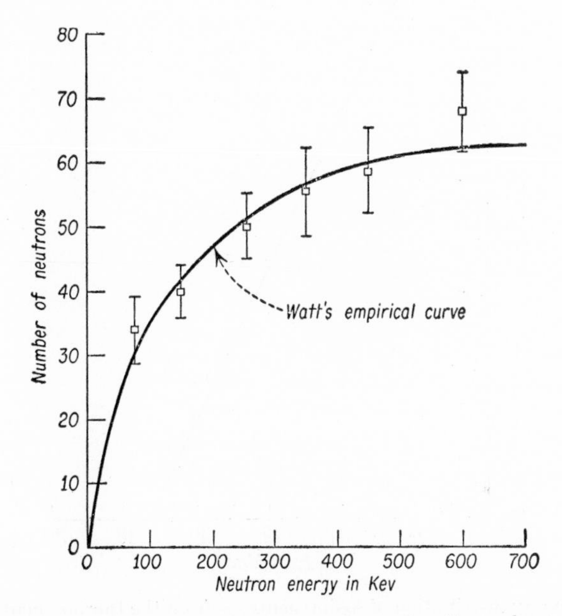

FIG. 13-7. Energy distribution of neutrons from the thermal neutron fission of uranium 235 in the low energy range. (After Bonner, Ferrell, and Rinehart, *Phys. Rev.*, 87, 1033, 1952.)

13-6. Energy of Neutrons from Thermal Fission of U 235

The energy spectrum of the neutrons emitted in the thermal fission of uranium 235 has been determined by measuring the energy of the recoil protons ejected by the neutrons from hydrogen or a substance containing hydrogen. The energy spectrum was found to extend from about 0.05 Mev to about 17 Mev. In the low energy range, Bonner, Ferrell, and Rinehart (1952) used a cloud chamber containing hydrogen at a pressure of $\frac{1}{3}$ of an atmosphere. Neutrons from the thermal fission of uranium entered the cloud chamber and produced recoil protons by collisions with hydrogen. The energy spectrum of the fission neutrons was determined from the number of tracks produced by these recoil protons and the lengths of these tracks. This spectrum is shown in Figure 13-7. The graph shows the number of neutrons $N(\mathcal{E})$ per 100 kev energy interval as a function of the neutron energy from about 75 to 600 kev.

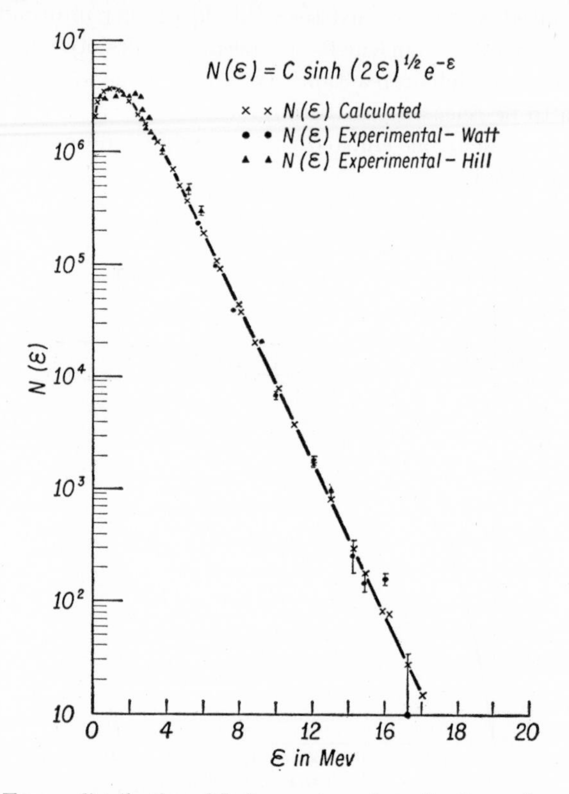

FIG. 13-8. Energy distribution of fission neutrons from the thermal neutron fission of uranium 235. (After Watt, *Phys. Rev.*, 87, 1040, 1952.)

The spectrum of the fission neutrons in the energy range from 0.4 to 7 Mev was measured by D. L. Hill (1952). The fission neutrons emitted in the thermal fission of uranium 235 ejected protons from a layer of paraffin; these protons then passed through an absorbing material and were detected in a series of counters. The amount of absorbing material between the paraffin and the counters yielded the range of the protons. The energy of the protons, and hence the energy of the neutrons, could be determined from the range-energy relationship of the protons. A different technique was used by B. E. Watt (1952) to determine the energy spectrum of the neutrons in the range from 3.3 to 17 Mev. The fission neutrons ejected protons from a polyethylene foil and were detected by a set of counters. Different thicknesses of aluminum absorbers were placed in the path of the protons; the range of the protons reaching the counters could then be determined from the amount of absorbing material in their path. The energy of the protons was determined from the known range-energy relationship, and the energy of the incident neutrons calculated from it. The results of the measurements of both Hill and Watt are shown on the single graph of Figure 13-8. This curve shows a maximum in the region of 0.75 Mev. This distribution in energy is well represented by the equation

$$N(\mathcal{E}) = C \sinh (2\mathcal{E})^{1/2} e^{-\mathcal{E}}, \qquad (4)$$

where $N(\mathcal{E})$ is the number of neutrons within a given energy interval, and C is an empirically determined constant. The results obtained by Bonner, Ferrell, and Rinehart are also represented by the above equation.

13-7. Delayed Neutron Emission by Fission Fragments

A nucleus which has an excess of neutrons may decay either by β^--emission or by neutron emission, depending upon the energy of the nucleus with respect to each of these processes. Bohr and Wheeler (1939), in their theory of nuclear fission, predicted the possibility of neutron emission from some of the fission products. Neutron emission would most likely occur if, in the process of beta decay, the product nucleus is left in an excited state with an energy in excess of the binding energy of a neutron in that nucleus. The neutron would then be emitted promptly, that is, with an immeasurably short lifetime. However, since the nucleus emitting the neutron was formed in a beta-decay process, the neutron activity of a sample will have the same period or half-life as the beta activity of the parent nuclide. Such neutron emission is called *delayed neutron emission*, and the neutrons emitted in this process are termed *delayed neutrons.*

Delayed neutrons from fission products of uranium were first detected by Roberts, Meyer, and Wang (1939), who observed the continued emission of neutrons after the fission of uranium had ceased. Booth, Dunning, and Slack (1939) also observed delayed neutron emission and measured two different half-lives of the neutron activity. Because of the importance of the delayed neutrons in the control of a chain reaction, they were intensively studied for the design of the first uranium pile. More recently, Hughes, Dabbs, Cahn, and Hall (1948) made accurate determinations of the half-lives of the delayed neutrons accompanying the fission of uranium 235 in the heavy water pile of the Argonne Laboratory. Their results are given in Table 13-2.

The origins of some of the delayed neutrons have been established by chemical tests. A. H. Snell and his co-workers (1947) showed that the 55.6-second delayed-neutron activity came from an excited state of krypton

Table 13-2

Delayed Neutrons from Fission of U^{235}		
Half-Life in Seconds	Energy of Neutrons in Kev	Yield (Relative to Total Neutron Emission) in Percentages
55.6	250	0.025
22.0	560	0.166
4.51	430	0.213
1.52	620	0.241
0.43	420	0.085
0.05	—	0.025
Total Yield		0.755

87 formed by the beta decay of bromine 87 with a half-life of 56 seconds. Figure 13-9(a) shows the nuclear disintegration scheme suggested by them

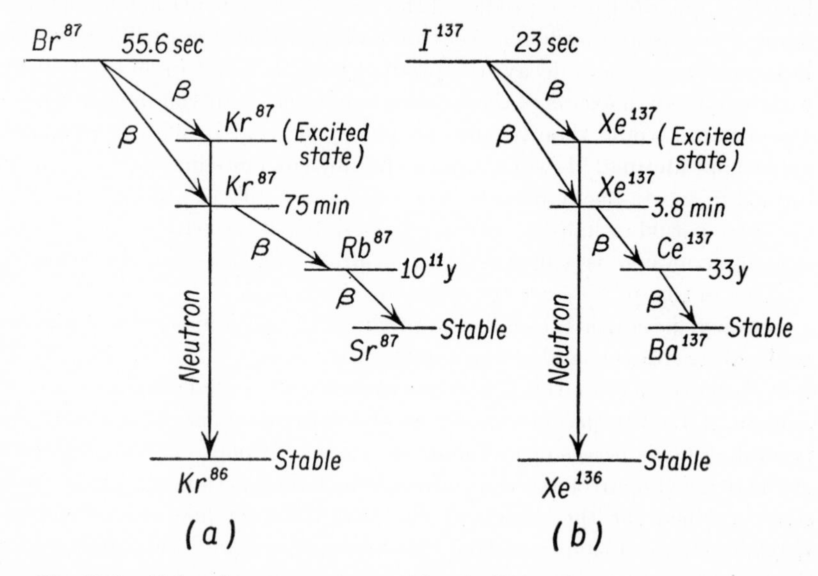

Fig. 13-9. Delayed neutron emitters. (After Snell, Levinger, Meiners, Sampson, and Wilkinson, *Phys. Rev.*, 72, 545, 1947.)

for the delayed neutron emission. Bromine 87 may disintegrate with the emission of a beta particle of small energy, forming krypton 87 in an excited state; the latter promptly emits a neutron forming krypton 86 in the ground state. A branching process also occurs in which bromine 87 emits a beta particle with a larger energy, forming krypton 87 in a lower energy state. This is followed by a beta decay to rubidium 87 with a half-life of 75 minutes. This nuclide of rubidium is found in nature and has a very long half-life of about 10^{11} years, undergoing beta decay to a stable form of strontium 87. An exactly analogous decay scheme was found by Snell and his co-workers for the 23-minute delayed-neutron activity. This follows the beta decay of iodine 137 to xenon 137 as shown in Figure 13-9(b).

13-8. Transuranic Elements—Neptunium and Plutonium

The capture of a neutron by uranium does not necessarily lead to the fission of the compound nucleus. Uranium 238, for example, has a small capture cross section for neutrons of low energy. For certain values of the neutron energy, the capture cross section becomes very large. These values are known as the resonance energies. One value of this resonance energy has been determined by H. L. Anderson (1940) as about 11 ev. The importance of the capture of neutrons by uranium 238 is that it leads, through a series of disintegrations given below, to the formation of two transuranic elements, *neptunium* (Np), $Z = 93$, and *plutonium* (Pu), $Z = 94$.

It was not until 1940 that the existence of transuranic elements was definitely established. McMillan and Abelson discovered the first transuranic element, neptunium, by bombarding uranium with low energy neutrons. The capture of neutrons by uranium 238 in an n-γ reaction led to the formation of a new isotope of uranium, $A = 239$, which decays by beta-ray emission with a half-life of 23.5 minutes resulting in the formation of neptunium. The following are the nuclear reactions:

$$_{92}U^{238} + {}_0n^1 \rightarrow ({}_{92}U^{239}) \rightarrow {}_{92}U^{239} + h\nu \qquad (5)$$

followed by

$$_{92}U^{239} \rightarrow {}_{93}Np^{239} + \beta^-, \quad T = 23.5 \text{ min.} \qquad (6)$$

McMillan and Abelson performed chemical experiments with the minute quantities, so-called *tracer* amounts, of the element formed in the above process and showed that its oxidation states differed from those of uranium. This was the first time that the existence of a new element was established by chemical experiments on a tracer scale of investigation.

The neptunium formed in the above reaction is also radioactive, emitting a beta particle to form a new transuranic element of atomic number 94, now known as *plutonium*. The following is the nuclear reaction for this process:

$$_{93}Np^{239} \rightarrow {}_{94}Pu^{239} + \beta^-, \quad T = 2.3 \text{ da.} \qquad (7)$$

This isotope of plutonium is radioactive with a long half-life and emits an alpha particle according to the following reaction:

$$_{94}Pu^{239} \rightarrow {}_{92}U^{235} + {}_2He^4, \quad T = 24{,}000 \text{ yr.} \qquad (8)$$

This isotope of plutonium plays an important part in an atomic bomb project because it is fissionable with both slow neutrons and fast neutrons.

A different isotope of plutonium was discovered shortly after the discovery of neptunium. This transuranic element was discovered by Seaborg, McMillan, Wahl, and Kennedy late in 1940. They bombarded uranium with deuterons and showed that the following reactions occurred:

$$_{92}U^{238} + {}_1H^2 \rightarrow ({}_{93}Np^{240}) \rightarrow {}_{93}Np^{238} + {}_0n^1 + {}_0n^1 \tag{9}$$

followed by $$_{93}Np^{238} \rightarrow {}_{94}Pu^{238} + \beta^-, \quad T = 2.1 \text{ da}, \tag{10}$$

and then $$_{94}Pu^{238} \rightarrow {}_{92}U^{234} + {}_2He^4, \quad T = 92 \text{ yr}. \tag{11}$$

The chemical properties of plutonium determined with the minute amounts available from the above reactions formed the basis for setting up the so-called *chain-reacting* units at Clinton, Tennessee, and Hanford, Washington, for the production of plutonium on a large scale for use in the atomic bomb. Once the chemical properties of plutonium were known it seemed reasonable to hunt for these elements in nature. Pitchblende ore, one of the sources of uranium, was examined by Seaborg and Perlman; they made a chemical separation of neptunium and plutonium and were able to show the presence of a small quantity of alpha activity in the transuranium fraction which they attributed to plutonium, $A = 239$. The amount of plutonium in the pitchblende corresponds to about 1 part in 10^{14}, an amount which could not possibly be found had the chemical properties not been known. It probably is being formed continuously as a result of the radiative capture of neutrons by some of the uranium present in the ore.

Another isotope of neptunium, $A = 237$, was discovered by Wahl and Seaborg in 1942. This is produced in the following reactions:

$$_{92}U^{238} + {}_0n^1 \rightarrow ({}_{92}U^{239}) \rightarrow {}_{92}U^{237} + {}_0n^1 + {}_0n^1 \tag{12}$$

followed by $$_{92}U^{237} \rightarrow {}_{93}Np^{237} + \beta^-, \quad T = 7 \text{ da}, \tag{13}$$

and $$_{93}Np^{237} \rightarrow {}_{91}Pa^{233} + {}_2He^4, \quad T = 2.25 \times 10^6 \text{ yr}. \tag{14}$$

The fact that this isotope is comparatively stable makes it particularly suitable for the chemical investigations of the properties of neptunium.

A large number of isotopes of neptunium, ranging in mass number from 231 to 239, have since been produced. Similarly, a large number of isotopes of plutonium have since been produced; they range in mass number from 232 to 242.

Other transuranic elements, of atomic numbers 95, 96, 97, and 98, have also been produced. These will be discussed in Chapter 15.

13-9. Photofission of Nuclei

Almost any method which will make a nucleus sufficiently unstable can be used to produce the fission of uranium and thorium. One method is to bombard these nuclei with high energy photons. Haxby, Shoupp, Stephens, and Wells (1941) were the first to produce such fission with gamma rays. Gamma-ray photons of 6.3 Mev energy, obtained by bombarding fluorite, CaF_2, with high energy protons, were used to irradiate a 12 cm^2 piece of uranium metal placed on the high-voltage plate of an ionization chamber. The fission products were measured by the pulses of ionization they produced in this chamber. Baldwin and Koch (1945) used the high energy x-ray photons produced by the betatron to induce the fission of uranium. Uranium oxide coated on a cylinder was irradiated with x-ray photons of energies from 8 Mev to 16 Mev. The fission fragments were collected on a paper cylinder held over this sample. The beta decay of the fission fragments was then examined with a counter. Fission products were observed for all values of the x-ray energies used in irradiating the uranium down to about 8 Mev. They estimate that the threshold for the photofission of uranium is less than 7 Mev.

Baldwin and Koch also tried to produce photofission in lead but were unsuccessful, even with x-ray photons of 16 Mev energy.

Koch, McElhinney, and Gasteiger (1950) were able to make more accurate determinations of the photofission thresholds by allowing the x-rays from a 20 Mev betatron, operated at suitable energies, to be incident on samples of separated isotopes of uranium, plutonium, and thorium. The values obtained by them are given in Table 13-3. It will be noted that these values do not vary very much from nuclide to nuclide in this range of mass numbers.

Table 13-3

Nuclide	Photofission Threshold in Mev
90 Th 230	5.40
92 U 233	5.18
92 U 235	5.31
92 U 238	5.08
94 Pu 239	5.31

The photofission of uranium and thorium was investigated by E. W. Titterton and co-workers (1950), using the continuous x-ray beam from the Harwell synchrotron with a maximum energy of 24 Mev. They used a photographic plate technique; for studying the photofission of uranium, the emulsion of an Ilford D_1 plate of 100μ thickness was impregnated with uranium from a saturated solution of uranium nitrate. When dry, it was exposed to the x-ray beam and then developed. For the study of the photofission of thorium, a similar plate was impregnated with thorium from a thorium nitrate solution. In each case they observed the typical tracks in the emulsion produced by the fission fragments moving in opposite directions. They measured the ranges of these particles and compared the kinetic energies of the fission fragments from thorium with those produced in slow neutron fission of U^{235}. They found that the average kinetic energy released in the photofission of Th^{232} was about 0.8 of that released in the slow-neutron fission of U^{235}.

In addition to the tracks of the fission fragments, they occasionally found a thin, long-range track produced by an alpha particle. This alpha particle is probably released at the instant of fission and travels approximately at right angles to the tracks of the fission fragments. There were a few cases in which a third track accompanying fission was an extremely short track, about 5μ in length, indicating the emission of a more massive particle than an alpha particle. Dewan and Allen (1949), in an investigation of *ternary fission* of uranium 235 for slow neutrons, had similarly observed short-range particles, of ranges less than 1 cm in air, and concluded that these particles had masses of the order of $A = 13$.

13-10. Ternary Fission

Shortly after nuclear fission was discovered, R. Present (1941), using the Bohr liquid drop model of the nucleus, predicted the possibility of the tripartition, or ternary fission; that is, the division of an excited heavy nucleus disintegrating by division into three nuclei of comparable masses. This process is comparatively rare and, at present, the evidence for it is meager. L. Rosen and A. M. Hudson (1949), in a preliminary report on the tripartition of U^{235} bombarded with slow neutrons, found about 4.3 ternary fissions per 10^6 binary fissions. In other work on ternary fission, two massive fragments have been observed with the third particle usually a long-range alpha particle, and in a few cases a somewhat heavier particle. For example, K. W. Allen and J. T. Dewan (1950), in their investigation of the ternary fission of U^{233}, U^{235}, and Pu^{239} bombarded by slow neutrons, found that a long-range alpha particle accompanied the fission of these nuclei in about 0.2 per cent of the fissions. The average kinetic energy of the alpha particles was found to be about 15 Mev with a maximum energy of about 26 Mev. This is in agreement with the results reported for the ternary fission in the photofission of uranium.

In an investigation of the ternary fission of U^{235} by slow neutrons, E. W. Titterton, using the photographic emulsion technique, observed that most of the long-range alpha particles were emitted at right angles to the line of motion of the two massive fission fragments. The distribution of energy among these alpha particles showed a maximum at about 29 Mev, with the greatest number having energies in the neighborhood of 15 Mev. The observed maximum alpha-particle energy suggests the idea that the alpha particle is left between the massive fission fragments at the instant of fission and acquires its kinetic energy from the electrostatic fields of these nuclei. He found that the frequency of occurrence of ternary fission is about 1 in 400 binary fissions, in agreement with the results of Allen and Dewan. He also found a few very short tracks which seemed to indicate the formation of nuclei with charges $Z > 2$, but found no evidence of ternary fission into three approximately equal masses. Allen and Dewan (1951) also investigated these short-range (< 1 cm air equivalent) particles accompanying nuclear fission of uranium; from the initial specific ionization along their tracks, the masses were estimated to be of the order of $A = 13 \pm 4$. Their frequency of occurrence was comparatively high, about 1 in 72 fissions.

13-11. Spontaneous Fission

The occurrence of the spontaneous fission of a heavy nucleus was first observed by Petrzhak and Flerov (1940), who detected the spontaneous fission of natural uranium. E. Segrè (1952) reported on the work done on the spontaneous fission of heavy nuclei at Los Alamos up to January, 1946, by himself and co-workers. The substance under investigation was deposited in a thin layer on a platinum disk and placed inside an ionization chamber connected to a linear amplifier; the ionization pulses produced by the fission fragments were then counted. They detected spontaneous fission in several of the heavy nuclei ranging from thorium, $Z = 90$, $A = 230$, to americium, $Z = 95$, $A = 241$, and measured their disintegration constants. They also measured the number of neutrons produced per spontaneous fission of uranium, $A = 238$, and obtained the value 2.2 ± 0.3 neutrons per fission.

The spontaneous fission of curium, $Z = 96$, $A = 242$, was first observed and studied by Hanna, Harvey, Moss, and Tunnicliffe (1951). They compared the fission rate with the rate of alpha-particle disintegration of curium and found 6.2 fission per 10^8 alpha particles. Using a half-life value of 162.5 days for alpha-particle disintegration, they obtained a spontaneous fission half-life of 7.2×10^6 years, the shortest such half-life thus far observed. They also measured the distribution in energies of the fission fragments and found that the most probable energy of the lighter fragment was about 95 Mev, while that of the heavier fragment was about 65 Mev, results very similar to those obtained in the slow-neutron fission of uranium and plutonium. This is in accord with the idea that the energy of the fission fragment is due entirely to the electrostatic field between them and is independent of the method of inducing fission.

13-12. Fission of Heavy Nuclei

Calculations based on the liquid drop model of the nucleus indicate that it should be possible to produce the fission of any heavy nucleus by providing sufficient energy of excitation. Probably the first definitely successful experiments on the fission of normally stable heavy nuclei were those performed by Perlman, Goeckermann, Templeton, and Howland (1947) in which high energy helium ions, deuterons, and neutrons from the 184-inch Berkeley cyclotron were used to bombard tantalum, $Z = 73$, platinum, $Z = 78$, thallium, $Z = 81$, and bismuth, $Z = 83$. The occurrence of fission for each of these nuclei was verified by chemical identification of radioactive fission products. The energies of the bombarding particles were these: 200 Mev deuterons, 400 Mev helium ions or alpha particles, and 100 Mev neutrons. The fission yield curve for each of these elements differed from that of the slow-neutron fission of uranium in that it did not show the pronounced asymmetrical division of the fission products. They also found that, in some cases, the lighter isotopes of an element were produced, and that the most probable type of fission was one in which the sum of the mass numbers of the fission products was much smaller than the target element mass number. This indicates that several neutrons are emitted in this process, probably before the actual occurrence of fission.

A similar result was observed by O'Connor and Seaborg (1948) in the fission of uranium 238 by 380 Mev helium ions. The fission yield curve showed a maximum in the neighborhood of $A = 115$, extending to a low value of about $A = 27$, much lower than that of the slow-neutron fission of uranium 235. On the high mass number side, it extended up to about $A = 180$. They also found nuclei in the mass number range of 180 to 200 which were produced in the process of spallation rather than fission. The fission of thorium by alpha particles of 37.5 Mev average energy was investigated by A. S. Newton (1948), who found that the fission yield curve had a broad plateau extending from mass number 80 to about 150, with a small trough in the neighborhood of mass number 117. It is thus apparent that the fission yields depend upon the excitation energy. Tewes and James (1951) investigated the fission of thorium when bombarded with protons of energies ranging from 6.7 Mev to 21.1 Mev. They observed the trough in the fission yield curve at the position corresponding to symmetrical fission, and noted that the trough became shallower with increasing proton energy. Thus the probability of symmetrical fission increases with increasing energy of the bombarding particle.

13-13. Fission of Lighter Nuclei

The concept of nuclear fission as a type of nuclear disintegration in which the nucleus splits into two nuclei of comparable masses can be extended to the entire range of complex atomic nuclei. The fission of nuclei of elements of medium atomic weight has been investigated by Batzel and Seaborg (1951), using the high energy protons from the 184-inch Berkeley cyclotron. For example, copper, $A = 63$, was bombarded by protons and one of the products looked for was chlorine, $A = 38$. Cl^{38} has a half-life of 38 minutes. The production of Cl^{38} was detected with proton energies as low as about 60 Mev, with the cross section for its production increasing with increasing bombarding energy, as shown in Figure 13-10. Of the several

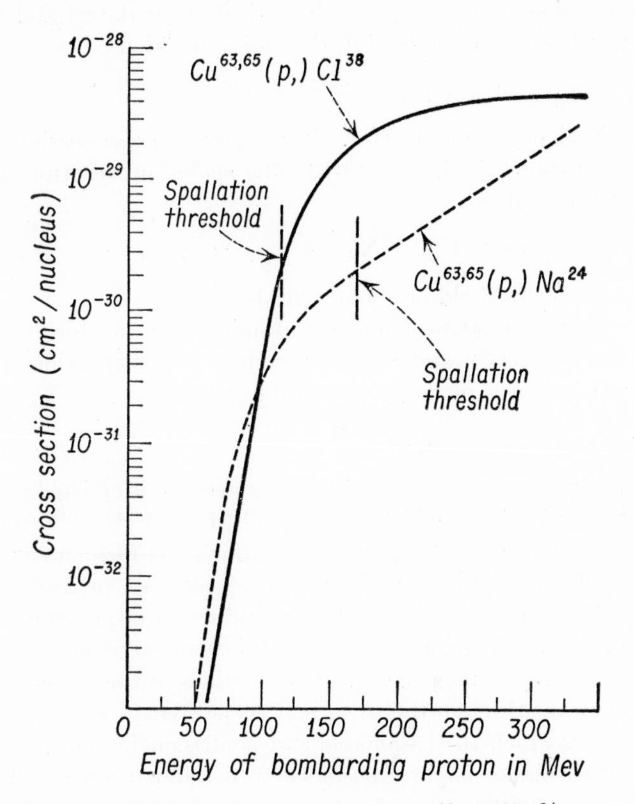

FIG. 13-10. Cross section for the formation of Cl^{38} and Na^{24} from copper as a function of the energy of the bombarding proton. (After Batzel and Seaborg, *Phys. Rev.*, 82, 609, 1952.)

reactions by which Cl^{38} could be produced, calculations can be made of the energy requirements for the following fission reaction:

$$Cu^{63} + p \rightarrow Cl^{38} + Al^{25} + n \tag{15}$$

and the spallation reaction

$$Cu^{63} + p \rightarrow Cl^{38} + p + n + 6\alpha. \tag{16}$$

The spallation reaction would require a threshold value of about 110 Mev, while the fission process would require a threshold energy of about 50 Mev. Of the latter amount about 30 Mev is needed for the excitation energy for passage over the potential barrier, and the remainder for the mass difference between the reactants and the products. As shown in Figure 13-10, since Cl^{38} is formed at energies less than the spallation threshold, Cu^{63} is fissionable.

Another fission product of Cu^{63} investigated by Batzel and Seaborg was Na^{24}, which would be formed in the fission reaction

$$Cu^{63} + p \rightarrow Na^{24} + K^{39} + n \tag{17}$$

with a threshold of about 50 Mev. The observed cross section for this reaction is also shown in Figure 13-10. The spallation reaction in which Na^{24} could be formed is

$$Cu^{63} + p \rightarrow Na^{24} + p + 3n + 9\alpha \tag{18}$$

and would have a threshold of about 170 Mev.

Other nuclei of elements of medium atomic weight in which fission was produced are Br^{79}, Ag^{107}, and Sn^{118}. In each case identification of one of the fission products was made by chemical analysis.

13-14. Fission Chain Reaction

The fact that, on the average, more than one neutron is emitted per fission in the neutron fission of such isotopes as Th^{232}, U^{233}, U^{235}, U^{238}, and Pu^{239} leads to the possibility of a chain reaction in a mass of fissionable material. Whether the chain reaction remains steady, builds up, or dies down depends upon the competition between the production of neutrons through fission and the loss of neutrons through a variety of processes such as nonfission capture of neutrons, primarily n-γ reactions in the system, and the leakage of neutrons through the surface of the system.

A system in which the fissionable and nonfissionable materials are so arranged that the fission chain reaction can proceed in a controlled manner is called a *nuclear reactor*. In contrast, an *atomic bomb* is a device designed to produce a chain reaction that builds up at an explosive rate. The latter will not concern us here.

A nuclear reactor is a source of the products of the fission process, namely, energy, neutrons, and radioactive isotopes. As we have shown (§13-2), energy is released at the rate of 200 Mev per fission of one atom or about 23×10^6 kw-hr per fission of one kilogram of fissionable material of mass number 235. As a source of neutrons, a nuclear reactor can provide a large number of neutrons per unit time with a wide range of energies (§13-6). Of the ν neutrons emitted per fission, only one neutron is required to cause further fission in order to maintain the chain reaction at a steady rate. The remaining $\nu - 1$ neutrons per fission are thus available for other purposes; these purposes are always taken into consideration in the design of the reactor. For example, a reactor may be designed for neutron experiments such as those discussed in earlier chapters. Or the reactor may be designed to produce desired isotopes by neutron capture, such as the production of plutonium from U^{238}, the production of C^{14} from N^{14}, or the production of fissionable U^{233} from Th^{232} through the reaction

$$_{90}\mathrm{Th}^{232} + {}_0n^1 \rightarrow {}_{90}\mathrm{Th}^{233} + h\nu$$

followed by $$_{90}\mathrm{Th}^{233} \rightarrow {}_{91}\mathrm{Pa}^{233} + \beta^-, \quad T = 23 \text{ min} \tag{19}$$

and $$_{91}\mathrm{Pa}^{233} \rightarrow {}_{92}\mathrm{U}^{233} + \beta^-, \quad T = 27.4 \text{ da.}$$

Once a fission chain reaction has started, the *effective multiplication factor* k_e will determine whether the chain reaction will continue at a steady rate, increase, or decrease. The effective multiplication factor is defined as *the ratio of the rate of production of neutrons, P, to the combined rate of absorption A and rate of leakage L of neutrons, or*

$$k_e = \frac{P}{A + L}; \tag{20}$$

the term *absorption* includes all types of absorption, such as those which produce fission and those which produce n-γ processes in the material of the reactor. The fission chain reaction will be *critical* or steady when $k_e = 1$, it will be building up or *supercritical* when $k_e > 1$, and it will be dying down or *subcritical* when $k_e < 1$.

If F is the rate at which fission processes occur, and if ν is the average number of neutrons emitted per fission, then

$$P = \nu F. \tag{21}$$

Equation (20) may then be written as

$$k_e = \frac{\nu F}{A + L},$$

from which $$k_e = \nu \frac{F}{A} \frac{1}{1 + (L/A)}. \tag{22}$$

The ratio F/A depends upon the amount of fissionable and nonfissionable material and on their cross sections for fission and neutron capture. The ratio L/A depends upon the ability of the reactor to contain and absorb neutrons before they can escape through the surface. As the size of a reactor decreases, the rate of neutron leakage through the surface increases, and the rate of neutron absorption decreases, so that L/A increases and approaches infinity, and hence in the limit k_e approaches zero. As the size of the reactor increases, L/A decreases toward zero, and k_e increases toward the limiting value $\nu F/A$. Hence if the composition of the reactor is such that

$$\nu F/A > 1,$$

then there is some size of this reactor for which $k_e = 1$; for this size, the reactor is critical. This size is called the *critical size* and *the mass of fissionable material at this size is called the critical mass.* The region containing the fissionable material is called the *reactor core.* The core may be surrounded by nonfissionable material capable of reflecting neutrons back into the core; in such a case both the critical size and the critical mass are reduced. On the other hand, if there is an insufficient amount of fissionable material or an excess of absorbing material in the reactor core so that $\nu F/A < 1$, then there is no size for which a steady chain reaction can occur, irrespective of whether or not a reflector is used.

13-15. Processes within a Reactor

The power level at which a reactor operates is proportional to the number of fissions occurring per unit time and this, in turn, is proportional to the number of neutrons in the reactor. Hence the power level of the reactor can be controlled by controlling the number of neutrons in it. A common method of doing this is to introduce a neutron-absorbing material, usually in the form of a steel rod containing boron, and to adjust the position of this rod in the core. This essentially changes the value of k_e in the desired direction. As the reactor continues in operation, fissionable material is used up and the ratio F/A decreases. To keep the power level constant the control rods containing the neutron-absorbing material should be moved out of the reactor at a suitable rate. When the limit of such compensation is reached, all the control rods are out; the reactor will then become subcritical and die down unless new fissionable material is added.

It has already been shown that the neutron is unstable and decays with a half-life of about 12 minutes. However, this has practically no effect on the operation of a nuclear reactor because the lifetime of the neutron is very long in comparison with the time interval between the emission of a neutron in a fission process and its subsequent absorption or leakage. This time interval, sometimes called the time of a neutron generation, is usually smaller than 10^{-3} second. Thus, only negligible fractions of the neutrons produced are lost by the decay process.

The determination of the effective multiplication constant for a given distribution of fissionable material in a nuclear reactor is a very difficult problem owing to the fact that the neutron-fission cross sections and absorption cross sections are complicated functions of the neutron energy. The latter, in turn, are governed by the neutron-fission spectrum (§13-6), by the elastic and inelastic scattering cross sections of neutrons, and, to some extent, by the size of the reactor. When these calculations are carried out, it can be shown that pure natural uranium, no matter how large the amount, cannot support a chain reaction, that is $\nu F/A < 1$. However, natural uranium, suitably arranged with either graphite (carbon) or heavy water, can support a chain reaction. The graphite or the heavy water acts as a *moderator* to slow down the highly energetic neutrons produced in the fission of uranium. The moderator has a very small capture cross section, so that most of the collisions between neutrons and moderator nuclei result in the scattering of neutrons at reduced energies. With a sufficient amount of moderator in the reactor, the neutrons are reduced to thermal energies. The values of the thermal cross sections are such that $\nu F/A > 1$, and thus a chain reaction can be produced. Table 13-4 lists the different cross sections of uranium for thermal neutrons.

Table 13-4

Thermal Neutron Cross Sections for Uranium

Process	Cross Sections in Barns		Natural U
	U^{235}	U^{238}	
Fission	549	0	3.92
Capture	101	2.80	3.5
Scattering	8.2	8.2	8.2

A glance at this table shows that thermal neutron fission in natural uranium is due entirely to the presence of the isotope U^{235}, which has an abundance of only 0.71 per cent in natural uranium. A small amount of fission will take place in U^{238} with some of the fast neutrons being released in the fission process before they are reduced to thermal energies. The first reactor ever built, the so-called uranium-graphite pile, used natural uranium with graphite as the moderator.

It will be interesting to consider the processes that occur during one generation of neutrons in a natural uranium graphite-moderated reactor operated at a constant power level. In one example, starting with 100 neutrons captured by uranium, mostly thermal neutrons captured by U^{235} and the remainder captured in fast fission process by both U^{235} and U^{238}, 256 new neutrons are produced. Of these

100 neutrons will be used to carry on new fissions;
90 neutrons will undergo radiative capture by U^{238};
20 neutrons will undergo radiative capture by U^{235};

30 neutrons will be absorbed by the moderator;
5 neutrons will be absorbed by structural material;
9 neutrons will escape from core; and
2 neutrons will be in excess, normally absorbed by control rods but otherwise available for increasing the power level.

13-16. Types of Nuclear Reactors

The design, construction, and operation of a nuclear reactor are part of a very large and rapidly expanding field of nuclear engineering. There are many nuclear reactors now in operation throughout the world, but only a very few produce power for consumption outside the reactor. Some of the nuclear reactors use natural uranium for the production of plutonium, Pu^{239}, which is fissionable by both fast and slow neutrons. A reactor which could produce useful power from a natural fuel such as uranium, and in the process produce additional fissionable nuclides equal to or exceeding the amount of the fuel used is called a *breeder* reactor. Most nuclear reactors now in operation are used for experimental purposes and for the training of personnel.

Uranium ores are plentiful and widely dispersed over the surface of the earth, and even though the concentration of uranium in these ores is small, the amount of uranium in existence is probably very large. In constructing nuclear reactors, the fuel may be natural uranium, or it may be uranium enriched with the lighter isotope, $A = 235$. The enrichment may be produced in a number of ways, of which gaseous diffusion through a porous barrier and thermal diffusion are perhaps the most common, although separation by electromagnetic methods has also been used.

Reactors may be classified in a wide variety of ways. For example, they may be classified by the manner in which the fuel and the moderator are mixed. A *homogeneous reactor* is one in which the fuel and the moderator form a mixture which has uniform composition. One of the common types of homogeneous reactors consists of a solution of uranyl nitrate in water, with the uranium enriched with the lighter isotope by as much as 1 part of U^{235} to 6 parts of U^{238}, as compared with natural uranium, where the ratio is 1 to 140. The solution is put in a steel sphere and this is surrounded by a neutron reflector such as beryllium oxide and graphite. The entire reactor is shielded by lead, cadmium, and concrete. The operation of the reactor can be controlled by means of cadmium rods which penetrate the beryllium oxide reflector. These control rods can be positioned accurately to control the power level of the reactor, and one or more may be used as safety rods, to be dropped into position should the power level get too high.

Most of the nuclear reactors, especially the larger ones, are of the *heterogeneous* type; that is, the fissionable material is concentrated in containers suitably distributed throughout the moderator. In many cases the fissionable materials, in the form of cylinders of uranium or uranium oxide enclosed in aluminum tubes, are spaced in a lattice work in the moderator, usually graphite but sometimes heavy water, as shown in Figure 13-11. A heterogeneous reactor suitable for research work, designed and built at the Oak Ridge National Laboratory, consists of a set of fuel elements immersed in a large tank of ordinary water. This set of fuel elements consists of plates of uranium-aluminum alloy inside an aluminum container.

FIG. 13-11. Top of the reactor core of Argonne National Laboratory's heavy water reactor. The shield has been removed to show the ends of the uranium rods which are suspended in a tank of heavy water. The large hole in the center is the thimble which extends nearly to the bottom of the tank. Materials to be made radioactive are lowered into this hole. (Courtesy of Argonne National Laboratory.)

A set of these fuel elements containing sufficient uranium to become critical when immersed in water is mounted on a frame with suitable control rods of boron-carbide. This fuel is lowered into a large concrete tank of water which acts as the moderator, as shown in Figure 13-12. About 3 kg of U^{235} are sufficient for the critical amount of fuel, but if beryllium oxide is used as a reflector, a smaller amount, about 2.4 kgm of U^{235}, will produce criticality. This reactor will develop approximately 100 kw and provide a thermal neutron flux of about 10^{12} neutrons/cm^2/sec. Samples to be irradiated by thermal neutrons can be placed conveniently anywhere in the water. Neutrons above thermal energy are also available for irradiating

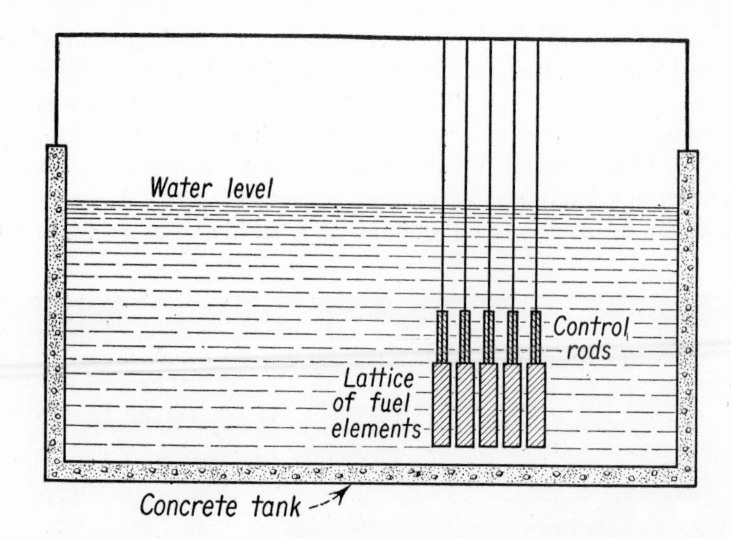

FIG. 13-12. Simplified diagram of "swimming pool" type of nuclear reactor.

materials by placing the substances between the fuel elements, or close to them.

A fair amount of technical information about the design, construction, and operation of some nuclear reactors is now available in the technical literature. Reference to some of this literature is given below.

Problems

13-1. Calculate the electrostatic potential energy of two nuclei of atomic numbers $Z_1 = 36$ and $Z_2 = 56$, when their centers are 1.5×10^{-12} cm apart.

13-2. Show that the ratio of the kinetic energies of two fission fragments that have equal and opposite momenta is M/m, where M and m are their respective masses. Which fragment has the greater kinetic energy?

13-3. (**a**) Determine the potential, in volts, at a distance of 10^{-12} cm from a nucleus of charge $Ze = 45e$, where e is the electronic charge. (**b**) Determine the potential energy, in Mev, of two such nuclei when the distance between their centers is 10^{-12} cm.

13-4. Calculate the energy released in the fission of uranium, $A = 235$, by a slow neutron if the fission products have mass numbers 72 and 162, respectively.

13-5. (**a**) Calculate the energy released in the fission of uranium, $A = 235$, by a slow neutron if the two fission products have equal mass numbers and two neutrons are emitted promptly. (**b**) Calculate the kinetic energies of the two fission particles, assuming that these are acquired as a result of the Coulomb repulsion at the instant of fission. (**c**) Account for any difference between (**a**) and (**b**).

13-6. Assuming that the average kinetic energy of a nucleus in thermal equilibrium at absolute temperature T is kT, where k is the Boltzman constant ($k = 1.38 \times 10^{-16}$ erg/deg), calculate the average energy, in Mev, of a neutron at 300°K; of a proton at 14×10^6 °K; of a helium nucleus at 10^8 °K.

13-7. The neutrons in a beam have an average energy of 0.025 ev. Calculate the average velocity of the neutrons.

13-8. Assume that the excitation energy required for passage over the nuclear potential barrier is equal to the Coulomb potential energy of the two nuclei formed in the fission process. (**a**) Calculate the excitation energy for the disintegration of Be^8 into two alpha particles. (**b**) Compare this value with the known disintegration energy of 17 Mev and account for the difference.

13-9. In the fission reaction

$$Cu^{63} + p \rightarrow Na^{24} + K^{39} + n$$

determine (**a**) the excitation energy necessary for passage over the potential barrier; (**b**) the energy equivalent of the mass difference between reactants and products; and (**c**) the threshold energy for the reaction.

13-10. In the fission reaction

$${}_{50}Sn^{118} + p \rightarrow {}_{11}Na^{24} + {}_{40}Zr^{94} + n,$$

determine (**a**) the excitation energy necessary for passage over the potential barrier; (**b**) the energy equivalent of the mass difference between reactants and products; and (**c**) the threshold energy for the reaction.

Ans. (**a**) 58 Mev.
(**b**) −8 Mev.
(**c**) 50 Mev.

13-11. In the fission reaction

$${}_{50}Sn^{118} + p \rightarrow {}_{31}Ga^{66} + {}_{20}Ca^{49} + 4n,$$

determine (**a**) the excitation energy necessary for passage over the potential barrier; (**b**) the energy equivalent of the mass difference between reactants and products; and (**c**) the threshold value for the reaction.

Ans. (**c**) ~70 Mev.

13-12. On the liquid drop model of the nucleus the probability of spontaneous fission increases rapidly with Z^2/A. G. T. Seaborg found that if Z^2/A is plotted against the half-life, it approaches the value 47 for a half-life of 10^{-20} seconds, which may be considered the rate of instantaneous fission. Use this value to determine an upper limit to the number of new elements which may be produced by nuclear processes.

13-13. Determine the kinetic energy that an alpha particle can acquire from the Coulomb field of a fission fragment of $Z = 56$ and $A = 140$, assuming that the alpha particle is released at rest at the instant of fission.

Ans. 17 Mev.

13-14. (a) Show that the kinetic energy $\mathcal{E}_k$ of the fission fragments, in Mev, for the slow-neutron fission of U^{235} can be expressed in terms of the atomic masses of the particles involved in the fission process by the equation

$$\mathcal{E}_k = 931[m(U^{235}) - m(L) - m(H) - (\nu - 1)m(n)] - \nu\mathcal{E}_n - \mathcal{E}_\gamma$$

where $m(L)$ is the mass of the light fragment, $m(H)$ the mass of the heavy fragment, $m(n)$ the mass of the neutron, ν the average number of neutrons emitted per fission, $\mathcal{E}_n$ the average kinetic energy of these neutrons, and $\mathcal{E}_\gamma$ the average energy of the prompt gamma rays.

(b) Using the data from the table of atomic masses, and taking $\nu = 2.5$, $\mathcal{E}_n = 2$ Mev, and $\mathcal{E}_\gamma = 4.6$ Mev, calculate the kinetic energy of the fission fragments for the most probable fission mode.

13-15. Assuming that the energy released per fission of U^{235} is 200 Mev, calculate the rate at which fission should occur in a nuclear reactor in order to operate at a power level of 1 watt.

Reference

Glasstone, S., and M. C. Edlund, *The Elements of Nuclear Reactor Theory*. New York: D. Van Nostrand Company, Inc., 1952.

Goodman, Clark (ed.), *The Science and Engineering of Nuclear Power*. Cambridge, Mass.: Addison-Wesley Press, 1947, Vol. I.

Isbin, H. S., "Nuclear Reactor Catalog," *Nucleonics*, 10, No. 3, 10, 1952; and 11, No. 6, 65, 1953.

Nucleonics. Special Report on *Materials and Equipment for Reactors*. 2, No. 6, 17–64, June, 1953.

Soodak, H., and E. C. Campbell, *Elementary Pile Theory*. New York: John Wiley & Sons, Inc., 1950.

chapter 14

Fundamental Particles

14-1. Subatomic Particles

For a period of about thirty-five years prior to 1932, an atom was assumed to consist only of two different elementary, stable particles—electrons and protons—in equal numbers. On the Bohr-Rutherford nuclear picture of the atom, there were A electrons and A protons in the atom, where A is the mass number of the isotope; all of the A protons were in the nucleus, together with $A - Z$ electrons, with Z electrons outside the nucleus of the neutral atom of atomic number Z. With the discovery of the neutron in 1932, the picture changed radically. There are still Z electrons outside the nucleus, but now there are only Z protons in the nucleus, no electrons whatever in it, and N neutrons, where $N + Z = A$. The neutron, however, when outside the nucleus, is not a stable particle; it undergoes beta decay with a half-life of about 12 minutes, the process being given by the equation

$$n \rightarrow p + \beta^- + \nu \qquad (1)$$

in which ν represents the neutrino.

After 1932, the number of subatomic particles began to increase at a rapid rate. The positron was discovered in 1934 among the particles in cosmic rays, and shortly thereafter was found as one of the particles emitted in the radioactive disintegration of many of the artificially produced radioactive nuclides. In the case of positron emission, the theory of beta decay assumed that a proton in the nucleus disintegrates, emitting the positron, with the process given by

$$p \text{ (in nucleus)} \rightarrow n \text{ (in nucleus)} + \beta^+ + \nu. \qquad (2)$$

The positron has no independent existence; ultimately it combines with an electron to produce annihilation gamma-ray photons (§14-4), with the process usually written as

$$e^+ + e^- \rightarrow h\nu. \qquad (3)$$

The reverse of the process given in equation (3) also occurs, that is, the production of a positron-electron pair from a gamma-ray photon of sufficient energy (§14-3).

The neutrino has been, for over twenty years, a very elusive particle. Its existence was predicated by Pauli in 1931, but the first direct experimental proof of the existence of a free neutrino has only recently been established (1953), by its interaction with a proton (§12-9), in the process given by

$$\nu + p \rightarrow n + \beta^+. \tag{4}$$

These particles have charges of either zero or one, in terms of the electronic charge e as the unit; the charges of all other particles known have values which are integral multiples of e: that is, the *charges are quantized.* The masses of the above subatomic particles vary considerably, with the neutrino having either zero mass or a mass which is less than 0.05 per cent of that of the electronic mass, m_e, while the proton mass is about 1835 m_e, and the neutron mass is only slightly larger, that is, about 1836 m_e. In 1937, a new charged particle, now called a *mu meson*, was discovered in the cosmic radiation; its mass is about 200 m_e. Very little additional work was done in this field until after World War II. Beginning in 1947 a whole series of new particles, some charged, others uncharged, were discovered among the particles in cosmic radiation. Many of them have masses intermediate between that of the electron and that of the proton and are designated as *mesons*. Some have masses in excess of the proton mass. All of them are unstable. Some of these particles have also been produced in nuclear reactions with the high energy particles and radiation now available in several laboratories. In this chapter we shall consider the modes of production, decay, and other properties of these new unstable particles. Just how they fit into the picture of the nucleus and the atom is not very clear at present. Whether there is any limit to the number of such particles, or whether mass is a quantized property like charge and angular momentum, is not certain, but some theoretical work is being done along these lines.

14-2. Cosmic Rays

In the early part of the twentieth century electroscopes were widely used in experiments on x-rays, radioactivity, and electrical discharge through gases. It was soon found that even though no known radiations were present in the neighborhood of such an electroscope, and no known electrical discharges were taking place in any circuit near the electroscope, a charged electroscope would gradually lose its charge. It was early surmised that the discharge of a well-insulated and shielded electroscope could be produced only by the action of some type of radiation which came either from below the surface of the earth or from outside the atmosphere. Experiments designed to test these hypotheses were begun about 1910. The rate of discharge of an electroscope at different altitudes was measured by several experimenters. In 1912, W. Kolhorster and V. F. Hess found that the amount of ionizing radiation incident on the electroscope, as measured by its rate of discharge, decreases at first with increasing altitude up to about 700 meters; after this, the amount of ionizing radiation increases with increasing altitude. This dependence upon altitude showed that these radiations were extremely penetrating and probably had their origin outside the earth; hence the name *cosmic rays.* The great penetrating power of these rays was also demonstrated by other experiments in which the cosmic rays had to penetrate various thicknesses of absorbing materials before reaching the detector.

Very little work was done in cosmic-ray studies until after World War I. It was then believed that cosmic rays were hard gamma rays, that is, rays of very high frequencies. However, in 1927, J. Clay found that the intensity of cosmic rays at sea level was not constant but varied with latitude; hence the cosmic rays must contain some charged particles whose motion was affected by the earth's magnetic field. This latitude effect was confirmed by a series of measurements (1930–1933) made by a group of observers at different stations throughout the world; this group was headed by A. H. Compton. The latitude effect was found to amount to about a 10 per cent decrease in intensity in going from high geomagnetic latitudes toward the equator.

The subject of cosmic rays is too vast to be dealt with in this book. Hence we shall confine ourselves only to those cosmic-ray events and phenomena which have a direct bearing on nuclear physics. We have already discussed one such important event, the discovery of the *positron* in 1932 by C. D. Anderson. Other particles have since been discovered in cosmic rays, particularly different kinds of *mesons*, that is, *particles of mass intermediate between the mass of an electron and that of a proton.* Furthermore, the energies available with cosmic-ray particles greatly exceed those produced by the largest particle accelerators. Estimates of the energies of cosmic rays are of the order of 10^{12} to 10^{15} ev.

Our knowledge of cosmic rays owes a great deal to the development of three types of detectors other than the electroscope. These are (1) the Geiger counter, (2) the Wilson cloud chamber, and (3) the photographic plate with specially prepared photographic emulsions. In cosmic-ray investigations, several Geiger counters are generally used in a single experiment; these counters may be connected in a variety of ways to recording devices. Geiger counters are also used in conjunction with Wilson cloud chambers; a common procedure is to use the discharge produced by a particle passing through one or more counters to actuate the expansion mechanism of the cloud chamber. The expansion of the chamber can thus be timed to coincide with the passage of a particle through it; hence practically every cloud-chamber photograph will yield some information.

Photographic plates have been used in nuclear physics since the day Becquerel discovered radioactivity. Modern photographic plates with so-called "nuclear" emulsions differ from ordinary photographic plates in that the emulsions are much thicker, usually from 25 to 2000 microns thick (1 micron = 10^{-3} mm). Further, these emulsions contain greater concentrations of silver halide than ordinary emulsions; sensitivity of the emulsion to different types of ionizing particles can also be controlled. Reproductions of photographs showing the tracks of different types of ionizing particles are shown in many of the figures in this chapter.

14-3. Production of Pairs of Charged Particles

In cloud-chamber experiments on the passage of high energy gamma rays through a heavy element such as lead, pairs of oppositely charged particles were observed to originate from a common point. From the densities of the tracks it was evident that these particles had exactly the same mass as that

Fig. 14-1. Cloud-chamber photograph of the paths of a pair of oppositely charged particles, an electron and a positron, formed by the disintegration of a 5.7 Mev gamma-ray photon in its passage through a sheet of lead 0.002 inch thick. Magnetic field of 1680 gausses is directed into the paper. (Photograph by H. R. Crane.)

of an electron. The velocities and hence the kinetic energies of these particles could be determined from the measurements of the radii of curvature of their paths in a magnetic field. The results of these measurements support the view that a positron and an electron are formed as the result of the interaction of a gamma-ray photon with a heavy nucleus. From calculations on the number produced, it is believed that this pair formation occurs in the intense electric field outside the nucleus rather than inside it.

If a gamma-ray photon of energy $h\nu$ is transformed into a pair of particles, each of rest mass m_e, then, according to the principle of conservation of energy,

$$h\nu = 2m_ec^2 + \mathcal{E}_1 + \mathcal{E}_2, \tag{5}$$

where m_ec^2 is the rest mass energy of each particle and $\mathcal{E}_1$ and $\mathcal{E}_2$ are the kinetic energies of the particles at the instant of production. Now, m_ec^2 is

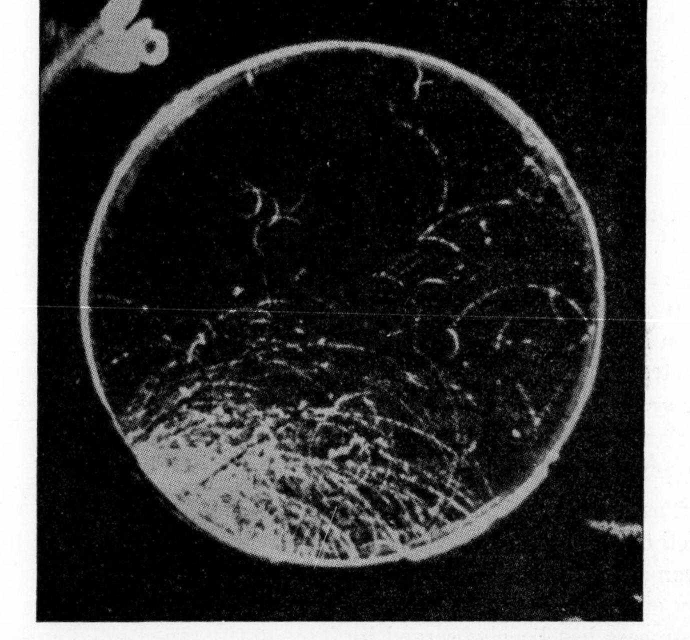

FIG. 14-2. Cloud-chamber photograph of a triplet which consists of the paths of a positron and two electrons. The triplet was produced by the conversion of a gamma-ray photon into a positron and an electron in the field of another electron. The magnetic field is directed into the paper. (From a photograph by P. Gerald Kruger and W. E. Ogle.)

equivalent to 5.11×10^5 ev energy; hence only gamma-ray photons whose energies are greater than 1.02 Mev can form a pair of charged particles.

Experiments on the production of pairs of charged particles have been performed successfully with the gamma-ray photons from ThC″ ($h\nu = 2.62$ Mev). In this case the total kinetic energy of the positron and electron formed by each photon should be 1.6 Mev. Cloud-chamber measurements of the energies of these particles are in good agreement with this calculated value. Figure 14-1 is a cloud-chamber photograph, taken by Crane, showing the paths of a pair of oppositely charged particles, a positron and an electron, which were produced by a gamma-ray photon which entered the lead foil 0.002 inch thick. The gamma-ray photon came from a target of fluorine which had been bombarded by protons. The known energy of the photon is 5.7 Mev. From measurements of the radii of curvature of the paths of the particles in the known magnetic field, Crane computed the sum of energies of these two particles to be 4.7 Mev. This checks very well with equation (5) when the rest mass energy of the two particles, 1.02 Mev, is added to the sum of their kinetic energies.

The production of pairs of charged particles—electrons and positrons—is one method by which gamma rays give up their energy in their passage through matter. Pair production can also be used for the measurement of gamma-ray energies in excess of 1.02 Mev. An example of this has already been given in §11-11 in which the gamma-ray energies were measured with a scintillation counter. When pair production is studied with the aid of a cloud chamber, triplet paths are observed occasionally. A photograph of such a triplet is shown in Figure 14-2. This photograph was taken by Kruger and Ogle during their investigation of the gamma rays emitted by Na^{24}. These triplets consist of the paths of a positron and two electrons, and are accounted for by the production of a pair of particles by the splitting up of a gamma-ray photon when it is in the field of an electron. This electron suffers a recoil when the gamma-ray photon is transformed into an electron and a positron. Measurements show that both the momentum of the system and the energy of the system are conserved in this process.

14-4. Annihilation of Charged Particles

The transformation of a photon into a positron and an electron is sometimes referred to as the *materialization of energy*. The reverse process, in which a positron and an electron combine and their energy is transformed into the energy of gamma rays, is usually referred to as the *annihilation of matter*. This process has been observed by Thibaud, Crane, and Lauritsen, and others. A convenient source of positrons is a block of carbon which has been bombarded with deuterons producing radioactive nitrogen according to the reaction

$$_6C^{12} + {}_1H^2 \rightarrow ({}_7N^{14}) \rightarrow {}_7N^{13} + {}_0n^1, \tag{6}$$

followed by

$$_7N^{13} \rightarrow {}_6C^{13} + \beta^+.$$

In one experiment, some recently activated carbon was placed at the bottom of an ionization chamber and the ionization measured. To distinguish between the ionization produced by the positrons and that produced by the gamma rays, a second ionization chamber was placed directly below the first one. The walls and window of the ionization chamber were sufficiently thick to prevent any of the charged particles from entering the chamber, so that only the ionization produced by the gamma rays was recorded. It was found that the ionization produced by the gamma rays decreased exponentially with time in exactly the same way as that due to the positrons; that is, the half-life was the same whether determined from the rate of emission of positrons or from the intensity of the gamma rays associated with this process. It seems reasonable to assume that the gamma rays have their origin in the annihilations of the positrons by electrons. To check this assumption, a freshly activated piece of carbon was placed, with the activated side upward, directly above one of the ionization chambers. It may be assumed that as many positrons are emitted upward as downward. Those that are emitted downward are absorbed in the rest of the carbon and give rise to gamma rays which are measured by the ionization produced in the chamber. The upward-moving positrons escape into the air. However, when a thin sheet of aluminum is placed on top of the carbon, the upward-moving positrons will be absorbed in the aluminum and give rise to gamma rays. The amount of ionization produced with the aluminum on the carbon was found to be about twice as great as that produced without the aluminum, indicating that the positrons were annihilated in the aluminum, giving rise to gamma-ray photons.

Measurements of the intensity of the ionization produced by the gamma rays showed that the number of photons produced was twice the number of positrons absorbed. The energy of these gamma-ray photons has been measured and found to be about 0.5 Mev. This is approximately the same as the rest mass energy of the positron and of the electron; hence positrons and electrons are most likely to combine when their speeds are small. Since the combined mass of the electron and positron is equivalent to about 1 Mev, the result of their annihilation must be the production of two gamma-ray photons each of 0.5 Mev energy, but traveling in opposite directions in order to conserve momentum. The fact that two photons traveling in opposite directions are produced by the annihilation of a positron and an electron was demonstrated by the use of two Geiger-Mueller counters, one on each side of an activated carbon block. The counters were arranged so that they would record only *coincidences*, that is, photons entering the two counters simultaneously. The number of coincidences observed, and their decrease with time, checked very well with the known rate of emission of positrons by the carbon block.

14-5. Wavelength of Annihilation Radiation

When a positron goes through a substance the probability that it will combine with an electron of the substance is greatest when the velocity of the positron is almost zero. It will most likely combine with one of the electrons in an outer shell rather than with a K or an L electron because the positron would be strongly repelled by the electric field of the nucleus were it to approach the K or L electronic orbits. In most cases, the result of the annihilation of an electron-positron pair is the production of two gamma-ray photons of equal and opposite momenta and of equal energies. The energy of each photon is equal to the rest mass energy of an electron, $\mathcal{E} = m_e c^2$ and hence the wavelength of the annihilation radiation should be

$$\lambda = \frac{h}{m_e c}, \tag{7}$$

which is identical with the Compton wavelength.

The wavelength of the annihilation radiation was measured with very high precision by DuMond and his co-workers (1952), using a two-meter focusing curved-crystal spectrometer (see §5-9). The source of the annihilation radiation was a rectangular piece of copper which had been irradiated with neutrons. Cu^{64} formed by the capture of a neutron is radioactive, decaying by β^- emission to Zn^{64}, and by positron emission or electron capture to Ni^{64}. The positrons have a range in copper of only about 0.3 mm. A narrow beam of the annihilation radiation was allowed to go through a long narrow slit of lead and then through the curved crystal and detected by an NaI(Tl) crystal scintillation counter. A tapered lead collimator was placed between the crystal and the counter to prevent the direct radiation from reaching the counter.

A single sharp line was obtained for the annihilation radiation. The wavelength λ of this radiation was found to be

$$\lambda = 0.024262\text{A},$$

in very good agreement with the Compton wavelength.

14-6. Formation of Positronium

When a positron slows down in its passage through matter, it may join an electron to form a positron-electron system, called *positronium*, which lasts for a measurable time before combining to produce annihilation radiation. One may think of positronium as an atom analogous to that of hydrogen in which an electron and a positron move in a Bohr orbit about the center of mass, which is halfway between them. This is an unusual type of atom in that it has no nucleus; it may be described by assigning to it the values $Z = 0$, $A = 0$, and $M = 2m_e$.

The lowest Bohr orbit of positronium is one for which $n = 1$ and $l = 0$, so that the lowest state is an S state. However, this state has fine structure owing to the spins of the particles; when the two spins are oppositely directed, the atom is in a ^1S state; when the two spins are parallel, it is in a ^3S state and has the higher energy. The triplet state is a metastable state and has an appreciably longer lifetime than the singlet state. Theoretical calculations predicting the existence of these states were made by

J. Pirenne (1944) and J. A. Wheeler (1946), who showed that the lifetime of the singlet state should be of the order of 10^{-10} sec. Furthermore, the annihilation radiation emitted by the combining of a positron-electron pair in the ^1S state should consist of two gamma-ray photons emitted simultaneously; but the radiation from the ^3S state of this system should consist of three gamma-ray photons emitted simultaneously. Theoretical calculations by Ore and Powell (1949) showed that the lifetime of the ^3S state of positronium decaying and producing this three-photon annihilation should be about 1.4×10^{-7} sec.

The first experimental evidence for the formation of positronium was obtained by M. Deutsch (1951), who observed a time delay between the emission of a positron from Na^{22} and the appearance of the annihilation photon from the substance in which the positrons were absorbed. Several different gases, such as N_2, O_2, or methane, were used as absorbers of the positrons. He also observed that the delay time increased with an increase in pressure of the gas. He concluded that the time delay was due to the formation of positronium. To show the existence of the two states, ^1S and ^3S, and to distinguish them, Deutsch made use of the fact that the triplet state, being a metastable state with an energy of only 0.013 ev above the ^1S state, could be converted to the singlet state by interaction with some substance such as NO, which has an odd number of electrons. He found that by adding a small amount, about 5 per cent, of NO to the gas in which positronium was being formed, the triplet state was quickly converted to the singlet state. The evidence for this was the rapid decrease in the number of delayed counts which would otherwise have come from the decay of the longer-lived triplet state. An examination of the gamma-ray spectrum with an NaI scintillation spectrometer showed an increase in intensity of the 0.51 Mev line when NO was added to the gas, such as N_2, and a decrease in intensity at the lower energy region corresponding to the three-photon annihilation radiation.

Deutsch (1951) measured the lifetime of the ^3S state of the positronium formed in O_2 and in freon ($C\,Cl_2F_2$). The latter seems to have a special affinity for positrons. Deutsch found the disintegration constant λ, extrapolated to zero pressure of the gas, to be 6.8×10^6 sec^{-1}, so that the lifetime of the ^3S state becomes 1.5×10^{-7} sec, in good agreement with the theoretical prediction.

The simultaneity of emission of the three photons in the decay of the ^3S state of positronium was recently verified by De Benedetti and Siegel (1952), using three coplanar scintillation counters set at angles of 120° around a circle with the source at the center. The latter consisted of Na^{22} in a small vessel containing freon at 6 atmospheres pressure. The three counters were connected in coincidence; when one of the counters was moved out of the plane of the circle, the number of coincidences obtained was reduced by a factor of 10. This showed that the radiation reaching the three counters simultaneously came from the positronium in the source. They also measured the energy of the radiation in one of the counters and found it to consist of a single line with its maximum point at an energy of $\frac{2}{3}m_ec^2$, which is to be expected since, for this special arrangement the three annihilation photons should have equal energies. They also used an arrangement with only two counters in coincidence to detect the two-photon annihilation radiation from the ^1S state of positronium and measured its energy in one of the counters, obtaining only one line with its maximum at an energy of m_ec^2, in agreement with other experiments.

14-7. Discovery of the Mu Meson

In 1935, H. Yukawa developed a theory in which he postulated the existence of short-range nuclear forces which act between nucleons; in this theory the nucleons are held together by a field of force known as a *meson*

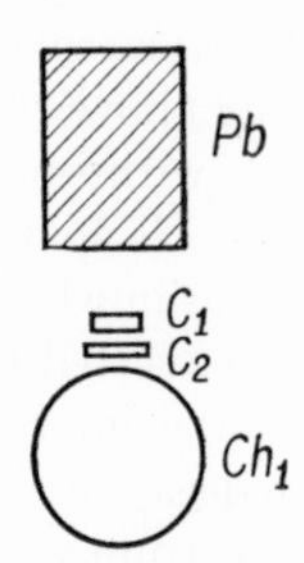

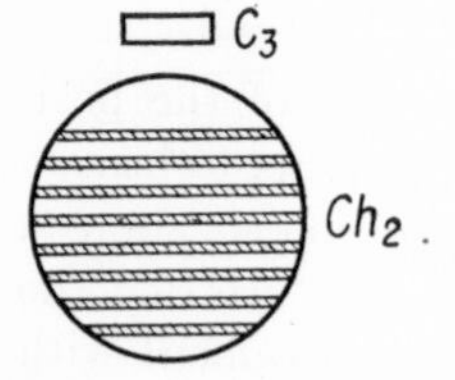

FIG. 14-3. A schematic drawing showing the two cloud chambers Ch_1 and Ch_2, and Geiger counters C_1, C_2, and C_3 which are connected in triple coincidence. The passage of a charged particle through the three counters actuated the simultaneous expansion of the two chambers. The upper cloud chamber was in a magnetic field directed at right angles to the plane of the paper. (After Fretter, *Phys. Rev.*, 70, 626, 1946.)

field. The meson field has associated with it particles, called *mesons*, in a manner analogous to the way photons are associated with the electromagnetic field which exists between charged particles. According to the Yukawa theory, a meson should have a mass intermediate between the mass of an electron and that of a proton and could carry a positive charge, a negative charge, or no charge. A particle of this type, then called a *mesotron* but now called a *mu meson* (μ-meson), was discovered in 1937 by

S. H. Neddermeyer and C. D. Anderson and independently by J. C. Street and E. C. Stevenson in cloud-chamber studies of cosmic rays. Estimates of the mass of this meson were made from measurements of the curvature of its track in a magnetic field, the density of ionization along this track as observed in the Wilson cloud-chamber photographs, or, sometimes, its range in the gas of the chamber. Such estimates yielded values for the mass of the meson in the neighborhood of 200 electronic masses.

W. B. Fretter (1946) made some very careful measurements of the masses of the mu mesons, using two cloud chambers, one above the other. They were expanded simultaneously whenever a penetrating particle passed through them. This was accomplished by placing Geiger counters above each chamber, the two sets of counters actuating the expansion mechanism whenever an ionizing particle passed through them, as shown in Figure 14-3. The upper cloud chamber was placed in a magnetic field of 5300 gausses so that the momentum of the particle could be measured. The lower cloud chamber had a set of lead plates 0.5 inch thick and placed 1.5 inches apart, so that the range in lead of the particles could be measured. Of the 2100 particle tracks observed, 26 were found suitable for measurement. The mass determinations of these yielded a value of 202 m_e. The present accepted value is 207 m_e.

14-8. Properties of Mu Mesons

Some of the mu mesons were found to be positively charged, others negatively charged. It was found that they were unstable particles, disintegration occurring near the end of the range by the emission of an electron. The average lifetime of a mu meson against spontaneous decay was found to be 2.15×10^{-6} sec. This was much larger than that predicted by Yukawa's theory.

The decay of a *muon* (shortened version of mu meson) has been observed in cloud-chamber photographs and in nuclear photographic emulsions. In one series of experiments (1949), Leighton, Anderson, and Seriff measured the energies of the electrons, both positive and negative, produced in the decay of cosmic-ray μ-mesons at sea level. The observations were made with a Geiger counter-controlled cloud chamber placed in a magnetic field of 7200 gausses. They found a range of values from 9 Mev to 55 Mev for the decay electrons. This wide range of energies for the decay electron spectrum, together with the principles of conservation of energy and momentum, suggests that this decay process is accompanied by the emission of two neutral particles of very small mass, probably two neutrinos. The decay of the mu meson can thus be represented by the reaction

$$\boxed{\mu^{\pm} \rightarrow e^{\pm} + 2\nu.} \tag{8}$$

In the decay of the muon, one must account for its rest mass, which is about 210 m_e or about 105 Mev. The maximum energy carried away by the electron is 55 Mev; hence the minimum energy carried away by the two neutrinos is about 50 Mev. Further, using the principle of conservation of angular momentum, the spin of the muon probably is $\frac{1}{2}$ but may be $\frac{3}{2}$ (in units of $\hbar$) since the spin of the electron is $\frac{1}{2}$; the sum of the spins of the neutrinos can be zero.

An interesting example of the disintegration of a muon is shown in Figure 14-4, taken by C. F. Powell (1947). This shows the path of a muon in a nuclear emulsion; the muon disintegrates into an electron which is

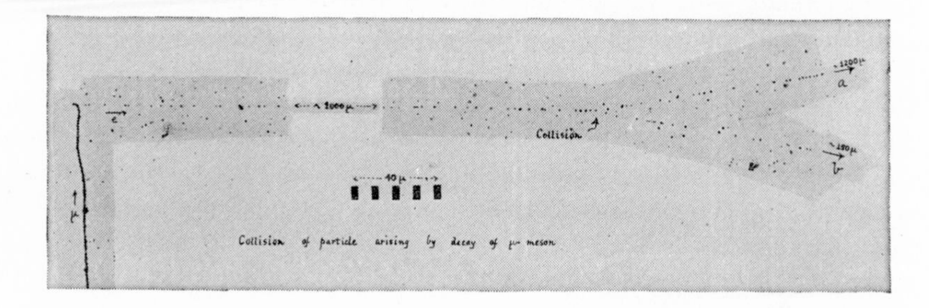

FIG. 14-4. Photograph showing the track, in a photographic emulsion, of a mu meson which decays, emitting an electron; the latter then collides with another electron. (Photograph by C. F. Powell, 1947.)

emitted at right angles to the original path of the muon. As the electron proceeds through the emulsion, it collides with another electron, the two proceeding on through the emulsion, their paths making a small angle with each other

Of special interest in nuclear physics is whether these mu mesons are the nuclear particles of the Yukawa theory. One of the most decisive experiments which settled the question in the negative was performed by Conversi, Pancini, and Piccioni (1947), who investigated the difference in behavior between positive and negative mu mesons stopped in iron and carbon. They used a magnetic field of 15,000 gausses between pole faces 20 cm high to sort out positive from negative mesons. They found that only the positive mu mesons disintegrated in the iron; the negative mesons were probably captured by the nuclei of iron. But in the case of the passage of mu mesons through carbon, both the positive and the negative meson, together with disintegration electrons, both positive and negative, were observed. This result was interpreted by Fermi, Teller, and Weisskopf (1947) as showing a much weaker interaction between mu mesons and nuclei than that required by Yukawa particles. They calculated that as the negative mu meson slows down in its passage through matter, losing energy by electron collision and radiation, it gets to a distance from a nucleus corresponding to a K orbit of the Bohr type in a time of the order of 10^{-12} sec. The radius of the K orbit of a meson is smaller than the K orbit of an electron about the same nucleus in the ratio of the masses of the two particles, that is, about 200:1. In the case of carbon, the radius of this K orbit is about 10 times the nuclear radius. The mu meson apparently moves in this orbit for about 2.5×10^{-6} sec and then decays. On the basis of the Yukawa theory, a nuclear meson should be captured in a time of the order of 10^{-18} sec. The disagreement between the two is of the order of 10^{12}, showing a much weaker interaction between mu meson and nucleus than that needed for a Yukawa particle.

That mu mesons are captured by nuclei of iron can be accounted for by the fact that the radius of the K orbit of a mu meson in iron is not more than twice the nuclear radius, and hence the probability of finding it within the nucleus is much greater for iron than for carbon. Later work on the passage of mu mesons through matter shows that the capture cross section varies as Z^4. In substances of small values of Z, the probability of decay exceeds that of capture, and at $Z = 13$, capture and decay processes compete equally.

One of the results of the capture of mu mesons in a heavy element such as lead is the production of neutrons, probably by the reaction

$$\mu^- + p \text{ (in nucleus)} \rightarrow n + \nu. \tag{9}$$

The production of neutrons by the capture of μ^--mesons has been investigated by Sard and co-workers for the past few years (1948–1953) by allowing cosmic-ray μ-mesons to pass through various materials. They found very few neutrons produced in the lighter materials such as Mg and Ca, but found that, on the average, about two neutrons produced for every μ^--meson stopped in lead.

In the capture of μ-mesons by matter the observed excitation energy is of the order of 10 to 20 Mev, whereas the mass energy that disappears in this process is about 100 Mev. Hence it is necessary to postulate that a neutrino be emitted, as in equation (9), to carry off this energy. If this reaction does take place, then the μ-meson must have a spin of $\frac{1}{2}$, (or $\frac{3}{2}$), in order to conserve spin angular momentum. A second conclusion that follows if equation (9) is correct, is that the μ-meson is not the particle required by the Yukawa theory, for in this theory the meson and proton should combine to produce a neutron only.

14-9. Discovery of the Pi Meson

It was suggested by R. E. Marshak and H. Bethe (1947) that the fact that mesons are produced in the atmosphere by nuclear interactions but that μ-mesons have very small interactions with nuclei could be explained only by assuming that the mesons produced in the primary nuclear interactions are heavy mesons which have a short lifetime of about 10^{-8} sec and that these heavy mesons decay into mu mesons. At about this time, Occhialini and Powell, and D. H. Perkins, using special nuclear emulsion photographic plates exposed at high altitudes, observed that some of the mesons stopped

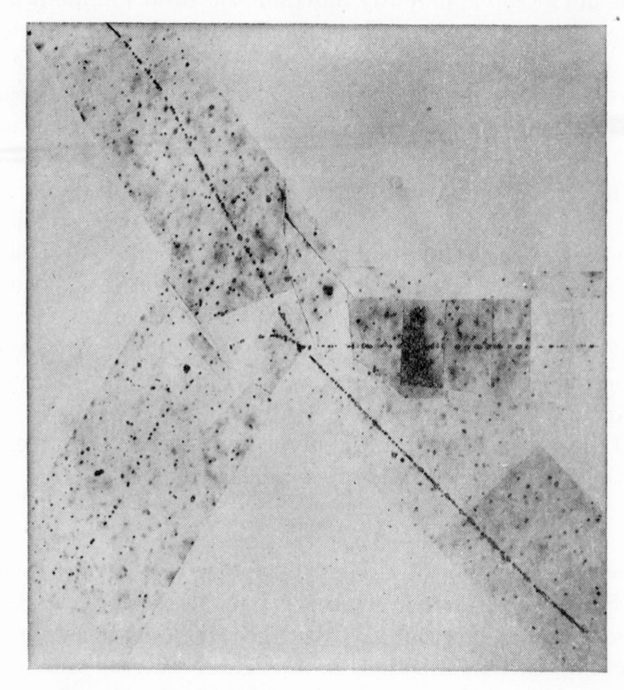

FIG. 14-5. Capture of a π^--meson by a nucleus producing a star in an Ilford C-2 emulsion. (Photograph by Perkins, *Nature*, 159, 126, 1947.)

in the photographic emulsions and produced so-called "stars," that is, nuclear disintegrations with the emission of slow protons or alpha particles. The photograph in Figure 14-5 shows the star observed in the photographic emulsion of an Ilford C-2 plate by Perkins. The noticeably curved track is that of the heavy meson, now known as the *π-meson*; when captured by a nucleus in the emulsion the resulting nuclear disintegration produces a star in which three charged particles are emitted. Shortly after this, Lattes, Muirhead, Occhialini, and Powell (1947), using similar nuclear photographic emulsions exposed at high altitudes, found tracks of some mesons each of which, when brought to rest in the emulsion, decayed with the emission of a mu meson. This was interpreted as the decay of a π^+-meson into a μ^+-meson. The Ilford C-2 plate was not sensitive enough to show the further disintegration of the μ-meson into a positive electron. With improved photographic emulsions the complete π^+-μ^+-e^+ decay scheme has been successfully recorded many times. Figure 14-6 is a photograph showing the tracks in a more sensitive nuclear emulsion of a π^+-meson which, when stopped, decays into a μ^+-meson, the latter then continuing until its characteristic kinetic energy has been expended in the emulsion, and

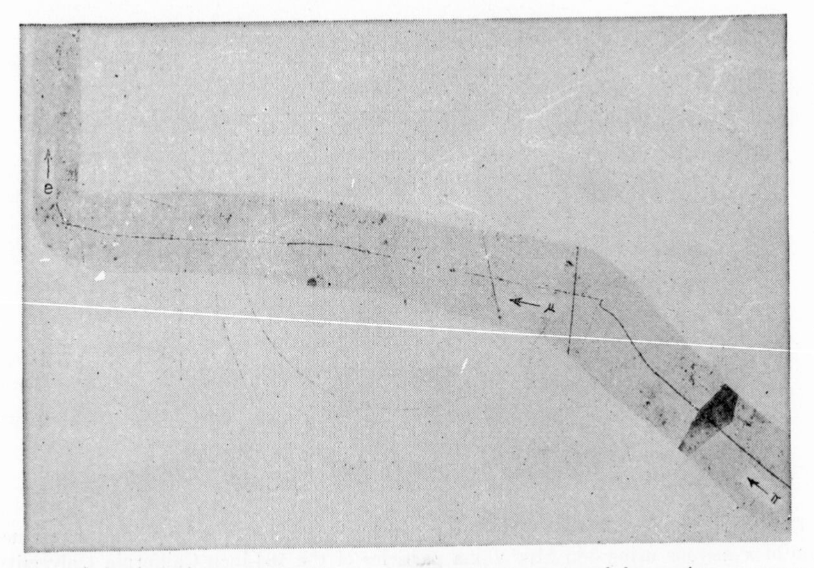

FIG. 14-6. π-μ-e decay. A positive pi meson comes to rest and decays into a μ-meson and a neutrino. The muon track shows the rapid increase in grain density (ionization) and multiple coulomb scattering characteristic of slow mesons. Upon coming to rest, the muon disintegrates into an electron (thin track at minimum ionization) and two neutrinos. (Photomosaic courtesy of Maurice M. Shapiro and Nathan Seeman, Naval Research Laboratory.)

then decaying into an electron. The kinetic energy of the muon emitted in the decay of a pi meson is always the same and is equal to 4 Mev. To conserve energy and also momentum in this process, an additional particle, most likely a neutrino, must be emitted simultaneously. Thus the disintegration scheme for a positive pi meson is

$$\boxed{\pi^+ \rightarrow \mu^+ + \nu.} \tag{10}$$

Examples have also been found of the decay of a negative pi meson *in flight*, as shown in Figure 14-8; its mode of decay is similar to that of the positive pi meson, thus

$$\pi^- \rightarrow \mu^- + \nu. \tag{11}$$

Early estimates of the rest mass of the charged π-meson yielded values of about 330 m_e, or about 165 Mev; this value is now known to be too high. At the time of the discovery of the pi meson, the new, large, modulated

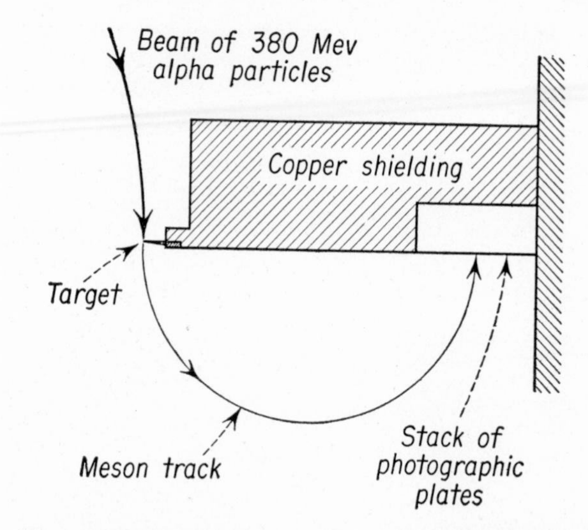

Fig. 14-7. Schematic diagram of the apparatus in the first experiment on the production of π-mesons using 380 Mev alpha particles of the 184-inch California University synchrocyclotron to bombard a target. π^--mesons travel in semicircular paths from place of origin in the target to stack of photographic plates.

frequency cyclotron at the University of California was already in operation, producing alpha particles of about 380 Mev. Gardner and Lattes (1948) performed experiments in which these high energy alpha particles bombarded a thin target, made of a material such as carbon, beryllium, or uranium, to determine whether π-mesons can be produced by the bombardment of nuclei by alpha particles. A stack of photographic plates (Ilford C-2 emulsions) was placed at an appropriate position so that any π^--mesons produced by this bombardment would be deflected by the magnetic field of the cyclotron so as to reach the plates, as shown in Figure 14-7. Examination of the tracks in the emulsion showed them to be of the same type as the cosmic-ray meson tracks. In later experiments on the artificial production of π-mesons, high energy protons were used as the bombarding particles, with a variety of substances used as targets. A plentiful supply of *pions* (shortened version of pi meson) thus became readily available wherever there were high energy particle accelerators.

14-10. Pi-Meson Decay in a Cloud Chamber

Cloud-chamber investigations have also been made to study the properties and modes of disintegration of the mesons. Pi mesons, produced artificially by the 385 Mev proton beam of the synchro-cyclotron at Nevis (Columbia

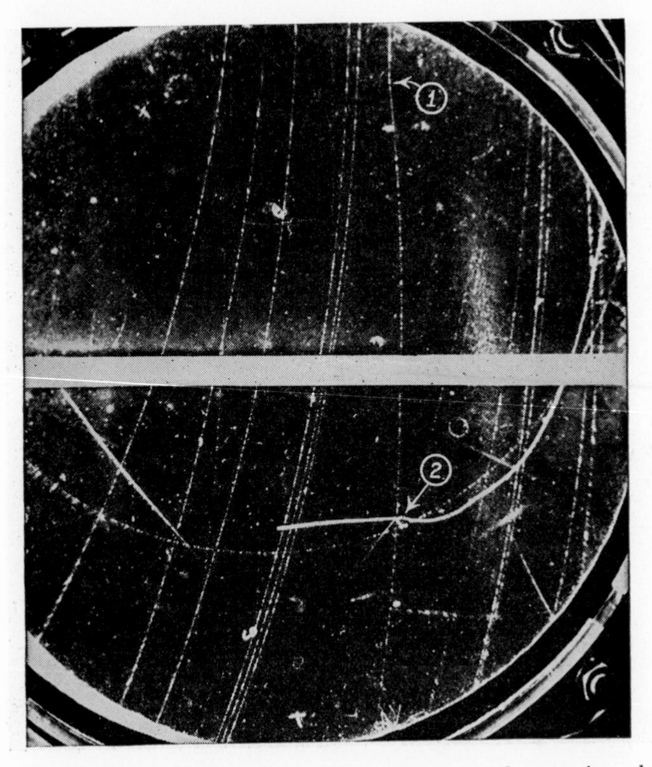

FIG. 14-8. Photograph of π^--meson tracks and associated events in a cloud chamber placed in a magnetic field of 4500 gausses. At (1) π^--meson decays in flight into μ^--meson. At (2), a meson, which lost some energy in a brass bolt, was slowed sufficiently so that it came to rest in the gas and was captured by a nucleus, resulting in a nuclear explosion forming a *star*. (Photograph courtesy of L. Lederman, Nevis Cyclotron Laboratory, Columbia University.)

University), were allowed to enter a cloud chamber 16 inches in diameter and working in a magnetic field of 4500 gausses. The charge of the meson could be determined from the direction of curvature of the tracks. Figure 14-8 is a photograph of π^--meson tracks in the cloud chamber showing two interesting events. Event (1) shows a π^--meson decaying in flight into a μ^--meson. This process is inferred from the change in direction of the path and from the change in density of the tracks; the μ-meson track is less dense than the end of the π^--meson track. Event (2) shows the path of a slow

π^--meson which, at the end of its range, is absorbed or captured by a nucleus of one of the atoms of the gas; the nucleus so produced is unstable and disintegrates into at least three charged particles. This nuclear explosion is an example of a nuclear *star* in a cloud chamber. One of the prongs

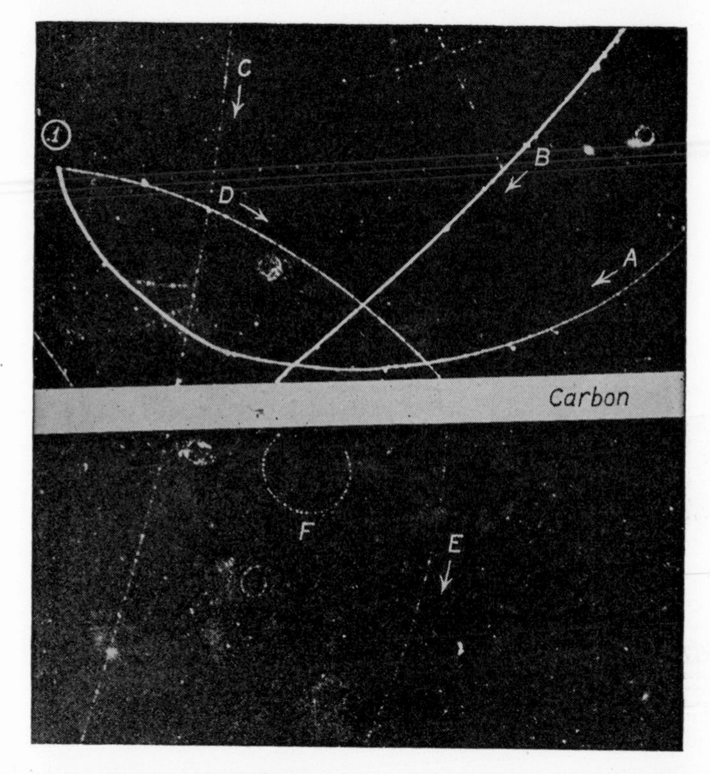

Fig. 14-9. Photograph of π^+-meson tracks and associated events in a cloud chamber placed in a magnetic field of 4500 gausses. Track A is that of a slow π^+-meson which comes to rest in the gas at (1) and decays into a μ^+-meson moving along track D; it enters the carbon plate and decays into a positron which moves along track E. This track shows minimum ionization. C is the track of a 70 Mev π^+-meson; B is a proton track of about the same curvature but greater ionization. F is a low momentum electron track of minimum ionization. (Track F retouched.) (Photograph courtesy of L. Lederman, Nevis Cyclotron Laboratory, Columbia University.)

of the star forms a typical "hammer" track; that is, it disintegrates into two charged particles traveling in opposite directions.

Tracks of π^+-mesons, produced under similar conditions at Nevis, are shown in the cloud-chamber photograph of Figure 14-9. Track C is that of a positive pion of high energy, about 70 Mev; it passes through the carbon block placed across the cloud chamber. This photograph is especially interesting because it shows the π^+-μ^+-e^+ decay. Track A is that of a positive pion near the end of its range, as evidenced by the increase in ionization and curvature along the track. When the pion comes to rest at point (1) it disintegrates into a positive mu meson, D, which has an energy of about 4 Mev, and a neutrino; the latter is a non-ionizing particle and produces no track. The muon enters the carbon plate, which is thick enough to stop muons of energies up to 10 Mev. The particle which emerges from the carbon and forms track E is a positron formed in the decay of the μ^+-meson. The fact that it is an electron rather than a muon track is inferred from its momentum, which is about 40 Mev/c, and also from its small ionization; these two factors combined indicate a very small mass. In this same photograph there are a low energy (a few Mev) and low momentum electron, track F, and also a heavily ionizing proton, track B.

14-11. Origins of the Pi Mesons

The results of cosmic-ray investigations led to the conclusion that pi mesons are produced both in nucleon-nucleon interactions and in the interaction of high energy photons with nucleons. For laboratory production of pi mesons, the most obvious target materials are hydrogen and deuterium or substances rich in these isotopes. More complex nuclides can also be used as targets, particularly to study the dependence of π-meson production on the mass number A.

The simplest nucleon-nucleon interaction involving protons as projectile and target is evidently

$$p + p \rightarrow \pi^+ + d \tag{12a}$$

or

$$p + p \rightarrow \pi^+ + (n + p). \tag{12b}$$

The symbol $(n + p)$ is used to indicate the fact that the neutron and proton may act as free particles, since the deuteron is a comparatively loosely bound structure; its binding energy is about 2.3 Mev, whereas the average binding energy per nucleon of the heavier nuclides is about 8 Mev.

The interaction between a high energy proton and a deuteron may be considered as an interaction between the proton and one of the nucleons, either the proton or the neutron, which constitute the deuteron. The possible reactions with deuterium as the target are thus

$$p + p \text{ (in } d) \rightarrow \pi^+ + p + n, \tag{13}$$

or

$$p + p \text{ (in } d) \rightarrow \pi^+ + d. \tag{14}$$

$$p + n \text{ (in } d) \rightarrow \pi^+ + n + n. \tag{15}$$

$$p + n \text{ (in } d) \rightarrow \pi^- + p + p. \tag{16}$$

Pi mesons can also be produced by the interaction of high energy photons, $h\nu$, with nucleons; the reactions which take place are probably those given by

$$h\nu + p \rightarrow \pi^{+} + n \tag{17}$$

and

$$h\nu + n \rightarrow \pi^{-} + p. \tag{18}$$

In addition to the charged pi mesons, the existence of neutral pi mesons, symbol π^0, has been definitely established. The neutral pion has been produced by bombarding hydrogen and deuterium with high energy photons; their existence has also been established from cosmic-ray evidence. The reactions for the production of neutral pi mesons by high energy photons are probably

$$h\nu + p \rightarrow \pi^{0} + p; \tag{19}$$

and

$$h\nu + d \rightarrow \pi^{0} + (n + p) \tag{20}$$

or

$$h\nu + d \rightarrow \pi^{0} + d. \tag{21}$$

The reaction given by equation (19) shows that there should be a minimum or threshold energy for the production of neutral pions equal to the energy equivalent for the mass of π^0.

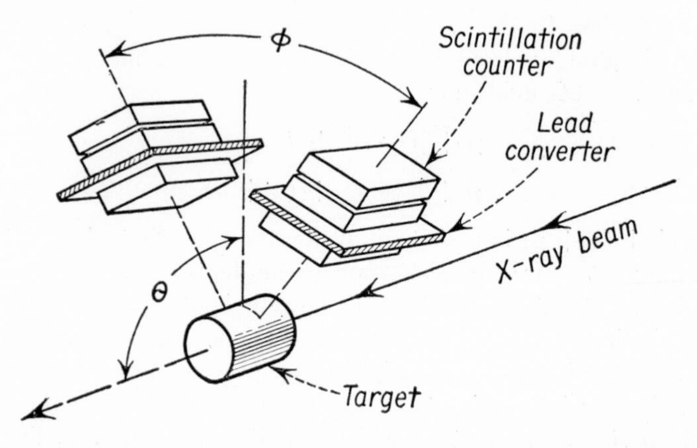

FIG. 14-10. Experimental arrangement for the production of π^0-mesons. The gamma rays coming from the decay of π^0-mesons produced when a target of hydrogen or beryllium is bombarded with 330 Mev x-rays are detected by the scintillation counters. (After Steinberger, Panofsky, and Steller, *Phys. Rev.*, 78, 802, 1950.)

14-12. Production of Neutral Pi Mesons

The production of neutral pi mesons by the interaction of high energy photons with matter was first definitely established by Steinberger, Panofsky, and Steller (1950), using the 330 Mev x-ray beam of the Berkeley synchrotron, although their production was inferred in earlier experiments by Bjorklund, Crandall, Moyer, and York (1949), who detected high energy photons coming from targets bombarded with protons from the Berkeley cyclotron. The latter suggested that a possible explanation of these high energy photons was that they were produced by the disintegration of a neutral meson into two gamma-ray photons, thus

$$\pi^0 \rightarrow \gamma + \gamma. \tag{22}$$

In the experimental arrangement used by Steinberger, Panofsky, and Steller, a narrow beam of x-rays from the synchrotron is incident on a

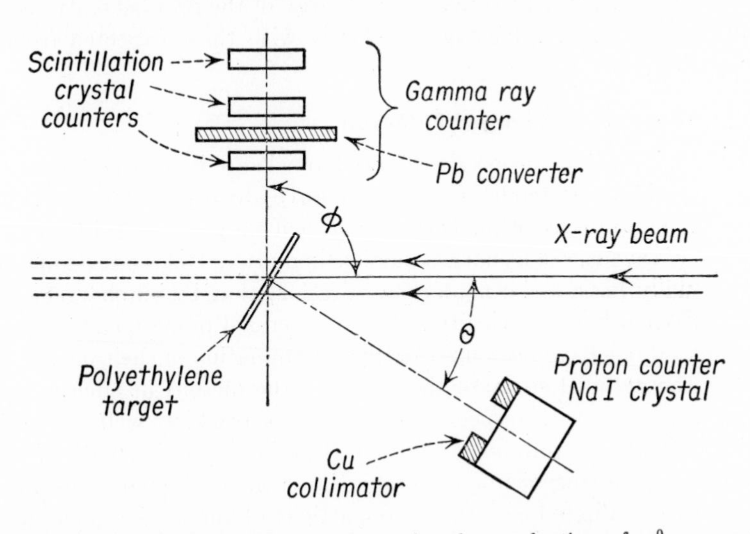

Fig. 14-11. Experimental arrangement for the production of π^0-mesons in a polyethylene target bombarded by x-ray photons. (After Silverman and Stearns, *Phys. Rev.*, 88, 1225, 1952.)

target, either of beryllium or hydrogen, as shown in Figure 14-10, and the products of this bombardment are detected by two gamma-ray counters which make an angle φ with each other in a plane at an angle θ with the x-ray beam. Each gamma-ray counter consists of three crystal scintillation counters with a thin piece of lead between the first two crystals to convert the gamma-ray photons into electron-positron pairs. The two counters were connected in a coincidence circuit with a resolving time of 10^{-8} sec. The measured values of the coincidence rates for different values of θ and φ agreed well with the calculated values based on the assumption that a π^0-meson of about 135 Mev rest mass disintegrates into two gamma-ray photons, each of approximately half this energy.

The threshold value of the energy of the photons to produce neutral pi mesons in the reaction

$$h\nu + p \rightarrow \pi^0 + p \tag{19}$$

was determined by Silverman and Stearns (1952) as about 145 Mev. In their experiment, a beam of x-rays (bremsstrahlung radiation) from the 315 Mev Cornell synchrotron was allowed to strike a polyethylene $(CH_2)_n$ target, as shown in Figure 14-11. Only one gamma-ray counter was used, set at an angle φ to the incident beam, and a proton counter consisting of an NaI crystal was set at a suitable angle θ to the incident beam. The two detectors were connected so that a proton pulse was registered only when there was a coincidence between the two counters. Using four different values between 215 Mev and 295 Mev for the energy of the incident photons, they measured the maximum energy of the protons scattered at a given angle θ. These values agreed closely with those expected from the reaction above.

14-13. Mass of the Charged Pi Meson

Among the important properties of any particle are its charge, mass, spin, average lifetime, and mode of decay. We have already shown the evidence for the modes of decay of the charged and neutral pi mesons. In the determination of the mass of a charged particle in motion, two separate measurements usually have to be made, one of E/M, that is, its charge-to-mass ratio, and the other, its velocity v. For the charged pi mesons, two general types of methods have been used in the determination of their masses. One involves the detailed study of the tracks of the mesons in nuclear photographic emulsions with respect to the length of track, as well as the grain density, that is, the number of developed grains per unit length of track. In all of these measurements, the properties of the particular nuclear emulsion used are evaluated with the aid of particles of known charge, mass, and energy; the tracks of protons of known energy are commonly used for this purpose. The results of these studies show that the ratio of the ranges in an emulsion of two particles, each of the same velocity v, is equal to the ratio of their masses. The energy $\mathfrak{E}$ of a particle which has a range R in an emulsion is given by

$$\mathfrak{E} = kR^n, \tag{23}$$

where k and n are constants for a particular emulsion. The grain density of a track is proportional to $d\mathfrak{E}/dR$, the loss of energy per unit length of path in the emulsion. The latter depends only upon the charge of the particle and its velocity, and is independent of the mass. For particles of a given charge, say electronic charge, the rate of loss of energy is a function of the velocity only. This function has a minimum for a velocity approaching the velocity of light—approximately that velocity for which the total mass of the particle is about twice its rest mass. Since a track, either in an emulsion or in a cloud chamber, is produced by ionization, the density of a track is sometimes expressed in terms of the density at minimum ionization. For certain electron-sensitive emulsions (Kodak NT-4 and Ilford G-5), tracks of minimum ionization contain about 300 to 400 grains per millimeter. At this density, the arrangement of grains is just barely recognizable as a track. From the above, it follows that tracks of minimum ionization are produced by electrons of about 1 Mev and by protons of about 2000 Mev.

The study of tracks in either photographic emulsions or cloud chambers may be supplemented by independent determinations of the momenta

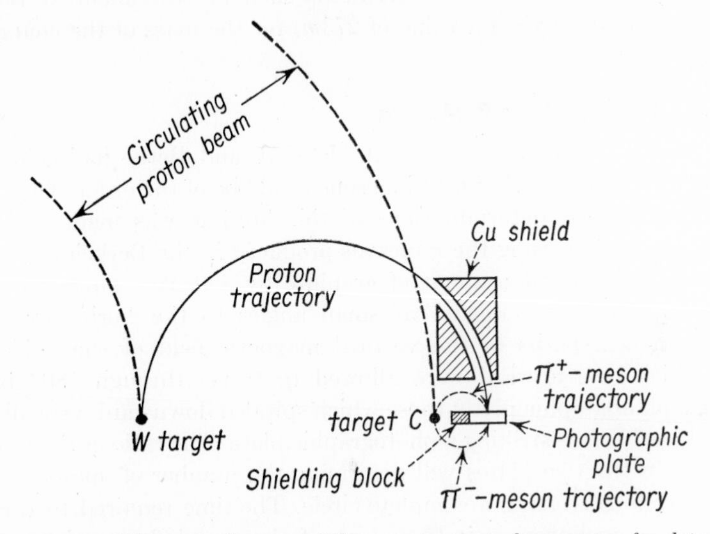

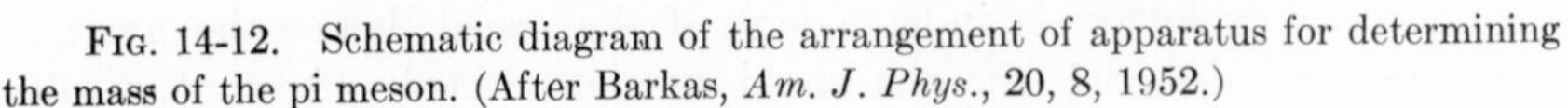

FIG. 14-12. Schematic diagram of the arrangement of apparatus for determining the mass of the pi meson. (After Barkas, *Am. J. Phys.*, 20, 8, 1952.)

of the particles by having them pass through magnetic fields and determining the curvature of the paths in these fields.

Another very useful method is the determination of the average angular deviation $\bar{\alpha}$ of the trajectory per unit length of path as a function of the grain density. The angular deviation of the path is due to the Coulomb interaction between the charged particle and the nuclei of the material of the emulsion. The value of the angular deviation for a particle of given charge, mass, and velocity can be calculated as a function of the grain density, and the experimental result compared with theoretical predictions. Such measurements have been used to determine the nature of the particle producing the track as well as the mass of the particle.

One of the most accurate determinations of the mass of the charged pi meson was made with pi mesons produced by the bombardment of a carbon target by high energy protons in the Berkeley cyclotron. These pions traveled in semicircular paths in the magnetic field of the cyclotron and were detected by nuclear photographic plates, as shown in Figure 14-12.

To avoid errors involved in direct measurements of the intensity of the magnetic field, the same photographic plate received protons scattered from a thin tungsten target placed in the circulating proton beam of the cyclotron. A copper block with a suitably cut circular channel was placed in front of the photographic plate so that only protons whose velocity was practically the same as that of the mesons could reach the photographic plate. For particles of the same velocity, the ratio of their ranges is equal to the ratio of their masses. The results of such an experiment by Barkas, Smith, and Gardner yield a value of $273m_e$ for the mass of the charged pi meson.

14-14. Lifetimes of the Pi Mesons

It has already been mentioned that Marshak and Bethe had calculated that the lifetime of the charged pi mesons would be of the order of 10^{-8} sec. One of the earliest determinations of this lifetime was made by J. R. Richardson (1948), using the π-mesons produced in the Berkeley synchro-cyclotron by the bombardment of graphite by 380 Mev alpha particles. Pi mesons which are emitted at small angles to the horizontal plane travel in helical paths in the vertical magnetic field of the cyclotron. Those which rose upward were allowed to travel through 180° before striking a photographic plate; those which spiraled downward were allowed to travel 540° before striking a photographic plate. The ratio of the number of mesons in the two plates will determine the number of mesons which decayed while traversing a complete circle. The time required to traverse a circle in a cyclotron is independent of the speed; hence the average lifetime of the decaying mesons could be determined. The first results obtained for the mean life of a charged pi meson yielded the value of about 1.1×10^{-8} sec. Using a similar method with improved technique, Martinelli and Panofsky (1950) obtained a value of 1.97×10^{-8} sec for the mean life of π^+-mesons.

A more recent experiment on the decay in flight of π^+-mesons was performed by Durbin, Loar, and Havens (1952) for the determination of their mean lifetimes. A beam of π-mesons produced in the Nevis cyclotron by the bombardment of a beryllium target with 385 Mev protons came out through a channel in the concrete shielding. The mesons in the beam had an energy of about 73 Mev. By reversing the magnetic field of the cyclotron, mesons of the opposite charge could be taken out through an appropriate channel. The meson beam was deflected by a magnet outside the channel and directed through three stilbene scintillation counters operated in coincidence, as shown in Figure 14-13. A much larger scintillation counter, C_4, eight inches in diameter and containing xylene, a liquid, was set at a distance L from C_3. This distance L could be varied from a few inches to about 8 ft. The coincidence counters C_1, C_2, C_3 defined the beam of the

π-mesons; some of these mesons decayed in flight between C_3 and C_4, the remaining ones being detected by C_4. It was shown that for $L \gtrless 2$ ft, practically all the μ-mesons produced in the π-decay miss the detector C_4. After suitable corrections for beam impurities, angular divergence, accidental coincidences, and so forth, the difference in counts between $C_1C_2C_3$ detectors and the C_4 detector represented the number of π-mesons decaying in flight along the path of length L. Knowing the average velocity of the

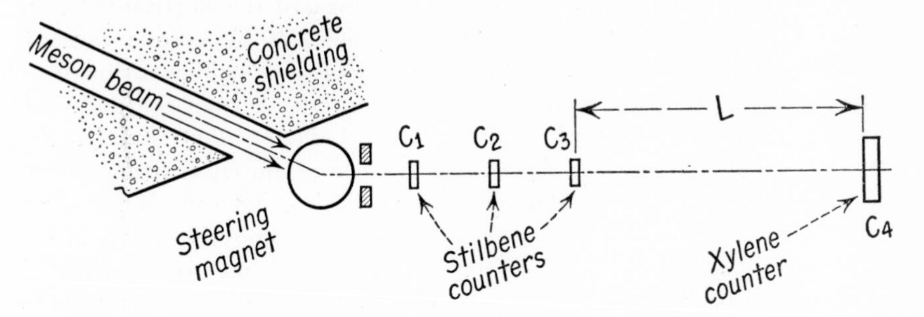

FIG. 14-13. Schematic diagram of the apparatus for measuring the lifetime of charged pi mesons. (After Durbin, Loar, and Havens, *Phys. Rev.*, 88, 180, 1952.)

π-mesons, and determining the mean free path from the above experiment, the mean lifetime could be calculated. The values so determined are, for π^+-mesons, 2.54×10^{-8} sec, and for π^--mesons, 2.44×10^{-8} sec, with an error of about 0.19×10^{-8} sec. Thus within the limits of experimental error, the mean lifetimes of the π^+- and π^--mesons are identical. Adopting the value for the mean life $T_m = 2.5 \times 10^{-8}$ sec, the half-life of a $\pi^\pm$-meson is

$$T = 0.693 \times 2.5 \times 10^{-8} \text{ sec},$$

or

$$T = 1.75 \times 10^{-8} \text{ sec}.$$

The lifetime of the π^0-meson seems to be considerably shorter than that of the charged π-mesons. Present estimates of this lifetime are of the order of 10^{-15} to 10^{-14} sec.

14-15. Nuclear Interactions of π^--Mesons

The interaction of negative pi mesons with nuclei can be considered in two general categories: (a) the interaction with the simplest type of nucleus, the proton, and (b) the interaction with more complex nuclei which lead to the production of *stars*.

The interaction of π^--mesons with protons has been studied with artificially produced mesons and with cosmic-ray mesons. The most probable reactions are

$$\pi^- + p \rightarrow n + \gamma \tag{24}$$

and

$$\pi^- + p \rightarrow n + \pi^0, \tag{25}$$

followed by

$$\pi^0 \rightarrow 2\gamma. \tag{26}$$

Carlson, Hooper, and King (1950) investigated the electron-positron pairs produced in nuclear photographic emulsions by cosmic rays at 70,000 ft elevation. The distribution in energy of these pairs was similar to that expected from the gamma-ray spectrum arising from the decay of neutral mesons. Panofsky, Aamodt, and Hadley (1951) studied the gamma-ray spectrum using the π^--meson beam produced in the Berkeley 184-inch cyclotron. The π^--mesons bombarded hydrogen under pressure; the gamma rays formed in this reaction passed through a slit system into a thin sheet of tantalum in which the gamma-ray photons were converted into electron-positron pairs. The pairs were deflected by a strong magnetic field into two trays of Geiger counters. The pair spectrum showed two peaks, a fairly narrow one centered about 130 Mev, and a rather wide one centered about 70 Mev. The narrow peak was ascribed to the gamma-ray photons formed in the reaction (24) by π^--mesons stopped in hydrogen. From an analysis of this peak, they obtained a value of $275m_e$ for the mass of the π^--meson. The wide peak ranged in values from 53.6 to 85 Mev and was ascribed to reactions (25) and (26), in which two gamma-ray photons were produced by the disintegration of each π^0-meson. This range of values is due to the Doppler broadening of the frequencies of the gamma rays owing to the initial velocities of the π^0-mesons. From this range of values, and the known difference in mass between neutron and proton, the difference in mass between the π^--meson and the π^0-meson could be calculated. The value obtained from this experiment was

$$m_{\pi^-} - m_{\pi^0} = 10.2 \pm 2m_e. \tag{27}$$

Using the present value of $273m_e$ for the mass of the π^--meson, the mass of the π^0-meson becomes $262m_e$

The stars produced by the capture of slow π^--mesons in the nuclei of the elements composing nuclear emulsions were investigated by Menon, Muirhead, and Rochat (1950). They studied more than 2500 stars, about half of them produced by artificially generated mesons, the remainder produced by cosmic-ray mesons. They classified the stars according to the number of prongs in each. The particles forming the prongs were identified by means of their grain densities and the scattering along their tracks. Tracks were observed which were ascribed to protons, alpha particles, and

Li^8 nuclei, the last identified by their characteristic hammer tracks. (See Figures 14-5 and 14-8 for typical stars.) About 46 per cent of all visible stars were ascribed to the interaction of π^--mesons with light nuclei such as C^{12}, N^{14}, and O^{16}; about 54 per cent were ascribed to interaction with the heavy nuclei, silver and bromine. About 28 per cent of all π^--mesons absorbed in the emulsion were captured by nuclei without producing visible stars.

The reactions between π^--mesons and light nuclei were identified as

$$_6C^{12} + \pi^- \rightarrow 2\,_2He^4 + {}_1H^1 + 3\,_0n^1 \quad \text{(3 prongs)} \tag{28}$$

$$_7N^{14} + \pi^- \rightarrow 3\,_2He^4 + 2\,_0n^1 \quad \text{(3 prongs)} \tag{29}$$

$$_8O^{16} + \pi^- \rightarrow 3\,_2He^4 + {}_1H^1 + 3\,_0n^1. \quad \text{(4 prongs)} \tag{30}$$

From the above reactions, it would seem that the alpha particle acts as a single unit inside the lighter nuclei, giving additional evidence that alpha particles are subgroups within such nuclei. The stars produced by the capture of π^--mesons by heavy nuclei had, on the average, fewer prongs than those produced by the lighter nuclei. Further, the ratio of alpha particles to protons was very small, about 0.3. The energy spectrum of the protons ejected in these disintegrations had a Maxwellian distribution. It appears that in the absorption of a π^--meson by a heavy nucleus, the energy is given to many nucleons in a small region of the nucleus, and as these nucleons proceed outward, they give up most of their energy to the other particles, with very few nucleons ultimately having enough energy to escape from the nucleus.

14-16. Mesic Atoms

There is a certain probability that negative mesons, either mu or pi, in their passage through matter, will be stopped; these will be captured in orbits about the nuclei, forming a type of Bohr atom. Since the radius of a Bohr orbit varies inversely as the mass of the negatively charged particle, the radius of a mesic orbit will be about 1/200 or 1/300 that of an electronic orbit. The energies of the mesic atoms will be correspondingly higher and hence energy changes produced by the motion of a meson from a high energy orbit to one of lower energy will result in the emission of x-ray photons characteristic of the mesic atoms. The emission of x-rays from both the mu mesic atoms and the pi mesic atoms has been observed.

X-rays due to the transition from the $2P$ states to $1S$ states of mesic atoms formed in the passage of π^--mesons through beryllium, carbon, and oxygen have been detected in a series of experiments performed by Camac, McGuire, Platt, and Schulte (1952), using the π^--meson beam from the Rochester cyclotron. Calculations of the $2P \rightarrow 1S$ transition yield photon energies of 44.3 kev in beryllium, 100 kev in carbon, and 178 kev in oxygen.

The x-rays from these transitions were detected with an NaI (Tl) scintillation counter which had been calibrated with x-ray lines of known energy. X-rays were observed at the expected energies within the limits of experimental error.

X-rays from mu-mesic atoms were investigated by Rainwater and Fitch (1953), using a negative meson beam of well-defined momentum from the Nevis cyclotron. The beam was allowed to pass through a piece of copper, three inches thick, to absorb all the pi mesons; the mu mesons, which constituted about 5 per cent of the original beam, passed through the

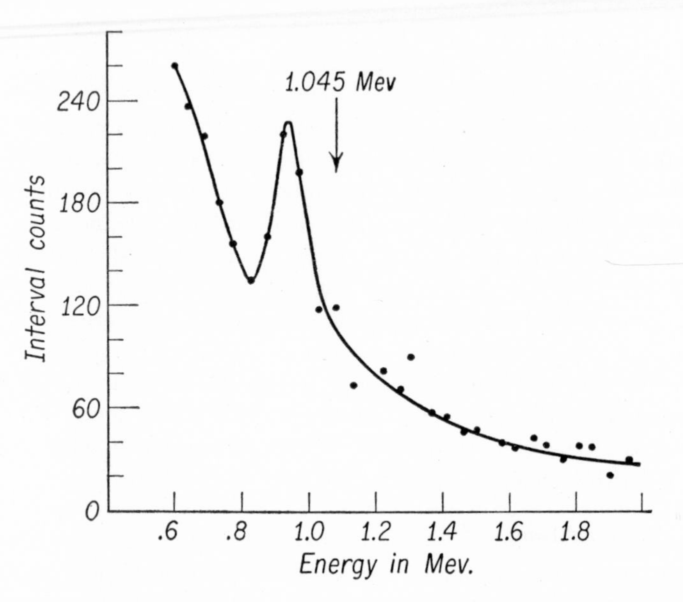

Fig. 14-14. X-ray spectrum from mu-mesic atom of titanium. (After Fitch and Rainwater, *Phys. Rev.*, 92, 796, 1953.)

copper into an absorber or target. X-rays produced in this absorber by the mu-mesic atoms were then detected by an NaI crystal. The crystal was calibrated with photons of 1.38 and 2.76 Mev energy. Absorbers of different atomic numbers, ranging from $Z = 13$ to $Z = 83$, were used in this experiment. The most probable transition in each case would be a $2P \rightarrow 1S$ transition for the mesic atom, giving rise to a characteristic line. A typical x-ray spectrum obtained from titanium is shown in Figure 14-14; this spectrum consists of a characteristic line at 0.955 Mev. The calculated energy of this line, assuming the nucleus to be a point charge, is 1.045 Mev. Similar results were obtained with the other mu-mesic atoms. Fine structure was observed in the x-ray lines of Pb, $Z = 82$, and Bi, $Z = 83$. This fine structure could be explained in terms of the fine structure of the $2P$ level due to the spin of the meson, the transitions being $2P_{3/2} \rightarrow 1S$ and $2P_{1/2} \rightarrow 1S$.

Since the orbit of the μ^--meson is very close to the nucleus, the energy of the orbit, and hence also the transition energy, will be sensitive to the size of the nucleus. This accounts for the shift in energy shown in Figure 14-14. Similar results were obtained for the energies of the other x-ray lines investigated. Hence the results of these experiments can be used to determine the nuclear radius. We have already shown that the nuclear radius R, as determined from a variety of nuclear phenomena, such as the scattering of particles and alpha-decay lifetimes, is given by

$$R = r_0 A^{1/3} \tag{31}$$

where r_0 is the radius parameter. These experiments have usually yielded values of r_0 of the order of $(1.4 - 1.5) \times 10^{-13}$ cm. From the results of their experiments on x-rays from mu-mesic atoms, Rainwater and Fitch found that the best fit between theory and experiment could be obtained by assigning the value

$$\boxed{r_0 = 1.2 \times 10^{-13} \text{ cm}} \tag{32}$$

to the radius parameter. This value is based on the assumption that the nucleus is a sphere of radius R in which the protons are uniformly distributed throughout its volume; also, the known values for the mass, spin, and magnetic moment of the μ^--meson were used in the calculations.

The value of the radius parameter obtained from these experiments is significantly smaller than those values obtained from other experiments. This reduction leads to an increase by a factor of $(1.5/1.2)^3 \approx 2$ in the proton density of the nucleus, assuming the correctness of the homogeneous nuclear model. This lower value of r_0 is in agreement with other recent experiments and may lead to a change in our concept of the distribution of charge in the nucleus.

14-17. Tau Mesons

Among the different particles classified as mesons, one interesting type is called a tau (τ) meson. Its mass is approximately 1000 m_e, and it decays at rest into three π mesons. It was first discovered by Brown, Camerini, Muirhead, Powell, and Ritson in 1949, in a nuclear emulsion exposed to cosmic radiation. It has since been observed by others in photographic emulsions exposed to cosmic rays at high altitudes, under varying thicknesses of absorbers, usually ice or aluminum. Figure 14-15 is a photograph of a typical decay of a τ-meson into three π-mesons. Tracks a, b, and c, are those of the π-mesons. These three tracks are coplanar, indicating that the probability of the simultaneous emission of another particle, such as a neutrino, is negligible. The measured values of the kinetic energies of the particles forming these tracks are 17.1, 27.8, and 41.6 Mev, respectively, or a total of 86.5 Mev, corresponding to about 173 m_e. If the mass of a π-meson is taken to be 275 m_e, then the mass of the τ-meson becomes 998 m_e. In the case cited above, the path of the τ-meson in the nuclear emulsion is

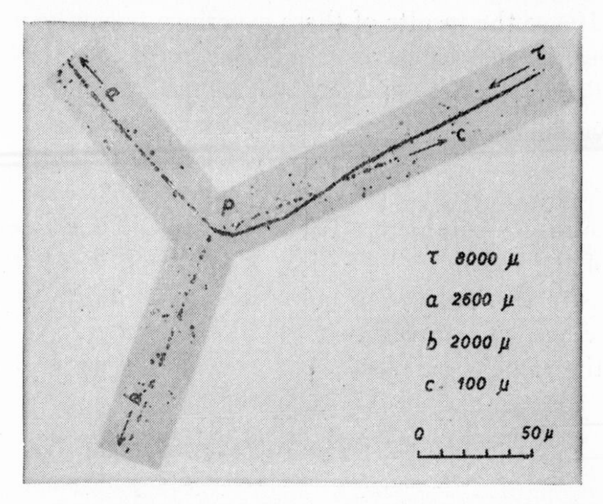

FIG. 14-15. Photograph of tracks of a τ-meson decaying at rest into three π-mesons, *a*, *b*, and *c*. Tracks are in an Ilford G-5 nuclear emulsion, 1200 microns thick, which was exposed on Mt. Rosa, 4500 meters above sea level, surrounded by an aluminum absorber 5 cm thick. The numbers on the photograph indicate the respective lengths of the tracks in the emulsion. Tracks *a* and *b* end in the glass plate, track *c* goes into the air after only 100 microns in the emulsion. (From photograph supplied by Ceccarelli, Dallaporta, Merlin, and Rostagni, *Nature*, 170, 454, 1952.)

8000 microns, sufficient to allow an independent determination of its mass to be made. Ceccarelli, Dallaporta, Merlin, and Rostagni, (1952) obtained a value of $(946 \pm 140)m_e$ from such a measurement.

The role of τ-mesons in nuclear phenomena other than that described above is at present unknown. To produce mesons in the laboratory for more intensive investigations would require particles with energies in excess of 500 Mev, the rest mass energy of the τ-meson. There is at present only one particle accelerator, the cosmotron at Brookhaven National Laboratory, capable of producing such high energy particles. Other accelerators capable of producing such high energy particles will probably be in operation in the near future. Until then, we shall have to rely upon the fortuitous appearance of τ-decay processes for our knowledge of these particles and their relationship to other nuclear particles and to nuclear forces generally.

14-18. *V*-Particles

Interesting groups of unstable particles, generally classified as *V particles*, have been observed in photographs of cloud-chamber investigations of penetrating showers in cosmic rays. The first observations of such particles were made by G. D. Rochester and C. C. Butler (1947). In one observation they found two tracks having a common origin, making an angle of about 65° with each other, which they attributed to the disintegration of a neutral particle, now called a V^0-*particle,* into two charged particles, as shown in

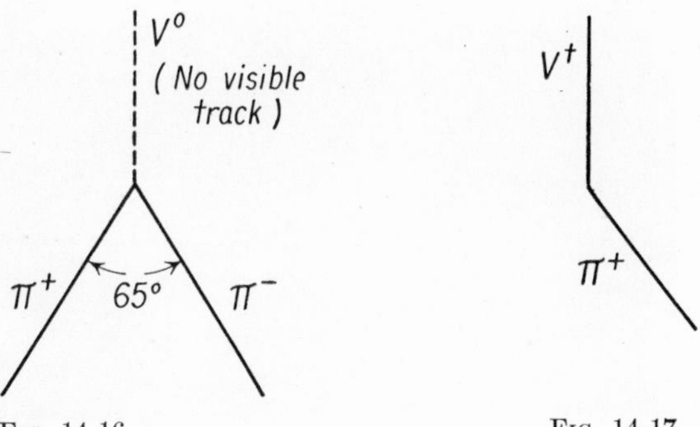

FIG. 14-16. FIG. 14-17.

FIG. 14-16. Schematic diagram showing the tracks formed in a cloud chamber by the products of disintegration of a neutral V^0 particle. The V^0 particle, shown moving along the dotted path, does not produce a track.

FIG. 14-17. Schematic diagram showing the tracks formed by the disintegration of charged V particle in flight.

Figure 14-16. From the curvature of the tracks in the magnetic field in the cloud chamber, the charges had opposite signs. The masses of the particles were approximately those of π-mesons. They estimated the energy of the neutral particle to be greater than $800m_e$. In the second case, they observed the path of a charged particle which suffered a sudden deviation; this deviation could not be accounted for by nuclear scattering in the gas of the cloud chamber. Better consistency was obtained by assuming that the charged particle, called a V^+ particle, disintegrated in flight into a charged π-meson, and at least one neutral particle, as shown in Figure 14-17. The mass of the V^+ particle was estimated to be about 1000 m_e.

These events are comparatively rare, but nonetheless many V particles have been observed since then. An idea of the frequency of occurrence of these events can be gathered from the following statistics. In counter-controlled cloud-chamber studies of penetrating showers, Seriff, Leighton, Hsiao, Cowan, and Anderson (1950) found 34 V particles in 11,000 photographs. Of these 30 were classified as V^0 particles and 4 as V^+ particles. In similar experiments, Leighton, Wanlass, and Anderson (1953) found 152 V particles in 23,000 photographs, 134 classified as V^0 particles and 18 as V^+ particles. Figure 14-18 shows a V^0 particle obtained in these experiments. The decay particles are formed below a lead plate in the cloud chamber. A

V^0 particle, which does not produce a track since it is not charged, originates in a nuclear event in the lead plate and then decays in flight into two charged particles which form the V. The shorter track on the left is that of a positively charged particle with a momentum of about 390 Mev/c and

FIG. 14-18. Cloud-chamber photograph of the decay of a V^0 particle. The V^0 particle originated in a nuclear event in the lead plate in the cloud chamber and decayed below it into two particles of opposite sign as shown by the opposite curvatures of the tracks in a magnetic field. (Photograph supplied by R. B. Leighton, California Institute of Technology.)

a mass estimated as between 1350 m_e and 1650 m_e; it is probably a proton. The negative particle produces less ionization, has momentum of about 150 Mev/c and a mass less than 370 m_e, and is probably a π^--meson. The Q value, or the energy released in this reaction, is about 33 Mev.

Figure 14-19 shows two unrelated V^0 particles in the same photograph. The V^0 particle in the upper left of the photograph was probably formed in a nuclear event or star produced in the lead blocks above the cloud chamber. This nuclear event probably also gave rise to the penetrating shower particles seen in the upper right of the chamber. One of these penetrating particles produced a star in the lead plate in the center of the chamber producing some penetrating particle and a V^0 particle. The latter disinte-

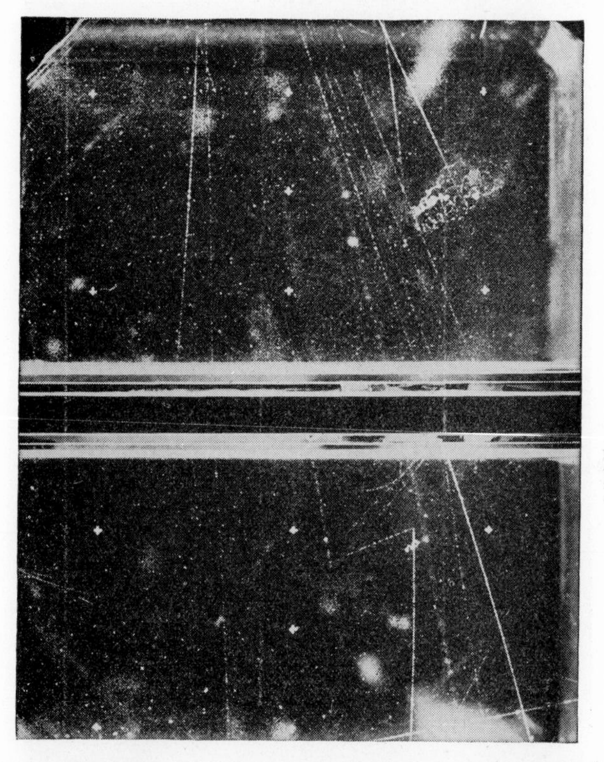

FIG. 14-19. Cloud-chamber photograph showing two unrelated V^0 decays. One V^0 decay occurs near the top and to the left of the center of the upper chamber, yielding a heavily ionizing positive particle and a lightly ionizing negative particle whose track is very short. This V^0 particle probably originated in the same nuclear event, in the lead blocks above the chamber, which gave rise to the penetrating shower particles to the right. One of these particles, colliding with a nucleus in the lead plate between the chambers, produced another V^0 particle which decayed below it, right of center, yielding a heavily ionizing positive particle which travels almost vertically downward, and a short, lightly ionizing negative particle. The positive particles in both cases are probably protons. (From a photograph by Leighton, Wanlass, and Anderson, *Phys. Rev.* 89, 151, 1953.)

grates below the lead plate into a long, heavily ionizing positive track and a short track due to a lightly ionizing negative particle. The tracks of both negative particles are too short for measurements; the particles producing these tracks probably leave through the walls of the cloud chamber. The positively charged particles in both cases are probably protons.

One of the important tests as to whether we are dealing with a V^0 particle or with two tracks which are unrelated is the test of *coplanarity*, that is, the plane containing the two decay particles must also contain the

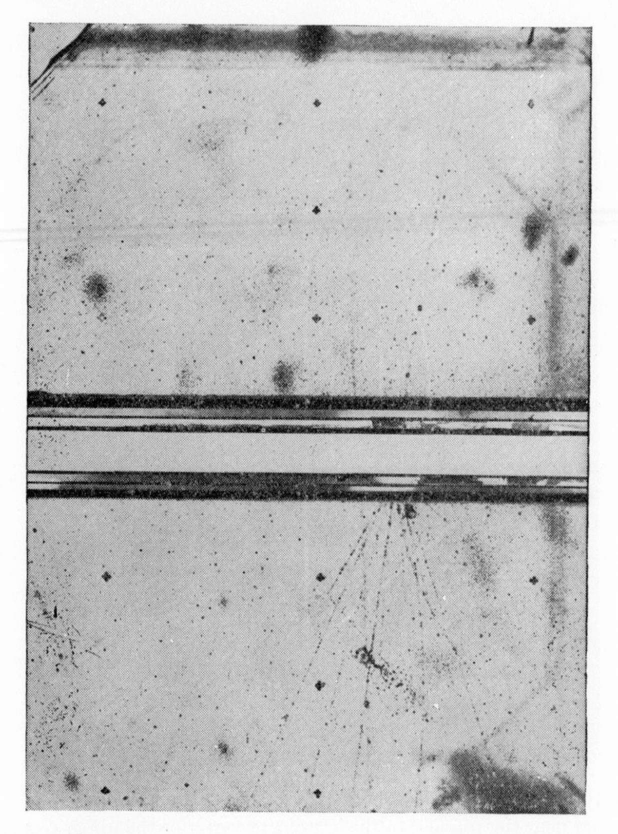

FIG. 14-20. Cloud-chamber photograph of the decay of a V^+ particle in flight. The V^+ particle is formed in the nuclear event giving rise to a star in the lead plate between the chambers. The V^+ particle travels slightly toward the left below the plate and then disintegrates into a π^+-meson which moves down toward the right, and a neutral particle which leaves no track. (From a photograph supplied by R. B. Leighton, California Institute of Technology.)

line of travel of the V^0 particle. The latter is taken as a line from the center of the star to the vertex of the V.

As has been shown, charged V disintegrations are comparatively rare events. Figure 14-20 shows a V^+ particle coming from a star produced in the lead plate in the cloud chamber; the V^+ particle disintegrates in flight below the plate with the emission of a charged particle. To conserve momentum, at least one other particle, a neutral one, must be emitted simultaneously. Penetrating charged particles produced in the star can be seen in the photograph coming from the same point in the lead plate from which the V^+ particle originated.

The present consensus is that there are several different kinds of V^0 particles. One of these, called V_1^0, has a mass of about 2200 m_e and decays into a proton and a pi meson:

$$V_1^0 \rightarrow p + \pi^- + Q_1. \tag{33}$$

The value of Q_1 is approximately 35 Mev; the lifetime of the V_1^0 particle is about 2.5×10^{-10} sec.

Another group of particles classified as V_2^0 is probably a complex group. One well-substantiated type of disintegration is into two pi mesons:

$$V_2^0 \rightarrow \pi^+ + \pi^- + Q_2. \tag{34}$$

The value of Q_2 is approximately 200 Mev. Its rest mass is of the order of 850 m_e; its lifetime is probably less than that of V_1^0, of the order of 10^{-10} sec.

Many of the observed V^0 particles do not fall in the above classifications. Their masses fall between those of V_1^0 and V_2^0 and their modes of decay are uncertain.

14-19. Mass Spectrum of Fundamental Particles

The fundamental particles discussed thus far do not exhaust the list of known particles. New particles are being discovered with great frequency. As we have seen, most of the newly discovered particles have very short lifetimes and produce unusual events. The same type of particle may be discovered by different physicists under different experimental conditions. The names assigned to such particles are usually related to the phenomena which led to their discovery; hence several names may be assigned to the same particle and will persist until some consensus is reached concerning the name. Recently (1953), a group of physicists, meeting at the International Cosmic-Ray Congress at Bagnères-de-Bigorre, France, proposed a new method of classifying the fundamental particles in three large groups, depending upon their masses, with sufficient flexibility for the inclusion of additional particles that may be discovered later. These are the groups:

1. *L*-mesons: light mesons such as π and μ and any other meson whose mass is less than that of the π-meson.
2. *K*-mesons: heavy mesons, such as the τ-meson; any meson with a mass between that of the π-meson and the mass of the proton.
3. *Y*-particles or *hyperons:* particles with mass between the mass of the neutron and that of the deuteron. This classification may be extended if fundamental particles heavier than the deuteron are discovered.

These three groups are shown in the mass spectrum in Figure 14-21.

The names and symbols for the older fundamental particles are left unchanged in this new scheme. These are electron, e; proton, p; neutron, n; neutrino, ν. All the other new particles are to be designated by Greek letters: small Greek letters for mesons, and capital Greek letters for hyperons or Y particles. Under this new proposal, the μ-, π-, and τ-mesons retain their designations, but the names of the V particles will be changed,

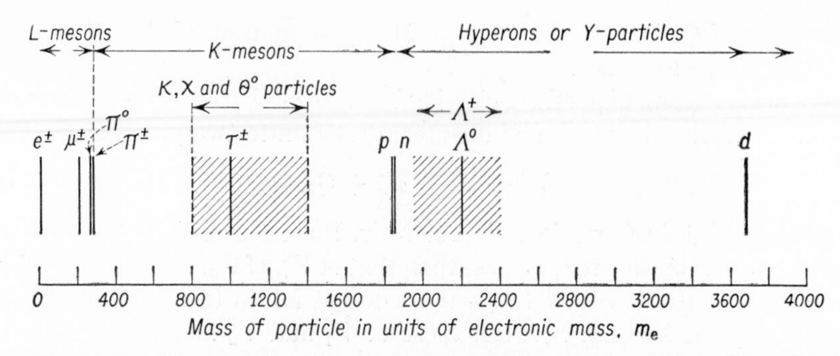

FIG. 14-21. Diagram showing mass spectrum of the fundamental particles with the proposed new classification. The unit of mass is the electronic rest mass.

depending upon whether they are classified as Y particles or K mesons. For Y particles, the names suggested are as follows:

Λ^0 (lambda zero)—old name V_1^0—with the decay scheme

$$\Lambda^0 \rightarrow p + \pi^-.$$

Λ^+ for the positive counterpart of Λ^0, with the possible decay schemes

$$\Lambda^+ \rightarrow n + \pi^+,$$

$$\Lambda^+ \rightarrow p + \pi^0.$$

For those V particles which are K mesons, and which have previously been designated as v^0, V_2^0, V_4^0, the new name suggested is θ^0. These particles are characterized by the decay scheme

$$\theta^0 \rightarrow \pi^{\pm} + \pi^{\mp}$$

or

$$\theta^0 \rightarrow \pi^{\pm} + \mu^{\mp}.$$

Among the newly discovered particles not listed above are the kappa meson and the chi meson, both K mesons, and both discovered by O'Ceallaigh and co-workers (1951). Their decay schemes are

$$\kappa \rightarrow \mu + 2 \text{ neutral particles (nature unknown)},$$

and

$$\chi \rightarrow \pi + 1 \text{ neutral particle (nature unknown)}.$$

We have already discussed some of the atomic and nuclear events involving the L mesons. Very little is now known about the part played by K mesons and Y particles in nuclear processes. Until recently the only sources of these particles were cosmic-ray events, but with the recent completion of the cosmotron (see §16-7) capable of producing protons of 2.3 Bev, it has become possible to produce Λ^0 particles in the laboratory.

FIG. 14-22. Cloud chamber photograph showing the production of a Λ^0 particle by the interaction of a π^--meson with a proton. The direction of motion of the Λ^0 particle from the end of the π^--meson track is shown by the broken arrow. The Λ^0 particle disintegrates into a proton p and a π^--meson whose tracks form the V. A heavy meson is probably emitted simultaneously with the Λ^0 particle; its direction of motion is shown by the broken arrow marked K^0. (Fowler, Shutt, Thorndike and Whittemore, *Phys. Rev.*, 91, 1287, 1953. Photograph courtesy of Brookhaven National Laboratory.)

In one experiment, Fowler, Shutt, Thorndike, and Whittemore allowed a beam of π^--mesons of 1.5 Bev to enter a diffusion cloud chamber containing hydrogen at a pressure of 18 atmospheres placed in a magnetic field of 11,000 gausses. One section of a stereoscopic photograph obtained in this experiment is shown in Figure 14-22. The track of the incident π^--meson can be seen to end in the chamber, and at a distance of 0.65 cm from it is the vertex of a V formed by the tracks of two particles labelled p and π^-. The identification of the particles that produced these tracks was made from measurements of their momenta and densities of ionization. Assuming that these particles are the products of the disintegration of a Λ° particle formed as a result of the interaction of the negative pi meson with a proton, its energy was found to be 1.26 Bev and its momentum 610 Mev/c. The direction of motion of this particle is shown by the broken arrow marked Λ°. The lifetime of this Λ° particle, calculated from its velocity and distance of travel, was found to be 4×10^{-11} sec. To conserve energy and momentum in the production of the Λ° particle by the interaction of the pion and the proton, it would be necessary for at least one other neutral particle, probably a heavy meson, to be produced at the same time. The direction of motion of such a particle is indicated by the broken arrow marked K^0. Since there is no evidence for its disintegration in a path 23 cm long, its lifetime must be greater than 4×10^{-10} sec.

14-20. Primary Cosmic-Ray Particles

Most of the cosmic-ray particles observed in the atmosphere are of secondary origin, that is, they are the products of the interaction between the primary cosmic-ray particles and nuclei in the atmosphere. Experiments must be conducted at altitudes above 60,000 ft to observe appreciable amounts of primary cosmic-ray particles. These experiments are usually made with nuclear emulsion photographic plates or with automatically operated cloud chambers which are sent aloft attached to balloons. When the equipment is recovered, the plates are developed and the cloud-chamber records and photographs scanned. Examinations of the photographic plates and cloud-chamber photographs show the presence of high energy protons and also of heavier nuclei, some with nuclear charges Ze in excess of $+40e$.

The primary cosmic-ray particles must have very large amounts of energy in order to pass through the earth's magnetic field and enter the atmosphere. M. S. Vallarta has calculated the minimum energies that protons must possess in order to penetrate the earth's magnetic field at a given angle as a function of the geomagnetic latitude. For example, in order to enter the earth's atmosphere vertically at about 45°N geomagnetic latitude protons must possess energies in excess of 2500 Mev. Heavier nuclei, because of their greater charge, must have still greater energies, probably in excess of 10^{11} ev, in order to penetrate the earth's magnetic field.

The first records of the heavy primary cosmic rays were obtained by Freier, Lofgren, Ney, Oppenheimer, Bradt, and Peters (1948), who sent up photographic plates and a cloud chamber attached to free balloons, to an altitude of 94,000 ft. The photographic plates, in stacks of 12, were placed above and below the cloud chamber, with the emulsion surfaces in a vertical plane. The photographic plates showed tracks of particles much denser and heavier than those usually associated with nuclear disintegra-

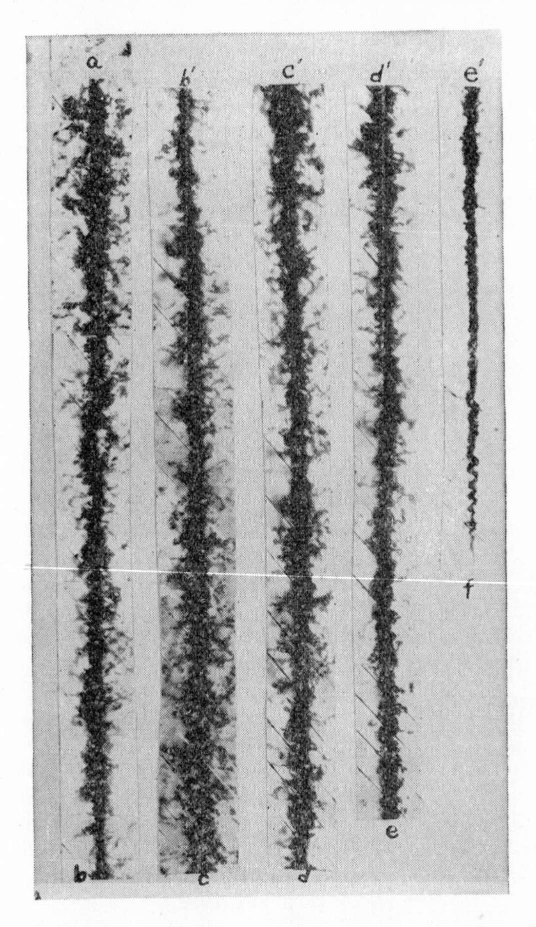

FIG. 14-23. Photomicrograph of a very heavy primary nucleus of the cosmic rays with $Z = 42 \pm 4$, observed in a stack of photographic pellicles (nuclear emulsions without glass support), exposed at an altitude of 100,000 ft. The primary particle entered the stack at *a* and slowed down in 1800 microns of continuously recorded path *abb'cc'dd'ee'f*. The primary particle came to rest in the third pellicle, producing the characteristic taper associated with successive electron capture. The peculiar corkscrew appearance of the track at *f* is due to the buckling of the column of developed silver as the emulsion shrinks during processing by a factor of approximately 2.5. This buckling occurs throughout the track but is most readily discernible at its end. (Photomicrograph courtesy of Maurice M. Shapiro and Nathan Seeman, Naval Research Laboratory.)

tions. The estimated values of Z for some of these tracks were as high as 40. Cloud-chamber photographs showed tracks of heavily ionizing particles but with values of Z generally lower than those observed with photographic emulsions.

The investigation of the primary cosmic-ray particles has continued with great improvement in nuclear emulsions and techniques for using and processing them. Figure 14-23 shows the track of a heavy primary nucleus observed in a stack of photographic "pellicles," that is, nuclear emulsions without glass supports, exposed at an altitude of 100,000 ft, obtained by

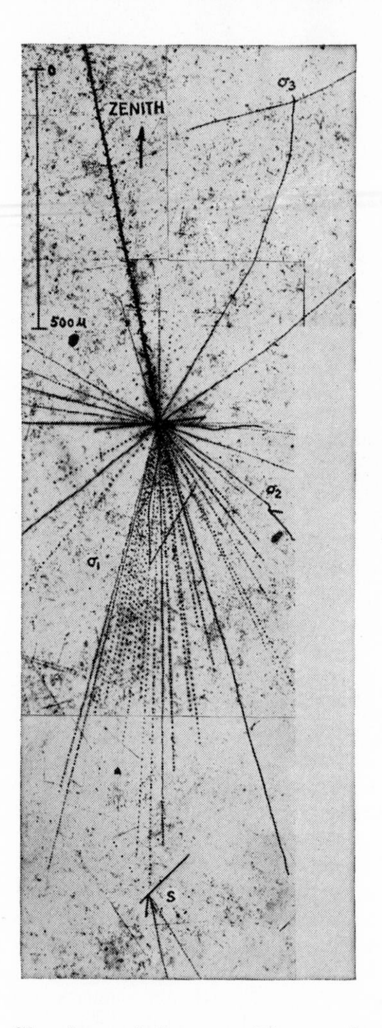

FIG. 14-24. A heavy primary cosmic ray with estimated value of $Z = 11 \pm 1$, passing through a nuclear photographic emulsion, interacts with a heavy nucleus, possibly silver, and produces a giant star. This star consists of 31 black and gray tracks and a shower of about 30 tracks of relativistic particles, the latter collimated in a broom of 52° angular spread. One of the fast shower particles is captured in flight and produces a 7-pronged star *S*. The giant star also contains three slow meson tracks with energies $\sigma_1 = 3$ Mev, $\sigma_2 = 4.9$ Mev, and $\sigma_3 = 8.2$ Mev. A number of tracks, directed at large angles to the plane of the emulsion, have been omitted from the horizontal projection of the event. (From a photograph by Yagoda, *Phys. Rev.*, 85, 891, 1952.)

Shapiro and Seeman. They estimate the value of Z to be about 42. Because of its high charge, this nucleus produces thousands of times as many ions along its path as would a fast, singly charged particle. The dense track has associated with it a series of short tracks along most of its length. These short tracks are the paths of secondary electrons, sometimes called *delta rays*. The delta rays are produced by the effect of the intense electric field of the primary particle on the material through which it passes. A count of the number of delta rays per unit length of track, combined with a measurement of the range of the particle in the emulsion, can be used to measure the charge Ze of the primary particle. A characteristic of such a track is the thinning down near the end of the track, noticeable in section e^1f. This

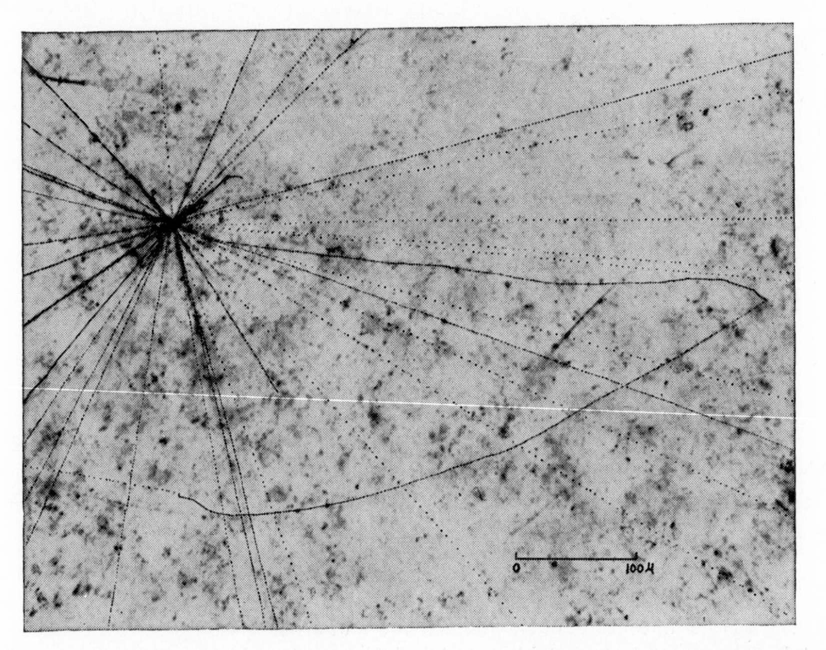

FIG. 14-25. Emission of a slow π^+-meson in the disruption of a heavy nucleus. The π-μ-e-decay events can be seen clearly in this photo-drawing. Although apparently emerging in the same direction as the fast shower particles, this slow π^+-meson is probably a member of an independent group of slow mesons. (From a photograph by Yagoda, *Phys. Rev.*, 85, 891, 1952.)

"thin-down length" can also be used to estimate Z on the assumption that, as the primary nucleus slows down, it captures electrons from the atoms through which it passes. Two methods are thus available for the determination of the charge of the heavy primary cosmic-ray particle.

Although the number of heavy primaries is small in comparison with the primary protons, their contribution to the total energy of the cosmic rays is comparable to that of the protons because the energy of a heavy primary is much larger than that of a proton.

Figure 14-24 shows a nuclear disintegration produced by a heavy primary cosmic-ray particle in a nuclear emulsion flown at about 100,000 ft altitude. The experiment was conducted by H. Yagoda (1951); Ilford G-5 plates with thick emulsions were flown in several stratosphere balloon flights at Minnesota at altitudes whose maxima ranged from 90,000 to

106,000 ft. The figure is a photo-drawing prepared by inking in details on an enlargement print obtained from a low-power photomicrograph. About 61 tracks of ionizing particles were observed, some heavy black tracks, others relativistic particles forming the collimated cosmic-ray shower, shown as dotted tracks. The primary particle is recognized by the delta rays associated with it. From a count of the delta rays, the value of Z for the primary particle is found to be about 11. The heavy nucleus with which the primary particle interacted is probably silver. The neutrons ejected in this event, since they are uncharged, do not produce any tracks. A secondary star S, with seven prongs, is produced in the emulsion by one of the shower particles. In addition, there are tracks of three slow mesons with energies of 3, 4.9, and 8.2 Mev. Another giant star produced in one of these emulsions is shown in Figure 14-25. The particle initiating the nuclear disruption is not known; it may have been a high energy neutron. Accompanying this event is the track of a π^+-meson which decays into a μ^+-meson of 4 Mev energy; the latter then decays into an electron.

Problems

14-1. Using the equation for the momentum of a relativistic particle of rest mass m_0 and total energy $\mathcal{E}$, calculate the momentum of an electron of 300 Mev.

14-2. (**a**) Calculate the momentum of a proton whose kinetic energy is 400 Mev. (**b**) Determine the velocity of this proton.

14-3. (**a**) Plot a graph of the momentum p of a relativistic particle against its total energy $\mathcal{E}$, using a set of units in which $c = 1$ and $m_0 = 1$. On this scale, select values of $\mathcal{E} = 1, 2, 3, \ldots 10$. (**b**) Determine the momentum of an electron whose total energy is $2m_0c^2$. Express this momentum in units of Mev/c. (**c**) Determine the momentum of a proton whose total energy is $2m_0c^2$. Express its momentum in units of Mev/c.

Ans. (**b**) 0.885 Mev/c.
(**c**) 1630 Mev/c.

14-4. Determine (**a**) the velocity and (**b**) the momentum of a mu meson whose kinetic energy is 4 Mev. (**c**) Determine the radius of curvature of the path of this meson in a magnetic field of 5000 gausses.

Ans. (**a**) $0.264c$.
(**b**) 29 Mev/c = 15.5×10^{-16} gm cm/sec.
(**c**) 19.3 cm.

14-5. Calculate (**a**) the velocity and (**b**) the momentum of a charged pi meson whose kinetic energy is 10 Mev. (**c**) Calculate the radius of curvature of its path in a magnetic field of 6000 gausses.

Ans. (**a**) $0.36c$.
(**b**) 54 Mev/c = 28.8×10^{-16} gm cm/sec.
(**c**) 30.0 cm.

14-6. A gamma-ray photon incident upon a hydrogen target produces a π^+-meson which moves off with an initial kinetic energy of 70 Mev in a direction at 90° to the direction of motion of the incident photon. (**a**) Determine the momentum of the meson. (**b**) Determine the energy of the incident gamma-ray photon.

14-7. (**a**) Show that the kinetic energy $\mathcal{E}_k$ of a charged meson of rest mass m_0 moving in a magnetic field of intensity H in a circular path of radius R satisfies the equation

$$\mathcal{E}_k\left(1 + \frac{\mathcal{E}_k}{2m_0c^2}\right) = \frac{e^2}{2m_0c^2}(HR)^2$$

in which e, the charge of the meson, is measured in es units.

(**b**) Calculate the radius of curvature of the path of a π^+-meson in a magnetic field of 15,000 gausses when its kinetic energy is 14 Mev.

(**c**) Calculate the radius of curvature of a μ^+-meson in the same magnetic field when its kinetic energy is 4 Mev.

14-8. (**a**) Show that the rest mass energy of a particle is given by

$$m_0c^2 = \frac{p^2c^2 - \mathcal{E}_k^2}{2\mathcal{E}_k}$$

where p is its momentum and $\mathcal{E}_k$ is its kinetic energy. Measurements on the track of a meson in a photographic emulsion yield the values of 215 Mev for its kinetic energy and 330 Mev/c for its momentum. Determine (**b**) its mass, and (**c**) its velocity. Identify the particle.

Ans. (**b**) $290m_e$.
(**c**) $0.917c$.

14-9. The kinetic energy of a positively charged particle is found to be 62 Mev and its momentum 335 Mev/c. Determine (**a**) its mass, and (**b**) its velocity. Identify the particle.

Ans. (**a**) 880 Mev or $1760m_e$.
(**b**) $0.374c$.

14-10. Suppose that a neutral particle decays into two charged particles which make an angle of 40° with each other. The measured kinetic energy of one particle is 62 Mev and its momentum is 335 Mev/c, and the kinetic energy of the second particle is 215 Mev and its momentum is 330 Mev/c. (See problems 14-8 and 14-9.) Determine (**a**) the mass of the neutral particle, (**b**) its kinetic energy, and (**c**) its momentum.

Ans. (**a**) $2240m_e$.
(**b**) 164 Mev.
(**c**) 624 Mev/c.

14-11. Assuming the nucleus to be a point charge, (**a**) calculate the radii of the mu-mesic Bohr orbits of titanium, $Z = 22$, for quantum numbers $n = 1$ and 2.

(**b**) Compute the energy radiated from such an atom in a transition between these orbits.

Ans. (**a**) 1.15×10^{-12} cm, 4.60×10^{-12} cm.
(**b**) 1.04 Mev.

14-12. Assuming the nucleus to be a point charge, (**a**) calculate the radii of the pi-mesic Bohr orbits of beryllium, $Z = 4$, for quantum numbers $n = 1$ and 2. (**b**) Compute the energy radiated from this atom in a transition between these orbits.

Ans. (**a**) 4.8×10^{-12} cm, 19.2×10^{-12} cm.
(**b**) 44.4 kev.

14-13. Assuming the nucleus to be a point charge, calculate the radius of the mu-mesic Bohr orbit of lead, $Z = 82$, $A = 208$, for which $n = 1$. Compare this value with the radius of the nucleus of lead.

Ans. 3.08×10^{-13} cm.

References

Bierman, L., "Origin and Propagation of Cosmic Rays," *Annual Review of Nuclear Science*, 2, 335–364, 1953.

Blair, J. S., and G. F. Chew, "Subnuclear Particles," *Annual Review of Nuclear Science*, 2, 163–186, 1953.

Leprince-Ringuet, L., *Cosmic Rays*. New York: Prentice-Hall, Inc., 1951.

Powell, C. F., "Mesons," in *Reports on Progress in Physics*. London: The Physical Society of London, 1950, XIII, 350.

Rochester, G. D., and C. C. Butler, "The New Unstable Cosmic-Ray Particles," in *Reports on Progress in Physics*. London: The Physical Society of London, 1951, XIV, 364.

Yagoda, Herman J., *Radioactive Measurements with Nuclear Emulsions*. New York: John Wiley & Sons, Inc., 1949.

New Elements and Isotopes

15-1. Naturally Occurring Elements

It has already been noted that fewer than 100 elements are found in nature and that these have approximately 300 isotopes, varying from 1 for an odd Z-odd N element such as bismuth $_{83}Bi^{209}$ to 10 for the magic number element tin, $Z = 50$. Most of these isotopes are stable, but a few of them are radioactive with long lifetimes. The latter have been considered in our discussion of natural radioactive transformations. In addition, two lighter isotopes, C^{14} and H^3, are being continually produced in the atmosphere by the n-p reaction of cosmic-ray neutrons with N^{14} of the atmosphere (see §11-13). C^{14} has become widely distributed over the surface of the earth through the formation of $C^{14}O_2$ and the subsequent reactions of CO_2 with organic and inorganic matter.

The formation of tritium in the nuclear reaction with cosmic-ray neutrons can take place only with fast neutrons; the nuclear reaction is

$$_7N^{14} + {_0n^1} \rightarrow (_7N^{15}) \rightarrow {_6C^{12}} + {_1H^3}. \tag{1}$$

Tritium, as an isotope of hydrogen, should be widely distributed over the surface of the earth, but partly owing to its short lifetime, it occurs in minute concentrations. The relative abundance of tritium in Norwegian surface water has been measured by Grosse, Johnston, Wolfgang, and Libby (1951), and found to be about one atom of tritium to 10^{18} atoms of ordinary hydrogen. The samples of water tested were all highly enriched with the heavier isotope D_2O, by electrolytic methods. The enrichment factor was of the order of 10^6. The ratio of tritium to deuterium in these samples was found to be of the order of 10^{-12}. The presence of tritium was determined by counting the rate at which beta rays were emitted by the sample. The natural abundance was then calculated from the measured beta-ray activity, the probable enrichment factor of the sample, its age, and the known half-life of tritium. It was noted that with a concentration of 3×10^{-18} gm of tritium per gram of ordinary hydrogen, it is the rarest atomic species discovered in nature. It was further concluded that most, if not all, of He^3 found in the atmosphere has its origin in the disintegration of cosmic-ray-produced tritium.

Methods have been developed by W. F. Libby and others for dating archaeological and geological samples by determining the C^{14} content. The basic assumption of the carbon dating method is that the relative abundance of the carbon isotopes has remained unchanged for the past few thousand years. When a living organism dies, its intake of carbon ceases and the amount of radioactive C^{14} in it decreases continually. A determination of its present C^{14} content per gram of substance, together with a knowledge of its half-life, yields the age of the sample. Wherever other reliable methods for determining the ages of such samples were available, the two methods gave consistent results. Ages of such samples extend up to 5000 years. One conclusion that can be drawn from this is that the neutron flux in cosmic radiation has been fairly constant for the extent of about 10,000 to 15,000 years, that is, about two or three times the half-life of C^{14}.

15-2. Filling Gaps in the Periodic Table

The discovery of the neutron in 1932 may be said to be the beginning of modern nuclear physics. At about this time several methods of producing high energy charged particles were also in use. There were then still three places vacant in the periodic table for elements of atomic numbers less than 92; one at $Z = 43$, another at $Z = 85$, and the third at $Z = 87$. With the number of different types of particles available as projectiles for bombarding nuclei, and the variety of nuclear reactions already known, it became possible to produce these missing elements by bombarding nuclei of neighboring atoms of the periodic table with suitable particles. One of the first produced in this manner was the element $Z = 43$, now known as technetium (symbol Tc); it was produced by Perrier and Segrè (1937) by bombarding molybdenum, $Z = 42$, with deuterons in a *d-n* reaction. Seaborg and Segrè showed that the particular isotope formed in this reaction has a mass number $A = 96$; the nuclear reaction is therefore

$$_{42}\mathrm{Mo}^{95} + {}_{1}\mathrm{H}^{2} \rightarrow ({}_{43}\mathrm{Tc}^{97}) \rightarrow {}_{43}\mathrm{Tc}^{96} + {}_{0}n^{1}. \tag{2}$$

This isotope of technetium has also been produced in a *p-n* reaction with molybdenum and in an α-n reaction with niobium, $Z = 41$. This isotope is radioactive, decaying by electron capture with a half-life of 4.3 days.

Since its original discovery, technetium has been produced by a variety of nuclear reactions; it is also one of the products of nuclear fission. There are now about 12 known isotopes of technetium, ranging in mass numbers from 92 to 105. All of them are radioactive.

The element of atomic number $Z = 85$, now called astatine (symbol At), was first produced by Corson, MacKenzie, and Segrè by bombarding bismuth with 32 Mev alpha particles. They found six different activities as a result of this bombardment, but all had exactly the same half-life, $T = 7.5$ hr. These activities were (1) an alpha-particle group of 6.55 cm range, (2) another alpha-particle group of 4.52 cm range, (3) a gamma ray with an energy of 0.5 Mev, (4) an x-ray or gamma-ray photon of about 80 Kev, (5) a low energy x-ray photon, and (6) a few low energy electrons. Their analysis of this experiment is as follows: since bismuth has only one stable isotope, the first reaction is

$$_{83}\text{Bi}^{209} + {}_2\text{He}^4 \rightarrow ({}_{85}\text{At}^{213}) \rightarrow {}_{85}\text{At}^{211} + {}_0n^1 + {}_0n^1. \quad (3)$$

Astatine then disintegrates in one of two ways, either by electron capture to actinium C′, or by alpha-particle emission to bismuth, according to the following reactions:

$$_{85}\text{At}^{211} + {}_{-1}e^0 \rightarrow {}_{84}\text{AcC}'^{211} \quad (4)$$

and

$$_{85}\text{At}^{211} \rightarrow {}_{83}\text{Bi}^{207} + {}_2\text{He}^4. \qquad (4.55 \text{ cm range}) \quad (5)$$

Actinium C′ disintegrates immediately, $T = 5 \times 10^{-3}$ sec, with the emission of an alpha particle of 6.55 cm range; this is very close to the known range of the alpha particles of the actinium C′ formed in the actinium radioactive series. This reaction is

$$_{84}\text{AcC}'^{211} \rightarrow {}_{82}\text{Pb}^{207} + {}_2\text{He}^4, \qquad T = 5 \times 10^{-3} \text{ sec.} \quad (6)$$

If the actinium C′ is formed by electron capture, this must be followed by the emission of K-series x-rays. The x-rays were measured by absorption methods and found to be identical with those of polonium, $Z = 84$, an isotope of AcC′. The x-ray photons were also counted with the same thin-walled Geiger counter that was used for counting the alpha particles, and, taking into account the difference in the counting efficiencies for the two types of radiation, it was estimated that there were equal numbers of alpha particles and x-ray photons emitted. This is to be expected if astatine decays by electron capture to AcC′; electron capture is followed by the emission of an x-ray photon and the AcC′ immediately disintegrates with the emission of an alpha particle.

Astatine is a chemical homologue of iodine although it is found to have some of the properties of a metal. Its resemblance to iodine was shown in a series of experiments by Hamilton and Soley, who found that it is concentrated in the thyroids of normal and thyrotoxic guinea pigs in a manner similar to that of iodine.

There are about 15 different isotopes of astatine now known, ranging in mass numbers from 203 to 219, all of them radioactive. One of these, $A = 217$, occurs in the neptunium radioactive series as the daughter of $_{87}\text{Fr}^{221}$ (see §10-4). Karlik and Bernert (1942) discovered other isotopes of astatine in the other radioactive series.

Element $Z = 87$, now called francium, was first discovered by Mlle Perey (1939) as one of the products in the radioactive disintegration of actinium; this isotope was called actinium K. About 1 per cent of the actinium nuclei disintegrate with the emission of alpha particles forming actinium K,

$$_{89}\mathrm{Ac}^{227} \rightarrow {}_{87}\mathrm{AcK}^{223} + {}_{2}\mathrm{He}^{4}$$

followed by $\quad {}_{87}\mathrm{AcK}^{223} \rightarrow {}_{88}\mathrm{AcX}^{223} + \beta^{-}, \quad T = 21 \text{ min.} \qquad (7)$

The branching of actinium is shown in the actinium series of Figure 10-4.

There are now about eight isotopes of francium known, with mass numbers ranging from 211 to 223. All of them are radioactive.

Element $Z = 61$, originally called illinium, was not included in the above list of missing elements because its existence had been inferred from spectroscopic data, but it had not been definitely isolated. It was first produced in an α-p reaction with neodymium by Law, Pool, Kurbatov, and Quill (1941), and in p-n and d-n reactions with neodymium by Kurbatov and Pool (1943). The isotope formed in these reactions had a mass number $A = 146$. Element $Z = 61$ is now called promethium (symbol Pm). There are now about 10 isotopes of promethium known with mass numbers ranging from 141 to 156. All of them are radioactive. Some of these isotopes are formed in nuclear fission.

15-3. Production of Transuranic Elements

We have already discussed the discovery and production of the first two transuranic elements, neptunium and plutonium, formed as a result of the n-γ process with uranium (see §13-8). In the period from 1945 to 1950 four additional transuranic elements were produced by using as projectiles the charged particles obtained from the 60-inch Berkeley cyclotron. These transuranic elements are given in Table 15-1.

Table 15-1

Transuranic Elements

Atomic No.	Name	Chemical Symbol	Range of Mass Nos.
93	Neptunium	Np	231–241
94	Plutonium	Pu	232–243
95	Americium	Am	237–244
96	Curium	Cm	238–245
97	Berkelium	Bk	243–245
98	Californium	Cf	244–246

We have already described methods for producing some of the isotopes of the first of the transuranic elements, neptunium and plutonium (see §13-8), and the fact that these elements have been found in small concentrations in pitchblende. Recently neptunium, $A = 237$, has been isolated in small amounts from this ore. The next transuranic elements, americium and curium, were first produced by G. T. Seaborg, L. O. Morgan, and A. Ghiorso in 1945, by bombarding uranium 238 and plutonium 239 with 40 Mev helium ions. The identification of these elements from their chemical and radioactive properties was done by Seaborg and J. G. Hamilton. These elements have since been produced in a variety of ways. Only a few of the reactions will be given here. For example, americium can be produced in an α-n reaction with U^{238} as follows

$$ {}_{92}U^{238} + {}_2He^4 \rightarrow {}_{94}Pu^{241} + {}_0n^1, \tag{8} $$

followed by

$$ {}_{94}Pu^{241} \rightarrow {}_{95}Am^{241} + \beta^-, \quad T = 14 \text{ yr.} \tag{9} $$

Pu^{241} also disintegrates by alpha-particle emission to Np^{237}. The branching ratio of alpha-particle decay to beta decay is about 10^{-5}.

Several different isotopes of curium are formed when Pu^{239} is bombarded with alpha particles of 30 to 40 Mev. Two of the reactions are

$$ {}_{94}Pu^{239} + {}_2He^4 \rightarrow {}_{96}Cm^{241} + 2{}_0n^1 \tag{10} $$

and

$$ {}_{94}Pu^{239} + {}_2He^4 \rightarrow {}_{96}Cm^{240} + 3{}_0n^1. \tag{11} $$

These are followed by the radioactive disintegration of curium as follows:

$$ {}_{96}Cm^{240} \rightarrow {}_{94}Pu^{236} + {}_2He^4, \quad T = 26.8 \text{ da.} \tag{12} $$

$$ {}_{96}Cm^{241} \rightarrow {}_{94}Pu^{237} + {}_2He^4 $$

and

$$ {}_{96}Cm^{241} + {}_{-1}e^0 \rightarrow {}_{95}Am^{241}, \quad T = 35 \text{ da.} \tag{13} $$

In addition, Cm^{240} disintegrates by spontaneous fission with a half-life of 7.9×10^5 yr.

Thompson, Ghiorso, and Seaborg (1950) produced berkelium by bombarding americium with 35 Mev alpha particles, the nuclear reaction being

$$ {}_{95}Am^{241} + {}_2He^4 \rightarrow {}_{97}Bk^{243} + 2{}_0n^1. \tag{14} $$

This isotope of berkelium disintegrates mostly by electron capture and about 0.1 per cent by alpha-particle emission, the reactions being

$$ {}_{97}Bk^{243} + {}_{-1}e^0 \rightarrow {}_{96}Cm^{243}, $$

$$ {}_{97}Bk^{243} \rightarrow {}_{95}Am^{239} + {}_2He^4, \quad T = 4.6 \text{ hr.} \tag{15} $$

Thompson, Ghiorso, Seaborg, and Street (1950) produced californium by bombarding curium with 35 Mev alpha particles, the reaction being

$$_{96}\mathrm{Cm}^{242} + {}_2\mathrm{He}^4 \rightarrow {}_{98}\mathrm{Cf}^{244} + 2{}_0n^1, \tag{16}$$

followed by $$_{98}\mathrm{Cf}^{244} \rightarrow {}_{96}\mathrm{Cm}^{240} + {}_2\mathrm{He}^4, \quad T = 45 \text{ min}. \tag{17}$$

The same group of investigators (1951) bombarded natural uranium with carbon nuclei, charge $+6e$, having an energy of approximately 120 Mev. They separated the elements of $Z > 94$ chemically and investigated its alpha-particle activity. They found one with a half-life of 45 min and an alpha-particle energy of 7.15 Mev, which is characteristic of Cf^{244}. The reaction in which Cf^{244} was formed was most likely

$$_{92}\mathrm{U}^{238} + {}_6\mathrm{C}^{12} \rightarrow {}_{98}\mathrm{Cf}^{244} + 6{}_0n^1. \tag{18}$$

They also found an alpha-particle activity with a longer half-life of 35 hr after the decay of Cf^{244}. They ascribed this activity to the formation of a new isotope of californium, $A = 246$, the reaction being

$$_{92}\mathrm{U}^{238} + {}_6\mathrm{C}^{12} \rightarrow {}_{98}\mathrm{Cf}^{246} + 4{}_0n^1. \tag{19}$$

This isotope can also be produced in an α-n reaction with Cm^{243}. Californium, $A = 246$, disintegrates by alpha-particle emission to Cm^{242}.

All of the transuranic elements are radioactive, and several of them disintegrate by spontaneous fission, Cf^{246} being one of these (see § 13-11).

15-4. Electronic Structure of the Heavy Elements

As a result of the intensive analysis of the chemical properties of the heavier elements, Seaborg suggested that the elements of atomic numbers greater than 88 probably form another transition group analogous to the rare-earth group of atomic numbers 58 to 71. In this latter group (see Table 8-2), each succeeding element is formed by the addition of an electron to the $4f$ shell until this shell is completed with 14 electrons. Seaborg suggested that in this new transition group electrons are added to the $5f$ shell, the first $5f$ electron probably appearing in thorium. Just as the rare-earth group of elements is called the *lanthanide series*, so the new group of heavy elements is called the *actinide series*.

J. K. Dawson (1952), from a study of the magnetic properties of the ions of the transuranic elements, has suggested a somewhat different electronic structure in which, beginning with actinium, electrons are added to the $6d$ shell until neptunium is reached. The evidence for neptunium is that 5 electrons may be either in the $6d$ or the $5f$ shell. There is a sudden change in magnetic properties at plutonium which is interpreted on the basis of 5 electrons in the $5f$ shell and 1 electron in the $6d$. In the formation of the transuranic elements, the additional electrons are placed in the $5f$ shell. On this basis, only the transuranic elements belong in a special series, say the transuranide series, in a manner analogous to the lanthanide series. However, other chemical properties do not seem to fit this assignment as well as the one suggested by Seaborg. Further experimental evidence is needed to resolve this problem.

15-5. Stellar Energy of Nuclear Origin

Ever since the discovery of the transmutation of elements, it has been thought that the conversion of mass into other forms of energy, which occurs during such transmutation, would provide a possible explanation of the origin of a great part of the energy radiated by the stars, but it was not until sufficient evidence had been accumulated in the laboratory concerning the probabilities of various types of reactions and their energy releases that it became possible to develop a fairly quantitative explanation. Astrophysical evidence shows that the most abundant type of nucleus present in the stars classified in the *main sequence* is the proton. Bethe (1939) developed the theory for the production of stellar energy in which protons, by suitable nuclear reactions, are transmuted into helium nuclei, thereby releasing energy which is transformed into radiation. One possible series of reactions, sometimes referred to as the *proton-proton* chain, which may occur in a star starts with the reaction between a proton and a proton to form a dueteron, that is,

$$_1H^1 + {}_1H^1 \rightarrow ({}_2He^2) \rightarrow {}_1H^2 + \beta^+, \tag{20}$$

followed by

$$_1H^2 + {}_1H^1 \rightarrow {}_2He^3. \tag{21}$$

The chain ends either with the reaction

$$_2He^3 + {}_1H^1 \rightarrow ({}_3Li^4) \rightarrow {}_2He^4 + \beta^+, \tag{22}$$

or, more probably, with the reaction

$$_2He^3 + {}_2He^3 \rightarrow ({}_4Be^6) \rightarrow {}_2He^4 + {}_1H^1 + {}_1H^1. \tag{23}$$

Another possible series of reactions in which protons are converted into helium nuclei is one in which carbon and nitrogen act as catalysts; this series is usually referred to as the *carbon-nitrogen cycle*, and consists of the following series of reactions:

$$\begin{aligned} {}_6C^{12} + {}_1H^1 &\rightarrow ({}_7N^{13}) \rightarrow {}_7N^{13} + h\nu \\ &\qquad {}_7N^{13} \rightarrow {}_6C^{13} + \beta^+, \quad T = 9.9 \text{ min.} \\ {}_6C^{13} + {}_1H^1 &\rightarrow ({}_7N^{14}) \rightarrow {}_7N^{14} + h\nu; \\ \text{and} \quad {}_7N^{14} + {}_1H^1 &\rightarrow ({}_8O^{15}) \rightarrow {}_8O^{15} + h\nu \\ &\qquad {}_8O^{15} \rightarrow {}_7N^{15} + \beta^+, \quad T = 2.1 \text{ min.} \\ {}_7N^{15} + {}_1H^1 &\rightarrow ({}_8O^{16}) \rightarrow {}_6C^{12} + {}_2He^4. \end{aligned} \tag{24}$$

It will be noted that this chain of reactions can start with either nitrogen or carbon, since each one is reproduced in the reaction, except that in about one case in 10^5, the last reaction will lead to the formation of $_8O^{16}$ and the emission of a gamma ray. Since the positrons will combine readily with electrons resulting in the formation of gamma rays, the net result is the combination of four protons and two electrons to form an alpha particle with the consequent release of energy. The mass difference released as energy in this chain of reactions is thus simply the difference between the masses of four protons and one helium nucleus or 0.0276 amu which is equivalent to about 41×10^{-6} erg or 25.7 Mev. A small amount of this energy is carried away by the neutrinos which are emitted during the radioactive parts of the cycle. Bethe estimates this to be about 3×10^{-6} erg, leaving about 38×10^{-6} erg for each alpha particle formed or approximately 10×10^{-6} erg for each proton consumed. In the particular case of the sun, it has been estimated that a gram of its mass contains about 2×10^{23} protons; hence if all the protons were consumed, the energy released would be 2×10^{18} ergs. If the sun were to continue to radiate at its present rate, it would take about 30 billion years to exhaust its supply of protons.

15-6. Stellar Evolution

It is interesting to speculate concerning the evolution of the stars. It is generally agreed that the first stage in the process of evolution is the contraction of a large mass of very tenuous matter from a large cloud of gas to a more compact star under the action of the gravitational attraction of the particles of the cloud. This produces a higher temperature at the center of the star and causes a flow of heat toward the surface of the star, and thus radiation of energy from the surface. A type of equilibrium may be reached in which the rate of radiation of energy from the surface is just equal to the rate of change in gravitational energy. The time scale for this event is rather short in terms of the estimated age of our galaxy; the latter is of the order of a few billion years.

At some stage in the process of contraction the temperature at the center of the star must become sufficiently high that collisions between nuclei take place with sufficient relative kinetic energy of the particles so that nuclear reactions occur with the subsequent release of energy. Furthermore, such collisions must occur with sufficient frequency to account for the rate at which energy is known to be radiated by different classes of stars. With the data on capture cross sections which are now available for several of the processes in the proton-proton chain and in the carbon-nitrogen cycle, it is possible to estimate the rate at which energy can be radiated from a star under a variety of conditions of temperature and density. Recently (1952), H. Bondi and E. E. Salpeter have developed empirical equations for the rate at which energy is liberated in each of the above chains of reaction. For the case of the sun, they estimate that the rate of generation of energy in the proton-proton chain is about the same as that in the carbon-nitrogen cycle. For much more luminous stars, the carbon-nitrogen cycle predominates as a source of energy, while for the less luminous stars the proton-proton chain supplies the greater fraction of the energy radiated.

When all of the hydrogen is used up in the above thermonuclear reactions the star will consist mostly of helium. The temperature of the star is probably not sufficiently high for nuclear reactions to take place among the helium nuclei. At this stage gravitational contraction will occur once again until a temperature of about 10^8°K is reached with the density of the star about 10^4 gm/cm^3. Under these conditions it will be possible for three helium nuclei to combine to form C^{12} with the release of about 7.3 Mev. F. Hoyle estimates that such processes can occur sufficiently often to provide for the radiation of energy for an additional 10^7 years. When all the helium is used up, further gravitational contraction of the star will occur, producing a further rise in the temperature of the star and making conditions right for the formation of atoms of medium atomic weights. A glance at the packing fraction curve will show that the region of mass number 60 is the most stable one, and that any appreciable combination of these atoms to form heavier ones will lead to endothermic rather than exothermic reactions. Bondi and Salpeter, tracing this life history of a star, suggest that the endothermic reactions may account for the sudden collapse of a star, identified as the sudden appearance of a supernova.

Problems

15-1. Using the data of Appendix IV, calculate the energy released in the $N^{14}(n,p)C^{14}$ reaction.

Ans. 670 kev.

15-2. Using the data of Appendix IV, calculate the neutron threshold energy for the formation of tritium in the reaction $N^{14}(n,t)C^{12}$.

Ans. 4.0 Mev.

15-3. Write the nuclear reactions in which ${}_{61}Pr^{146}$ is produced by *p-n*, *d-n*, and α-*p* reactions with Nd, $Z = 60$.

15-4. Using the data of Appendix IV, calculate the energy released in the $H^3(d,n)He^4$ reaction.

15-5. Using the data of Appendix IV, calculate the energy released in the $He^3(d,p)He^4$ reaction.

15-6. Determine the isotope produced in a *d*-4*n* reaction with Pu^{239}.

15-7. Determine the isotope produced when carbon nuclei are used to bombard Th^{232} in a C-4n reaction.

15-8. Determine the isotope produced in a Pu^{239}, α-$p3n$ reaction.

References

Hollander, J. M., I. Perlman, and G. T. Seaborg, Table of Isotopes, *Revs. Modern Phys.*, 25, 469, 1953.

New Nuclear Data, 1952 Cumulation. Nuclear Science Abstracts. Oak Ridge, Tenn.: Technical Information Service, December 31, 1952, Vol. VI, No. 2413.

Salpeter, E. E., "Energy Production in Stars," *Annual Review of Nuclear Science*, 2, 41, 1953.

Way, Katherine, Lilla Fano, Millicent R. Scott, and Karin Thew (Comps.), *Nuclear Data.* Washington, D. C.: National Bureau of Standards, Circular 499, and Supplements 1, 2 and 3. Washington, D. C.: Government Printing Office, 1950.

Particle Accelerators

16-1. Introduction

In this chapter we shall consider the fundamental principles underlying the operations of the particle accelerators which are currently in use. The design, construction and operational details are engineering problems, and data are available on these aspects in the literature; references to some of this literature are given at the end of this chapter.

The term *particle accelerator* will be generalized to include devices, such as the Van de Graaff generator, which, in themselves, provide only large differences of potential, but, when combined with appropriate ion tubes, accelerate the ions to high energies. One of the most common methods of obtaining a large difference of potential from a low-voltage alternating current source is the step-up transformer. Most frequently direct current rather than alternating current is needed for the experiments with electrons and positive ions. For such work, two-element thermionic tubes are used for either half-wave or full-wave rectification. Sometimes the secondaries of the step-up transformers are connected in series; potential differences of over one million volts have been obtained in this way. This high voltage is used to accelerate positive ions which have been produced in an auxiliary tube by the ionization of the gas in the tube. Some sources of positive ions are adaptations of the type of positive-ray tubes used in measurements of E/M; other sources of positive ions are low-voltage arcs maintained in a tube containing a gas. The most common kinds of positive ions used in nuclear experiments are protons, deuterons, and helium nuclei.

In addition to these types of accelerators, there is a second group, exemplified by the cyclotron (for positive ions) and the betraton (for electrons), consisting of devices in which the charged particle makes several or many trips around a circular path, receiving additional energy during each trip. Although the energy acquired during each revolution may be comparatively small, after a sufficient number of revolutions, the particle will acquire a very large amount of energy. When the particle has acquired the desired energy, it is taken out of the device and used in nuclear experiments.

The third group is a modification of the second group and utilizes the phenomenon of *phase stability* in its operation. Among these devices are the synchro-cyclotron, the proton synchrotron, the betatron-synchrotron, and the cosmotron. This third group is capable of producing particles of much higher energies than those in the second group.

The fourth group contains the *linear accelerators* in which the particles travel in straight paths, receiving additions to their energies at given positions along the path. Linear accelerators have been designed for operation with electrons and with protons.

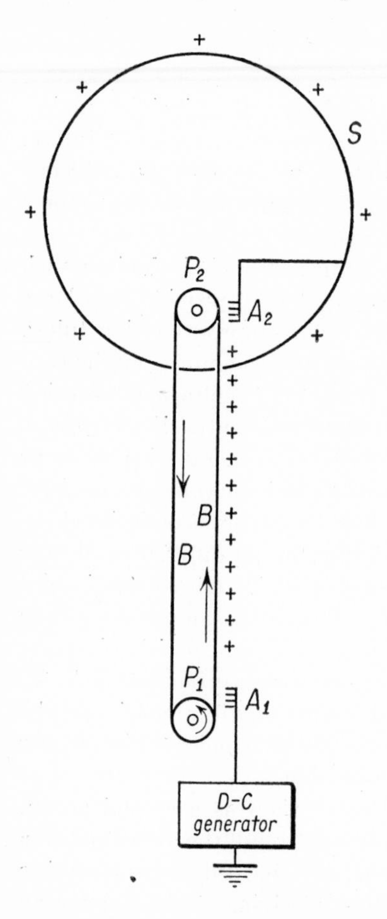

FIG. 16-1. Schematic diagram of a Van de Graaff electrostatic generator.

16-2. Van de Graaff Electrostatic Generator

Van de Graaff (1931) designed a direct current electrostatic generator which can develop a potential difference of several million volts and, when used with positive ion tubes, can impart energies of several Mev to the ions. This type of generator consists essentially of a continuous belt B, made of some insulating material such as rubber, silk, linen, or paper, which passes over two pulleys P_1 and P_2, as shown in Figure 16-1. Pulley P_1 is at ground potential and is driven by a motor; pulley P_2 is mounted inside a hollow metal sphere S of large radius or a metal cylinder with curved bases. The hollow metal body S is insulated from the rest of the apparatus. In the operation of this generator, an electric charge is sprayed onto the side of the belt which is moving upward. The source of this charge is usually a small transformer-rectifier set capable of developing a potential difference of about 10 to 100 kilovolts. The charge is sprayed on the belt from a set of sharp points A_1, and then removed from the upper end of the belt by another series of sharp points A_2 and conducted to the surface S. If Q is the charge on this surface at any instant, its potential with respect to ground is simply

$$V = Q/C, \tag{1}$$

where C is the capacitance of the system.

The conditions which limit the charge on the surface S, and hence its potential V, are the nearness of other objects, such as the walls and ceilings of the laboratory, and the breakdown of the air near the surface owing to the intense electric field around it. To improve the operation of the Van de Graaff generator, and to reduce its size for a given maximum potential difference, the entire generator is placed inside a steel container in which the air is maintained at a high pressure, about 150 pounds per square inch. At the higher pressures, air can withstand stronger electric fields before breakdown occurs. Also, since the air is in a closed steel tube, it may be dried and cleaned, and other gases may be mixed with it to improve the operating conditions. Van de Graff generators can now be obtained commercially to provide voltages up to 6 to 8 million volts and proton beam currents of the order of 6 to 8 microamperes.

16-3. The Cyclotron

Another device for producing high energy particles which has come into fairly common use is the *cyclotron* originally developed by E. O. Lawrence and M. S. Livingston (1931). It consists essentially of a short hollow cylinder divided into two sections, A and B, as shown in Figure 16-2. Each section is usually referred to as a "dee" because of its resemblance to the letter D. These dees are placed between the poles of a very large electromagnet. Some of the cyclotrons at present in use have magnets whose pole pieces are from 30 to 60 inches in diameter; the diameters of the dees are approximately the same as those of the pole pieces. The dees are placed in another metal cylinder, as shown in Figure 16-3, and the whole assembly is placed between the poles of the electromagnet so that the magnetic field is perpendicular to the base of the cylinder and parallel to its axis.

There are two methods in general use for producing ions inside the dees. One method is to introduce a gas such as hydrogen into the system at a low pressure. A filament situated in the center of the chamber just outside the dees is heated, and a small difference of potential is applied between the filament and the metal box to give the electrons from the filament sufficient energy to ionize some of the hydrogen atoms. This produces a vertical column of positive ions, some of which travel into the space between the dees. Another method is to produce the ions in a separate small source with a narrow opening into the space between the dees; this is usually referred to as a capillary ion source. The pressure of the gas in the ion source can be adjusted for optimum conditions while the rest of the system is maintained at as low a pressure as possible. This avoids electrical discharges inside the dees and also makes it possible to use narrower dees and a smaller air gap between the poles of the magnet.

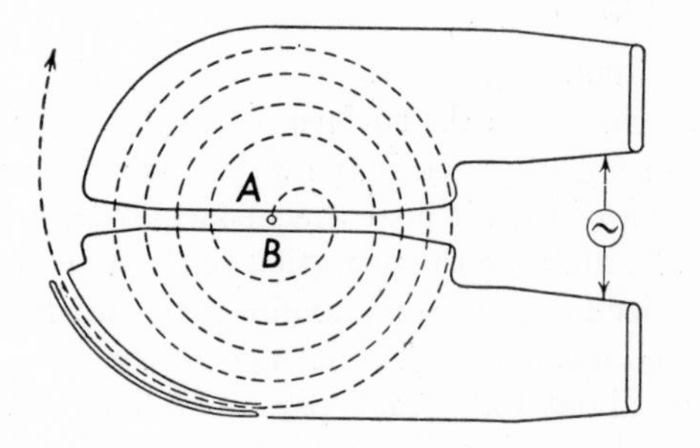

FIG. 16-2. Schematic diagram showing the path of a charged particle in a cyclotron. Magnetic field is perpendicular to the paper.

The two dees, A and B, are connected to the terminals of a high frequency alternating current circuit so that the charge on each half changes a few million times per second. When A is positive, the protons are accelerated toward B. The magnetic field causes each proton inside B to travel in a circle of radius r given by

$$HEv = \frac{Mv^2}{r} \cdot \tag{2}$$

After it has traversed half a circle, the proton comes to the edge of B. If, in the meantime, the potential difference between A and B has changed direction so that B is now positive and A negative, the proton will receive an additional acceleration, go across the gap from B to A, and then travel in a circular path of larger radius inside A. After traversing a half circle in A, it will reach the edge of A and receive an additional acceleration from A to B because, in the meantime, the potential difference between A and B will have changed sign. The proton will continue traveling in semicircles of increasing radii each time it goes from A to B and from B to A. This is due to the fact that the time required by the proton to travel half a circumference is independent of the radius of the circle. This can be shown very simply since the time t required to travel the distance πr, when the particle

FIG. 16-3. Shop assembly photograph of the M.I.T. cyclotron chamber, showing the construction of the chamber and dees. (From *J. Appl. Phys.*, January, 1944. Courtesy of the Radioactivity Center at the Massachusetts Institute of Technology.)

is moving with velocity v, is

$$t = \frac{\pi r}{v};$$

but

$$v = \frac{HEr}{M},$$

so that

$$t = \frac{\pi M}{HE}. \tag{3}$$

For any given value of M/E, the time required to traverse half a circumference is determined by the magnetic field intensity. By adjusting the magnetic field intensity H, the time can be made the same as that required to change the potentials of A and B.

After the protons have traversed many semicircular paths and approach the circumference of the cylinder, an auxiliary electric field is used to deflect them from the circular path and make them come out through a thin window. The substance to be bombarded by the protons is placed near the window, and the investigation of the results of this bombardment can then be performed in a suitable manner.

Instead of ordinary hydrogen, heavy hydrogen or deuterium can be introduced into the chamber of the cyclotron, so that deuterons become available as bombarding particles; or if helium is used in this chamber, we have an artificial source of alpha particles.

The voltage between the sections A and B may have any value from about 10,000 to 200,000 volts. The particle, as it emerges from the cyclotron, may have an energy of several million electron volts due to the successive accelerations it experiences in going from one section to the other. The cyclotron is thus a comparatively low-voltage source of high energy particles.

16-4. Frequency-Modulated Cyclotron

The practical limit to the energy that can be imparted to an ion in the conventional constant-frequency cyclotron is due to the fact that the mass increases with increasing velocity. This puts the motion of the ions out of

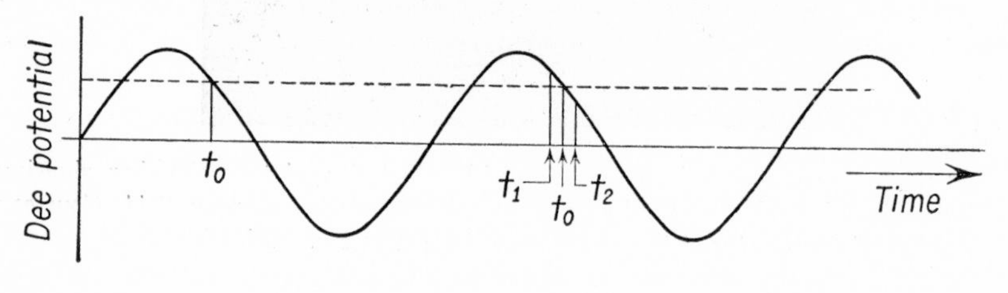

Fig. 16-4.

phase with the frequency applied to the dees. This limitation is overcome in the *frequency-modulated cyclotron*, also sometimes called the *synchrocyclotron*, by the property known as *phase stability* possessed by charged particles moving in unidirectional magnetic fields and alternating electric fields of varying frequency. This property was discovered independently in 1945 by V. Veksler and E. M. McMillan. Suppose, for example, that a positive ion is moving within the dees of a cyclotron at the proper frequency, and that during each cycle of the alternating potential it arrives at the edge of the dee at a time t_0 as shown in Figure 16-4. This time is shortly after the time that the dee potential has reached its maximum value. In the ordinary cyclotron, where the change of mass with velocity is negligible, the period of the motion of an ion is independent of its velocity and is the same as that of the alternating current applied to the dees, so that the ion arrives in the same phase during each cycle, that is, at the same time t_0. Suppose, however, that the increment in velocity is smaller during the transit across the dees because of the relativistic change in mass; then the ion will move in a circle of smaller radius and arrive at the edge of the dee in a shorter time, represented by t_1 on the diagram; it will thus receive a larger acceleration from the ac field and may get into phase again during the next cycle or cycles. If, on the other hand, an ion receives more than the normal increment of velocity, it will move in a circle of larger radius

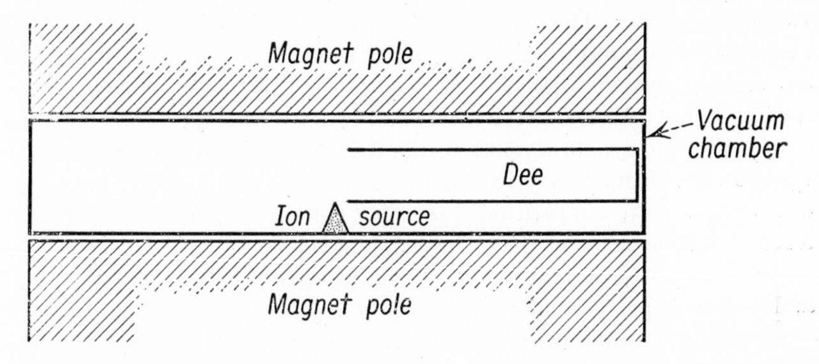

Fig. 16-5. Schematic diagram showing a single dee inside the vacuum chamber between the poles of a synchro-cyclotron.

and arrive at the edge of the dee at a later time t_2, at which time it will receive less energy from the ac field and fall into phase during the next cycle or cycles. Once a particle gets into phase, it can continue in the same orbit as long as the magnetic field and the frequency of the voltage applied to the dees remain constant. In order to increase the energy of the ion, it must be made to move in an orbit of larger radius. Both Veksler and McMillan showed that this could be accomplished either by increasing the magnetic field, or by decreasing the frequency of the applied voltage, or both. In the frequency-modulated cyclotron the magnetic field is kept constant while the frequency of the applied voltage is decreased slowly.

A frequency-modulated cyclotron consists of only a single dee placed inside a vacuum chamber between the poles of a very large electromagnet, as shown in Figure 16-5. The pole piece of the magnet of the Berkeley synchrocyclotron is 184 inches in diameter, that at the University of Chicago is 170 inches, and the one at Columbia University (Nevis) is 164 inches. The pole faces are specially shaped or contoured to provide a field which decreases almost linearly from the center out to the position of maximum orbital radius. For example, the magnetic field of the Nevis synchrocyclotron decreases from a maximum of about 17,400 gausses at the center to about 16,600 gausses at a radius of 74 inches, while the magnetic field at the Chicago synchrocyclotron decreases from a maximum of about 18,600 gausses at the center to 17,600 gausses at a radius of 76 inches. The reason for contouring the magnet is to provide a magnetic field which will focus the ions in the median plane. The contoured pole faces of the magnet go through circular holes in the top and bottom of the vacuum chamber.

The potential difference between the dee and the grounded plane is comparatively low, about 10 to 30 kilovolts. The radiofrequency is supplied by a tube oscillator circuit which is modulated by being coupled to a variable capacitor. The capacitance is varied by rotating one set of plates by means of a motor. This variable capacitor is sometimes placed inside the vacuum system between the pole faces, as in the Nevis synchrocyclotron, or it may be outside the magnet to avoid effects due to eddy currents. In the Chicago synchrocyclotron, the frequency of the voltage applied to the dee varies from 28.6 to 18.0 megacycles per second to accelerate protons to 450 Mev with a repetition rate of 60 per second; the oscillator of the Nevis synchrocyclotron goes through a frequency range of 28 to 16.9 megacycles per second with a repetition rate which can be varied from 60 to 120 pulses per second when accelerating protons to about 435 Mev.

Targets for nuclear experiments can be introduced through a vacuum lock in the vacuum chamber into the region where the ion beam is circulating. A variety of particle energies is thus available by simply placing the target at appropriate positions in the chamber. Furthermore, the magnetic field of the synchrocyclotron will also act on any charged particles produced by the bombardment of the target. There is also room enough for suitable detectors to be placed inside the vacuum chamber. This method has been widely used for the production and detection of charged π-mesons (see Chapter 14). Neutrons produced by bombarding a target with protons will come out of the walls of the chamber; channels are usually provided in the shielding around the synchrocyclotron so that a collimated beam of neutrons is available at a large distance from the magnet for experimental purposes.

It can readily be shown that the total energy $\mathcal{E}$ of a charged particle moving in a circular orbit with constant angular velocity ω in a magnetic field of strength H is given by

$$\boxed{\mathcal{E} = Hec/\omega} \tag{4}$$

where H is in em units and e is in es units (see problem 16-3). Its kinetic energy will then be given by

$$\boxed{\mathcal{E}_k = Hec/\omega - m_0c^2.} \tag{5}$$

For particles moving in synchronism with the radiofrequency field impressed on the dee, the angular velocity $\omega = 2\pi f$, where f is the frequency appropriate to the phase stable orbit. The above equations are perfectly general; they apply to all types of positive ions and to electrons.

Frequency-modulated cyclotrons are commonly operated with protons which are obtained from a suitable ion source placed at the center of the vacuum chamber. These cyclotrons can be modified to operate with more massive ions, such as deuterons, helium ions, beryllium ions, and so forth. Recently, (1952) Chou, Fry, and Lord introduced CO_2 in the ion source of the Chicago synchrocyclotron and observed carbon nuclei, C^{6+}, that is, carbon atoms stripped of their electrons. They also observed stripped beryllium atoms, that is, beryllium nuclei, Be^{4+}, probably produced by the evaporation of an internal beryllium target which was bombarded by protons circulating in the vacuum chamber. The carbon nuclei were observed in orbits up to 65 inches in radius, while the beryllium nuclei were observed in orbits of radii up to 50 inches. They estimated that the carbon ions had energies up to 1.1 Bev. Nuclear emulsion photographic plates were placed in the cyclotron and nuclear disintegrations produced in the emulsions by these heavy ions were studied.

16-5. The Betatron

Electrons may be accelerated to high energies by having them move in a circular path of constant radius and, at the same time, increasing the magnetic flux through the circular orbit so that the electrons acquire additional energy during each revolution. Attempts to build such an accelerator, now known as a *betatron*, were made more than thirty years ago, but the first successful betatron was designed and built by D. W. Kerst (1940) from the theory worked out by Kerst and R. Serber. The original betatron, as shown in Figure 16-6, which accelerated electrons up to 2.3 Mev, was operated as an x-ray tube; the x-rays were produced in the conventional manner by allowing the high energy electrons to strike a target. Most betatrons built since then have also been used as x-ray sources, while some have been used as sources of high energy electrons for nuclear experiments. Betatrons have been built which accelerate electrons up to about 300 Mev.

In the operation of the betatron, electrons from the heated filament F are injected into the circular or doughnut-shaped tube by applying a difference of potential between the filament and the plate P, as shown in Figure 16-7. The electrons are focused with the aid of the grid G. When an alternating magnetic field is applied parallel to the axis of the tube, two effects are produced: an electromotive force is produced in the electron orbit by the changing magnetic flux which gives the electrons additional energy; a radial force is produced by the action of the magnetic field whose

Fig. 16-6. Photograph showing the original 2.3 Mev betatron in front of a 20 Mev betatron. Each machine has its doughnut-shaped vacuum tube in place between the poles of the magnet. (From a photograph supplied to the author by Professor D. W. Kerst.)

direction is perpendicular to the electron velocity, which keeps the electron moving in a circular path. The magnetic flux through the orbit has to be chosen in such a way that the electrons will move in a stable orbit of fixed radius R. The electrons make several hundred thousand revolutions in this circular path while the alternating magnetic field is increasing in intensity from zero to a maximum, that is, during a quarter of a cycle. With each revolution they gain additional energy. When the electrons have acquired the desired amount of energy, a capacitor is discharged through two coils of wire, one directly above and the other directly below the stable orbit producing a sudden addition to the magnetic flux. This destroys the condition for the stability of this orbit and the electron beam moves out to larger radii until it strikes the back of the injector P which acts as the x-ray target.

We can think of the circular electron path of fixed radius R as a circuit; the emf V induced in this circuit by the changing magnetic flux is, according to Faraday's law,

$$V = \frac{d\Phi}{dt}$$

where Φ is the instantaneous value of the magnetic flux which is perpendicu-

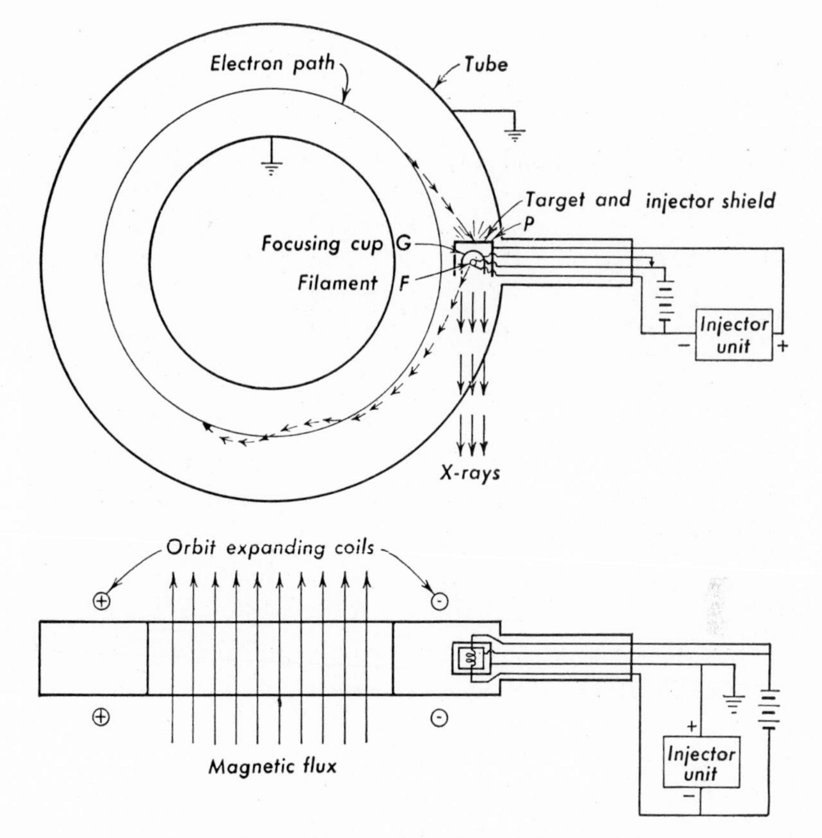

FIG. 16-7. Path of an electron in a betratron tube.

lar to the plane of the circuit. The work done on an electron of charge e in one revolution is therefore

$$Ve = e\frac{d\Phi}{dt}\cdot$$

This work can also be expressed in terms of the tangential force F which, acting on the electron over a distance ds, does an amount of work dW given by

$$dW = F \cdot ds,$$

from which

$$F = \frac{dW}{ds}\cdot$$

Thus the tangential force acting on the electron is equal to the work done per unit length of path. Evaluating this for one revolution for which the path length is $2\pi R$, we get

$$F = \frac{Ve}{2\pi R} = \frac{e}{2\pi R}\frac{d\Phi}{dt}.$$

Now, from Newton's second law,

$$F = \frac{d}{dt}(mv);$$

hence

$$\frac{d}{dt}(mv) = \frac{e}{2\pi R}\frac{d\Phi}{dt}$$

or

$$d(mv) = \frac{e}{2\pi R}d\Phi. \tag{6}$$

Because of the presence of the magnetic flux perpendicular to the plane of the electron orbit, the electron will experience a radial force inward given by

$$Hev = \frac{mv^2}{R}$$

where H is the value of the magnetic field intensity at the electron orbit of constant radius R. From the above equation,

$$mv = HeR.$$

If R is kept constant, then

$$d(mv) = eR \cdot dH. \tag{7}$$

Comparing equations (6) and (7), we see that

$$\frac{e}{2\pi R}d\Phi = eRdH,$$

from which

$$d\Phi = 2\pi R^2 dH.$$

Integrating this equation between the limits of zero and Φ and zero and H, respectively, we get

$$\Phi = 2\pi R^2 H \tag{8}$$

for the instantaneous relationship between the total magnetic flux Φ and the intensity of the magnetic field H at a distance R from the center. This equation shows that the magnetic flux within the orbit of radius R is always proportional to the intensity of the magnetic field at the orbit, and, furthermore, that the magnetic flux through the orbit is twice what it would have been if the magnetic field intensity were uniform throughout the orbit at the value H. This distribution of magnetic flux is obtained in an air gap between specially shaped pole faces of an electromagnet.

Most modern betatrons are operated from a 60 cycle/sec ac source. Since the magnet and its coils constitute a large inductance, a very large capacitance is introduced into the circuit to bring the power factor closer to unity for efficient operation. In the 100 Mev betatron, the electrons are accelerated during a quarter of a cycle, that is, during 1/240 sec. The energy acquired by an electron per revolution is 400 ev; hence it has to make 250,000 revolutions to acquire the maximum energy. In practice, the energy of the electrons, and hence that of the x-ray photons, can be varied from about 10 Mev to 100 Mev by applying the orbit-shifting magnetic field at different times during the quarter cycle that the field is increasing.

16-6. The Betatron-Synchrotron

The total energy $\mathcal{E}$ of a particle in a phase stable orbit moving with angular velocity ω at a place where the magnetic field intensity is H is given by

$$\mathcal{E} = \frac{eHc}{\omega} \cdot \tag{5}$$

An electron having an energy of a few million electron volts has a linear velocity practically equal to c, so that an increase in its energy produces no significant change in ω, but does produce an increase in its mass. Using the relativistic equation between energy and mass, $\mathcal{E} = mc^2$, we obtain

$$\boxed{\omega = \frac{eH}{mc};} \tag{9}$$

thus to increase the total energy or mass of the electron, it is necessary to increase the magnetic field acting on it in the same ratio.

The condition for a stable electron orbit, given by equation (8) for a betatron, must still be fulfilled, but it is no longer necessary to have a very heavy solid magnet over the entire area of the tube. The electromagnet need be built with its poles above and below the tube only, and with some steel bars, called flux bars, inside the hollow center near the tube. This is illustrated schematically in Figure 16-8, where a section of one side of the magnet, the tube, and a flux bar are shown. The steel flux bars become saturated magnetically very early in the magnetic cycle and further time variation in the magnetic field H then takes place in the region of the electron orbit. Figure 16-9 is a photograph of a 70 Mev betatron synchrotron in operation.

The doughnut-shaped vacuum tube shown in Figure 16-10 differs from the regular betatron tube in that a coating of silver is placed on a small section of the inside of the tube forming a metallic cavity, but a small break in the coating separates it into two parts. A high frequency electric field from a radiofrequency oscillator is applied across this gap at the proper time in the magnetic cycle. This frequency is in synchronism with the angular velocity of the electrons so that the electrons will be accelerated when they go through the cavity and cross the gap. The property of phase

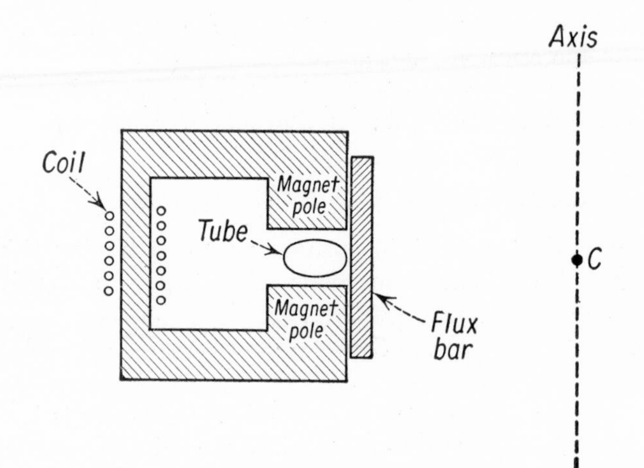

FIG. 16-8. Cross section of one side of a betatron-synchrotron showing the position of the vacuum tube between the poles of a C-shaped magnet with a flux bar. This synchrotron may be visualized by rotating this section through 360° about the verticle axis through the center C.

stability is also utilized in its operation so that electrons which have deviated from the normal orbit get the necessary decrease or increase in energy to bring them back to the normal orbit.

When the electrons are injected at the beginning of the magnetic cycle, the device operates as a betatron for a short time, of the order of microseconds, until the electrons have acquired an energy of about 2 Mev. The high frequency field is then automatically applied across the gap. It remains on while the magnetic field is increasing and is automatically cut off when the electrons have acquired their maximum energy or, if desired, at an earlier time in the cycle. Once the electrons have acquired the desired energy, the magnetic flux condition for a stable orbit is destroyed by sending a large current through additional coils to make the electrons spiral toward the target. In the case of the 70 Mev synchrotron, the electrons spiral inward to the target, which consists of a tungsten wire. X-rays come from the target in a narrow cone in the forward direction.

Betatron-synchrotrons (sometimes simply called synchrotrons) which can accelerate electrons up to 300 Mev and produce photons of this energy are now in operation. There are designs for higher energy synchrotrons.

FIG. 16-9. Photograph of a 70 Mev synchrotron. The brilliant spot of light just left of the center of the picture is caused by visible radiation emitted by the accelerated electrons. (Courtesy of the General Electric Company.)

However, there is a practical limit to the size of a synchrotron because of the radiation of electromagnetic waves, a large amount of it in the visible region, coming from the accelerated electrons. The light which is observed coming from the synchrotron in Figure 16-9 is evidence of this radiation. Electrons can be accelerated to higher energies without appreciable radiation losses by means of a *linear accelerator* (see §16-8).

The power radiated from accelerated charges moving with speeds v comparable with the speed of light c was calculated by Schwinger (1946), using the theory of relativity. For the case of a circular trajectory, such as exists in a betatron, cyclotron, and similar devices, the power S radiated was shown to be given by

$$S = \frac{2}{3}\omega^2 \frac{e^2}{R}\left(\frac{v}{c}\right)^3 \left(\frac{\mathcal{E}}{m_0c^2}\right)^4 . \tag{10}$$

in which R is the radius of the trajectory, ω is the angular velocity of the

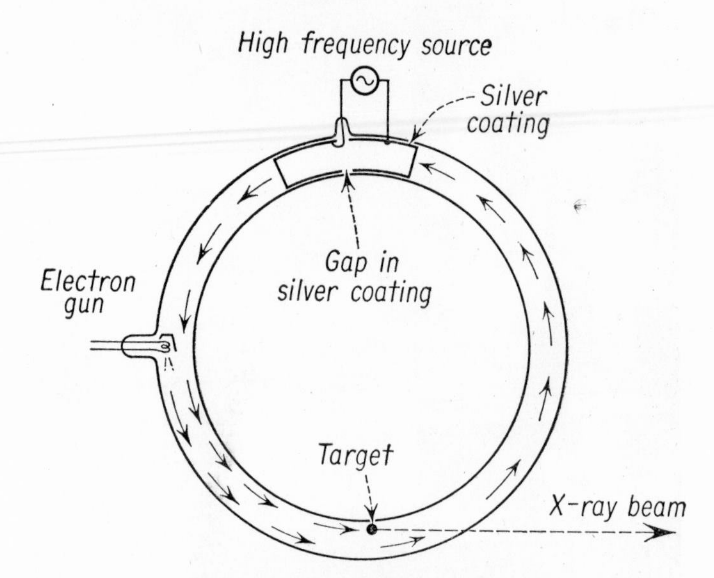

FIG. 16-10. Schematic diagram of the vacuum tube of a betraton-synchrotron showing the method of applying a high frequency potential difference across a gap in the silver-coated section of the tube.

particle, and $\mathcal{E}$ is its total energy. For the case of particles in a betatron or synchrotron whose speed $v \cong c$, this equation becomes

$$\boxed{S = \frac{2}{3}\omega^2 \frac{e^2}{R}\left(\frac{\mathcal{E}}{m_0c^2}\right)^4 .} \tag{11}$$

The energy $\mathcal{E}_1$ radiated during one revolution is

$$\mathcal{E}_1 = S\frac{2\pi}{\omega} \tag{12}$$

or

$$\boxed{\mathcal{E}_1 = \frac{4\pi}{3}\frac{e^2}{R}\left(\frac{\mathcal{E}}{m_0c^2}\right)^4 .} \tag{13}$$

Hence, for relativistic charged particles, the energy radiated per revolution varies directly with the fourth power of the total energy, and inversely as the fourth power of the rest mass.

16-7. Proton Synchrotron

At present, the device which accelerates particles to highest energies is the *proton synchrotron*. Several are in advanced stages of construction, and one, at Brookhaven, is in operation, producing protons of about 2.3 Bev. These machines are sometimes given different names at different localities; the one at Brookhaven is called the *cosmotron;* the one at Berkeley, designed to accelerate protons to 6 Bev, is called the *bevatron*. The fundamental

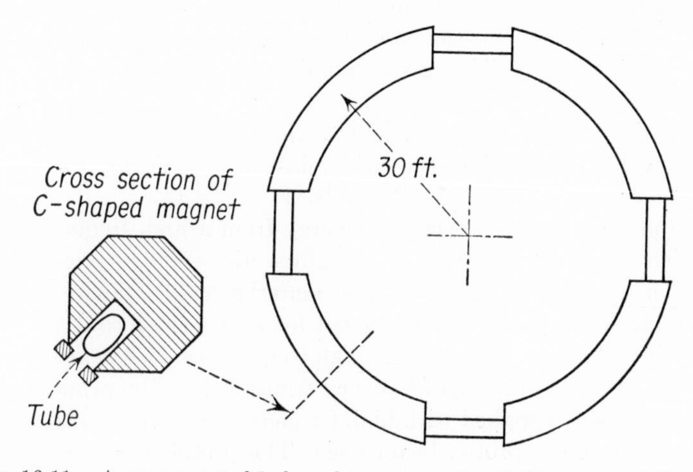

FIG. 16-11. Arrangement of C-shaped magnets and straight sections of the vacuum chamber of the cosmotron shown schematically.

principles underlying the operation of the proton synchrotron are the same as those for the electron synchrotron. Protons from some other accelerator, such as a Van de Graaff generator, are injected into the vacuum tube with energies up to about 10 Mev. The vacuum tubes are ring-shaped or else shaped like a race track, with straight sections connecting circular sections, as shown in Figure 16-11. The latter is the type used in the cosmotron and bevatron. The Birmingham accelerators use the ring-shaped tube with a ring-shaped magnet surrounding the entire tube. In the cosmotron, the ring-shaped magnet is in four sections surrounding the circular portions of the tube. A cross section of the magnet has the shape of the letter C with the solid iron on the inside of the circle and the vacuum tube in the open section of the C.

The proton synchrotrons are very large machines; the average radius of the Birmingham machine is 450 cm (15 ft); that of the cosmotron, 900 cm (30 ft); and that of the bevatron, 1500 cm (50 ft).

The vacuum tube of the cosmotron has an aperture of 7 in. × 30 in. and is pumped continuously. Protons of about 4 Mev energy are injected into one of the straight portions of the tube when the magnetic field has reached a value of about 300 gausses and is being built up to a value of about 14,000 gausses. Rectified direct current is supplied to the magnet coils rather slowly, taking one second to build up to its maximum value. An electrostatic deflector in one of the straight portions of the tube forces the ions initially toward the outer periphery, and as the magnetic field increases, the ions are forced closer to the center. A good proportion of the ions oscillates about, and finally moves into, the equilibrium orbit. The decrease in the magnetic field also takes place during a period of one second. The energy that was stored in the magnetic field, instead of being fed into a bank of capacitors as in the case of the electron synchrotron, is used to drive a large flywheel. During the building up of the magnetic field, the energy stored in the flywheel is returned to the magnetic circuit. The flywheel is driven by an induction motor which keeps the flywheel running between cycles and provides the energy lost in heat during the operation. The cycle is repeated every five seconds.

The protons receive their high energy from a high frequency electric field which is applied to one of the straight sections. This straight section is made of a nonmetallic ferromagnetic material, called ferrite, which has poor conductivity, so that eddy current losses are small, but which has a permeability of about 1000 at these high frequencies. In essence this ferrite tube forms the core of a high frequency transformer. The primary consists of one turn of wire supplied with high frequency current from an oscillator; the secondary is the proton beam itself. The proton receives an average energy of about 1000 ev per passage through the transformer and thus makes about 2.3×10^6 revolutions per second. The frequency has to be varied over a comparatively large range, from about 0.3 to 4.2 megacycles/sec owing to the fact that the initial velocity of the protons is rather low and does not approach the speed of light until its energy is about 1 Bev. Figure 16-12 is a photograph of the cosmotron.

There are plans now (1954) for building proton synchrotrons capable of accelerating protons to energies of about 100 Bev. Although the radius of the vacuum tube will be much larger, probably about 800 ft, the tube itself will have a very small aperture of about 2 in. × 1.5 in. Such a small aperture is made possible by the discovery of a new principle of focusing ions magnetically. This principle was discovered independently by N. Christophilos and by M. S. Livingston, E. D. Courant, and H. S. Snyder (1952), and is called the principle of *strong focusing*. By appropriate design of the magnetic pole faces and the use of a large number of magnets separated by short straight sections, the amplitude of the oscillation about the equilibrium orbit can be kept very small. The magnets will still have the shape of a

FIG. 16-12. View of the Cosmotron at Brookhaven National Laboratory, Upton, N.Y., from the angle at which protons enter the machine from the Van de Graaff generator. The proton beam coming from the generator tank passes through the magnetic field of a small magnet which analyzes the beam. Protons of the proper energy then enter the vacuum chamber through the straight section. Note the C-magnets in which the vacuum chamber rests. Twelve large cylindrical vacuum pumps, one of which can be seen to the left of the small analyzing magnet, are attached to the vacuum tube. (Courtesy of Brookhaven National Laboratory.)

C, but alternate magnets will have the solid portion inside while the others will have the solid portion outside the ring.

16-8. Linear Accelerators

The development of the linear accelerator for charged particles was started at about the same time as that of the cyclotron. The success of the latter type of accelerator and the unavailability of high-powered high frequency sources shifted the interest from linear accelerators. Interest in linear accelerators was renewed about 1945 as the result of the development of magnetrons, klystrons, and other tubes capable of delivering power of several megawatts for periods of several microseconds with repetition rates up to a few hundred pulses per second. Among the advantages of a linear accelerator are that no magnet is needed to guide the particles, and that the particles readily emerge from the apparatus since they travel in straight lines down the length of the vacuum tube. Linear accelerators have been developed for both electrons and protons, though the actual number in operation at present is not large.

One of the earliest of the modern linear accelerators is the proton accelerator designed by L. Alvarez (1947) at Berkeley. It consists essentially of a long steel vacuum chamber containing a 12-sided copper tube which is about 40 ft long and 1 meter in diameter and which acts as a resonant cavity for a radiofrequency wave of 202.5×10^6 cycles/sec. Protons with an energy of 4 Mev obtained from a Van de Graaff generator are injected along the axis of the copper cylinder. The protons travel through a set of 46 *drift tubes* aligned with their axes coincident with the axis of the copper tube, as shown in Figure 16-13. The drift tube shields the protons from the electric field of the wave traveling down the tube during

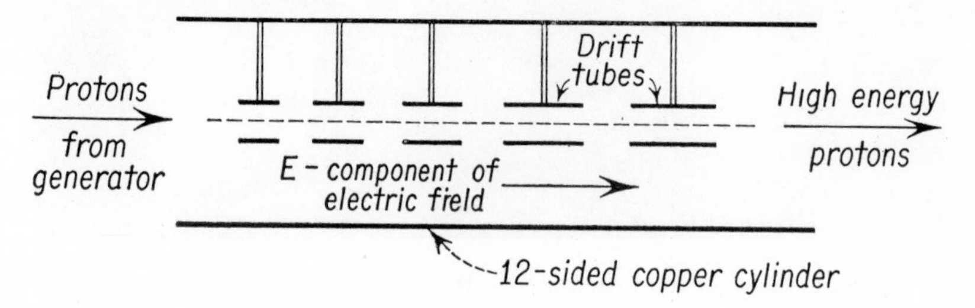

FIG. 16-13. Simplified diagram showing arrangement of drift tubes within copper cavity resonator of the linear proton accelerator.

the time that the phase of the wave is such as to produce a negative acceleration of the protons. The protons are accelerated in the forward direction only while they pass from one drift tube to the other. As the velocity of the proton increases, the length of the drift tube must also increase, so that the proton will remain in the same phase with respect to the electric field. The drift tubes vary in length from 4.4 in. to 10.9 in. and the distance between their centers along the axis also increases. Power is supplied to the resonator from 26 triode oscillators delivering a peak power of 2.15×10^6 watts. The power is delivered in pulses of 3×10^{-4} second duration with a repetition rate of 15 per second. This linear accelerator delivers protons with an energy of 32 Mev.

Linear accelerators for electrons are, in a sense, simpler than proton accelerators because the electrons acquire a speed practically equal to the speed of light at a comparatively low energy, in the neighborhood of a few Mev. Hence, if electrons are supplied to a linear accelerator from an outside source with an energy of 3 or 4 Mev, and in the correct phase with the electric field traveling down the tube, they will remain in phase and acquire energy from it. The problem in the design of a linear accelerator for electrons is to produce an electromagnetic wave which progresses along the tube with a controlled phase or wave velocity slightly less than or equal to the velocity of light. In order to supply energy to the electrons, the electric field of the wave must have a component in the direction of propagation of the wave. Methods of accomplishing this are known from microwave techniques, and several linear electron accelerators are now in operation and others are in advanced stages of construction. Electrons of energies up to about 200 Mev have been obtained with the Stanford linear accelerator 80 ft long, built of sections each 10 ft long. This is being increased to 220 ft with predicted value for the energy of the electron beam of 1000 Mev. The power is supplied through a series of klystrons operated as amplifiers and producing a traveling wave in the tube of 3×10^9 cycles/sec. The power is pulsed with a peak value of 10^7 watts for 1 to 2 microseconds and a repetition rate of 60 per second. At these high energies, the linear accelerator has one decided advantage over the cyclic accelerator in that there is negligible loss of energy in the form of radiation from the accelerated charges, since the speed of the electrons is practically constant and equal to c.

Problems

16-1. (**a**) Show that the energy of an ion of mass M and charge E which is circulating within the dees of a cyclotron along a path having a radius of curvature R is such as to correspond to a total acceleration through an equivalent voltage V given by

$$V = \tfrac{1}{2}H^2R^2\frac{E}{M}$$

in which V, H, and E are in em units.

(**b**) Show that the energy of this particle, in Mev, is given by

$$\mathcal{E} = 3.12 \times 10^5 H^2R^2\frac{E^2}{M}$$

with E and H in em units.

(**c**) Calculate the energy of a proton which is moving in a circle of 60 cm radius in a magnetic field of 10,000 gausses.

Ans. 17.2 Mev.

16-2. Show that the radius of curvature R of the path of a particle inside the dees of a cyclotron is proportional to the $\sqrt{n}$ where n is the number of times the particle has been accelerated across the space between the dees.

16-3. A particle of total mass m and charge e is moving in a stable orbit of radius R with angular velocity ω and linear velocity v. The orbit is perpendicular to the magnetic field of intensity H. Starting with the equation for the momentum p of the particle

$$p = HeR/c$$

where H is in em units and e in es units, and the relativistic expression for the momentum of a particle of total energy $\mathcal{E}$ and rest mass m_0:

$$p^2 = \frac{\mathcal{E}^2}{c^2} - m_0^2c^2,$$

show that the total energy is given by

$$\mathcal{E} = \frac{Hec}{\omega}.$$

16-4. (**a**) Calculate the kinetic energy, in Mev, of a proton which is moving in a circular orbit in a magnetic field of 17,000 gausses in resonance with the applied dee frequency of 18 megacycles per sec. (**b**) Determine the momentum of this proton in units of Mev/c. (**c**) Determine the linear velocity of the proton. (**d**) Determine the radius of this orbit.

Ans. (**a**) 415 Mev.
(**b**) 974 Mev/c.
(**c**) 0.72c.
(**d**) 192 cm.

16-5. (**a**) Calculate the kinetic energy, in Mev, of a deuteron which is moving in a circular orbit in a magnetic field of 17,000 gausses in resonance with the applied dee frequency of 12 megacycles per second. (**b**) Calculate the momentum of the deuteron in units of Mev/c. (**c**) Determine the linear velocity of the deuteron. (**d**) Determine the radius of this orbit.

Ans. (**a**) 185 Mev.
(**b**) 855 Mev/c.
(**c**) 0.42c.
(**d**) 163 cm.

16-6. Assume that, in the 70 Mev betatron synchrotron, the radius of the stable electron orbit is 28 cm. Calculate (**a**) the angular velocity of the electrons; (**b**) the frequency of the applied electric field; and (**c**) the value of the magnetic field intensity at the orbit for this energy.

Ans. (**a**) 1.07×10^9 rad/sec.
(**b**) 1.7×10^8 cycles/sec.
(**c**) 8300 gausses.

16-7. The radius of the stable electron orbit of a small betatron-synchrotron is 12.0 cm and the maximum magnetic field available at this position is 9000 gausses. Calculate (**a**) the angular velocity of the electron in the stable orbit, (**b**) the frequency of the applied electric field in synchronism with these electrons, and (**c**) the maximum electron energy produced.

Ans. (**a**) 2.50×10^9 rad/sec.
(**b**) 4.04×10^8 cycles/sec.
(**c**) 32.4 Mev.

16-8. In problem 16-7, the energy of the electron is increased from 2 to 32 Mev in a quarter of the magnetic cycle which is operated from a 50-cycle ac line.

Determine the average energy given to the electron by the high frequency electric field during each revolution.

Ans. 15 ev.

16-9. Show that the radius of a positive ion of rest mass m_0 moving in a circular orbit within a synchrocyclotron is given by

$$R = \left[\frac{\omega^2}{c^2} - \left(\frac{m_0c^2}{He}\right)^2\right]^{1/2}$$

where ω is its angular velocity and H is the magnetic field strength, in em units, and e is the charge of the ion in es units.

16-10. (**a**) Calculate the ratio of ω/H for a stripped carbon atom, $A = 12$' to move in a stable orbit in a synchrocyclotron with a kinetic energy of 1 Bev· (**b**) If the value of H at the orbit is 10,000 gausses, calculate the frequency of the electric field applied to the dee. (**c**) Determine the radius of this orbit.

16-11. (**a**) Calculate the power radiated from an electron synchrotron operated at 70 Mev when the electron orbit radius is 30 cm. (**b**) Calculate the energy lost by radiation during a single revolution of an electron. (**c**) Determine the ratio of the radiated energy to the total energy of the electron.

16-12. (**a**) Calculate the power radiated from an electron synchrotron operated at 300 Mev when the electron orbit radius is 100 cm. (**b**) Calculate the energy lost by radiation during a single revolution of an electron. (**c**) Determine the ratio of the radiated energy to the total energy of the electron.

16-13. (**a**) Calculate the power radiated from a proton synchrotron operated at 350 Mev when the orbit radius is 200 cm. (**b**) Calculate the energy lost by radiation during a single revolution of the proton. (**c**) Determine the linear and angular velocities of the protons in this orbit.

References

Chu, E. L., and L. I. Schiff, "Recent Progress in Accelerators," *Annual Review of Nuclear Science*, 2, 79–92, 1953. Contains extensive references to earlier literature.

Fremlin, J. H., and J. S. Gooden, "Cyclic Accelerators," in *Reports on Progress in Physics*. London: The Physical Society of London, 1950, XIII, 295.

Frisch, O. R. (ed.), *Progress in Nuclear Physics*. New York: Academic Press, Inc., 1950, Vol. I, Chap. I, "Cyclotrons," by T. G. Pickavance; Chap. II, "High Voltage Direct Current Generators," by R. L. Fortescue.

Fry, D. W., and W. Walkinshaw, "Linear Accelerators," in *Reports on Progress in Physics*. London: The Physical Society of London, 1948–1949, XII, 102.

Livingston, M. S., "High Energy Accelerators," *Annual Review of Nuclear Science*, 1, 157–174, 1952.

Review of Scientific Instruments, September, 1953. Entire issue devoted to articles on the cosmotron.

Slater, J. C., "Design of Linear Accelerators," *Revs. Modern Phys.*, 20, 473, 1948.

APPENDIXES

appendix I Values of Some Physical Constants*

Physical Quantity	Symbol	Value
1. Velocity of light	c	2.997929×10^{10} cm/sec.
2. Electronic charge	e	4.80288×10^{-10} esu
3. Avogadro number	N_0	6.02472×10^{23} at/gm atwt. (phys.)
4. Faraday constant	F	9652.01 emu/gm mole (phys.)
5. Specific electronic charge	e/m_e	1.75888×10^{7} emu/gm
6. Planck constant	h	6.6252×10^{-27} erg sec.
7. Rydberg constant for infinite mass	R_∞	109,737.309 cm^{-1}
8. Electron rest mass	m_e	9.1085×10^{-28} gm 5.48760×10^{-4} amu
9. Bohr magneton	M_B	9.2732×10^{-21} erg/gauss
10. Boltzmann constant	k	1.38042×10^{-16} erg/deg

Conversion Factors

Conversion	Value
Atomic mass units to Mev	931.162 Mev/amu
Electron volts to ergs	1.60207×10^{-12} erg/ev
Grams to Mev	5.60999×10^{26} Mev/gm

* Values taken from Jesse W. M. Du Mond and E. Richard Cohen, "Least-Squares Adjustment of the Atomic Constants, 1952," *Rev. Modern Phys.*, 25, 691, 1953.

appendix II Atomic Weights of the Elements*

Element	Symbol	Atomic Number	Atomic Weight[a]	Element	Symbol	Atomic Number	Atomic Weight[a]
Actinium	Ac	89	227	Molybdenum	Mo	42	95.95
Aluminum	Al	13	26.98	Neodymium	Nd	60	144.27
Americium	Am	95	[243]	Neptunium	Np	93	[237]
Antimony	Sb	51	121.76	Neon	Ne	10	20.183
Argon	A	18	39.944	Nickel	Ni	28	58.69
Arsenic	As	33	74.91	Niobium (Columbium)	Nb	41	92.91
Astatine	At	85	[210]	Nitrogen	N	7	14.008
Barium	Ba	56	137.36	Osmium	Os	76	190.2
Berkelium	Bk	97	[245]	Oxygen	O	8	**16**
Beryllium	Be	4	9.013	Palladium	Pd	46	106.7
Bismuth	Bi	83	209.00	Phosphorus	P	15	30.975
Boron	B	5	10.82	Platinum	Pt	78	195.23
Bromine	Br	35	79.916	Plutonium	Pu	94	[242]
Cadmium	Cd	48	112.41	Polonium	Po	84	210
Calcium	Ca	20	40.08	Potassium	K	19	39.100
Californium	Cf	98	[246]	Praseodymium	Pr	59	140.92
Carbon	C	6	12.010	Promethium	Pm	61	[145]
Cerium	Ce	58	140.13	Protactinium	Pa	91	231
Cesium	Cs	55	132.91	Radium	Ra	88	226.05
Chlorine	Cl	17	35.457	Radon	Rn	86	222
Chromium	Cr	24	52.01	Rhenium	Re	75	186.31
Cobalt	Co	27	58.94	Rhodium	Rh	45	102.91
Copper	Cu	29	63.54	Rubidium	Rb	37	85.48
Curium	Cm	96	[243]	Ruthenium	Ru	44	101.7
Dysprosium	Dy	66	162.46	Samarium	Sm	62	150.43
Erbium	Er	68	167.2	Scandium	Sc	21	44.96
Europium	Eu	63	152.0	Selenium	Se	34	78.96
Fluorine	F	9	19.00	Silicon	Si	14	28.09
Francium	Fr	87	[223]	Silver	Ag	47	107.880
Gadolinium	Gd	64	156.9	Sodium	Na	11	22.997
Gallium	Ga	31	69.72	Strontium	Sr	38	87.63
Germanium	Ge	32	72.60	Sulfur	S	16	32.066[b]
Gold	Au	79	197.2	Tantalum	Ta	73	180.88
Hafnium	Hf	72	178.6	Technetium	Tc	43	[99]
Helium	He	2	4.003	Tellurium	Te	52	127.61
Holmium	Ho	67	164.94	Terbium	Tb	65	159.2
Hydrogen	H	1	1.0080	Thallium	Tl	81	204.39
Indium	In	49	114.76	Thorium	Th	90	232.12
Iodine	I	53	126.91	Thulium	Tm	69	169.4
Iridium	Ir	77	193.1	Tin	Sn	50	118.70
Iron	Fe	26	55.85	Titanium	Ti	22	47.90
Krypton	Kr	36	83.80	Tungsten	W	74	183.92
Lanthanum	La	57	138.92	Uranium	U	92	238.07
Lead	Pb	82	207.21	Vanadium	V	23	50.95
Lithium	Li	3	6.940	Xenon	Xe	54	131.3
Lutetium	Lu	71	174.99	Ytterbium	Yb	70	173.04
Magnesium	Mg	12	24.32	Yttrium	Y	39	88.92
Manganese	Mn	25	54.93	Zinc	Zn	30	65.38
Mercury	Hg	80	200.61	Zirconium	Zr	40	91.22

[a] A value given in brackets denotes the mass number of the isotope of longest known half-life.
[b] Because of natural variations in the relative abundances of the isotopes of sulphur the atomic weight of this element has a range of ± 0.003.

* From *J. Am. Chem. Soc.*, 74, 2447, 1952.

appendix III Periodic Table of the Elements

	I	II	III	IV	V	VI	VII	VIII
1	1 H 1.0080							2 He 4.003
2	3 Li 6.940	4 Be 9.03	5 B 10.82	6 C 12.010	7 N 14.008	8 O 16.0000	9 F 19.00	10 Ne 20.183
3	11 Na 22.997	12 Mg 24.32	13 Al 26.98	14 Si 28.09	15 P 30.975	16 S 32.066	17 Cl 35.457	18 A 39.944
4	19 K 39.100	20 Ca 40.08	21 Sc 44.96	22 Ti 47.90	23 V 50.95	24 Cr 52.01	25 Mn 54.93	26 Fe 55.85 27 Co 58.94 28 Ni 58.69
	29 Cu 63.54	30 Zn 65.38	31 Ga 69.72	32 Ge 72.60	33 As 74.91	34 Se 78.96	35 Br 79.916	36 Kr 83.80
5	37 Rb 85.48	38 Sr 87.63	39 Y 88.92	40 Zr 91.22	41 Nb 92.91	42 Mo 95.95	43 Tc [99]	44 Ru 101.7 45 Rh 102.91 46 Pd 106.7
	47 Ag 107.880	48 Cd 112.41	49 In 114.76	50 Sn 118.70	51 Sb 121.76	52 Te 127.61	53 I 126.91	54 Xe 131.3
6	55 Cs 132.91	56 Ba 137.36	57–71 Rare Earths[a]	72 Hf 178.6	73 Ta 180.88	74 W 183.92	75 Re 186.31	76 Os 190.2 77 Ir 193.1 78 Pt 195.23
	79 Au 197.2	80 Hg 200.61	81 Tl 204.39	82 Pb 207.21	83 Bi 209.00	84 Po 210	85 At [210]	86 Rn 222
7	87 Fr [223]	88 Ra 226.05	89–96 Actinide[b] Series					

[a] Rare Earth or Lanthanide Series.

57 La 138.92	58 Ce 140.13	59 Pr 140.92	60 Nd 144.27	61 Pm [147]
62 Sm 150.43	63 Eu 152.0	64 Gd 156.9	65 Tb 159.2	66 Dy 162.46
67 Ho 164.94	68 Er 167.2	69 Tm 169.4	70 Yb 173.04	71 Lu 174.99

[b] Actinide Series.

89 Ac 227	90 Th 232.12	91 Pa 231	92 U 238.07
93 Np [237]	94 Pu [242]	95 Am [243]	96 Cm [243]
97 Bk [245]	98 Cf [246]		

appendix IV Table of Isotopic Masses

Mass No.	Atomic No.	Element	Atomic Mass
1	0	n	1.008987
1	1	H	1.008145
2	1	H	2.014741
3	1	H	3.016997
3	2	He	3.016977
4	2	He	4.003879
5	2	He	5.0137
5	3	Li	5.0136
6	2	He	6.020833
6	3	Li	6.01697
7	3	Li	7.01822
7	4	Be	7.01916
8	3	Li	8.02502
8	4	Be	8.00785
8	5	B	8.0264
9	4	Be	9.01503
9	5	B	9.01620
10	4	Be	10.01677
10	5	B	10.016110
10	6	C	10.0206
11	5	B	11.012811
11	6	C	11.01495
12	6	C	12.003844
12	7	N	12.0227
13	6	C	13.007505
13	7	N	13.00988
14	6	C	14.00767
14	7	N	14.007550
15	6	C	15.0143
15	7	N	15.004902
15	8	O	15.0078
16	7	N	16.0109
16	8	O	16.000000
17	7	N	17.0139
17	8	O	17.004533
17	9	F	17.007505
18	8	O	18.004883
18	9	F	18.006651
19	8	O	19.0091
19	9	F	19.004444
19	10	Ne	19.007952

CONTINUED

Mass No.	Atomic No.	Element	Atomic Mass
20	9	F	20.006350
20	10	Ne	19.998772
21	10	Ne	21.000504
21	11	Na	21.004286
22	10	Ne	21.998382
22	11	Na	22.001409
23	10	Ne	23.001768
23	11	Na	22.997055
23	12	Mg	23.001453
24	11	Na	23.998568
24	12	Mg	23.992628
25	12	Mg	24.993745
26	12	Mg	25.990802
27	12	Mg	26.992876
27	13	Al	26.990109
28	13	Al	27.990760
28	14	Si	27.985825
29	14	Si	28.985705
30	14	Si	29.983307
31	14	Si	30.985140
31	15	P	30.983619
32	15	P	31.984016
32	16	S	31.982274
33	15	P	32.982166
33	16	S	32.981941
34	16	S	33.978709
35	17	Cl	34.980064
36	18	A	35.97926
37	17	Cl	36.977675
38	18	A	37.97491
39	19	K	38.97606
40	18	A	39.975148
40	20	Ca	39.97545
41	19	K	40.97490
42	20	Ca	41.97216
43	20	Ca	42.97251
44	20	Ca	43.96924
45	21	Sc	44.97010
46	22	Ti	45.96697
47	22	Ti	46.96668
48	20	Ca	47.96778

CONTINUED

Mass No.	Atomic No.	Element	Atomic Mass
48	22	Ti	47.96317
49	22	Ti	48.96358
50	22	Ti	49.96077
50	24	Cr	49.96210
51	23	V	50.96052
52	24	Cr	51.95707
53	24	Cr	52.95772
54	24	Cr	53.9563
54	26	Fe	53.95704
55	25	Mn	54.95581
56	26	Fe	55.95272
57	26	Fe	56.95359
58	26	Fe	57.9520
58	28	Ni	57.95345
59	27	Co	58.95182
60	27	Co	59.95250
60	28	Ni	59.94901
61	28	Ni	60.94907
62	28	Ni	61.94681
63	29	Cu	62.94926
64	28	Ni	63.94755
64	30	Zn	63.94955
65	29	Cu	64.94835
66	30	Zn	65.94722
67	30	Zn	66.94815
68	30	Zn	67.94686
70	30	Zn	69.94779
70	32	Ge	69.9447
74	32	Ge	73.9426
74	34	Se	73.9439
75	33	As	74.9432
76	32	Ge	75.9433
79	35	Br	78.944
81	35	Br	80.943
82	36	Kr	81.938
84	36	Kr	83.938
85	37	Rb	84.931
86	38	Sr	85.93533
87	37	Rb	86.9295
88	38	Sr	87.93374
94	42	Mo	93.9343

CONTINUED

Mass No.	Atomic No.	Element	Atomic Mass
98	42	Mo	97.93610
102	46	Pd	101.9375
104	46	Pd	103.93655
105	46	Pd	104.9384
106	46	Pd	105.9368
106	48	Cd	105.93984
108	46	Pd	107.93801
108	48	Cd	107.93860
110	46	Pd	109.93965
110	48	Cd	109.93857
111	48	Cd	110.93978
112	48	Cd	111.93885
113	48	Cd	112.94061
113	49	In	112.94045
114	48	Cd	113.93997
115	49	In	114.94040
115	50	Sn	114.94014
116	48	Cd	115.94202
116	50	Sn	115.93927
117	50	Sn	116.94052
118	50	Sn	117.93978
119	50	Sn	118.94122
120	50	Sn	119.94059
120	52	Te	119.94288
122	50	Sn	121.94249
122	52	Te	121.94193
123	52	Te	122.94368
124	50	Sn	123.94490
124	52	Te	123.94278
124	54	Xe	123.94578
125	52	Te	124.94460
126	52	Te	125.94420
126	54	Xe	125.94476
127	53	I	126.94528
128	52	Te	127.94649
128	54	Xe	127.94446
129	54	Xe	153.94601
130	52	Te	129.94853
130	54	Xe	129.94501
131	54	Xe	130.94673
132	54	Xe	131.94615

appendix  **Table of Isotopic Masses**

CONTINUED

Mass No.	Atomic No.	Element	Atomic Mass
134	54	Xe	133.94803
136	54	Xe	135.95046
136	56	Ba	135.9488
137	56	Ba	136.9502
138	56	Ba	137.9498
140	58	Ce	139.9489
141	59	Pr	140.9514
142	58	Ce	141.9537
144	60	Nd	143.9560
150	60	Nd	149.9687
176	72	Hf	175.9923
178	72	Hf	177.9936
180	72	Hf	180.0029
181	73	Ta	181.0031
182	74	W	182.0033
183	74	W	183.0059
184	74	W	184.0052
194	78	Pt	194.0256
196	78	Pt	196.02744
205	82	Pb	205.04559
206	81	Tl	206.04702
206	82	Pb	206.04519
207	81	Tl	207.04934
207	82	Pb	207.04725
208	81	Tl	208.05290
208	82	Pb	208.04754
208	83	Bi	208.04968
209	81	Tl	209.05778
209	82	Pb	209.05398
209	83	Bi	209.05325
209	84	Po	209.05496
210	81	Tl	210.06264
210	82	Pb	210.05622
210	83	Bi	210.05614
210	84	Po	210.05488
211	82	Pb	211.06196
211	83	Bi	211.06047
211	84	Po	211.05927
212	82	Pb	212.06487
212	83	Bi	212.06345
212	84	Po	212.06094

appendix IV Table of Isotopic Masses

CONTINUED

Mass No.	Atomic No.	Element	Atomic Mass
212	85	At	212.06079
213	83	Bi	213.06824
213	83	Po	213.06696
214	82	Pb	214.07362
214	83	Bi	214.07225
214	84	Po	214.06852
214	85	At	214.06955
215	84	Po	215.07392
215	85	At	215.07313
216	84	Po	216.07617
216	85	At	216.07586
216	86	Em	216.07358
217	85	At	217.07979
217	86	Em	217.07939
218	84	Po	218.08407
218	85	At	218.08369
218	86	Em	218.08017
218	87	Fr	218.08108
219	86	Em	219.08527
219	87	Fr	219.08501
220	86	Em	220.08693
220	87	Fr	220.08706
220	88	Ra	220.08567
221	87	Fr	221 09057
221	88	Ra	221 09060
222	86	Em	222 09397
222	88	Ra	222.09116
222	89	Ac	222.09342
223	87	Fr	223.09697
223	88	Ra	223.09559
223	89	Ac	223.09615
224	88	Ra	224.09703
224	89	Ac	224.09769
224	90	Th	224.09743
225	88	Ra	225.10102
225	89	Ac	225.10081
225	90	Th	225.10170
226	88	Ra	226.10309
226	90	Th	226.10193
226	91	Pa	226.10494
227	88	Ra	227.10723

CONTINUED

Mass No.	Atomic No.	Element	Atomic Mass
227	89	Ac	227.10666
227	90	Th	227.10642
227	91	Pa	227.10710
228	88	Ra	228.11005
228	89	Ac	228.11005
228	90	Th	228.10685
228	91	Pa	228.10823
228	92	U	228.10863
229	90	Th	229.11021
229	91	Pa	229.11088
229	92	U	229.11258
230	90	Th	230.11206
230	91	Pa	230.11441
230	92	U	230.11222
231	90	Th	231.11628
231	91	Pa	231.11607
231	93	Np	231.11776
232	90	Th	232.11852
232	91	Pa	232.11768
232	92	U	232.11650
232	94	Pu	232.11973
233	90	Th	233.12198
233	91	Pa	233.12027
233	92	U	233.11937
234	90	Th	234.12394
234	91	Pa	234.12281
234	92	U	234.12115
234	94	Pu	234.12269
235	92	U	235.12517
236	94	Pu	236.12667
237	92	U	237.13010
237	93	Np	237.12932
238	92	U	238.13232
238	93	Np	238.13255
238	94	Pu	238.13106
239	92	U	239.13704
239	93	Np	239.13620
239	94	Pu	239.13494
239	95	Am	239.13568
240	96	Cm	240.13744
241	94	Pu	241.13909

CONCLUDED

Mass No.	Atomic No.	Element	Atomic Mass
241	95	Am	241.13919
242	95	Am	242.14215
242	96	Cm	242.14160

Collins, T. L., A. O. Nier, and W. H. Johnson, Jr., *Phys. Rev.*, 86, 408, 1952.
Duckworth, H. E., C. L. Kegley, J. M. Olson, and G. S. Stanford, *Phys. Rev.*, 83, 1114, 1951.
Halsted, R. E., *Phys. Rev.*, 88, 660, 1952.
Hays, E. E., P. I. Richards, and S. A. Goudsmit, *Phys. Rev.*, 84, 824, 1951.
Hornyak, W. F., T. Lauritsen, P. Morrison, and W. A. Fowler, *Rev. Modern Phys.*, 22, 291, 1950.
Ogata, K., and H. Matsuda, *Phys. Rev.*, 89, p. 27, 1953.
Stern, N. O., *Revs. Modern Phys.*, 21, 316, 1949.

appendix V Table of Naturally Occurring Isotopes

Atomic No.	Atom	Mass No.	Abundance (%)
1	H	1	99.985
1	H	2	0.015
2	He	3	0.00013
2	He	4	~100.
3	Li	6	7.52
3	Li	7	92.48
4	Be	9	100.
5	B	10	18.98
5	B	11	81.02
6	C	12	98.892
6	C	13	1.108
7	N	14	99.635
7	N	15	0.365
8	O	16	99.759
8	O	17	0.037
8	O	18	0.204
9	F	19	100.
10	Ne	20	90.92
10	Ne	21	0.257
10	Ne	22	8.82
11	Na	23	100.
12	Mg	24	78.60
12	Mg	25	10.11
12	Mg	26	11.29
13	Al	27	100.
14	Si	28	92.18
14	Si	29	4.71
14	Si	30	3.12
15	P	31	100.
16	S	32	95.018
16	S	33	0.750
16	S	34	4.215
16	S	36	0.017
17	Cl	35	75.4
17	Cl	37	24.6
18	A	36	0.337
18	A	38	0.063
18	A	40	99.600
19	K	39	93.08
19	K	(40)	0.012
19	K	41	6.91
20	Ca	40	96.92

CONTINUED

Atomic No.	Atom	Mass No.	Abundance (%)
20	Ca	42	0.64
20	Ca	43	0.13
20	Ca	44	2.13
20	Ca	46	0.0032
20	Ca	48	0.179
21	Sc	45	100.
22	Ti	46	7.95
22	Ti	47	7.75
22	Ti	48	73.45
22	Ti	49	5.51
22	Ti	50	5.34
23	V	50	0.24
23	V	51	99.76
24	Cr	50	4.31
24	Cr	52	83.76
24	Cr	53	9.55
24	Cr	54	2.38
25	Mn	55	100.
26	Fe	54	5.90
26	Fe	56	91.52
26	Fe	57	2.25
26	Fe	58	0.33
27	Co	59	100.
28	Ni	58	67.76
28	Ni	60	26.16
28	Ni	61	1.25
28	Ni	62	3.66
28	Ni	64	1.16
29	Cu	63	69.09
29	Cu	65	30.91
30	Zn	64	48.89
30	Zn	66	27.81
30	Zn	67	4.11
30	Zn	68	18.56
30	Zn	70	0.62
31	Ga	69	60.2
31	Ga	71	39.8
32	Ge	70	20.52
32	Ge	72	27.43
32	Ge	73	7.76
32	Ge	74	36.54
32	Ge	76	7.76

CONTINUED

Atomic No.	Atom	Mass No.	Abundance (%)
33	As	75	100.
34	Se	74	0.96
34	Se	76	9.12
34	Se	77	7.50
34	Se	78	23.61
34	Se	80	49.96
34	Se	82	8.84
35	Br	79	50.57
35	Br	81	49.43
36	Kr	78	0.354
36	Kr	80	2.27
36	Kr	82	11.56
36	Kr	83	11.55
36	Kr	84	56.90
36	Kr	86	17.37
37	Rb	85	72.15
37	Rb	(87)	27.85
38	Sr	84	0.56
38	Sr	86	9.86
38	Sr	87	7.02
38	Sr	88	82.56
39	Y	89	100.
40	Zr	90	51.46
40	Zr	91	11.23
40	Zr	92	17.11
40	Zr	94	17.40
40	Zr	96	2.80
41	Nb	93	100.
42	Mo	92	15.05
42	Mo	94	9.35
42	Mo	95	14.78
42	Mo	96	16.56
42	Mo	97	9.60
42	Mo	98	24.00
42	Mo	100	9.68
44	Ru	96	5.68
44	Ru	98	2.22
44	Ru	99	12.81
44	Ru	100	12.70
44	Ru	101	16.98
44	Ru	102	31.34
44	Ru	104	18.27

CONTINUED

Atomic No.	Atom	Mass No.	Abundance (%)
45	Rh	103	100.
46	Pd	102	0.8
46	Pd	104	9.3
46	Pd	105	22.6
46	Pd	106	27.1
46	Pd	108	26.7
46	Pd	110	13.5
47	Ag	107	51.35
47	Ag	109	48.65
48	Cd	106	1.22
48	Cd	108	0.89
48	Cd	110	12.43
48	Cd	111	12.86
48	Cd	112	23.79
48	Cd	113	12.34
48	Cd	114	28.81
48	Cd	116	7.66
49	In	113	4.16
49	In	115	95.84
50	Sn	112	0.95
50	Sn	114	0.65
50	Sn	115	0.34
50	Sn	116	14.24
50	Sn	117	7.57
50	Sn	118	24.01
50	Sn	119	8.58
50	Sn	120	32.97
50	Sn	122	4.71
50	Sn	124	5.98
51	Sb	121	57.25
51	Sb	123	42.75
52	Te	120	0.089
52	Te	122	2.46
52	Te	123	0.87
52	Te	124	4.61
52	Te	125	6.99
52	Te	126	18.71
52	Te	128	31.79
52	Te	130	34.49
53	I	127	100.
54	Xe	124	0.096
54	Xe	126	0.090

CONTINUED

Atomic No.	Atom	Mass No.	Abundance (%)
54	Xe	128	1.919
54	Xe	129	26.44
54	Xe	130	4.08
54	Xe	131	21.18
54	Xe	132	26.89
54	Xe	134	10.44
54	Xe	136	8.87
55	Cs	133	100.
56	Ba	130	0.101
56	Ba	132	0.097
56	Ba	134	2.42
56	Ba	135	6.59
56	Ba	136	7.81
56	Ba	137	11.32
56	Ba	138	71.66
57	La	138	0.089
57	La	139	99.911
58	Ce	136	0.193
58	Ce	138	0.250
58	Ce	140	88.48
58	Ce	142	11.07
59	Pr	141	100.
60	Nd	142	27.09
60	Nd	143	12.14
60	Nd	144	23.83
60	Nd	145	8.29
60	Nd	146	17.26
60	Nd	148	5.74
60	Nd	150	5.63
62	Sm	144	3.16
62	Sm	147	15.07
62	Sm	148	11.27
62	Sm	149	13.84
62	Sm	150	7.47
62	Sm	(152)	26.63
62	Sm	154	22.53
63	Eu	151	47.77
63	Eu	153	52.23
64	Gd	152	0.20
64	Gd	154	2.15
64	Gd	155	14.73
64	Gd	156	20.47

appendix V Table of Naturally Occurring Isotopes

CONTINUED

Atomic No.	Atom	Mass No.	Abundance (%)
64	Gd	157	15.68
64	Gd	158	24.87
64	Gd	160	21.90
65	Tb	159	100.
66	Dy	156	0.0524
66	Dy	158	0.0902
66	Dy	160	2.294
66	Dy	161	18.88
66	Dy	162	25.53
66	Dy	163	24.97
66	Dy	164	28.18
67	Ho	165	100.
68	Er	162	0.136
68	Er	164	1.56
68	Er	166	33.41
68	Er	167	22.94
68	Er	168	27.07
68	Er	170	14.88
69	Tm	169	100.
70	Yb	168	0.140
70	Yb	170	3.03
70	Yb	171	14.31
70	Yb	172	21.82
70	Yb	173	16.13
70	Yb	174	31.84
70	Yb	176	12.73
71	Lu	175	97.40
71	Lu	176	2.60
72	Hf	174	0.199
72	Hf	176	5.23
72	Hf	177	18.55
72	Hf	178	27.23
72	Hf	179	13.73
72	Hf	180	35.07
73	Ta	181	100.
74	W	180	0.126
74	W	182	26.31
74	W	183	14.28
74	W	184	30.64
74	W	186	28.64
75	Re	185	37.07
75	Re	(187)	62.93

CONCLUDED

Atomic No.	Atom	Mass No.	Abundance (%)
76	Os	184	0.018
76	Os	186	1.59
76	Os	187	1.64
76	Os	188	13.3
76	Os	189	16.1
76	Os	190	26.4
76	Os	192	41.0
77	Ir	191	38.5
77	Ir	193	61.5
78	Pt	190	0.012
78	Pt	192	0.78
78	Pt	194	32.8
78	Pt	195	33.7
78	Pt	196	25.4
78	Pt	198	7.23
79	Au	197	100.
80	Hg	196	0.146
80	Hg	198	10.02
80	Hg	199	16.84
80	Hg	200	23.13
80	Hg	201	13.22
80	Hg	202	29.80
80	Hg	204	6.85
81	Tl	203	29.50
81	Tl	205	70.50
82	Pb	202	<0.0004
82	Pb	204	1.37
82	Pb	206	25.15
82	Pb	207	21.11
82	Pb	208	52.38
83	Bi	209	100.
90	Th	(232)	100.
92	U	(234)	0.0058
92	U	(235)	0.715
92	U	(238)	99.28

NOTE: Parentheses denote a radioactive isotope.

Hollander, J. M., I. Perlman, and G. T. Seaborg, "Table of Isotopes," *Revs. Modern Phys.*, 25, 469, 1953.

Way, Katherine, Lilla Fano, Millicent R. Scott, and Karin Thew, (Comps.), *Nuclear Data*. Washington, D. C.: National Bureau of Standards, Circular 499, 1950.

appendix VI Path of an Alpha Particle in a Coulomb Field of Force

Consider a nucleus of charge Ze stationary at point C and an alpha particle of mass M and charge E approaching it along the line AB, Figure 3-8. The

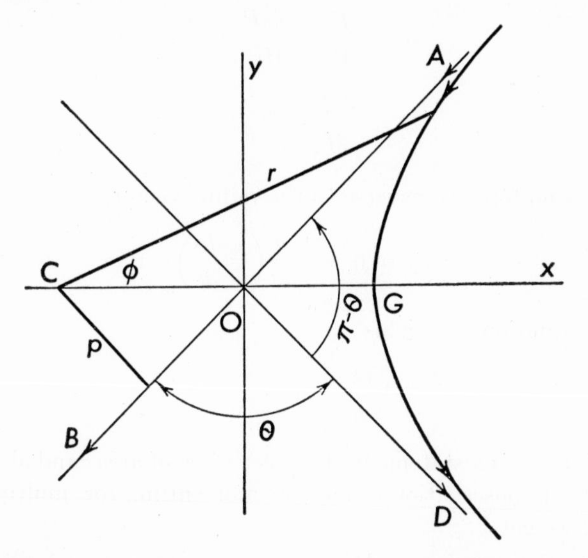

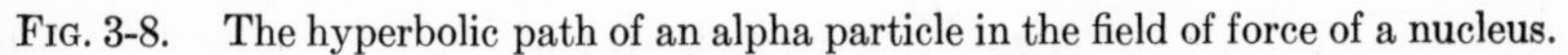
FIG. 3-8. The hyperbolic path of an alpha particle in the field of force of a nucleus.

original velocity of the alpha particle in the direction of AB is V. There will be a force of repulsion between the two charges given by Coulomb's law

$$F = \frac{ZeE}{r^2}, \tag{1}$$

where r is the distance of the alpha particle from the nucleus. The alpha particle will be deflected from its original direction of motion by this force of repulsion and its path will be a conic section since the motion is governed by an inverse square law of force. This conic section will be one branch of a hyperbola with the nucleus at the focus on the convex side of this branch.

To derive the expression for the path of the alpha particle, let us choose polar coordinates with the nucleus at the pole. The acceleration of the particle may be resolved into two components, one along the radius, a_r, and the other transverse to the radius a_ϕ. In texts on Mechanics, it is shown that these components are given by the equations

$$a_r = \frac{d^2r}{dt^2} - r\left(\frac{d\phi}{dt}\right)^2 \tag{2}$$

$$a_\phi = \frac{1}{r}\frac{d}{dt}\left(r^2\frac{d\phi}{dt}\right). \tag{3}$$

appendix VI Path of an Alpha Particle in a Coulomb Field of Force

CONTINUED

Since the force of repulsion is along the radius vector r, the radial component of the acceleration is

$$a_r = \frac{F}{M} = \frac{ZeE}{Mr^2} = \frac{J}{r^2}, \tag{4}$$

where $$J = \frac{ZeE}{M}.$$

Since there is no force transverse to the radius vector,

$$a_\phi = 0 = \frac{1}{r}\frac{d}{dt}\left(r^2\frac{d\phi}{dt}\right). \tag{5}$$

Integrating equation (5) yields

$$r^2\frac{d\phi}{dt} = K. \tag{6}$$

Equation (6) is a statement of Kepler's law of areas and also expresses the principle of conservation of angular momentum, for, multiplying both sides by M, we get

$$Mr^2\frac{d\phi}{dt} = MK = MVp, \tag{7}$$

where Mr^2 is the moment of inertia of the alpha particle with respect to an axis through C, $d\phi/dt$ is the angular velocity of the particle, and MVp is the initial angular momentum of the particle. The distance p from the nucleus to AB is called the *impact parameter*.

The differential equation of the path of the particle may be obtained by combining equations (2) and (4); this yields

$$\frac{d^2r}{dt^2} - r\left(\frac{d\phi}{dt}\right)^2 = \frac{J}{r^2}. \tag{8}$$

Before integrating this equation, let us change the independent variable from t to ϕ, and also, for convenience, let $u = \frac{1}{r}\cdot$ To carry out this transformation, note that

$$\frac{dr}{dt} = \frac{dr}{d\phi}\frac{d\phi}{dt}$$

$$\frac{dr}{d\phi} = -\frac{1}{u^2}\frac{du}{d\phi},$$

CONTINUED

and from equation (6) $$\frac{d\phi}{dt} = \frac{K}{r^2} = Ku^2$$

and $$\frac{d^2r}{dt^2} = -K^2u^2\frac{d^2u}{d\phi^2}.$$

Equation (8) now becomes

$$\frac{d^2u}{d\phi^2} + u = -\frac{J}{K^2}$$

or $$\frac{d^2}{d\phi^2}\left(u + \frac{J}{K^2}\right) = -\left(u + \frac{J}{K^2}\right). \tag{9}$$

This is a well-known differential equation and its solution is

$$u + \frac{J}{K^2} = A\cos(\phi - \delta), \tag{10}$$

where A and δ are constants of integration. To verify that this is the solution of the differential equation, one needs only to differentiate equation (10) twice.

By the proper choice of the x axis, the phase angle δ can be set equal to zero. Further, by setting

$$\epsilon = \frac{AK^2}{J} \tag{11}$$

equation (10) becomes

$$u + \frac{J}{K^2} = \frac{\epsilon J}{K^2}\cos\phi,$$

from which $$u = \frac{1}{r} = -\frac{J}{K^2}(1 - \epsilon\cos\phi). \tag{12}$$

Equation (12) is one form of the equation of a conic section in polar coordinates; ϵ is the eccentricity of this conic section. When ϵ is greater than unity, the conic section is a hyperbola. The eccentricity of this path can be determined with the aid of the principle of conservation of energy, which yields

$$\tfrac{1}{2}MV^2 = \tfrac{1}{2}Mv^2 + \frac{ZeE}{r} = \tfrac{1}{2}Mv^2 + \frac{JM}{r} \tag{13}$$

where ZeE/r is the potential energy of the particle at any point in its path.

CONTINUED

Resolving the velocity v into two components, one along the radius and one transverse to the radius, we get

$$v^2 = \left(\frac{dr}{dt}\right)^2 + \left(r\frac{d\phi}{dt}\right)^2 = \left[\left(\frac{dr}{d\phi}\right)^2 + r^2\right]\left(\frac{d\phi}{dt}\right)^2. \tag{14}$$

From equation (12) we get

$$\left(\frac{dr}{d\phi}\right)^2 = \frac{J^2\epsilon^2 r^4 \sin^2\phi}{K^4},$$

and since

$$\left(\frac{d\phi}{dt}\right)^2 = \frac{K^2}{r^4},$$

equation (14) becomes

$$v^2 = \frac{J^2\epsilon^2 \sin^2\phi}{K^2} + \frac{J^2}{K^2}(1 - \epsilon\cos\phi)^2. \tag{15}$$

Substituting this value of v^2 in equation (13) and the value for r from equation (12) and simplifying, we get

$$V^2 = \frac{J^2\epsilon^2}{K^2} - \frac{J^2}{K^2},$$

from which

$$\epsilon^2 - 1 = \frac{K^2}{J^2}V^2$$

or

$$\epsilon^2 - 1 = \left(\frac{MV^2p}{ZeE}\right)^2. \tag{16}$$

The eccentricity of the orbit is greater than unity and is expressed in terms of the initial energy of the alpha particle, the impact parameter p, and the nuclear charge Ze; thus

$$\epsilon = \sqrt{1 + \left(\frac{MV^2p}{ZeE}\right)^2}. \tag{17}$$

The orbit is therefore a hyperbola with the nucleus at the focus outside the branch of the curve followed by the alpha particle. The asymptote AB represents the direction of the initial velocity of the alpha particle, while the second asymptote OD represents the direction of the final velocity of the alpha particle. The angle θ between the two asymptotes is the angle through which the particle has been deflected and is the angle of scattering.

CONCLUDED

This angle can be expressed in terms of the eccentricity from a consideration of the properties of the hyperbola.

The equation of the hyperbola in rectangular coordinates is

$$\frac{x^2}{a^2} - \frac{y^2}{b^2} = 1, \tag{18}$$

where

$$a\epsilon = OC$$

and

$$b^2 = a^2(\epsilon^2 - 1).$$

The equations of the asymptotes are obtained by setting the left-hand side of equation (18) equal to zero, yielding

$$y = \pm \frac{b}{a} x.$$

From the figure

$$\frac{b}{a} = \tan \frac{\pi - \theta}{2} = \cot \frac{\theta}{2};$$

hence

$$\epsilon^2 - 1 = \cot^2 \frac{\theta}{2}. \tag{19}$$

Using equation (16), we get

$$\cot \frac{\theta}{2} = \frac{MV^2}{ZeE} p. \tag{20}$$

appendix VII Derivation of the Equations for the Compton Effect

The three equations derived in §5-19 are

$$h\nu = h\nu' + m_0c^2(K - 1) \tag{1}$$

$$\frac{h\nu}{c} = \frac{h\nu'}{c}\cos\phi + Km_0v\cos\theta \tag{2}$$

$$0 = \frac{h\nu'}{c}\sin\phi - Km_0v\sin\theta, \tag{3}$$

where

$$K = \frac{1}{\left(1 - \frac{v^2}{c^2}\right)^{1/2}}.$$

To solve these equations, let

$$\alpha = \frac{h\nu}{m_0c^2} = \frac{h}{m_0c\lambda}$$

$$\alpha' = \frac{h\nu'}{m_0c^2} = \frac{h}{m_0c\lambda'}$$

$$b = \sqrt{K^2 - 1} = \frac{Kv}{c},$$

or

$$K = \sqrt{1 + b^2}$$

$$l_1 = \cos\phi$$

$$n_1 = \sin\phi$$

$$l_2 = \cos\theta$$

$$n_2 = \sin\theta.$$

By dividing equation (1) by m_0c^2, we get

$$\alpha = \alpha' + \sqrt{1 + b^2} - 1, \tag{4}$$

and by dividing equations (2) and (3) by m_0c, we get

$$\alpha = \alpha' l_1 + bl_2 \tag{5}$$

and

$$0 = \alpha' n_1 - bn_2. \tag{6}$$

From equation (5) $\quad b^2l_2^2 = \alpha^2 - 2\alpha\alpha' l_1 + \alpha'^2 l_1^2, \tag{7}$

and from equation (6)

$$b^2 n_2^2 = \alpha'^2 n_1^2. \tag{8}$$

Adding equations (7) and (8), we get

$$b^2(l_2^2 + n_2^2) = \alpha^2 - 2\alpha\alpha' l_1 + \alpha'^2(l_1^2 + n_1^2)$$

or

$$b^2 = \alpha^2 - 2\alpha\alpha' l_1 + \alpha'^2, \tag{9}$$

since

$$l_2^2 + n_2^2 = 1 = l_1^2 + n_1^2.$$

From equation (4),

$$b^2 = \alpha^2 - 2\alpha\alpha' + \alpha'^2 + 2\alpha - 2\alpha'. \tag{10}$$

Subtracting (10) from (9), we get

$$0 = 2\alpha\alpha'(1 - l_1) - 2\alpha + 2\alpha',$$

from which

$$0 = \alpha(1 - l_1) - \left(\frac{\alpha}{\alpha'} - 1\right)$$

or

$$\frac{\alpha}{\alpha'} - 1 = \alpha(1 - l_1), \tag{11}$$

from which

$$\frac{\lambda'}{\lambda} - 1 = \frac{h}{m_0 c\lambda}(1 - \cos\phi)$$

or

$$\lambda' - \lambda = \frac{h}{m_0 c}(1 - \cos\phi), \tag{12}$$

which is the same as equation (34) in the text. To get the expression for the kinetic energy of the recoil electron, solve equation (11) for α', obtaining

$$\alpha' = \frac{\alpha}{1 + \alpha(1 - l_1)}. \tag{13}$$

Substitute this value in equation (4) to obtain

$$\sqrt{1 + b^2} - 1 = \alpha - \frac{\alpha}{1 + \alpha(1 - l_1)}$$

$$= \frac{\alpha^2(1 - l_1)}{1 + \alpha(1 - l_1)}.$$

CONTINUED

Now the kinetic energy $\mathcal{E}$ is given by

$$\mathcal{E} = m_0c^2(K - 1) = m_0c^2(\sqrt{1 + b^2} - 1)$$

$$= m_0c^2 \frac{\alpha^2(1 - \cos\phi)}{1 + \alpha(1 - \cos\phi)} \cdot$$

But

$$m_0c^2 = \frac{h\nu}{\alpha};$$

therefore

$$\mathcal{E} = h\nu \frac{\alpha(1 - \cos\phi)}{1 + \alpha(1 - \cos\phi)} \cdot \tag{14}$$

The energy of the recoil electron can also be put in terms of the angle θ by noting that, from equations (5) and (6),

$$\frac{l_2}{n_2} = \frac{\alpha - \alpha' l_1}{\alpha' n_1} = \frac{1}{n_1}\left(\frac{\alpha}{\alpha'} - l_1\right), \tag{15}$$

and eliminating α' with the aid of equation (11), we get

$$\frac{l_2}{n_2} = \frac{1}{n_1}(1 + \alpha)(1 - l_1). \tag{16}$$

Substituting the values of l_1, l_2, n_1, and n_2, we get

$$\cot\theta = (1 + \alpha)\frac{1 - \cos\phi}{\sin\phi} \cdot \tag{17}$$

Now

$$\frac{1 - \cos\phi}{\sin\phi} = \tan\frac{\phi}{2};$$

therefore

$$\cot\theta = (1 + \alpha)\tan\frac{\phi}{2}, \tag{18}$$

also

$$\tan\theta = \frac{\cot\frac{\phi}{2}}{1 + \alpha}, \tag{19}$$

which is equation (35) in Chapter 5 of the text.

By dividing equation (18) by equation (19), we get

$$\frac{\cos^2\theta}{\sin^2\theta} = \frac{\cos^2\theta}{1 - \cos^2\theta} = (1 + \alpha)^2\tan^2\frac{\phi}{2} \cdot$$

Now $$\tan^2 \frac{\phi}{2} = \frac{1 - \cos \phi}{1 + \cos \phi};$$

hence $$\frac{\cos^2 \theta}{1 - \cos^2 \theta} = (1 + \alpha)^2 \frac{1 - \cos \phi}{1 + \cos \phi}. \quad \textbf{(20)}$$

Solving equation (20) for $\cos \phi$ and then for $(1 - \cos \phi)$, we get

$$1 - \cos \phi = \frac{2\cos^2 \theta}{(1 + \alpha)^2 - 2\alpha \cos^2 \theta - \alpha^2 \cos^2 \theta}. \quad \textbf{(21)}$$

Substituting this value in equation (14) yields

$$\mathcal{E} = h\nu \frac{2\alpha \cos^2 \theta}{(1 + \alpha)^2 - \alpha^2 \cos^2 \theta}, \quad \textbf{(22)}$$

which is equation (36) in Chapter 5 of the text

appendix VIII Evaluation of $\oint p_r dr = n_r h$.

Evaluation of $$\oint p_r dr_r = n_r h. \tag{1}$$

Now $$p_r = m \frac{dr}{dt} \tag{2}$$

is the momentum along the radius. Changing the independent variable from t to ϕ, by the relationship

$$\frac{dr}{dt} = \frac{dr}{d\phi} \frac{d\phi}{dt}, \tag{3}$$

we get $$p_r = m \frac{d\phi}{dt} \frac{dr}{d\phi}; \tag{4}$$

and noting that $$p_\phi = mr^2 \frac{d\phi}{dt} \tag{5}$$

and $$dr = \frac{dr}{d\phi} d\phi, \tag{6}$$

we may write the integral as

$$\oint \frac{p_\phi}{r^2} \frac{dr}{d\phi} \cdot \frac{dr}{d\phi} \cdot d\phi = n_r h \tag{7}$$

or $$p_\phi \oint \frac{1}{r^2} \left(\frac{dr}{d\phi} \right)^2 d\phi = n_r h. \tag{8}$$

The equation of the ellipse may be written as

$$\frac{1}{r} = \frac{1 + \epsilon \cos \phi}{a(1 - \epsilon^2)}, \tag{9}$$

where a is the semimajor axis and ϵ is the eccentricity.

Therefore $$\frac{dr}{d\phi} = \frac{a(1 - \epsilon^2)\epsilon \sin \phi}{(1 + \epsilon \cos \phi)^2} \tag{10}$$

and $$\frac{1}{r} \frac{dr}{d\phi} = \frac{\epsilon \sin \phi}{1 + \epsilon \cos \phi}. \tag{11}$$

The integral equation now becomes

$$p_\phi \int_0^{2\pi} \frac{\epsilon^2 \sin^2 \phi}{(1 + \epsilon \cos \phi)^2} d\phi = n_r h. \tag{12}$$

CONTINUED

The integral
$$I = \int_0^{2\pi} \frac{\epsilon^2 \sin^2 \phi}{(1 + \epsilon \cos \phi)^2} \, d\phi \tag{13}$$

can be integrated by parts. In the usual standard form

$$\int u dv = uv - \int v du; \tag{14}$$

let
$$u = \epsilon \sin \phi$$
$$du = \epsilon \cos \phi d\phi$$
$$dv = \frac{\epsilon \sin \phi}{(1 + \epsilon \cos \phi)^2} \, d\phi,$$

so that
$$v = \frac{1}{1 + \epsilon \cos \phi};$$

then
$$I = \left. \frac{\epsilon \sin \phi}{1 + \epsilon \cos \phi} \right]_0^{2\pi} - \int_0^{2\pi} \frac{\epsilon \cos \phi}{1 + \epsilon \cos \phi} \, d\phi. \tag{15}$$

Upon substitution of the limits of integration, the first term on the right-hand side becomes zero. The value of the integral is

$$I = -\int_0^{2\pi} \frac{\epsilon \cos \phi}{1 + \epsilon \cos \phi} \, d\phi, \tag{16}$$

which may be written in the form

$$I = \int_0^{2\pi} \left(\frac{1}{1 + \epsilon \cos \phi} - 1 \right) d\phi, \tag{17}$$

yielding
$$I = \frac{2\pi}{(1 - \epsilon^2)^{1/2}} - 2\pi. \tag{18}$$

(See Peirce's *Table of Integrals*, page 41.)
Putting this back in the integral equation, we get

$$\frac{2\pi p_\phi}{(1 - \epsilon^2)^{1/2}} - 2\pi p_\phi = n_r h, \tag{19}$$

or
$$\frac{kh}{(1 - \epsilon^2)^{1/2}} - kh = n_r h \tag{20}$$

since
$$p_\phi = \frac{kh}{2\pi};$$

CONTINUED

hence
$$(n_r + k) = \frac{k}{(1 - \epsilon^2)^{1/2}}; \tag{21}$$

so that
$$\epsilon = \sqrt{1 - \left(\frac{k}{k + n_r}\right)^2}, \tag{22}$$

which is the expression for the eccentricity of the ellipse in terms of the azimuthal and radial quantum numbers.

Of great interest is the expression for the total energy $\mathcal{E}$ of an elliptic orbit. The potential energy is $-Ze^2/r$. The kinetic energy can be written as

$$\tfrac{1}{2}m\left[\left(\frac{dr}{dt}\right)^2 + \left(r\frac{d\phi}{dt}\right)^2\right]$$

where $\dfrac{dr}{dt}$ is the radial component of the velocity and $r\dfrac{d\phi}{dt}$ is the transverse component of the velocity. Now using equation (3) and equation (5), we get

$$\frac{dr}{dt} = \frac{p_\phi}{mr^2}\frac{dr}{d\phi} \tag{23}$$

and
$$\left(r\frac{d\phi}{dt}\right)^2 = \frac{p_\phi^2}{m^2r^2}. \tag{24}$$

The expression for the total energy then becomes

$$\begin{aligned} \mathcal{E} &= \tfrac{1}{2}m\left[\frac{p_\phi^2}{m^2r^4}\left(\frac{dr}{d\phi}\right)^2 + \frac{p_\phi^2}{m^2r^2}\right] - \frac{Ze^2}{r} \\ &= \frac{p_\phi^2}{2mr^2}\left[\left(\frac{1}{r}\frac{dr}{d\phi}\right)^2 + 1\right] - \frac{Ze^2}{r}. \end{aligned} \tag{25}$$

Solving this for $\left(\dfrac{1}{r}\dfrac{dr}{d\phi}\right)^2$ yields

$$\left(\frac{1}{r}\frac{dr}{d\phi}\right)^2 = \frac{2m\mathcal{E}r^2}{p_\phi^2} + \frac{2mZe^2r}{p_\phi^2} - 1. \tag{26}$$

From equation (11) we get

$$\left(\frac{1}{r}\frac{dr}{d\phi}\right)^2 = \frac{\epsilon^2 \sin^2\phi}{(1 + \epsilon\cos\phi)^2}. \tag{27}$$

CONCLUDED

Eliminating the angle ϕ between this equation and the equation of the ellipse (9) yields

$$\left(\frac{1}{r}\frac{dr}{d\phi}\right)^2 = -\frac{r^2}{a^2(1-\epsilon^2)} + \frac{2r}{a(1-\epsilon^2)} - 1. \tag{28}$$

By equating coefficients of like powers of r in equations (26) and (28), we get

$$\frac{2m\mathcal{E}}{p_\phi^2} = -\frac{1}{a^2(1-\epsilon^2)} \tag{29}$$

and

$$\frac{mZe^2}{p_\phi^2} = \frac{1}{a(1-\epsilon^2)}, \tag{30}$$

from which

$$\mathcal{E} = -\frac{Ze^2}{2a}. \tag{31}$$

The total energy depends only upon the major axis of the ellipse and is the same as that for a circle of radius a. Eliminating a from equations (29) and (30) yields

$$\mathcal{E} = -\frac{mZ^2e^4(1-\epsilon^2)}{2p_\phi^2}. \tag{32}$$

INDEX

Index

A

Aamodt, R. L., 456
Abelson, P. H., 415
Absorption, coefficient, 148, 291
    atomic, 149
  cross section, 93
    for x-rays, 150
  of energy, 257
  limit, x-ray, 291
  of neutrons, 423
  spectra, x-ray, 290
  spectrum, 257
  of x-rays, 148, 291
Abundance of naturally occurring isotopes, 522
Actinide series, 480
Actinium series, 308
Allen, J. S., 385
Allen, K. W., 418, 419
α-γ reaction, 347
α-n reaction, 340, 344
α-p reaction, 335, 345
Alpha particle, capture, radiative, 346
    simple, 346
  decay, 379
  disintegration energy, 311
  model of nucleus, 374
  path of, in a Coulomb field, 528
Alpha particles, angle of scattering of, 532
  charge of, 81
  E/M of, 77
  long-range, 327
  mass of, 81
  nature of, 79
  range of, 312
  resonance capture of, 348
  single scattering of, 85, 92
  velocities of, 82
  velocity spectrum of, 314
Alpha rays, 76, 77
Alvarez, L. W., 279, 504
amu, 62
Anderson, C. D., 341, 343, 433, 441, 461, 463
Anderson, H. L., 403, 415
Andrade, E. N. da C., 137
Angle of scattering of alpha particle, 532
Angular momentum, of electron, 219, 236
  nuclear, 273
  orbital, 236, 252
  spin, 237
  total, 239, 253
  unit of, 237
Angular quantum number, 219
Annihilation, of charged particles, 436
  gamma-ray photons, 431
  radiation, wavelength of, 437
Anomalous Zeeman effect, 102, 237, 265, 272
Arago, F., 97
Artificial disintegration, discovery of, 331
Artificial radioactivity (*see* Radioactivity, induced)
Aston, F. W., 53, 55, 217
Aston's mass spectrograph, 53
Atom, 32

Atom (*continued*)
nuclear theory of the, 83
Rutherford's theory of the, 83
structure of, 32
Atomic absorption coefficient, 149
Atomic bomb, 422
Atomic mass unit, 62
Atomic masses, physical scale of, 62
Atomic number, 61
Atomic spectra, 233
Atomic weights, 30
chemical system of, 31
table of, 512
Auger, P., 297
Auger effect, 297, 298
Auger electron, 298, 385
Auger transition, 298
Average lifetime, 304
Avogadro, 30
Avogadro number, 31, 34, 35, 132, 147, 148
Azimuthal quantum number, 219, 229

B

Baldwin, G. C., 355, 417
Baker, W. B., 341
Bainbridge, K. T., 53, 58, 59, 60, 61
Bainbridge and Jordan's mass spectrograph, 59
Bainbridge's mass spectrograph, 58
Balfour, J. G., 324
Balmer, J. J., 205
Balmer's equation, 205, 206, 210
Balmer series, 206, 210, 217, 223, 273
Barkas, W. H., 453, 454
Barkla, C. G., 121, 140, 154, 155
Barn, 93
Barrier, height, 376
potential, 375
probability of penetration of, 377
transparency of, 377, 380
Batzel, R. E., 420
Bearden, J. A., 147
Becker, H., 337
Becquerel, H., 75, 76, 77
Bell, P. R., 116
Bell, R. E., 360
Bennett, W. E., 347
Bergmann series, 234
Bernert, T., 477
Beta decay, comparative half-lives for, 382
Fermi selection rules for, 383
Fermi theory of, 361, 381
Gamow-Teller selection rules for, 383
induced, 344
Beta disintegration (*see* Beta decay)
Beta particle, 46
decay, 380
disintegration, 319, 380
Beta particles, 77
Beta-ray spectra, 316
continuous, 317
end-point energies of, 318
sharp line, 317
Beta rays, 46, 76, 77
Betatron, 123, 485, 493
Betatron-synchrotron, 486, 497
Bethe, H. A., 443, 454, 481, 482
Bevatron, 501
Binding energy, 65
of neutron and proton, 360
of a nucleus, 65
Biot, J. B., 15
Birge, R. T., 35, 41, 148, 217
Bjorklund, R., 451
Blackett, P. M. S., 332
Blake, F. C., 299
Bloch, F., 279, 280, 328
Bøggild, J. K., 404
Bohr, N., 89, 190, 206, 287, 333, 375, 404, 413
Bohr magneton, 242, 269, 275
Bohr theory of hydrogen, 206
Bohr's frequency condition, 233, 253, 289
Bohr's nuclear theory, 404
Bohr's postulates, 208, 214, 218, 228
Boltzmann constant, 181, 511
Bondi, H., 482, 483
Bonner, T. W., 411, 413
Booth, E. T., 404, 413
Bothe, W., 160, 337
Brackett series of hydrogen, 212

Bradt, H. L., 468
Bragg, W. L., 126, 130
Bragg equation, 128, 130, 139, 173
Bragg spectrometer, 130, 137, 139
Bragg's law, 140, 173, 175
modified form of, 142, 176
Branching, 307
in ThC, 326
Breeder reactor, 426
Bremsstrahlung, 134
from beta emitters, 327
external (outer), 327
inner, 328
Bretscher, E., 308
Brickwedde, F. G., 217
Brøstrom, K. J., 404
Brown, R., 34
Brown, R. H., 459
Brownian motion, 31, 34
Bucherer, A. H., 46
Burcham, W. E., 350
Butler, C. C., 461

C

Cahn, A., 413
Camac, M., 457
Camerini, V., 459
Capture cross section, for neutrons, 375
Capture gamma rays, 348
Carbon 14, 476
Carbon-nitrogen cycle, 481
Carlson, A. G., 456
Cathode rays, 43
Cauchois, Y., 138
Ceccarelli, M., 460
Cerenkov, P. A., 117
Cerenkov radiation, 117
Chadwick, J., 62, 84, 90, 331, 338, 355, 361
Chain reaction, 402
critical, 423
Chang, W. Y., 82
Characteristic x-ray spectra (*see* X-ray, spectra), 296
Charge, of beta particles, 77
of an electron, 35, 38, 41, 136, 147
nuclear, determination of, 90
quantization of, 432
Charged particles, annihilation of, 436
pair production of, 434
Chemical equivalent, 33
Chi meson, 466
Chou, C. N., 493
Christophilos, N., 502
Clay, J., 433
Cleavage planes, 125
Cloud chamber, 312
Collins, G. B., 117
Comparative half-life, 382
Compound nucleus, 333, 335, 348, 375
Compton, A. H., 155, 157, 160, 433
Compton effect, 157, 166
equations for the, 534
modified line of, 159
Compton recoil electrons, 160
Compton wavelength, 438
Condon, E. U., 379
Conduction electrons, 111
energy distribution of, 111
Constants, table of values of, 511
Contact potential difference, 108
Continuous bremsstrahlung from beta emitters, 327
Continuous spectra of beta rays, 317
Continuous spectrum, of hydrogen, 227
x-ray, 132, 134
short wavelength limit of, 134
Conversi, M., 442
Conversion factors, 64
table of, 26
Cook, C. F., 351
Cook, C. S., 382, 383
Coolidge type of x-ray tube, 122
Coplanarity of tracks, 464
Cork, J. M., 147, 370
Corson, D. R., 476
Cosmic rays, 432
energies of, 433
latitude effect of, 433
primary particles, 468
Cosmotron, 486, 501
Coulomb, the, 4
Coulomb, C. A., 4
Coulomb barrier, 376

Coulomb field, 376
Coulomb force, 376
Coulomb scattering, 92
Coulomb's law of force between electric charges, 3, 84, 207
Coulomb's law of force between magnetic poles, 10
Courant, E. D., 502
Cowan, C. L., Jr., 386
Cowan, E. W., 461
Crandall, W. E., 451
Crane, H. R., 318, 385, 434, 435, 436
Critical chain reaction, 423
Critical mass, 424
Critical size, 424
Critical voltage, x-ray, 293
Crookes dark space, 42
Cross, W. G., 161
Cross section, for absorption, 93
  differential, 93
  geometrical, 92
  nuclear, 92
  of a process, 92
  for scattering, 92
Crystals, 125
Curie, I., 401
Curie, M., 76
Curie, P., 76
Curie-Joliots, the, 337, 343, 344
Curran, S. C., 324
Curved crystal spectrometer, 138
Cyclotron, 485, 487

D

d-α reactions, 352
d-*n* reactions, 352, 396
d-*p* reaction, 351, 397
d-*t* reactions, 397
Dabbs, J., 413
Dallaporta, N., 460
Dalton, J., 30, 50
Dash, J. G., 126
Davisson, C., 170, 175
Dawson, J. K., 480
De Benedetti, S., 439
Debierne, A., 76
De Broglie, L., 169
De Broglie waves, 170, 173, 194
  velocity of, 185, 187
    group, 189
De Broglie's hypothesis, 169, 171, 180
  and quantization of orbits, 228
Debye, P., 140, 157
Dee, P. I., 348
Delayed neutrons, 404, 413
  emission, 413
  emitters, 393
Delta rays, 470
Dempster, A. J., 53, 55, 56, 58
Dempster's mass spectrometer, 56
Deuterium, discovery of, 217
Deuteron, 218
  disintegration of the, 354
  magnetic moment of, 279, 282
Deutsch, M., 439
Dewan, J. T., 418, 419
Diamagnetism, 269
Dielectric constant, 4
Diffraction, of electrons, 171, 177, 190, 194
  of neutrons, 181
  gratings, reflection of x-rays from, 146
  of x-rays, by powder crystals, 139
Diffuse series, 234, 256
Dirac, P. A. M., 111
Discovery, of the neutron, 337
  of nuclear fission, 401
  of the positron, 341
Disintegration, artificial, 331
  constant, 305
  by deuterons, 350
  energy, 311, 333, 345
    alpha particle, 311
    for β^- emission, 319
    for β^+ emission, 345
  by neutrons, 357
  by photons, 354
  by protons, 348
Dispersion of x-rays, 143
Distribution of electrons, in atom, 246
  in atoms, table of, 248
Distribution-in-range curve, 336
Drift tubes, 504

Duane, W., 134
Du Mond, J. W. M., 138, 139, 438
Dunning, J. R., 404, 413
Durbin, R. P., 454, 455
Dynode, 113

E

Edwards, J. E., 299
Effective multiplication factor, 423
Eigen functions, 230
Einstein, A., 34, 63, 98, 110
Einstein's photoelectric equation, 110, 227
Einstein's special theory of relativity, 46, 63, 98
Electric current, 14
  electromagnetic unit of, 17
  magnetic effect of an, 14
Electric discharge through gases, 41
Electric field, 5, 23
  intensity of, 5, 98
Electrochemical equivalent, 33
Electrolysis, 31
Electromagnetic induction, 21
  Faraday's law of, 22
Electromagnetic radiation, 98
Electromagnetic system of units, 10
Electromagnetic theory of light, 97
Electromagnetic wave, 97
  intensity of, 99
  linearly polarized, 100
Electromotive force, induced, 21
Electron, 32, 38, 43
  capture, 299
    by nuclei, 364
  charge of an, 35, 38, 41, 136
  e/m of an, 45, 49
  magnetic moment of, in orbit, 241
  mass of an, 45
    reduced, 213
  radius of, 69
  ratio of mass of, to mass of proton, 45, 217
  recoil, 157, 160
  spin, 220, 224, 237, 267
  state of, 246
  waves, refraction, 174
Electron microscope, 196
Electron optics, 196
Electron-positron pair, 352, 434
Electron volt, 63
Electronic charge, 35
Electronic cloud, 231
Electronic structure, of the heavy elements, 480
Electrons, conduction, 111
  diffraction of, 171, 177
  distribution of, in atom, 246
  number of, per atom, 153
Electrostatic system of units, 4, 17
Elements, naturally occurring, 475
  periodic table of the, 513
  table of, 512
Elliott, L. G., 360
Elliptic orbit, precession of, 222
Elliptic orbits for hydrogen, 218
Elsasser, W., 392
e/m, of cathode rays, 43, 45
  determination of, from Zeeman effect, 105
End-point energy, 319
Energy, in electric field, 13
  in electromagnetic wave, 99
  end-point, 319
  in magnetic field, 14
  of a relativistic particle, 68
Energy level, 246
  diagram, of calcium, 271
    for hydrogen, 224
    nuclear, 324, 325
    of sodium, 255
  x-ray, 287, 296
Ether, luminiferous, 97
ev, 63
Evans, G. R., 364
Evolution of the stars, 482
Excitation energy, 373
Excited state, 253, 373
  of hydrogen atom, 212

F

Faraday, the, 35
Faraday, M., 21, 32, 102
Faraday constant, 33, 147

Faraday dark space, 42
Faraday's law of electromagnetic induction, 22
Faraday's laws of electrolysis, 33
Feather, N., 308
Feder, H., 135
Fermi, E., 111, 361, 381, 401, 402, 442
Fermi selection rules for beta decay, 383
Fermi theory of beta decay, 381
Ferrell, R. A., 411, 413
Ferromagnetism, 270
Fine structure, constant, 223
  of spectral lines, 253
    of hydrogen, 220
Fission, chain-reaction, 422
  fragments, energies of, 405
    velocities of, 406
  of heavy nuclei, 419
  of lighter nuclei, 420
  nuclear, 401
  spontaneous, 419
  ternary, 418
  of uranium, 402
    neutrons released in, 409
Fitch, V. L., 458
Fizeau, A. H. L., 97, 169
Flerov, G. N., 419
Fletcher, H., 34
Fluorescent radiation, 149, 227, 258, 298
Fluorescent transformation coefficient, 149
Fluorescent x-ray spectra, 298
Flux density, magnetic, 19, 22
Force, on a moving charge in a magnetic field, 20
  on a wire carrying current in a magnetic field, 18
Forces, short range, 166
Foucault, J. B. L., 97, 169
Fowler, J. L., 405
Fowler, W. A., 349
Fowler, W. B., 467
Frank, I. M., 117
Freeman, J. M., 350
Freier, P., 468
Frequency-modulated cyclotron, 490
Fresnel, A., 97
Fretter, W. B., 440
Friedrich, W., 125
Fry, W. F., 493
Fundamental particles, mass spectrum of, 465
Fundamental series, 234, 256

G

g factor, 262, 265
  nuclear, 276
γ-α reactions, 356
γ-d reactions, 356
γ-n reactions, 354
γ-p reactions, 356
Gamma-ray counter, 451
Gamma rays, 76, 77
  from alpha-particle emitters, 324
  from beta-particle emitters, 322
  nature of, 137
  spectra, 321
  wavelengths of, 137
γ-t reactions, 356
Gamow, G., 379
Gamow-Teller selection rules for beta decay, 383
Gardner, E., 446, 454
Gasteiger, E. L., 417
Gauss, the, 19, 22
Geiger, H., 81, 83, 87, 160
Geiger counter, 79, 124, 433
Geiger-Nuttal law, 315, 380
Geiger's rule, 89, 315
Gerlach, W., 267
Germer, L. H., 170, 175
Ghiorso, A., 479
Goeckermann, R. H., 420
Goldhaber, M., 351, 355, 361, 391
Goudsmit, A., 237
Gram molecular volume, 31
Grating space, 131, 147
  of calcite, 132, 147
  of rocksalt, 131, 147
Gray, J. A., 327
Grosse, A. V., 404, 475
Ground state, 321, 378

Group velocity, 187
  and particle velocity, 189
  and wave velocity, 187
Gurney, R. W., 379

H

Hadley, J., 456
Haga, H., 121
Hagenow, C. F., 155
Hahn, O., 308, 401, 402
Halban, H. von, 411
Half-life, 304
  comparative, 382
Hall, D., 413
Halloway, M. G., 314
Hallwachs, W., 107
Halpern, J., 355, 385
Hamilton, J. G., 477, 479
Hammer track, 448
Hanna, G. C., 419
Hansen, W. W., 280, 281
Harvey, B. G., 419
Havens, W. W., Jr., 454, 455
Haxby, R. O., 417
Haxel, O., 393
Heisenberg, W., 189, 275
Heisenberg's "uncertainty principle," 189
Helmholtz, A. C., 396
Henderson, J. E., 117
Henry, Joseph, 21
Hertz, H. R., 97, 107
Herzberg, G., 206, 254, 257
Hess, V. F., 432
Heterogeneous reactor, 426
Hewlett, C. W., 154
High energy nuclear reactions, 396
Hill, D. L., 412, 413
Hill, R. D., 391
Hillier, J., 198, 199
Hoenigschmidt, O., 76
Hofstadter, R., 162, 353
Homogeneous reactor, 426
Hooper, J. E., 456
Hopper, V. D., 38, 39, 40
Hornyak, W. F., 349
Howland, J. J., 420
Hoyle, F., 483
Hsiao, C., 461
Hudson, A. M., 418
Hughes, D. J., 413
Hull, A. W., 140
Hunt, F. L., 134
Hunt, S. E., 378
Huygens, C., 97
Huygens construction, 126
Hydrogen, application of wave mechanics to, 228
  atom, mass of a, 45
    motion of nucleus, 212
    normal state of, 211
    permissible orbits of, 208
  Bohr theory of, 206
  Brackett series of, 212
  continuous spectrum of, 227
  elliptic orbits for, 218
  energy level diagram for, 225
  ionization potential of, 226
  Lyman series of, 211, 224
  multiplicity of orbits of, 220
  Paschen series of, 212, 224
  Pfund series of, 212
  relativistic change of mass in, 222
  spectrum of, 205
Hydrogenlike spectra, 215
Hyperfine quantum number, 274
Hyperfine structure, 273
Hyperons, 465

I

Impact parameter, 530
Independent particle model of nucleus, 374
Index of refraction (*see* Refraction, index of)
Induced beta decay, 344
Induced electromotive force, 21
Induced radioactivity, 343
Insch, G. M., 324
Intensity, of an electric field, 5
  of electromagnetic wave, 99
  of a magnetic field, 10
  of a spectral line, 231
  of x-rays, 123, 291

Intensity, of x-rays (*continued*)
scattered, 151, 156
Intercombination lines, 272
Internal conversion, 298, 323
Ionization, chamber, 123
potential, 226, 256
Ions, 31
Isobars, 304, 320, 372
Isomeric state, 367, 388
Isomers, nuclear, 308, 367, 388
Isotones, 392
Isotopes, 50
per cent abundance, 522
radioactive, of lighter elements, 309
table of naturally occurring, 522
Isotopic abundance, 392
Isotopic masses, 60
table of, 514

J

j-j coupling, 394
James, R. A., 420
Jensen, J. H. D., 393
Johnson, T. H., 181
Johnston, W. M., 475
Joliot, F., 411
Jones, W. M., 378
Jordan, E. B., 59, 60, 61
Jordan, W. H., 116

K

K absorption limit, 291
K capture, 364
K-mesons, 465
K-series lines, 285, 296
Kappa meson, 466
Karlik, B., 477
Kaufmann, W., 46
Kennedy, J. W., 416
Kepler's law, 219, 530
Kerst, D. W., 123, 493
King, D. T., 456
Klinkenberg, P. F. A., 395
Knipp, 328
Knipping, P., 125
Koch, H. W., 355, 417
Kolhorster, W., 432
Kowarski, L., 411
Kruger, P. G., 435, 436
Kurbatov, J. D., 478
Kurie, N., 382
Kurie plot, 382, 388
Kusch, P., 279

L

L absorption limit, 291
L-mesons, 465
L-S coupling, 240, 394
L-series lines, 285, 296
Laby, T. H., 38, 39, 40
Λ^+ particle, 466
Λ^0 particle, 466
Landé *g* factor, 262
Langer, L. M., 384, 388
Lanthanide series, 480
Larmor, J., 104, 260
Larmor precession, 260, 277
Larmor theorem, 260, 277
Latitude effect of cosmic rays, 433
Lattes, C. M. G., 444, 446
Laue, M. von, 121, 125
Laue diffraction pattern, 129, 130, 183
Lauritsen, C. C., 436
Lauritsen, T., 349, 404
Law, H. B., 478
Lawrence, E. O., 487
Leachman, R., 406, 407
Lederman, L., 447, 448
Leighton, R. B., 441, 461, 462, 463, 464
Levinger, J. S., 414
Libby, W. F., 475
Lifetime, average, 304
Light, electromagnetic theory of, 97
nature of, 97, 166
polarized, circularly, 102
linearly, 100
velocity of, 17, 511
Lillie, A. B., 357, 358
Lindner, M., 397
Linear accelerator, 486, 499, 503
Liquid drop model of nucleus, 374, 404, 419
Livingston, M. S., 314, 487, 502
Loar, H. H., 454, 455

Lofgren, E. J., 468
Long-range alpha particles, 327
Lord, J. J., 493
Lorentz, H. A., 103
Lorentz unit, 265
Lyman series, 211, 224

M

McDaniel, B. D., 350
McElhinney, J., 417
McGuire, A. D., 457
McIntyre, J. A., 162, 353
MacKenzie, K. R., 476
McKeown, M., 390
McMillan, E. M., 396, 415, 416, 490, 491
McReynolds, A. W., 48
Magnetic domains, 270
Magnetic field, force, on a moving charge in, 20
 on wire in, 18
 intensity, 10, 98
Magnetic flux, 22
 density, 19, 22
Magnetic induction, 19, 22
Magnetic moment, of Bohr magneton, 242
 due to spin, 242
 of a magnet, 12
 nuclear, 275
 of orbital electron, 241
 of a plane circuit, 21
Magnetic properties of atoms, 269
Magnetic quantum number, 243
Magnetic resonance absorption method, 281
Magnetic resonance method, 275
Magnetic spectrograph, 294, 317
Magnetic spectrum analysis, 294, 316
Magneton, nuclear, 276
Mann, A. K., 355
Marney, M. C., 183
Marquez, L., 398
Marsden, E., 83, 87
Marshak, R. E., 443, 454
Martinelli, E. A., 454
Mason, F. D., 136
Mass, absorption coefficient, 149, 291
 of charged pi meson, 452
 defect, 67
 and energy, 63
 number, 62
 scattering coefficient, 149
 spectrum of fundamental particles, 465
 transformation coefficient, 149
 variation of, with velocity, 45
Mass spectrograph, 53
Masses of isotopes, 514
Materialization of energy, 436
Mattauch, J., 53
Maxwell, the, 22
Maxwell, J. C., 17, 97
Mayer, Maria G., 392, 393
Meiners, E. P., Jr., 414
Meitner, L., 401
Menon, M. G. K., 456
Menzel, D. H., 217
Merlin, M., 460
Mesic atoms, 457
Meson field, 440
Mesons, 432, 440
 classification of, 465
Mesotron, 440
Metastable state, 272, 388
Meyer, N. C., 413
Microscope, resolving power of, 190, 196, 198
Millikan, R. A., 34, 36, 38, 109, 110, 147
Millman, S., 279
Minimum ionization, 452
Mirror nuclei, 394
mks system of units, 23, 26
Moderator, 425
Modified line of Compton effect, 159
Moffat, R. D., 384, 388
Mole, the, 31
Molecular beam method, 275
Momentum of a relativistic particle, 68
Morgan, L. O., 479
Morrison, P., 349
Moseley, H. G. J., 89, 285
Moseley diagram, 286
Moss, N., 419

Motion of the hydrogen nucleus, 212
Moyer, B. J., 451
Mu-mesic atoms, x-rays from, 458
Mu meson, 432
  Bohr orbit of a, 443
  capture of, 443
  decay of the, 441
  discovery of, 440
  lifetime of the, 441
  mass of the, 441
  properties of the, 441
  spin of the, 442
Muirhead, H., 444, 456, 459
Mukherjee, N. R., 178, 179
Multiplication factor, effective, 423
Multiplicity of orbits of hydrogen, 220
Muon, 441
Murphy, G. M., 217

N

n-α reaction, 357
n-d reactions, 397
n-γ reaction, 360
n-p reactions, 359
n-$2n$ reactions, 361
Natural radioactive transformations, 303
Naturally occurring elements, 475
Naturally occurring isotopes, table of, 522
Neddermeyer, S. H., 441
Neptunium, 415
  series, 309
Neutral pi meson, 450
Neutrino, 320, 431
  evidence for, 383
  rest mass of the, 388
Neutron, 62, 338, 431
  capture cross section, 375
  discovery of the, 337
  half-life of the, 362
  magnetic moment of, 279, 282
  number, 63, 372
  radioactive decay of, 361
  slow, 357, 359
Neutron-proton diagram, 373
Neutrons, absorption of, 423
  cross sections for, 425
  De Broglie wavelength of, 182
  delayed emission of, 413
  diffraction of, 181
  energy of, from fission of uranium, 411
  released in fission of uranium, 409
  source of, 422
  temperature equilibrium of, 181
Newton, the, 23
Newton, A. S., 420
Newton, I., 97, 166
Ney, E. P., 468
Nier, A. O., 53, 73, 404
Noddack, I., 401
Nondegenerate system, 222
Normal state of hydrogen atom, 211
Normal Zeeman effect, 102, 259, 272
  and the vector model, 259
Notation for nuclear reactions, 335
Nuclear angular momentum, 273, 394
Nuclear atom, 83
Nuclear charge, determination of, 90
Nuclear constitution, 60
Nuclear cross section, 92
Nuclear energy level diagram, 324, 325
Nuclear fission, discovery of, 401
  energy released in, 403
  products of, 407
  spontaneous, 419
Nuclear g factor, 276
Nuclear induction, 280
Nuclear isomers, 308, 367, 388
Nuclear magnetic moment, 275
Nuclear magneton, 276
Nuclear models, 374
Nuclear particles and nuclear spin, 273
Nuclear photographic emulsions, 434
  tracks in, 452
Nuclear processes, 397
  spallation, 397, 421
  star production, 397, 444, 470, 471
  stripping, 396, 397
Nuclear radius, 91, 376, 459
Nuclear reaction energy, 333
Nuclear reaction equation, 311, 333

Nuclear reactions, α-γ, 347
  α-n, 340, 344
  α-p, 335, 345
  d-α, 352
  d-n, 352, 396
  d-p, 351, 397
  d-t, 397
  γ-α, 356
  γ-d, 356
  γ-n, 354
  γ-p, 356
  γ-t, 356
  high energy, 396
  n-α, 359
  n-d, 397
  n-γ, 360
  n-p, 359
  n-$2n$, 361
  notation for, 335
  p-α, 348
  p-d, 349, 397
  p-γ, 350
Nuclear reactor, 402, 422
  breeder type, 426
  critical, 423
  heterogeneous type, 426
  homogeneous type, 426
  subcritical, 423
  supercritical, 423
Nuclear reactors, 426
Nuclear shell structure, 392
Nuclear spin, 273
  quantum numbers, table of, 274
Nuclei, stability of, 372
Nucleon, 62, 303
Nucleus, 32
  charge of, 84
  compound, 333, 348
  ground state of a, 321
  photofission of, 416
Nuclide, 388

O

Occhialini, G. P. S., 444
O'Ceallaigh, C., 466
O'Connor, P. R., 420
Oersted, the, 11, 22
Ogle, W. E., 435, 436
O'Neal, R. D., 351
Oppenheimer, F., 468
Oppenheimer-Phillips process, 397
Optical series, diffuse, 234, 256
  fundamental, 234, 256
  principal, 234, 253
  sharp, 234, 256
Optical spectra, 233
Optical spectral series, 234
Orbital angular momentum, 236, 252
Ore, A., 439
Orthohelium, 273
Owen, G. E., 382, 383

P

p-α reaction, 348
p-d reaction, 349, 397
p-γ reaction, 350
Packard, M., 280, 281
Packing fraction, 67
Pair production, 352, 434
Pancini, E., 442
Panofsky, W. K. H., 450, 454, 456
Paramagnetism, 269
Parhelium, 273
Parity, 382
Particle accelerator, 485
Paschen series of hydrogen, 212, 224
Pauli, W., 246, 273, 296, 320, 432
Pauli's exclusion principle, 246
  applied to nucleus, 393
Perey, M., 478
Periodic table, 513
  filling gaps in the, 476
Perkins, D. H., 444
Perlman, I., 397, 416, 420
Permeability, 10, 19, 22
Permissible orbits, 208
  radii of, of hydrogen, 209
Perrier, C., 476
Perrin, J., 34
Peters, B., 468
Petrzhak, K. A., 419
Pfund series of hydrogen, 212
Phase stability, 486, 490
Phosphors, 115

Photodisintegration, 354
Photoelectric effect, 107, 290, 294
  inverse of, 134
Photoelectric equation, Einstein's 110, 227, 298
Photoelectrons, velocity of, 108, 295
Photofission of nuclei, 416
Photographic emulsions for nuclear research, 434
Photomultiplier tube, 113
Photon, 111, 157, 169
Phototubes, 113
Physical constants, table of values of, 511
Physical scale of atomic masses, 62, 514
Pi meson, 443
  capture of a, 444
  decay of a, 444
    in a cloud chamber, 447
  discovery of the, 443
  mass of the charged, 452
  neutral, 450
    decay of, 451
    production of, 450
Pi mesons, lifetime of, 454
  origins of, 448
π^--mesons, nuclear interactions of, 455
Piccioni, O., 442
Pick-up, 397
Pions, 446
Pirenne, J., 439
Planck, M., 110
Planck constant, 110, 134, 136, 190
Platt, J. B., 457
Plutonium, 415
Polarization of x-rays, 155
Polarized wave, 100
Polonium, 76
Pool, M. L., 299, 478
Positive-ray analysis, 51
Positron, 341, 343
  discovery of the, 341
Positronium, 438
Potential, 6
Potential barrier, 375
Potential energy, electrostatic, 8
Pound, R. V., 281
Powell, C. F., 442, 444, 459
Powell, J. L., 439
Present, R., 418
Primary cosmic-ray particles, 468
Principal quantum number, 220, 236
Principal series, 234, 253
Principle of equivalence of mass and energy, 63
Probability concept, 192
Probability of penetration of barrier, 377
Probability of scattering, 85, 92
Prompt neutrons, 404
Proton, 431
  magnetic moment of, 279, 282
  number, 372
Proton-proton chain, 481
Proton synchrotron, 486, 501
Prout, W., 50
Purcell, E. M., 281

Q

Quantized charges, 432
Quantum of energy, 110, 157
Quantum number, 209, 229
  angular, 219
  angular momentum, orbital, 236, 252
    spin, 239
    total, 239
  azimuthal, 219, 229
  hyperfine, 274
  magnetic orbital, 243
  principal, 220, 236
  radial, 219
  spin, magnetic, 244
    nuclear, 273
Quantum state, nuclear, 393
Quill, L. L., 478

R

Rabi, I. I., 275, 277
Radial quantum number, 219
Radiation, from an accelerated charge, 98, 499
  electromagnetic, 97
  from radioactive substances, 76
Radiationless transitions, 297

Radiative capture of alpha particles, 346
Radioactive decay of the neutron, 361
Radioactive isotopes of lighter elements, 309
Radioactive series, 306
Radioactive transformations, 303
Radioactivity, discovery of, 75
  induced, 343
Radium, 76
Radius, of electron, 69
  of nucleus, 91, 380, 459
  parameter, nuclear, 91, 459
Rainwater, J., 458
Ramsey, N. F., 161, 279
Range of alpha particles, 312
  table of, 315
Reactions (*see* Nuclear reactions)
Reactor, core, 424
  nuclear, 422
  processes within a, 424
Recoil atoms, 339
Recoil electron, 157, 160
Recoil nucleus, velocity of, 339
Reduced electronic mass, 213
Reines, F., 386
Reflection of x-rays, 127
  from a mirror, 143
  from ruled gratings, 146
  total, 143, 146
Refraction, of electron waves, 174, 176
  index of, 166, 168, 169
    of electromagnetic waves, 145
    of x-rays, 140
  of particles, 166
  Snell's law of, 141, 166
  of waves, 166
  of x-rays, 140
Regener, E., 81
Reiling, V. G., 117
Relativistic motion of electron in hydrogen, 222
Relativistic particle, 68
Relativity, special theory of, 46, 63, 98
Relaxation time, 281
Resolving power of a microscope, 190, 196, 198
Resonance, 378
  capture, 348, 415
    of alpha particles, 348
  energy, 415
  potential, 259
  radiation, 258
Richardson, J. R., 454
Rinehart, M. C., 411, 413
Ritson, D. M., 459
Roberts, R. B., 413
Robinson, H. R., 77, 294, 316
Robson, J. M., 362
Rochat, O., 456
Rochester, G. D., 461
Rodeback, G. W., 385
Roentgen, W. C., 75, 121, 140
Roentgen rays, 121
Rogers, E. H., 281
Rogers, F. T., Jr., 48
Rogers, M. M., 48
Rosen, L., 405, 418
Rosenblum, S., 82
Rostagni, A., 460
Row, O., 178, 179
Rowland, H. A., 15
Royds, T., 81
Roys, P. A., 347
Russell-Saunders coupling, 240, 394
Rutherford, E., 76, 77, 81, 83, 137, 331
  theory of the atom, 83, 207
Rutherford scattering, 94
Rydberg, J. R., 205, 234
Rydberg constant, 205, 234
  for hydrogen, 205, 215
  for infinite mass, 215
  and mass of nucleus, 16
  table of values of, 216

S

Salpeter, E. E., 482, 483
Sampson, M. B., 414
Sard, R. D., 443
Savart, F., 15
Scattering, of alpha particles, 85, 92
  coefficient, 149
    for x-rays, 154
  cross section, 92

Scattering, cross section (*continued*)
differential, 93
of x-rays, 150
Scharff-Goldhaber, G., 390
Scherrer, P., 140
Schroedinger, E., 194
Schroedinger's equation, 194, 228, 377
for a single particle, 195
Schulte, H. J., 457
Schwinger, J., 499
Scintillation, method of counting, 79
Scintillation counter, 115, 124
Scintillation spectrometer, 116
Seaborg, G. T., 416, 420, 429, 476, 479, 480, 481
Secondary emission, 113
Seeman, N., 445, 469, 470
Segrè, E., 419, 476
Selection principle, rule, 224, 231, 256
Selection rule for x-ray lines, 296
Serber, R., 396, 493
Series, optical, 234
x-ray, 285, 296
Series limit, 206, 234
Seriff, A. J., 441, 461
Sewell, D., 396
Shapiro, M. M., 445, 469, 470
Sharp line beta-ray spectra, 317, 322
Sharp series, 234, 256
Shell, 246, 288, 392
model of nucleus, 374, 392
Sher, R., 355
Shiba, K., 38
Short wavelength limit of x-ray spectrum, 134
Shoup, W. E., 417
Shull, C. G., 182, 183, 184
Shutt, R. P., 467
Siegbahn, M., 132
Siegel, R., 439
Silverman, A., 451, 452
Simon, A. W., 160
Single crystal x-ray spectrometer, 130
Singlet states, 270
Slack, F. G., 413
Slow neutron, 357, 359
Smith, F. M., 454
Smith, J. R., 351
Smoluchowski, M., 34
Snell, A. H., 361, 413, 414, 415
Snell's law, 141, 166
Snyder, H. S., 502
Soddy, F., 51
Soley, 477
Sommerfeld, A., 111, 218, 222
Sommerfeld fine structure constant, 223
Space quantization, 246
Spallation, 397, 421
Specific inductive capacity, 4
Specifically nuclear forces, 374, 376
Spectra, of alpha particles, 314
atomic, 233
of beta rays, 316
of gamma rays, 321
optical, 233
of two-electron atoms, 270
x-ray, 233, 285
Spectral line, intensity of, 231
Spectral lines, hyperfine structure of, 273
Spectral notation, 252
Spectral series, optical, 234
Spectrometer, curved crystal, 138
Spectrum, of hydrogen, 205
of sodium, 253
Spin, angular momentum, 237, 273, 394
of electron, 220, 237, 267
of the mu meson, 442
nuclear, 273, 394
quantum number, 239
magnetic, 244
Spontaneous fission, 419, 479, 480
Stability of nuclei, 372
Stable isotopes, 372
Star production, 397, 444, 470, 471
Stars, 444, 470, 471
Statcoulomb, the, 4
Stationary orbits, 208
Staub, H. H., 281
Stearns, M., 451, 452
Steinberger, J., 450
Stellar energy of nuclear origin, 481
Stellar evolution, 482
Steller, J., 450

Stenström, W., 140
Stephens, W. E., 417
Stephenson, S. T., 136
Stern, O., 179, 267
Stern-Gerlach experiment, 267, 275
Stevenson, E. C., 441
Stokes's law, 38
Stopping potential, 109
Strassmann, F., 401, 402
Street, J. C., 441
Street, K., Jr., 479
Stripping, 396
Subatomic particles, 431
Suess, H. E., 393
Synchro-cyclotron, 486, 490
Szilard, L., 409, 410

T

Tamm, I. E., 117
Tau meson, 459
Teller, E., 442
Templeton, D. H., 420
Ternary fission, 418
Tewes, H. A., 420
Thermal neutrons, 182
Thermonuclear reactions, 483
Θ^0 particle, 466
Thibaud, J., 436
Thompson, S. G., 479
Thomson, G. P., 170, 177
Thomson, J. J., 3, 35, 43, 51, 154
Thorium series, 307
Thorndike, A. M., 467
Threshold frequency, 109
Titterton, E. W., 417, 418
Tolman, R. C., 15
Toppel, B. J., 347
Torrey, H. C., 281
Total angular momentum, of nucleus, 394
  quantum number, 239, 253, 273
Townsend, J. S., 35
Tracers, 361
Transparency of barrier, 377, 380
Transuranic elements, 309, 401, 415
  production of, 478
Transuranide series, 480
Triplet states, 270
Tritium, 351
  formation of, 475
  relative abundance of, 475
Tunnicliffe, P. R., 419

U

Uhlenbeck, G. E., 237, 328
Ulrey, C. T., 132
Uncertainty principle, 189
Uniform particle model of nucleus, 374
Unit of angular momentum, 237
Units, electromagnetic system of, 10
  electrostatic system of, 4, 17, 26
  mks system of, 23, 26
Uranium, 75, 76
  fission (*see* Fission of uranium)
  graphite pile, 402, 425
    processes within a, 425
  series, 306
Uranium-radium series, 306
Urey, H. C., 217

V

V-particles, 460
V^0-particle, 461
Vallarta, M. S., 468
Van de Graaff, R. J., 486
Van de Graaff generator, 485, 486, 503
Variation of mass with velocity, 46
Vector model of the atom, 236
Veksler, V., 490, 491
Velocity, of De Broglie waves, 185, 187
  of light, 17, 511
  of photoelectrons, 108, 295
  of recoil nucleus, 339

W

Wahl, A. C., 416
Walke, H., 364
Walker, R. L., 350
Walton, E. T. S., 348
Wang, P., 413
Wanlass, S. D., 461, 463
Watt, B. E., 412, 413

Wave, equation of Schroedinger, 194
  function, 195, 230
  mechanics, 194, 228, 236
    application of, to hydrogen, 228
  number, 170, 205, 210
  packet, 186, 190
  velocity, 145, 186
    and group velocity, 187
Wavelength, associated with a particle, 171
  of gamma rays, 137
  of x-rays, 128, 293
Waves associated with atoms and molecules, 179
Weisskopf, V. F., 442
Wells, W. H., 417
Westgren, 34
Wheeler, J. A., 404, 413, 439
Whitmore, B. G., 341
Whittemore, W. L., 467
Wigner, E., 374
Wilkinson, R. G., 414
Williams, E. J., 364
Wilson, C. T. R., 35
Wilson, H. A., 35, 36
Wilson cloud chamber, 312
Wind, C. H., 121
Wolfgang, R. L., 475, 476
Wollan, E. O., 182, 183, 184
Wood, R. W., 257
Work function, 113
Wu, C. S., 328
Wyckoff, H. O., 117
Wyman, L. L., 140

X

X-ray, absorption, edge, 291
    limit, 291
    spectra, 290
  critical voltage, 293
  energy level diagram, 287, 296
  powder crystal diffraction, 139
  spectra, 132, 233, 285
    characteristic, 285, 296
      production of, 298
    continuous, 132, 134
    fluorescent, 298
    selection rule for, 296
    sharp line, 132, 285
  spectrometer, curved crystal, 138
    single crystal, 130, 290
  terms, 296
  tube, 121
    betatron as an, 493
    Coolidge type, 122
X-rays, 121
  absorption of, 148, 291
  absorption coefficient of, 148, 291
    atomic, 149
    mass, 149
  absorption cross section for, 150
  from a betatron, 493
  critical angle for, 143
  diffraction of, 124
  discovery of, 121
  dispersion of, 143
  fluorescent radiation, 149, 298
  intensity of, 123
  K-series, 285
  L-series, 285
  from mesic atoms, 457
  from mu-mesic atoms, 458
  polarization of, 155
  production of, 121
  reflection of, 127, 143
    by ruled gratings, 146
  refraction of, 140
  scattering of, 150
  scattering coefficient of, 149, 154
    mass, 149
  secondary, 150
  total reflection of, 143
  transformation coefficient of, fluorescent, 149
    mass, 149
  wavelengths of, 128, 293

Y

Y-particles, 465
Yagoda, H., 470, 471
Yield, 336, 347
York, H. F., 451
Young, T., 97
Yukawa, H., 440

Yukawa theory, 440, 442

Z

Zacharias, J. R., 279
Zeeman, P., 102
Zeeman effect, 102, 259
  anomalous, 102, 237, 265
  Lorentz's theory of, 103
  normal, 102, 259
Zinn, W. H., 182, 183, 402, 409, 410